# Principles of
# Environmental
# Science

## ENGR 100W

San Jose State University

Materials from

**Principles of Environmental Science**
Inquiry & Applications
Sixth Edition

William P. Cunningham
*University of Minnesota*

Mary Ann Cunningham
*Vassar College*

Boston   Burr Ridge, IL   Dubuque, IA   New York   San Francisco   St. Louis
Bangkok   Bogotá   Caracas   Lisbon   London   Madrid
Mexico City   Milan   New Delhi   Seoul   Singapore   Sydney   Taipei   Toronto

Principles of Environmental Science
ENGR 100W
San Jose State University

This book is a McGraw-Hill Learning Solutions textbook and contains select material from *Principles of Environmental Science: Inquiry & Applications*, Sixth Edition by William P. Cunningham and Mary Ann Cunningham. Copyright © 2011 by The McGraw-Hill Companies, Inc. Previous editions © 2009, 2008 and 2006. Reprinted with permission of the publisher. Many custom published texts are modified versions or adaptations of our best-selling textbooks. Some adaptations are printed in black and white to keep prices at a minimum, while others are in color.

1 2 3 4 5 6 7 8 9 0 FRD FRD 14 13 12

ISBN-13: 978-0-07-766323-0
ISBN-10: 0-07-766323-3
Part of:
ISBN-13: 978-0-07-766324-7
ISBN-10: 0-07-766324-1

*Learning Solutions Consultant: Jill Albracht*
*Production Editor: Vanessa Arnold*
*Printer/Binder: Frederic Printing*

# About the
# Authors

## William P. Cunningham

William P. Cunningham is an emeritus professor at the University of Minnesota. In his 38-year career at the university, he taught a variety of biology courses, including Environmental Science, Conservation Biology, Environmental Health, Environmental Ethics, Plant Physiology, General Biology, and Cell Biology. He is a member of the Academy of Distinguished Teachers, the highest teaching award granted at the University of Minnesota. He was a member of a number of interdisciplinary programs for international students, teachers, and nontraditional students. He also carried out research or taught in Sweden, Norway, Brazil, New Zealand, China, and Indonesia.

Professor Cunningham has participated in a number of governmental and nongovernmental organizations over the past 40 years. He was chair of the Minnesota chapter of the Sierra Club, a member of the Sierra Club national committee on energy policy, vice president of the Friends of the Boundary Waters Canoe Area, chair of the Minnesota governor's task force on energy policy, and a citizen member of the Minnesota Legislative Commission on Energy.

In addition to environmental science textbooks, Cunningham edited three editions of an *Environmental Encyclopedia* published by Thompson-Gale Press. He has also authored or co-authored about 50 scientific articles, mostly in the fields of cell biology and conservation biology as well as several invited chapters or reports in the areas of energy policy and environmental health. His Ph.D. from the University of Texas was in botany.

His hobbies include backpacking, canoe and kayak building (and paddling), birding, hiking, gardening, and traveling. He lives in St. Paul, Minnesota with his wife, Mary. He has three children (one of whom is co-author of this book) and seven grandchildren.

## Mary Ann Cunningham

Mary Ann Cunningham is an associate professor of geography at Vassar College, in New York's Hudson Valley. A biogeographer with interests in landscape ecology, geographic information systems (GIS), and remote sensing, she teaches environmental science, natural resource conservation, and land-use planning, as well as GIS and remote sensing. Field research methods, statistical methods, and scientific methods in data analysis are regular components of her teaching. As a scientist and educator, Mary Ann enjoys teaching and conducting research with both science students and non-science liberal arts students. As a geographer, she likes to engage students with the ways their physical surroundings and social context shape their world experience. In addition to teaching at a liberal arts college, she has taught at community colleges and research universities.

Mary Ann has been writing in environmental science for over a decade, and she has been co-author of this book since its first edition. She is also co-author of *Environmental Science* (now in its eleventh edition), and an editor of the *Environmental Encyclopedia* (third edition, Thompson-Gale Press). She has published work on pedagogy in cartography, as well as instructional and testing materials in environmental science. With colleagues at Vassar, she has published a GIS lab manual, *Exploring Environmental Science with GIS,* designed to provide students with an easy, inexpensive introduction to spatial and environmental analysis with GIS.

In addition to environmental science, Mary Ann's primary research activities focus on land-cover change, habitat fragmentation, and distributions of bird populations. This work allows her to conduct field studies in the grasslands of the Great Plains as well as in the woodlands of the Hudson Valley. In her spare time she loves to travel, hike, and watch birds.

Mary Ann holds a bachelor's degree from Carleton College, a master's degree from the University of Oregon, and a Ph.D. from the University of Minnesota.

# Brief Contents

# Contents

*Preface xv*

# 6 Environmental Conservation: Forests, Grasslands, Parks, and Nature Preserves 128

# 7 Food and Agriculture 153

## 8 Environmental Health and Toxicology 180

## 9 Air: Climate and Pollution 205

## 11 Environmental Geology and Earth Resources  270

## 12 Energy  291

## List of Case Studies

# Preface

## Science for Changing Times

In 2009 an interdisciplinary group of 25 distinguished scientists warned that humans are approaching the limits or already exceeding thresholds for ten vital components of the earth's ecological systems. The most immediate crises, they reported, are climate change, biodiversity loss, and nitrogen pollution, all of which are already past sustainable rates of change. Among the other boundaries that we ought not transgress, they warned, are stratospheric ozone depletion, ocean acidification, global freshwater use, and chemical pollution. The massive oil spill in the Gulf of Mexico on Earth Day 2010 illustrates the environmental costs of our addiction to fossil fuels. The recent discovery of a pair of Texas-sized gyres of plastic garbage in the central Pacific Ocean also reminds us of our unsustainable lifestyles. All these signs caution us that we need a new attitude toward our planetary stewardship. Complacency about our collective impact on the earth is no longer a safe course.

At the same time, despite this litany of crises, there are also signs of hope. Human population growth is slowing nearly everywhere. New technologies offer alternatives to fossil fuels. Renewable sources, such as solar, wind, biomass, and geothermal heat could supply all the energy we need. Conservation measures are reducing wasteful uses of energy, water, soil, and materials. Communities and countries are cutting their carbon emissions, and better public health combined with improved diets has dramatically increased child survival rates around the world.

Citizen action is helping to bring about improved environmental conditions. In China, millions of people are demonstrating to demand enforcement of environmental laws. In the United States, a student-led group, called Step It Up, organized 1,400 demonstrations in 2007 to demand action to stop global warming. A successor group, 350.org is sponsoring thousands of additional rallies, work parties, and practical steps in 181 countries to do something about climate change. All these events show that people around the globe care about their communities and have a will to help in the survival of our species and others.

Environmental science can give you the knowledge to understand problems and the tools to help find solutions. In this book, you'll find a concise but comprehensive discussion of the principles of environmental science. You'll examine basic subjects, such as ecology, geology, climatology, and economics, as well as practical applications in preserving biodiversity, protecting landscapes, and sustainable resource use. The world ahead is yours to shape. We hope this book will help you grow as an environmental citizen and safeguard the earth's resources for future generations.

## What Sets This Book Apart?

### A Positive, Balanced Viewpoint

If students are to take the ideas of environmental science to heart, they need positive messages about ways all of us can contribute to a more sustainable world. This book presents the positive developments through **case studies** at the beginning of each chapter, illustrating an important current issue to demonstrate how it relates to practical environmental concerns. Most of these case studies present optimistic examples in which people are working to find solutions to environmental problems. These stories also demystify scientific investigation and help students understand how scientists study complex issues. In addition to these introductory stories, case studies and examples of how scientists investigate our environment appear periodically throughout the book to reiterate the practical importance of these issues.

### Integrated Approach Emphasizing Sustainability

Environmental problems and their solutions occur at the intersection of natural systems and the human systems that manipulate the natural world. In this book we present an **integrated approach** to physical sciences—biology, ecology, geology, air and water resources—and to human systems that affect nature—food and agriculture, population growth, urbanization, environmental health, resource economics, and policy. Although it is tempting to emphasize purely natural systems, we feel that students can never understand why coral reefs are threatened or why tropical forests are being cut down if they don't know something about the cultural, economic, and political forces that shape our decisions.

### Current and Accurate Data

Throughout this book, we present up-to-date tables and graphs with the most current available data. We hope this data will give students an appreciation of the kinds of information available in environmental science. Among the sources we have called upon here are geographic information systems (GIS) data and maps, current census and population data, international news and data sources, and federal data collection agencies. Every chapter in this book has numerous updates that reflect recent events in energy, food, climate, population trends, and other important issues.

## Active Learning and Critical Thinking

Learning how scientists approach problems can help students develop habits of independent, orderly, and objective thought. But it takes active involvement to master these skills. *Principles of Environmental Science* integrates numerous learning aids that will encourage students to think for themselves. Data and interpretations aren't presented as immutable truths, but rather as evidence to be examined and tested.

- **Exploring Science** essays promote scientific literacy by demonstrating the methodology scientists use to explore complex environmental questions.

- **What Can You Do?** boxes encourage students to "make a difference" by assuming personal responsibility for environmentally friendly decisions. The text offers many examples of how scientists and citizens have worked to resolve environmental questions, both basic and applied.

- **Data Analysis** exercises conclude each chapter to give students further opportunities to apply skills and put into practice the knowledge they've gained. We pay special attention to graphing techniques in these boxes because data display is such an important part of scientific information delivery. We don't limit this discussion to simple pie charts and line plots; we use this space to demonstrate a variety of ways to display and analyze data.

- **Critical Thinking and Discussion**, a challenging, open-ended set of questions at the end of each chapter, encourages students to think more deeply and independently about issues and principles presented in the chapter. These questions make excellent starting points for discussion sections. They also could be used to practice for essay exams, or might even serve as an essay exam themselves.

## What's New in This Edition?

A highpoint of this edition is a dramatic, contemporary new design that improves the readability and information transmission of the text. To complement this attractive layout, we've included two-page *A Closer Look* pieces in every chapter that highlight key ideas. These spreads integrate photographs, graphics, and extended captions to provide a closer focus on these central ideas. *Active Learning* exercises encourage students to practice critical thinking skills and apply their understanding of chapter concepts to propose solutions. Updated graphs, figures, and tables provide a clear and up-to-date discussion of the essential themes in environmental science.

## Learning Outcomes

Each chapter opens with a list of Learning Outcomes that will help students organize study priorities. Rather than being imperative requirements, these outcomes have been changed to more friendly questions that lead rather than command.

## New Chapter Content

- Chapter 1 has updated discussions of global environmental problems and improvements, critical thinking, probability, and statistics. A new Exploring Science essay discusses public databases that we use to understand trends throughout this book.

- Chapter 2 has an expanded discussion of uncertainty as a key aspect of skepticism in science. A new opening case study on the Everglades ecosystem provides a structure for discussing systems, nutrients, and flows of energy and matter in ecosystems.

- Chapter 3 has a new opening case study on Charles Darwin and his explanation of the principles of evolution. An Exploring Science box examines studies by Tilman, et al., of the relationship between biodiversity and stability. The two-page Closer Look for this chapter focuses on what evolution means and why it is an important idea.

- Chapter 4 adds a new boxed reading on China's one-child policy. Most statistics and population data have been updated. Ecological footprints are the focus of the Closer Look piece.

- Chapter 5 includes a new section on the economic benefits of ecosystems and biodiversity, emphasizing that economics and biodiversity are not necessarily opposing interests, as well as new discussion of endangered species protection.

- Chapter 6 has a new boxed reading on the northern spotted owl recovery plan. A new Data Analysis box gives practical directions for doing a field study on detecting edge effects in your local environment. The two-page Closer Look explores the REDD mechanism for protecting tropical forests. There are 11 new or revised figures.

- Chapter 7 has an updated examination of food production, nutrition, obesity, and health. Graphs and data have been updated, and an expanded discussion reviews pesticides and other agricultural inputs.

- Chapter 8 has a new box on the epigenome and its role in regulating gene expression. The Closer Look spread for this chapter illustrates household toxins.

- Chapter 9 is among the most completely updated in the book, including recent climate change evidence and debates. A new section examines arguments that dispute climate change evidence, and a new boxed reading discusses how we know that the climate is changing. Figures are updated with data and graphs from the Copenhagen climate conference, as well as new 800,000-year-old European (EPICA) ice core records. We also provide further explanation of the mechanisms and effects of climate change.

- Chapter 10 opens with a new case study on the drying of Lake Mead and water shortages in the western United States. Water treatment strategies are the focus of the two-page spread for this chapter. There are 11 new or revised figures.

- Chapter 11 opens with a new case study on the Haiti earthquake. New sections examine the strategic importance of rare earth metals and developments in coal-bed methane deposits in the eastern United States. The Closer Look for this chapter shows the complexity of material sources for consumer electronics and the problems of their waste disposal.

- Chapter 12 opens with a new case study on China's new lead in renewable energy using the specific example of Rizhao, one of the first carbon neutral cities in the world. The boxed reading on ethanol production has been updated, as has the discussion of fuel supplies, including the recent EPA restrictions on mountaintop removal. Discussions of recent events include methane deposits in the Marcellus Shale, which underlies much of the eastern United States, and the 2010 Gulf oil spill. Smart metering and conservation are also discussed, as is the new push to build nuclear plants in the U.S. An important addition to this chapter is the practical proposal by Jacobson and Delucchi for providing all the energy used in the U.S. with renewables. The Closer Look for this chapter shows how we might accomplish this task.

- Chapter 13 includes new discussions on plastic waste, oceanic garbage gyres, composting, and methane generation. We have updated waste production data and added an examination of how we consume, dispose of, and recover different components of the municipal waste stream.

- Chapter 14 has an enhanced emphasis on cities as places of opportunity for sustainability, as well as places facing major challenges. A new case study about Vauban, a car-free suburb of Freiburg, Germany, opens the chapter. The Closer Look pages illustrate principles of green city planning.

- Chapter 15 uses a new case study on the Cuyahoga River to focus on the benefits of environmental legislation. A new section reviews some of our key environmental laws. An updated discussion on policy formation includes a new look at the importance of the Supreme Court. The chapter ends with a focus on sustainability as a policy goal.

## Acknowledgements

We express our gratitude to Cindy Shaw, who did the expert artwork and graphic design for the new two-page *A Closer Look* pieces in this edition. Working with her was a real pleasure. The entire McGraw-Hill book team did wonderful work in putting together this edition. Thanks to Janice Roerig-Blong (publisher), Wendy Langerud (developmental editor), who oversaw the developmental stages and made many creative contributions to this book. Cathy Conroy has done a superb job of copy editing, correcting errors, and improving our prose. Lori Hancock and LouAnn Wilson found excellent photos for us. We are grateful for the patience and energy of April Southwood and Michelle Whitaker in managing the project through production and overseeing the attractive new design. Heather Wagner (marketing manager) has supported this project with her enthusiasm and creative ideas. A very special thanks is due to Marge Kemp (executive editor), whose ongoing support and close attention over many years has helped to make this book so successful.

This text has had the benefit of input from more than 400 researchers, professionals, and instructors who have reviewed this book or our larger text, *Environmental Science: A Global Concern*. These reviewers have helped us keep the text current and focused. We deeply appreciate their many helpful suggestions and comments. Space does not permit inclusion of all the excellent ideas that were provided, but we will continue to do our best to incorporate the ideas that reviewers have given us. In addition, all of us owe a great debt to the many scholars whose work forms the basis of our understanding of environmental science. We stand on the shoulders of giants. If errors persist in spite of our best efforts to root them out, we accept responsibility.

The following individuals provided reviews for this book. We thank them for their suggestions.

### Sixth Edition Reviewers

Eugene Beckham
*Northwood University*

Joanne Brock
*Kennesaw State University*

Huntting Brown
*Wright State University*

Kelly Cartwright
*College of Lake County*

Michelle Cawthorn
*Georgia Southern University*

Richard Clements
*Chattanooga State Technical Community College*

Danielle DuCharme
*Waubonsee Community College*

John B. Dunning, Jr.
*Purdue University*

William Ensign
*Kennesaw State University*

Brook E. Hall
*Folsom Lake College*

Suzanne Holt
*Cabrillo Community College*

Shane Jones
*College of Lake County*

Kurt Leuschner
*College of the Desert*

Heidi Marcum
*Baylor University*

Neil M. Mulchan
*Broward College*

Natalie Osterhoudt
*Broward College*

Barry Perlmutter
*College of Southern Nevada*

Neal Phillip
*Bronx Community College of City University of New York*

Robert Remedi
*College of Lake County*

Robert Ruliffson
*Minneapolis Community and Technical College*

Bruce Schulte
*Georgia Southern University*

Roy Sofield
*Chattanooga State Technical Community College*

Stinnett Danny
*Dakota County Technical College*

Michael Tveten
*Pima College—Northwest Campus*

Richard Waldren
*University of Nebraska-Lincoln*

Phillip Watson
*Ferris State University*

Amanda Zika
*Kishwaukee Community College*

# Guided Tour

## Application-based learning contributes to engaged scientific investigation

### A Closer Look

Key concepts from each chapter are presented in a beautifully arranged layout to guide the student through the often complex network of issues.

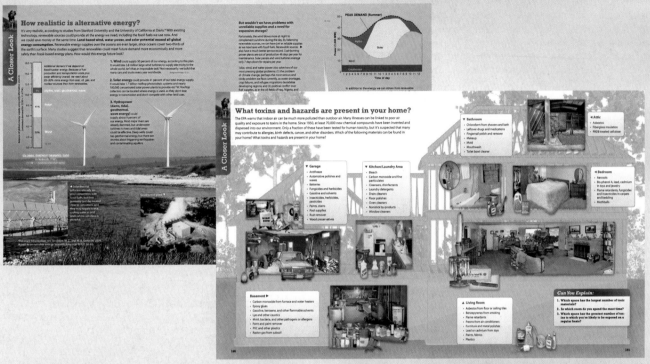

### Case Studies

All chapters open with a real-world case study to help students appreciate and understand how environmental science impacts lives and how scientists study complex issues.

### Google Earth™ Activities

Google Earth™ interactive satellite imagery gives students a geographic context for global places and topics discussed in the text. Google Earth™ icons indicate when to visit the text's website, where students will find links to locations mentioned in the text, and corresponding exercises that will help them understand environmental topics. Placemark links can be found at www.mhhe.com/cunningham6e.

## Active Learning

Students will be encouraged to practice critical thinking skills and apply their understanding of newly learned concepts and to propose possible solutions.

### Life Cycle Analysis

One step toward understanding your place in the waste stream is to look at the life cycle of the materials you buy. Here is a rough approximation of the process. With another student, choose one item that you use regularly. On paper, list your best guess for the following: (1) a list of the major materials in it; (2) the original sources (geographic locations and source materials) of those materials; (3) the energy needed to extract/convert the materials; (4) the distances the materials traveled; (5) the number of businesses involved in getting the item to you; (6) where the item will go when you dispose of it; (7) what kinds of reused/recycled products could be made from the materials in it.

## Exploring Science

Current environmental issues exemplify the principles of scientific observation and data-gathering techniques to promote scientific literacy.

### EXPLORING Science

**Rare Earth Metals: The New Strategic Materials**

Could shortages of a group of obscure minerals limit the growth of alternative energy supplies and green technology? A recent decision by China to limit exports of rare earth elements is seen by some experts as a serious threat to the global clean tech industry.

"Rare earth" elements are a collection of metallic elements including yttrium, scandium, and 15 lanthanides, such as neodymium, dysprosium, and gadolinium, that are essential in modern electronics. These metals are used in cell phones, high-efficiency lights, hybrid cars, superconductors, high-strength magnets, lightweight batteries, lasers, energy-conserving lamps, and a variety of medical devices. Because of their unusual properties, small amounts of these metals can make motors 90 percent lighter and lights 80 percent more efficient. Without these materials, MP3 players, hybrid vehicles, high-capacity wind turbines, and much other high-tech equipment would be impossible. A Toyota Prius, for example, uses about a kilogram of neodymium and dysprosium for its electric motor and as much as 15 kg of lanthanum for its battery pack.

Despite their name, these elements occur widely in the earth's crust, but commercially viable concentrations are found in only a few locations. China produces about 95 percent of all rare earth metals, an increase from about 30 percent two decades ago. China's dominance in mining these metals results partly because China uses these materials in electronics production, partly because of low labor costs in mining, and partly because the government has been willing to overlook the high environmental costs of extracting these metals from the ground. About half of all Chinese production of rare earth metals occurs in a single mine in Baotou in Inner Mongolia; most of the rest come from small, often unlicensed mines in southern China.

Like gold, silver, and other precious metals, rare earth elements are often separated from ore by crushing ore-bearing rocks and washing the ore in strong acids. Acids release metals from the ore, but when the metals are later separated from the acid slurry, tremendous amounts of toxic wastewater are produced. Often acids are pumped directly into a borehole drilled in the ground, and metals are dissolved from ores in place. The resulting slurry is then pumped to the surface for processing. Acidic wastewater is frequently stored behind earthen dams, which can leak into surface and ground waters. Processing also releases sulfur and radioactive uranium and thorium that frequently occur with rare earth elements. Establishing better control on illegal mines is one reason for China's interest in controlling export and production.

For China, maintaining control of supplies, as well as a near monopoly on production, ensures that domestic electronic needs will be met. Outside of China, there is concern about supplies for both strategic needs (such as military guidance systems), consumer electronics, and alternative energy supplies. Having a near

monopoly of rare earth metals production has helped China become a center of technology innovation, and other countries now wonder how to keep up in the high-tech race. Many firms are simply moving to China. The division of General Motors that deals with miniaturized magnet research, for example, shut down its U.S. office and moved its entire staff to China in 2006. The Danish wind turbine company Vestas moved much of its production to China in 2009.

In response to expected shortages and rising prices, several companies are working to reopen mines in North America and Australia. Molycorp Minerals expects to have its mine in Mountain Pass, California, back in production by 2012, meeting perhaps 10 percent of global demand, and Avalon Rare Metals of Toronto is working on a mine in Canada's Northwest Territories. Greenland is also jumping into this new gold rush, with hopes to produce up to 25 percent of rare earth metals from recently discovered ore bodies. It remains to be seen whether new environmental controls will be in place for this coming expansion.

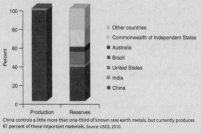

China controls a little more than one-third of known rare earth metals, but currently produces 97 percent of these important materials. Source: USGS, 2010.

## What Do You Think?

Students are presented with challenging environmental studies that offer an opportunity to consider contradictory data, special interest topics, and conflicting interpretations within a real scenario.

### What Do YOU Think?

**Northern Spotted Owls**

What's the most controversial bird in the world? If you count the number of scientists, lawyers, journalists, and activists who have debated its protection, as well as the amount of money, time, and effort spent on research and recovery, the answer must be the northern spotted owl (*Strix occidentalis caurina*). This brown, medium-size owl lives in the complex, old-growth forests of North America's Pacific Northwest. Before European settlement, it's thought that northern spotted owls occurred throughout the Coastal Ranges and Cascade Mountains from southern British Columbia to the San Francisco Bay.

Spotted owls nest in cavities in the huge, old-growth trees of the ancient forest. They depend on flying squirrels and wood rats as their primary prey, but they'll also eat voles, mice, gophers, hares, birds, and occasionally insects. With 90 percent of their preferred habitat destroyed or degraded, northern spotted owl populations are declining throughout their former range. When the U.S. Congress established the Endangered Species Act (ESA) in 1973, the northern spotted owl was identified as potentially endangered. After decades of study—but little action to protect them—northern spotted owls were listed as threatened in 1990 by the U.S. Fish and Wildlife Service. At that time, the population was estimated to contain 5,431 breeding pairs.

Several environmental organizations sued the federal government for its failure to do more to protect the owls. In 1991 a federal district judge agreed that the government wasn't following the requirements of the ESA, and temporarily shut down all logging in old-growth habitat in the Pacific Northwest. Timber sales dropped precipitously, and thousands of loggers and mill workers lost their jobs. Although mechanization and export of whole logs to foreign countries accounted for much of these job losses, many people blamed the owls for the economic woes across the region. Fierce debates broke out between loggers, who hung owls in effigy, and conservationists, who regarded them as protectors of the forest along with the whole biological community that lives in it.

In an effort to protect the remaining old-growth while still providing timber jobs, President Clinton started a broad planning process for the whole area. After a great deal of study and consultation, a comprehensive Northwest Forest Plan was adopted in 1994

as a management guide for about 9.9 million hectares (24.5 million acres) of federal lands in Oregon, Washington, and northern California. The plan was based on the latest science of ecosystem management and represented compromises on all sides. Nevertheless, loggers complained that this plan locked up forests on which their jobs depended, while environmentalists lamented the fact that millions of hectares of old-growth would still be vulnerable to logging.

In spite of the habitat protection provided by the forest plan, northern spotted owl populations continued to decline. By 2004, researchers could find only 1,044 breeding pairs. They reported that 80 percent of the nesting areas occupied two decades earlier no longer had spotted owls, and that 9 of the 13 geographic populations were declining. The courts ordered the Fish and Wildlife Service to establish a recovery plan as required by the ESA. After four more years of study and deliberation, a recovery plan was published in 2008. The plan identified 133 owl conservation areas encompassing 2.6 million hectares (6.4 million acres) of federal lands that will be managed to protect old-growth habitat and, hopefully, stabilize owl populations. Again, both sides complained about the compromise. Loggers accused the government of caring more for owls than people. Conservationists deplored the fact that although less than 10 percent of the original old-growth is left, nearly a third of that remnant is still open to harvesting.

Recently, barred owls (*Strix varia*) have been moving into the Pacific Northwest. These larger and more aggressive cousins of the spotted owl have a wider habitat and prey tolerance, giving them a competitive advantage. When barred owls move in, spotted owls generally move out. In addition, barred owls sometimes interbreed with spotted owls further diluting the endangered spotted owl gene pool. Some wildlife managers suggest that the only way to rebuild spotted owl populations is to kill barred owls, which are common across most of the middle of North America.

As you can see, there are a number of thorny ethical issues here. Is it right to kill one species to protect another? And where there are tradeoffs between jobs, local economies, and homes for people versus habitat for wildlife and the existence of pristine landscapes, how should we weigh these competing values? Can we coexist with these shy, highly specialized forest creatures? There aren't easy answers for these dilemmas. The solutions depend on your values and worldviews. How would you answer these questions?

Only about 2,000 pairs of northern spotted owls remain in the old-growth forests of the Pacific Northwest. Cutting old-growth forests threatens the endangered species, but reduced logging threatens the jobs of many timber workers.

## What Can You Do?

Students can employ these practical ideas to make a positive difference in our environment.

### What Can YOU Do?

**Tips for Staying Healthy**

- Eat a balanced diet with plenty of fresh fruits, vegetables, legumes, and whole grains. Wash fruits and vegetables carefully; they may have come from a country where pesticide and sanitation laws are lax.

- Use unsaturated oils, such as olive or canola, rather than hydrogenated or semisolid fats, such as margarine.

- Cook meats and other foods at temperatures high enough to kill pathogens; clean utensils and cutting surfaces; store food properly.

- Wash your hands frequently. You transfer more germs from hand to mouth than any other means of transmission.

- When you have a cold or flu, don't demand antibiotics from your doctor—they aren't effective against viruses.

- If you're taking antibiotics, continue for the entire time prescribed—quitting as soon as you feel well is an ideal way to select for antibiotic-resistant germs.

- Practice safe sex.

- Don't smoke; avoid smoky places.

- If you drink, do so in moderation. Never drive when your reflexes or judgment are impaired.

- Exercise regularly: walk, swim, jog, dance, garden. Do something you enjoy that burns calories and maintains flexibility.

- Get enough sleep. Practice meditation, prayer, or some other form of stress reduction. Get a pet.

- Make a list of friends and family who make you feel more alive and happy. Spend time with one of them at least once a week.

# Pedagogical Features Facilitate Student Understanding of Environmental Science

## Learning Outcomes

Questions at the beginning of each chapter challenge students to find their own answers.

### Learning Outcomes

*After studying this chapter, you should be able to answer the following questions:*

- What are our dominant sources of energy?
- What is peak oil production? Why is it hard to evaluate future oil production?
- How important is coal in domestic energy production?
- What are the environmental effects of coal burning? Is clean coal possible?
- How do nuclear reactors work? What are some of their advantages and disadvantages?
- What are our main renewable forms of energy?
- Could solar, wind, hydropower, and other renewables eliminate the need for fossil fuels?
- What are photovoltaic cells, and how do they work?
- What are biofuels? What are arguments for and against their use?

## Practice Quiz

Short-answer questions allow students to check their knowledge of chapter concepts.

### Practice Quiz

1. What is a *policy*? How are policies formed?
2. Describe three important provisions of NEPA.
3. List four important U.S. environmental laws (besides NEPA), and briefly describe what each does.
4. Why are international environmental conventions and treaties often ineffective? What can make them more successful?
5. Why is the World Trade Organization controversial?
6. List two broad goals of environmental education identified by the National Environmental Education Act.

## Critical Thinking and Discussion Questions

Brief scenarios of everyday occurrences or ideas challenge students to apply what they have learned to their lives.

### Critical Thinking and Discussion Questions

Apply the principles you have learned in this chapter to discuss these questions with other students.

1. Suppose that you were head of a family planning agency in a developing country. How would you design a scientific study to determine the effectiveness of different approaches to population stabilization? How would you account for factors such as culture, religion, education, and economics?
2. Why do you suppose that the United Nations gives high, medium, and low projections for future population growth? Why not give a single estimate? What factors would you consider in making these projections?
3. Some demographers claim that the total world population has already begun to slow, while others dispute this claim. How would you recognize a true demographic transition, as opposed to mere random fluctuations in birth and death rates?

4. Discuss the ramifications of China's "one-child policy" with a friend or classmate. Do the problems caused by rapid population growth justify harsh measures to limit births? What might the world situation be like today if China had a population of 2 billion people?
5. In northern Europe, the demographic transition began in the early 1800s, a century or more before the invention of modern antibiotics and other miracle drugs. What factors do you think contributed to this transition? How would you use historical records to test your hypothesis?
6. In chapter 3, we discussed carrying capacities. What do you think the maximum and optimum carrying capacities for humans are? Why is this a more complex question for humans than it might be for other species? Why is designing experiments in human demography difficult?

# Data Analysis

At the end of each chapter, these exercises give students further opportunities to apply skills and analyze data.

## Data Analysis | Examining Nutrients in a Wetland System

As you have read, movements of nitrogen and phosphorus are among the most important considerations in many wetland systems, because high levels of these nutrients can cause excessive algae and bacteria growth. This is a topic of great interest, and many studies have examined how nutrients move in a wetland, and in other ecosystems. Taking a little time to examine these nutrient cycles in detail will draw on your knowledge of atoms, compounds, systems, cycles, and other ideas in this chapter. Understanding nutrient cycling will also help you in later chapters of this book.

One excellent overview was produced by the Environmental Protection Agency. Go to this website and download a PDF document of the study: http://www.epa.gov/waterscience/criteria/nutrient/guidance/wetlands/index.html. If you prefer, you can also look at just one chapter at a time on this website.

Find chapter 2, An Overview of Wetland Science, and answer the following questions:

1. Look first at the page numbered 28 (section 2.1). How many nutrients are discussed in this chapter? Why are iron (Fe), aluminum (Al), and calcium of interest in understanding phosphorus?

2. Now look at the next page, with the photograph. What are the sources from which nutrients enter a wetland? Think of at least three ways in which human activities can increase these sources.

3. Proceed to page 30, figure 2.5. Study the online figure and fill in the boxes on figure 1 on the next page. How many different forms of nitrogen, or compounds containing nitrogen, are there? List them.

## Relevant Photos and Instructional Art Support Learning

Numerous high quality photos and realistic illustrations display detailed diagrams, graphs, and real-life situations.

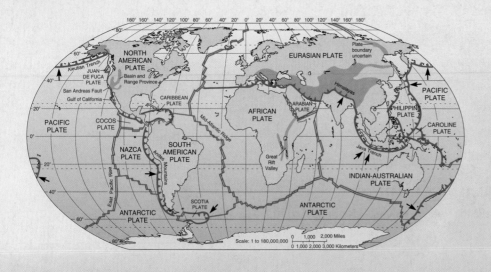

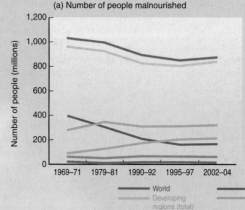

(a) Number of people malnourished

(b) Percentage malnourished

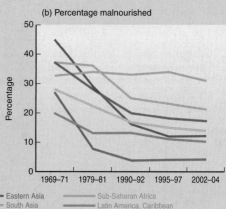

World — Developing regions (total) — Eastern Asia — South Asia — Sub-Saharan Africa — Latin America, Caribbean — Northern Africa

# Teaching and Learning Supplements

McGraw-Hill Connect™ Environmental Science provides online presentation, assignment, and assessment solutions. It connects your students with the tools and resources they'll need to achieve success.

With Connect™ Environmental Science you can deliver assignments, quizzes, and tests online. A robust set of questions and activities are presented and aligned with the textbook's Learning Outcomes. Instructors can edit existing questions and author entirely new problems. Track individual student performance—by question, assignment, or in relation to the class overall—with detailed grade reports. Integrate grade reports easily with Learning Management Systems (LMS), such as Blackboard, and much more. ConnectPlus™ Environmental Science provides students with all the advantages of Connect™ Environmental Science, plus 24/7 online access to an eBook. This media-rich version of the book is available through the McGraw-Hill Connect™ platform and allows seamless integration of text, media, and assessments. To learn more, visit **www.mcgrawhillconnect.com**

### Computerized Test Bank

A comprehensive bank of test questions is provided within a computerized test bank powered by McGraw-Hill's flexible electronic testing program, EZ Test Online. EZ Test Online allows you to create paper and online tests or quizzes in this easy to use program! A new tagging scheme allows you to sort questions by Bloom's difficulty level, topic, and section. Imagine being able to create and access your test or quiz anywhere, at any time, without installing the testing software. Now, with EZ Test Online, instructors can select questions from multiple McGraw-Hill test banks or author their own, and then either print the test for paper distribution or give it online.

### Presentation Tools

Everything you need for outstanding presentations in one place! **www.mhhe. com/cunningham6e.**

- Image PowerPoints—including every piece of art that has been sized and cropped specifically for superior presentations. Also included are tables, photographs, and unlabeled art pieces.
- Lecture PowerPoints—a base lecture outline that can be used to save you time in preparing for your course.
- Images files—Full-color digital files of all illustrations that can be readily incorporated into presentations, exams, or custom-made classroom materials.

### Presentation Center

In addition to the images from your book, this online digital library contains photos, artwork, animations, and other media from an array of McGraw-Hill textbooks that can be used to create customized lectures, visually enhanced tests and quizzes, compelling course websites, or attractive printed support materials.

### My Lectures—Tegrity

Tegrity Campus™ records and distributes your class lecture, with just a click of a button. Students can view anytime or anywhere via computer, iPod, or mobile device. It indexes as it records your PowerPoint presentations and anything shown on your computer so students can use keywords to find exactly what they want to study. Tegrity is available as an integrated feature of McGraw-Hill Connect™ Environmental Science or as stand-alone.

### Companion Website www.mhhe.com/cunningham6e

The Cunningham: Principles of Environmental Science companion website allows students to access a variety of free digital learning tools that include:

- Chapter-level practice quizzes
- Google Earth activities
- Printable textbook images for note taking
- Ecological footprint calculators
- Interactive maps

And much more.

# Flexible Options

You're in charge of your course, so why not be in control of the content of your textbook? At McGraw-Hill Custom Publishing, we can help you create the ideal text—the one you've always imagined. Quickly. Easily. With more than 20 years of experience in custom publishing, we're experts. But at McGraw-Hill, we're also innovators, leading the way with new methods and means for creating simplified value added custom textbooks. The options are never-ending. You already know what will work best for you and your students. And with Create, you can choose it.

Our custom book format choices are numerous and diverse. From printed black-and-white texts to full color customization, to cost saving eBooks that students buy online, we do it all.

# eBooks

McGraw-Hill eBooks offer a cheaper and eco-friendly alternative to traditional textbooks. By purchasing eBooks from McGraw-Hill students can save as much as 50% on selected titles delivered on the most advanced eBook platforms available. Contact your McGraw-Hill sales representative to discuss eBook options or go to **www.mhhe. com/ebooks.**

# Additional Materials in Environmental Science

**Additional Resources**
*Environment* 10/11 by Sharp (MHID: 0-07-351556-6)
This twenty-eighth edition provides convenient, inexpensive access to current articles selected from some of the most respected magazines, newspapers, and journals published today. Organizational features include: an annotated listing of selected World Wide Web sites, an annotated table of contents, a topic guide, a general introduction, brief overviews for each section, and an instructor's resource guide with testing materials. Using Annual Editions in the Classroom is also offered as a practical guide for instructors.

*Taking Sides: Clashing Views on Environmental Issues,* Fourteenth Edition by Easton (MHID: 0-07-351446-2)
This expanded thirteenth edition of *Taking Sides* presents two additional current controversial issues in a debate-style format designed to stimulate student interest and develop critical thinking skills. Each issue is thoughtfully framed with an issue summary, an issue introduction, and a postscript. *Taking Sides* readers also feature annotated listings of selected World Wide Web sites. An instructor's resource guide with testing material is available for each volume. Using *Taking Sides in the Classroom* is also an excellent instructor resource.

*Classic Edition Sources: Environmental Studies,* Third Edition, by Easton (MHID: 0-07-352758-0)
This reader provides over 40 selections of enduring intellectual value—classic articles, book excerpts and research studies—that have shaped our contemporary understanding of the environment.

*Student Atlas of Environmental Issues* by Allen (ISBN: 978-0-69- 736520-0; MHID: 0-69-736520-4)
This atlas is an invaluable pedagogical tool for exploring the human impact on the air, waters, biosphere, and land in every major world region. This informative resource provides a unique combination of maps and data that help students understand the dimensions of the world's environmental problems and the geographical basis of these problems.

# 1 Understanding Our Environment

Fish and the reefs that support them are essential to the livelihoods of people in the Philippines and most other tropical island nations.

*Today we are faced with a challenge that calls for a shift in our thinking, so that humanity stops threatening its life-support system.*

—WANGARI MAATHAI, WINNER OF 2004 NOBEL PEACE PRIZE

## Learning Outcomes

*After studying this chapter, you should be able to answer the following questions:*

- Explain several of the most important environmental problems facing the world.
- How can we work toward solving these problems?
- What do we mean by sustainability and sustainable development?
- Why are scientists cautious about claiming absolute proof of particular theories?
- Why is critical thinking essential for understanding environmental science?
- How can we use graphs and data to answer questions in science?
- Who are some of the people who helped shape our ideas of resource conservation and preservation? Why did they promote these ideas when they did?

# CASE STUDY

## Saving the Reefs of Apo Island

As their outrigger canoes glide gracefully onto Apo Island's beach after an early morning fishing expedition, villagers call to each other to ask how fishing was. "Tunay mabuti!" (very good!) is the cheerful reply. Nearly every canoe has a basketful of fish; enough to feed a family for several days with a surplus to send to the market. Life hasn't always been so good on the island. Thirty years ago, this island, like many others in the Philippines, suffered a catastrophic decline in the seafood that was the mainstay of their diet and livelihood. Rapid population growth coupled with destructive fishing methods such as dynamite or cyanide fishing, small mesh gill nets, deep-sea trawling, and *muroami* (a technique in which fish are chased into nets by pounding on coral with weighted lines) had damaged the reef habitat and exhausted fish stocks.

In 1979, scientists from Silliman University on nearby Negros Island visited Apo to explain how establishing a marine sanctuary could help reverse this decline. The coral reef fringing the island acts as a food source and nursery for many of the marine species sought by fishermen. Protecting that breeding ground, they explained, is the key to preserving a healthy fishery (fig. 1.1). The scientists took villagers from Apo to the uninhabited Sumilon Island, where a no-take reserve was teeming with fish.

After much discussion, several families decided to establish a marine sanctuary along a short section of Apo Island shoreline. Initially, the area had high-quality coral but few fish. The participating families took turns watching to make sure that no one trespassed in the no-fishing zone. Within a few years, fish numbers and sizes in the sanctuary increased dramatically, and "spillover" of surplus fish led to higher catches in surrounding areas. In 1985, Apo villagers voted to establish a 500 m (0.3 mi) wide marine sanctuary around the entire island.

Fishing is now allowed in this reserve, but only by low-impact methods such as hand-held lines, bamboo traps, large mesh nets, spearfishing without SCUBA gear, and hand netting. Coral-destroying techniques, such as dynamite, cyanide, trawling, and *muroami* fishing are prohibited. By protecting the reef, villagers are guarding the nursery that forms the base for their entire marine ecosystem. Young fish growing up in the shelter of the coral move out as adults to populate the neighboring waters and yield abundant harvests. Fishermen report that they spend much less time traveling to distant fishing areas now that fish around the island are so much more abundant.

Apo Island's sanctuary is so successful that it has become the inspiration for more than 400 marine preserves throughout the Philippines and many others around the world. Not all are functioning as well as they might, but many, like Apo, have made dramatic progress in restoring abundant fish populations in nearby waters.

Global recognition of the importance of fish breeding areas is also growing. The United Nations Environment Programme (UNEP) reports that 75 percent of the world's fisheries are at or past maximum supportable fishing levels. UNEP has encouraged countries worldwide to establish marine proteced areas and ensure their own sustainable fisheries.

The rich marine life and beautiful coral formations in Apo Island's crystal clear water now attract international tourists. Two small hotels and a dive shop provide jobs for island residents. Other villagers take in tourists as boarders or sell food and T-shirts to visitors. The island government collects a diving/snorkeling fee, which has been used to build schools, improve island water supplies, and provide electricity to most of the island's 145 households. Almost all the island men still fish as their main occupation, but the fact that they don't have to go so far or work so hard for the fish they need means they have time for other activities, such as guiding diving tours or helping with household chores.

Higher family incomes now allow most island children to attend high school on Negros. Many continue their education with college or technical programs. Some find jobs elsewhere in the Philippines, and the money they send back home is a big economic boost for Apo families. Others return to their home island as teachers or to start businesses such as restaurants or dive shops. Seeing that they can do something positive to improve their environment and living conditions has empowered villagers to take on self-improvement projects that they may not otherwise have attempted.

Finding ways to live sustainably within the limits of the resource base available to us and without damaging the life-support systems provided by our ecosystem is a preeminent challenge of environmental science. Our answers to these challenges must be ecologically sound, economically sustainable, and socially acceptable if they are to succeed in the long term. Sometimes, as this case study shows, actions based on ecological knowledge and local action can spread to have positive effects on a global scale. Economics, policy, planning, and social organization all play vital roles in finding answers to human/environment problems. We'll discuss those disciplines later in this book, but first we'll look at the basic principles of ecological science as a basis for understanding our global environment.

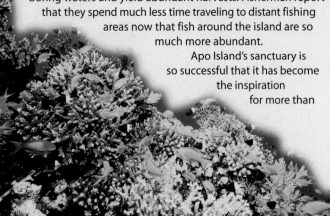

**Figure 1.1** Coral reefs are among the most beautiful, species-rich, and productive biological communities on the planet. They serve as the nurseries for many open-water species. At least half the world's reefs are threatened by pollution, global climate change, destructive fishing methods, and other human activities, but they can be protected and restored if we care for them.

## 1.1 Understanding Our Environment

Understanding the depletion of Apo Island's fishery, and finding solutions to the problem, required an appreciation of many aspects of the environment. Knowledge about population biology, reef ecology, the cultural history of fishing, and even economics of fishing all contribute to understanding environmental resource questions. The field of environmental science draws on many disciplines to help us understand pressing problems of resource supply, ecosystem stability, and sustainable living. Usually environmental science is also about identifying and solving problems that affect our lives, and those of future generations.

In this book you will read about serious environmental problems. You will also read about promising, exciting solutions to many of these problems. Your task as a student of environmental science is to gain an understanding of some of the larger issues, what some solutions might be, and how you might use your knowledge and skills to develop tomorrow's strategies for living on this planet.

### We live on a marvelous planet

Before proceeding in our discussion of current dilemmas and how scientists are trying to understand them, we should pause for a moment to consider the extraordinary natural world that we inherited and that we hope to pass on to future generations in as good—or perhaps even better—condition than we found it.

Imagine that you are an astronaut returning to the earth after a long trip to the moon or Mars. What a relief it would be, after experiencing the hostile environment of outer space, to come back to this beautiful, bountiful planet (fig. 1.2). Although there are dangers and difficulties here, we live in a remarkably prolific and hospitable world that is, as far as we know, unique in the universe. Compared with the conditions on other planets in our solar system, temperatures on the earth are mild and relatively constant. Plentiful supplies of clean air, fresh water, and fertile

Figure 1.3 Perhaps the most amazing feature of our planet is its rich diversity of life.

soil are regenerated endlessly and spontaneously by biogeochemical cycles and biological communities (discussed in chapters 2 and 3).

Perhaps the most amazing feature of our planet is its rich diversity of life. Millions of beautiful and intriguing species populate the earth and help sustain a habitable environment (fig. 1.3). This vast multitude of life creates complex, interrelated communities where towering trees and huge animals live together with, and depend upon, such tiny life-forms as viruses, bacteria, and fungi. Together, all these organisms make up delightfully diverse, self-sustaining ecosystems, including dense, moist forests; vast, sunny savannas; and richly colorful coral reefs.

From time to time, we should pause to remember that, in spite of the challenges and complications of life on earth, we are incredibly lucky to be here. We should ask ourselves: what is our proper place in nature? What *ought* we do and what *can* we do to protect the irreplaceable habitat that produced and supports us? These are some of the central questions of environmental science.

### What is environmental science?

We inhabit two worlds. One is the natural world of plants, animals, soils, air, and water that preceded us by billions of years and of which we are a part. The other is the world of social institutions and artifacts that we create for ourselves using science, technology, culture, and political organization. Both of these factors are part of our **environment** (from the French *environner*: to encircle or surround). Both the natural world and the "built" or technological, social, and cultural world, make up our environment.

**Environmental science** is the systematic study of our environment and our place in it. Because environmental problems are complex, environmental science draws on many fields of knowledge (fig. 1.4). Sciences such as biology, chemistry, earth science, and geography provide important information. Social sciences and humanities, from political science and economics to art and literature, help us understand how society responds to environmental crises and opportunities. Environmental science is also mission-oriented: generally we try to understand problems so that we can offer solutions in public health and environmental quality.

The distinguished economist Barbara Ward has pointed out that very often the difficulty is not in identifying remedies, but in making them socially, economically, and politically acceptable. Foresters know how to plant trees, but not how to establish conditions under which villagers in developing countries can manage plantations for themselves. Engineers know how to control pollution, but not how to persuade

**Figure 1.2** The life-sustaining ecosystems on which we all depend are unique in the universe, as far as we know.

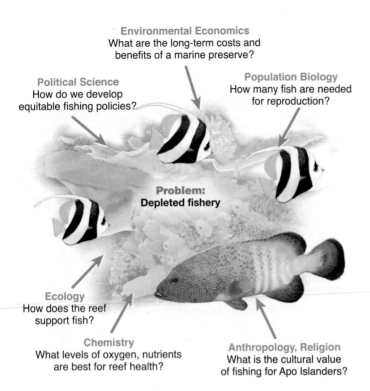

Political Science
How do we develop
equitable fishing policies?

Environmental Economics
What are the long-term costs and
benefits of a marine preserve?

Population Biology
How many fish are needed
for reproduction?

Problem:
Depleted fishery

Ecology
How does the reef
support fish?

Chemistry
What levels of oxygen, nutrients
are best for reef health?

Anthropology, Religion
What is the cultural value
of fishing for Apo Islanders?

**Figure 1.4** Many types of knowledge are needed in environmental science. A few examples are shown here.

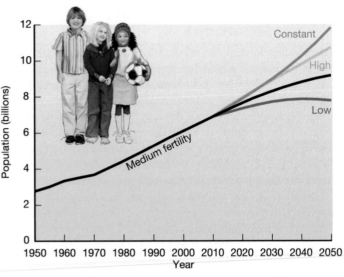

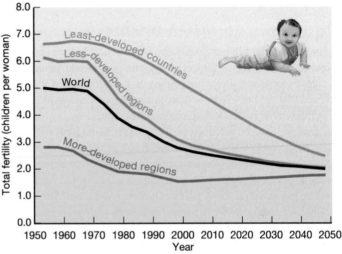

**Figure 1.5** Bad news and good news: globally, populations continue to rise, but our rate of growth has plummeted. Some countries are below the replacement rate of about two children per woman. *Source:* United Nations Population Program, 2007.

factories to install the necessary equipment. City planners know how to design urban areas, but not how to make them affordable for everyone. Solutions to these problems increasingly involve both social systems and natural science. One of your tasks in this class may be to discover where your knowledge and interests contribute to understanding questions in environmental science (see Active Learning, p. 5).

### Environmental science is a global subject

Learning environmental science involves understanding how principles play out in real places. Familiarity with these places will help you understand the problems and their context. Throughout this book we've provided links to places you can see in Google Earth, a free online mapping program that you can download from http://googleearth.com. When you see a blue globe in the margin, like the one at left, you can go to our web log (EnvironmentalScience_Cunningham.blogspot.com) and find a "place mark" that lets you virtually visit places discussed. In Google Earth you can also save your own place marks and share them with your class.

## 1.2 Problems and Opportunities

A first step in understanding environmental science is to identify some of the principal problems we face, and some of the recent changes in environmental quality and environmental health. Most issues you will read about are complex. Many have both positive and negative aspects. As you read, consider what factors contribute to these issues, and what steps might be taken to resolve some of these problems.

### What persistent challenges do we face?

There are about 7 billion people on earth, and we are adding about 80 million more each year. While demographers report a transition to slower growth rates in most countries, with improved education and health care, present trends project a population between 8 and 10 billion by 2050 (fig. 1.5). The impact of that many people on our natural resources and ecological systems is a serious concern that complicates many of the other problems we face.

**Climate Change**   The atmosphere has always trapped heat near the earth's surface, which is why it is warmer here than in space. But human activities such as burning fossil fuels, clearing forests and farmlands, and raising ruminant animals, have greatly increased concentrations of carbon dioxide and other "greenhouse gases." In the past 200 years, atmospheric $CO_2$ concentrations have increased about 30 percent. Climate models indicate that by 2100, if current trends continue, global mean temperatures will probably warm between

# Active Learning

**Hunger** Over the past century, global food production has increased faster than human population growth, but hunger remains a chronic problem because food resources are unevenly distributed. At the same time, soil scientists report that about two-thirds of all agricultural lands show signs of degradation. The biotechnology and intensive farming techniques responsible for much of our recent production gains are too expensive for many poor farmers. Can we find ways to produce the food we need without further environmental degradation? And can we distribute food more equitably? In a world of food surpluses, currently more than 850 million people are chronically undernourished, and at least 60 million people face acute food shortages due to weather, politics, or war (fig. 1.6b).

**Clean Water** Water may well be the most critical resource in the twenty-first century. Already at least 1.1 billion people lack access to safe drinking water, and twice that many don't have adequate sanitation. Polluted water contributes to the death of more than 15 million people every year, most of them children under age 5. About 40 percent of the world population lives in countries where water demands now exceed supplies, and the UN projects that by 2025 as many as three-fourths of us could live under similar conditions (fig. 1.6c).

**Energy Resources** How we obtain and use energy is likely to play a crucial role in our environmental future. Fossil fuels (oil, coal, and natural gas) presently provide around 80 percent of the energy used in industrialized countries. Supplies of these fuels are diminishing, however, and problems associated with their acquisition and use—air and water pollution, mining damage, shipping accidents,

about 2° and 6°C compared to 1990 temperatures (3.6° and 12.8°F: fig. 1.6a). For comparison, the last ice age was about 4°C cooler than now. Climate change already is leading to range shifts and population declines in many species. Increasingly severe droughts and heat waves will occur in many areas, but increased flooding is likely in others. Disappearing alpine glaciers and snowfields threaten water supplies on which large regions depend, including the western United States and much of Asia. Canadian Environment Minister David Anderson said that global climate change is a greater threat than terrorism because it could force hundreds of millions of people from their homes and trigger an economic and social catastrophe.

**Figure 1.6** Environmental and political challenges. (a) Climate change is projected to raise temperatures, especially in northern winter months. (b) Some 800 million people lack adequate nutrition. (c) Poor water quality is responsible for more than 15 million deaths each year. (d) Biodiversity including marine species, continues to decline. *Data:* NOAA 2010, WWF 2008.

(c) Water quality

(a) Climate change

(b) Hunger

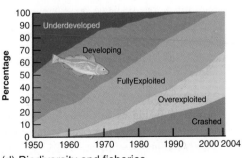
(d) Biodiversity and fisheries

and geopolitics—may limit what we do with remaining reserves. Cleaner, renewable energy resources—solar, wind, geothermal, and biomass power—together with conservation could give us cleaner, less destructive options if we invest in appropriate technology.

**Air Quality**   Air quality has worsened dramatically in many areas. Over southern Asia, for example, satellite images recently revealed a 3-km (2-mile)-thick toxic haze of ash, acids, aerosols, dust, and photochemical products, which regularly covers the entire Indian subcontinent for much of the year. Nobel laureate Paul Crutzen estimates that at least 3 million people die each year from diseases triggered by air pollution. Worldwide, the United Nations estimates, more than 2 billion metric tons of air pollutants (not including carbon dioxide or wind-blown soil) are released each year. Air pollution is also a problem far from its source. Mercury, polychlorinated biphenyls (PCBs), DDT, and other long-lasting pollutants accumulate in arctic ecosystems and native people after being transported by air currents from industrial regions thousands of kilometers to the south. On some days, 75 percent of the smog and particulate pollution recorded on the west coast of North America can be traced to Asia.

**Biodiversity Loss**   Biologists report that habitat destruction, overexploitation, pollution, and introduction of exotic organisms are eliminating species at a rate comparable to the great extinction that marked the end of the age of dinosaurs (fig. 1.6d). The UN Environment Programme reports that, over the past century, more than 800 species have disappeared and at least 10,000 species are now considered threatened. This includes about half of all primates and freshwater fish, together with around 10 percent of all plant species. Top predators, including nearly all the big cats in the world, are particularly rare and endangered. A nationwide survey of the United Kingdom in 2004 found that most bird and butterfly populations had declined between 50 and 75 percent over the previous 20 years. At least half of the forests existing before the introduction of agriculture have been cleared, and much of the diverse "old growth" on which many species depend for habitat is rapidly being cut and replaced by secondary growth or monoculture.

**Marine Resources**   As the opening case study for this chapter shows, the ocean is an irreplaceable food resource for many people. More than a billion people in developing countries depend on seafood for their main source of animal protein, but most commercial fisheries around the world are in steep decline. According to the World Resources Institute, more than three-quarters of the 441 fish stocks for which information is available are severely depleted or in urgent need of better management. Canadian researchers estimate that 90 percent of all the large predators, including bluefin tuna, marlin, swordfish, sharks, cod, and halibut, have been removed from the ocean.

## There are also many signs of hope

The problems facing us can seem overwhelming, but increasing awareness is leading to progress in many areas. As in Apo Island, both environmental scientists and ordinary people can invent new strategies for protecting nature and improving people's lives.

**Population and Pollution**   As you will see in subsequent chapters in this book, progress has been made in many areas in reducing pollution and curbing wasteful resource use. Many cities in Europe and North America, for example, are cleaner and much more livable now than they were a century ago. Population has stabilized in most industrialized countries and even in some very poor countries where social security and democracy have been established. Over the past 25 years, the average number of children born per woman worldwide has decreased from 6.1 to 2.6 (see fig. 1.5). By 2050, the UN Population Division predicts, all developed countries and 75 percent of the developing world will experience a below-replacement fertility rate of 2.1 children per woman. If this happens, the world population will stabilize at about 8.9 billion, rather than the 9.3 billion previously estimated.

**Health**   The incidence of life-threatening infectious diseases has been reduced sharply in most countries during the past century, while life expectancies have nearly doubled, on average (fig. 1.7a). Smallpox has been completely eradicated and polio has been vanquished except in a few countries. Since 1990 more than 800 million people have gained access to improved water supplies and modern sanitation. In spite of population growth that added nearly a billion people to the world during the 1990s, the number of people facing food insecurity and chronic hunger during this period actually declined by about 40 million.

**Renewable Energy**   Encouraging progress is being made in a transition to renewable energy sources. The European Union and China, particularly, are developing wind energy, solar, wave and tidal energy, and improvements in efficiency to cut reliance on fossil fuels. At the Copenhagen climate summit in late 2009, the world's wealthiest countries agreed to aid developing nations in finding alternative energy technologies that will help to reduce global dependence on fossil fuels while allowing economic growth.

**Information and Education**   Because so many environmental issues can be fixed by new ideas, technologies, and strategies, expanding access to knowledge is essential to progress. The increased speed at which information now moves around the world offers unprecedented opportunities for sharing ideas. At the same time, literacy and access to education are expanding in most regions of the world (fig. 1.7b). Although we continue to face many challenges, collectively we may be able to implement sustainable development that raises living standards for everyone while also reducing our negative environmental impacts.

**Conservation of Forests and Nature Preserves**
Deforestation has slowed in Asia, from more than 8 percent during the 1980s to less than 1 percent in the 1990s. Brazil, which has led global deforestation rates for decades, is working to protect forests. Nature preserves and protected areas have increased dramatically over the past few decades. In 2010 there were more than

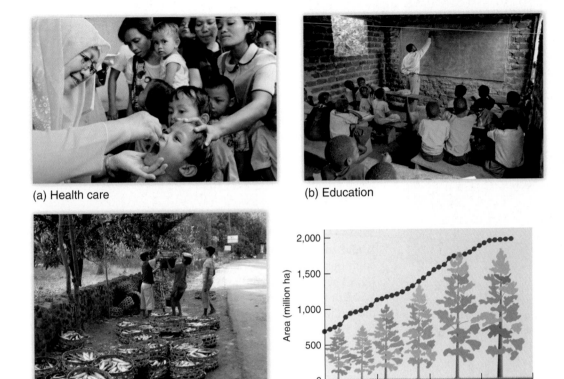

(a) Health care

(b) Education

(c) Sustainable resource use

(d) Increasing protected areas

**Figure 1.7** Conditions are improving in many areas, including access to (a) health care and (b) education. In many areas, (c) sustainable resource use is being improved by expanding (d) networks of protected areas. *Data:* IUCN and UNEP 2010.

condition into account. We live in a world of haves and have-nots; a few of us live in increasing luxury, while many others lack the basic necessities for a decent, healthy, productive life. The World Bank estimates that more than 1.4 billion people—about one-fifth of the world's population—live in acute poverty with an income of less than $1 (U.S.) per day. These poorest of the poor generally lack access to an adequate diet, decent housing, basic sanitation, clean water, education, medical care, and other essentials for a humane existence. Seventy percent of those people are women and children. In fact, four out of five people in the world live in what would be considered poverty in the richer countries (fig. 1.8).

Policymakers are becoming aware that eliminating poverty and protecting our common environment are inextricably interlinked because the world's poorest people are both the victims and the agents of environmental degradation. The poorest people are often forced to meet short-term survival needs at the cost of long-term sustainability. Desperate for croplands to feed themselves and their families, many move into virgin forests or cultivate steep, erosion-prone hillsides, where soil nutrients are exhausted after only a few years. Others migrate to the grimy, crowded slums and ramshackle shantytowns that now surround most major cities in the developing world. With no way to dispose of wastes, the residents often foul their environment further and contaminate the air they breathe and the water on which they depend for washing and drinking.

The cycle of poverty, illness, and limited opportunities can become a self-sustaining process that passes from one generation to another. People who are malnourished and ill can't work productively to obtain food, shelter, or medicine for themselves or their children, who also are malnourished and ill. About 250 million children—mostly in Asia and Africa and some as young as 4 years old—are forced to work under appalling conditions weaving carpets, making ceramics and jewelry, or working in the sex trade. Growing up in these conditions leads to educational, psychological, and developmental deficits that condemn these children to perpetuate this cycle.

Faced with immediate survival needs and few options, these unfortunate people often have no choice but to overharvest resources; in doing so, however, they diminish not only their own options but also those of future generations. And in an increasingly interconnected world, the environments and resource bases

100,000 parks and nature preserves in the world, representing more than 20 million km² (about 7.7 million mi²), or about 13.5 percent of the world's land area (fig. 1.7c). Ecoregion and habitat protection remains uneven, and some areas are protected only on paper. Still, this is dramatic progress in biodiversity protection.

**Protection of Marine Resources** After centuries of uncontrolled industrial exploitation of marine resources, global awareness of the value of marine protected areas is growing. Improved monitoring of fisheries and networks of marine protected areas promote species conservation as well as human development (fig. 1.7d). Much progress has yet to be made, but protecting fish nurseries represents an altogether new approach to protecting ocean systems and the people who depend on them.

Marine reserves are being established to protect reproductive areas in California, Hawaii, New Zealand, Great Britain, and many other areas, in addition to the Philippines.

## 1.3 Human Dimensions of Environmental Science

Because we live in both the natural and social worlds, and because we and our technology have become such dominant forces on the planet, environmental science must take human institutions and the human

**Figure 1.8** While many of us live in luxury, more than 1.4 billion people lack access to food, housing, clean water, sanitation, education, medical care, and other essentials for a healthy, productive life. Helping them meet their needs is not only humane, it is essential to protect our mutual environment.

damaged by poverty and ignorance are directly linked to those on which we depend.

## Affluence has environmental costs

The affluent lifestyle that many of us in the richer countries enjoy consumes an inordinate share of the world's natural resources and produces a shockingly high proportion of pollutants and wastes. The United States, for instance, with less than 5 percent of the total population, consumes about one-quarter of most commercially traded commodities, such as oil, and produces a quarter to half of most industrial wastes, such as greenhouse gases, pesticides, and other persistent pollutants.

To get an average American through the day takes about 450 kg (nearly 1,000 lbs) of raw materials, including 18 kg (40 lbs) of fossil fuels, 13 kg (29 lbs) of other minerals, 12 kg (26 lbs) of farm products, 10 kg (22 lbs) of wood and paper, and 450 liters (119 gal) of water. Every year, Americans throw away some 160 million tons of garbage, including 50 million tons of paper, 67 billion cans and bottles, 25 billion styrofoam cups, 18 billion disposable diapers, and 2 billion disposable razors (fig. 1.9).

This profligate resource consumption and waste disposal strains the planet's life-support systems. If everyone in the world tried to live at consumption levels approaching ours, the results would be disastrous. Unless we find ways to curb our desires and produce the things we truly need in less destructive ways, the sustainability of human life on our planet is questionable.

## Sustainability is a central theme

**Sustainability** is a search for ecological stability and human progress that can last over the long term. Of course, neither ecological systems nor human institutions can continue forever. We can work, however, to protect the best aspects of both realms,

and to encourage resiliency and adaptability in both of them. World Health Organization Director Gro Harlem Brundtland has defined **sustainable development** as "meeting the needs of the present without compromising the ability of future generations to meet their own needs." In these terms, development means bettering people's lives. Sustainable development, then, means progress in human well-being that we can extend or prolong over many generations, rather than just a few years. To be truly enduring, the benefits of sustainable development must be available to all humans and not just to the members of a privileged group.

## Where do the rich and poor live?

About one-fifth of the world's population lives in the 20 richest countries, where the average per capita income is above $25,000 (U.S.) per year. Most of these countries are in North America or Western Europe, but Japan, Singapore, Australia, New Zealand, the United Arab Emirates, and Israel also fall into this group (see Exploring Science, p. 9). Almost every country, however, even the richest, such as the United States and Canada, has poor people. No doubt everyone reading this book knows about homeless people or other individuals who lack resources for a safe, productive life. Some 35 million Americans—one-third of them children—live in households without sufficient food.

Eighty percent of the world's population lives in middle- or low-income countries, where nearly everyone is poor by North American standards. More than 3 billion people live in the poorest nations, where the average per capita income is below $620 (U.S.) per year. China and India are the largest of these countries, with a combined population of about 2.3 billion people. Among the 41 other nations in this category, 33 are in sub-Saharan Africa. All the other lowest-income nations, except Haiti, are in Asia. Although poverty levels in countries such as China and Indonesia have fallen in recent years, most

**Figure 1.9** "And may we continue to be worthy of consuming a disproportionate share of this planet's resources."
© Lee Lorenz/Condé Nast Publications/www.cartoonbank.com

# EXPLORING
## Science

### How Do We Know the State of Population, Poverty, and Other Issues?

How do we know about changes in global problems such as hunger, food production, or health, which are much too large to observe directly? We use data sets, usually collected by governments, such as the United States Census (www.census.gov) or the U.S. Census of Agriculture (http://www.agcensus.usda.gov/), or by organizations such as the United Nations Food and Agriculture Organization (http://faostat.fao.org/default.aspx) or the World Bank (http://www.worldbank.org/). If you have a question and some time, you can use these data sets to examine trends, too.

In general, a census agency contacts as many individuals in a country as they can reach. They ask a standard list of questions (for example, how old are you, how many people are in your household?). You may have answered some of these questions in the 2010 United States census, a count that happens every ten years. The census agency enters all the answers into an enormous set of data tables that anybody can access, with a little practice. International organizations such as the United Nations can't contact all persons in the world, but they can survey governments and attempt to gather answers to a standard set of questions (how many citizens are there, how many children died this year, how much clean water is available per person?). Not all countries are able—or willing—to answer all questions, so sometimes there are "no data" values in global data sets.

From these tables, we can calculate averages, high and low values, changes from previous surveys, or comparisons among regions. The graphs and maps you see in this book originate from these types of data, so will the data sources above, and many others, noted below the figures.

Newspapers and news magazines rely on these large data sources, too. Take a look at a some maps and graphs in your favorite newspapers, and see what data sources were used.

You can access these databases yourself. Some are very easy to use; others require some patience and persistence. Most data-distributing agencies also provide summaries of important findings in their data. Many educational and business agencies also compile and reorganize data from public sources. For example, the Gapminder project (http://www.gapminder.org) has entertaining animation to help you visualize global trends. Your school or university library may also keep data, and your reference librarians may be trained to help you use them.

Once you have a graph or map, how do you interpret it? Here are a few steps, with reference to the map shown here:

1. Look for areas of especially high or low values (for example, identify some blue areas and some white areas).

2. In the legend, find the difference in values between those high and low areas.

3. Find an area you know, and think about reasons for the values. (Does the blue United States fit your expectations? Can you think of reasons why U. S. income differs from that of Mexico or China, for example?)

4. Look for regions with contrasting values. For example, which countries in Africa are green? Why? Think of some explanations for those differences.

Data sources like these provide a large-scale view of issues such as hunger, poverty, education, or health across space or time. This view complements more subtle and complex, but less global, insights from case studies. The Apo Island case study, for example, provides a detailed perspective on the interaction of different factors, or the ways that individuals can influence progress. Both local and global views are often necessary for describing trends in environmental science.

Try exploring the websites noted earlier. They can provide rich and valuable information and entirely new insights on the issues that interest you.

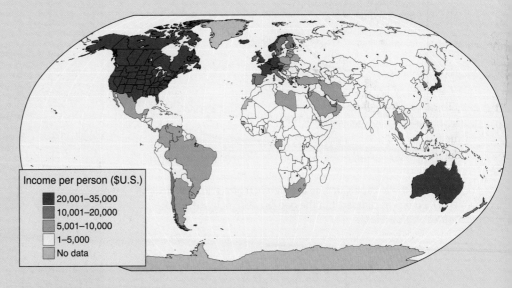

Income per person ($U.S.)
- 20,001–35,000
- 10,001–20,000
- 5,001–10,000
- 1–5,000
- No data

**Figure 1** About four-fifths of the world's population live in middle or low-income countries.

countries in sub-Saharan Africa and much of Latin America have made little progress. The destabilizing and impoverishing effects of earlier colonialism continue to play important roles in the ongoing problems of these countries. Meanwhile, the relative gap between rich and poor has increased dramatically.

The gulf between the richest and poorest nations affects many quality-of-life indicators (table 1.1). The average individual in the highest-income countries has an annual income more than 100 times that of those in the lowest-income nations. Because of high infant mortality rates, the average family in the

## Table 1.1 | Quality-of-Life Indicators

|  | Least-Developed Countries | Most-Developed Countries |
|---|---|---|
| GDP/Person[1] | (U.S.)$329 | (U.S.)$30,589 |
| Poverty Index[2] | 78.1% | ~0 |
| Life Expectancy | 43.6 years | 76.5 years |
| Adult Literacy | 58% | 99% |
| Female Secondary Education | 11% | 95% |
| Total Fertility[3] | 5.0 | 1.7 |
| Infant Mortality[4] | 97 | 5 |
| Improved Sanitation | 23% | 100% |
| Improved Water | 61% | 100% |
| $CO_2$/capita[5] | 0.2 tons | 13 tons |

[1]Annual gross domestic product.

[2]Percent living on less than (U.S.)$2/day.

[3]Average births/woman.

[4]Per 1,000 live births.

[5]Metric tons/yr/person.

*Source:* UNDP Human Development Index, 2006.

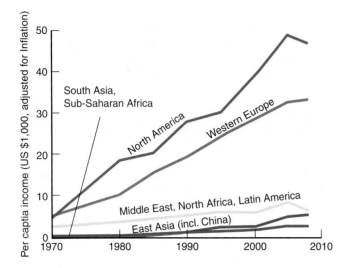

**Figure 1.10** Per capita income in different regions (in 2008 dollars). Overall income has climbed, but the gap between rich and poor countries as grown faster.
*Data Source:* World Bank.

poorest countries has more than four times as many children as those in richer countries. If it were not for immigration, the population in most of the richer countries now would be declining; the total population of poorer countries continues to grow at 2.6 percent per year.

The gulf between rich and poor is even greater at the individual level. The richest 200 people in the world have a combined wealth of $1 trillion. This is more than the total owned by the 3 billion people who make up the poorest half of the world's population (fig. 1.10).

## Indigenous peoples are guardians of much of the world's biodiversity

In both rich and poor countries, native or **indigenous people** are generally the least powerful, most neglected groups in the world. Typically descendants of the original inhabitants of an area taken over by more powerful outsiders, they are distinct from their country's dominant language, culture, religion, and racial communities. Of the world's nearly 6,000 recognized cultures, 5,000 are indigenous ones that account for only about 10 percent of the total world population. In many countries, traditional caste systems, discriminatory laws, economics, or prejudice repress indigenous people. Their unique cultures are disappearing, along with biological diversity, as natural habitats are destroyed to satisfy industrialized world appetites for resources. Traditional ways of life are disrupted further by dominant Western culture sweeping around the globe.

At least half of the world's 6,000 distinct languages are dying because they are no longer taught to children. When the last few elders who still speak the language die, so will the culture that was its origin. Lost with those cultures will be a rich repertoire of knowledge about nature and a keen understanding of a particular environment and way of life (fig. 1.11).

Nonetheless, in many places, the 500 million indigenous people who remain in traditional homelands still possess valuable ecological wisdom and remain the guardians of little-disturbed habitats that are refuges for rare and endangered species and undamaged ecosystems.

**Figure 1.11** Do indigenous people have unique knowledge about nature and inalienable rights to traditional territories?

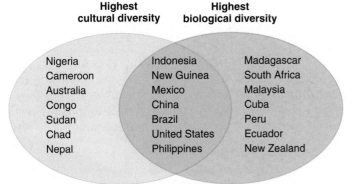

Highest cultural diversity | Highest biological diversity

Nigeria
Cameroon
Australia
Congo
Sudan
Chad
Nepal

Indonesia
New Guinea
Mexico
China
Brazil
United States
Philippines

Madagascar
South Africa
Malaysia
Cuba
Peru
Ecuador
New Zealand

**Figure 1.12** Cultural diversity and biodiversity often go hand in hand. Seven of the countries with the highest cultural diversity in the world are also on the list of "megadiversity" countries with the highest number of unique biological organisms (listed in decreasing order of importance).

*Source:* Norman Myers, Conservation International and Cultural Survival Inc., 2002.

In his book *The Future of Life*, the eminent ecologist E. O. Wilson argues that the cheapest and most effective way to preserve species is to protect the natural ecosystems in which they now live. Notably, just 12 countries account for 60 percent of all human languages (fig. 1.12). Seven of these are also among the "megadiversity" countries that contain more than half of all unique plant and animal species. Conditions that support evolution of many unique species seem to favor development of equally diverse human cultures as well.

Recognizing native land rights and promoting political pluralism can be among the best ways to safeguard ecological processes and endangered species. As the Kuna Indians of Panama say, "Where there are forests, there are native people, and where there are native people, there are forests." A few countries, such as Papua New Guinea, Fiji, Ecuador, Canada, and Australia, acknowledge indigenous title to extensive land areas.

Other countries, unfortunately, ignore the rights of native people. Indonesia, for instance, claims ownership of nearly three-quarters of its forestland and all waters and offshore fishing rights, ignoring the interests of indigenous inhabitants. Similarly, the Philippine government claims possession of all uncultivated land in its territory, while Cameroon and Tanzania recognize no rights at all for forest-dwelling pygmies who represent one of the world's oldest cultures.

## 1.4 Science Helps Us Understand Our Environment

Because environmental questions are complex, we need orderly methods of examining and understanding them. Environmental science provides such an approach. In this section, we'll investigate what science is, what the scientific method is, and why that method is important.

What is science? **Science** (from *scire*, "to know" in Latin) is a process for producing empirical knowledge by observing natural phenomena. We develop or test theories (proposed explanations of how a process works) using these observations. "Science" also refers to the cumulative body of knowledge produced by many scientists. Science is valuable because it helps us understand the

| **Table 1.2 | Basic Principles of Science** |
|---|
| 1. *Empiricism:* We can learn about the world by careful observation of empirical (real, observable) phenomena; we can expect to understand fundamental processes and natural laws by observation. |
| 2. *Uniformitarianism:* Basic patterns and processes are uniform across time and space; the forces at work today are the same as those that shaped the world in the past, and they will continue to do so in the future. |
| 3. *Parsimony:* When two plausible explanations are reasonable, the simpler (more parsimonious) one is preferable. This rule is also known as Ockham's razor, after the English philosopher who proposed it. |
| 4. *Uncertainty:* Knowledge changes as new evidence appears, and explanations (theories) change with new evidence. Theories based on current evidence should be tested on additional evidence, with the understanding that new data may disprove the best theories. |
| 5. *Repeatability:* Tests and experiments should be repeatable; if the same results cannot be reproduced, then the conclusions are probably incorrect. |
| 6. *Proof is elusive:* We rarely expect science to provide absolute proof that a theory is correct, because new evidence may always improve on our current explanations. Even evolution, the cornerstone of modern biology, ecology, and other sciences, is referred to as a "theory" because of this principle. |
| 7. *Testable questions:* To find out whether a theory is correct, it must be tested; we formulate testable statements (hypotheses) to test theories. |

world and meet practical needs, such as finding new medicines, new energy sources, or new foods. In this section, we'll investigate how and why science follows standard methods.

Science rests on the assumption that the world is knowable and that we can learn about it by careful observation and logical reasoning (table 1.2). For early philosophers of science, this assumption was a radical departure from religious and philosophical approaches. In the Middle Ages the ultimate sources of knowledge about matters such as how crops grow, how diseases spread, or how the stars move, were religious authorities or cultural traditions. While these sources provided many useful insights, there was no way to test their explanations independently and objectively. The benefit of scientific thinking is that it searches for testable evidence. As evidence improves, we can find better answers to important questions.

### Science depends on skepticism and accuracy

Ideally scientists are skeptical. They are cautious about accepting a proposed explanation until there is substantial evidence to support it. Even then, every explanation is considered only provisionally true, because there is always a possibility that some additional evidence may appear to disprove it. Scientists also aim to be methodical and unbiased. Because bias and methodical errors are hard to avoid, scientific tests are subject to review by informed peers, who can evaluate results and conclusions (fig. 1.13). The peer review process is an essential part of ensuring that scientists maintain good standards in study design, data collection, and interpretation of results.

Scientists demand **reproducibility** because they are cautious about accepting conclusions. Making an observation or obtaining a result just once doesn't count for much. You have to produce the

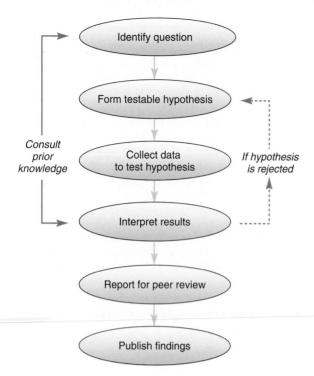

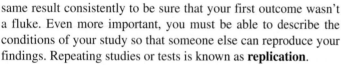

**Figure 1.13** Ideally, scientific investigation follows a series of logical, orderly steps to formulate and test hypotheses.

**Figure 1.14** Scientific studies rely on repeated, careful observations to establish confidence in their findings.

same result consistently to be sure that your first outcome wasn't a fluke. Even more important, you must be able to describe the conditions of your study so that someone else can reproduce your findings. Repeating studies or tests is known as **replication**.

Science relies on measurements that are accurate (close to the true value). Accuracy usually requires careful, precise measurement (fig. 1.14) and meticulous record keeping.

## Deductive and inductive reasoning are both useful

Ideally, scientists deduce conclusions from general laws that they know to be true. For example, if we know that massive objects attract each other (because of gravity), then it follows that an apple will fall to the ground when it releases from the tree. This logical reasoning from general to specific is known as **deductive reasoning**. Often, however, we do not know general laws that guide natural systems. Then we must rely on observations to find general rules. We observe, for example, that birds appear and disappear as a year goes by. Through many repeated observations in different places, we can infer that the birds move from place to place. We can develop a general rule that birds migrate seasonally. Reasoning from many observations to produce a general rule is **inductive reasoning**. Although deductive reasoning is more logically sound than inductive reasoning, it only works when our general laws are correct. We often rely on inductive reasoning to understand the world because we have few immutable laws.

Insight, creativity, and experience can also be essential in science. Often discoveries are made by investigators who are passionately interested in their subjects and who pursue hunches that appear unreasonable to fellow scientists. For example some of our most basic understanding of plant genetics come from the intuitive guesses of Barbara McClintock, a geneticist who discovered that genes in corn can move and recombine spontaneously. Where other corn geneticists saw random patterns of color and kernel size, McClintock's years of experience in corn breeding and an uncanny ability to recognize patterns, led her to guess that genes could recombine in ways that no one had previously imagined.

## The scientific method is an orderly way to examine problems

You may already be using the scientific method without being aware of it. Suppose you have a flashlight that doesn't work. The flashlight has several components (switch, bulb, batteries) that could be faulty. If you change all the components at once, your flashlight might work, but a more methodical series of tests will tell you more about what was wrong with the system—knowledge that may be useful next time you have a faulty flashlight. So you decide to follow the standard scientific steps:

1. *Observe* that your flashlight doesn't light; also, there are three main components of the lighting system (batteries, bulb, and switch).

2. Propose a **hypothesis**, a testable explanation: "The flashlight doesn't work because the batteries are dead."

3. Develop a *test* of the hypothesis and *predict* the result that would indicate your hypothesis was correct: "I will replace the batteries; the light should then turn on."

4. Gather *data* from your test: After you replaced the batteries, did the light turn on?

5. *Interpret* your results: If the light works now, then your hypothesis was right; if not, then you should formulate a new hypothesis, perhaps that the bulb is faulty, and develop a new test for that hypothesis.

In systems more complex than a flashlight, it is almost always easier to prove a hypothesis wrong than to prove it unquestionably true. This is because we usually test our hypotheses with observations, but there is no way to make every possible observation. The philosopher Ludwig Wittgenstein illustrated this problem as follows: Suppose you saw hundreds of swans, and all were white. These observations might lead you to hypothesize that all swans were white. You could test your hypothesis by viewing thousands of swans, and each observation might support your hypothesis, but you could never be entirely sure that it was correct. On the other hand, if you saw just one black swan, you would know with certainty that your hypothesis was wrong.

As you'll read in later chapters, the elusiveness of absolute proof is a persistent problem in environmental policy and law. Rarely can you absolutely prove that the toxic waste dump up the street is making you sick. You could, however, collect evidence to show that it was very probable that the waste made you and your neighbors sick. The elusiveness of proof often decides environmental liability lawsuits (fig. 1.15).

When an explanation has been supported by a large number of tests, and when a majority of experts have reached a general consensus that it is a reliable description or explanation, we call it a **scientific theory**. Note that scientists' use of this term is very different from the way the public uses it. To many people, a theory is speculative and unsupported by facts. To a scientist, it means just the opposite: While all explanations are tentative and open to revision and correction, an explanation that counts as a scientific theory is supported by an overwhelming body of data and experience, and it is generally accepted by the scientific community, at least for the present.

**Figure 1.15** How can you prove who is responsible for environmental contamination, such as the orange ooze in this stream? Careful, repeated measurements and well-formed hypotheses are essential.

## Understanding probability reduces uncertainty

One strategy to improve confidence in the face of uncertainty is to focus on probability. **Probability** is a measure of how likely something is to occur. Usually, probability estimates are based on a set of previous observations or on standard statistical measures. Probability does not tell you what *will* happen, but it tells you what is *likely* to happen. If you hear on the news that you have a 20 percent chance of catching a cold this winter, that means that 20 of every 100 people are likely to catch a cold. This doesn't mean that *you* will catch one. In fact, it's more likely, an 80 percent chance, that you *won't* catch a cold. If you hear that 80 out of every 100 people will catch a cold, you still don't know whether you'll get sick, but there's a much higher chance that you will.

Science often involves probability, so it is important to be familiar with the idea. Sometimes probability has to do with random chance: If you flip a coin, you have a random chance of getting heads or tails. Every time you flip, you have the same 50 percent probability of getting heads. The chance of getting ten heads in a row is small (in fact, the chance is 1 in $2^{10}$, or 1 in 1,024), but on any individual flip, you have exactly the same 50 percent chance, since this is a random test. Sometimes probability is weighted by circumstances: Suppose that about 10 percent of the students in your class earn an A each semester. Your likelihood of being in that 10 percent depends a great deal on how much time you spend studying, how many questions you ask in class, and other factors. Sometimes there is a combination of chance and circumstances: The probability that you will catch a cold this winter depends partly on whether you encounter someone who is sick (largely random chance) and also on whether you take steps to stay healthy (get enough rest, wash your hands frequently, eat a healthy diet, and so on).

Probability is often a more useful idea than proof. This is because absolute proof is hard to achieve, but we can frequently demonstrate a strong trend or relationship, one that is unlikely to be achieved by chance. For example, suppose you flipped a coin and got heads 20 times in a row. That could happen by chance, but it would be pretty unlikely. You might consider it very likely that there was a causal explanation, such as that the coin was weighted towards heads. Often we consider a causal explanation reliable (or "significant") if there is less than 5 percent probability that it happened by random chance (see Exploring Science, p. 15).

## Experimental design can reduce bias

The study of fishing success (case study) is an example of an observational experiment, one in which you observe natural events and interpret a causal relationship between the variables. This kind of study is also called a **natural experiment**, one that involves observation of events that have already happened. Many scientists depend on natural experiments: A geologist, for instance, might want to study mountain building, or an ecologist might want to learn about how species evolve, but neither scientist can spend millions of years watching the process happen. Similarly, a toxicologist cannot give people a disease just to see how lethal it is.

Other scientists can use **manipulative experiments**, in which conditions are deliberately altered, and all other variables are held

# Active Learning

constant. Most manipulative experiments are done in the laboratory, where conditions can be carefully controlled. Suppose you were interested in studying whether lawn chemicals contributed to deformities in tadpoles. You might keep two groups of tadpoles in fish tanks, and expose one to chemicals. In the lab, you could ensure that both tanks had identical temperatures, light, food, and oxygen. By comparing a treatment (exposed) group and a control (unexposed) group, you have also made this a **controlled study**.

Often, there is a risk of experimenter bias. Suppose the researcher sees a tadpole with a small nub that looks like it might become an extra leg. Whether she calls this nub a deformity might depend on whether she knows that the tadpole is in the treatment group or the control group. To avoid this bias, **blind experiments** are often used, in which the researcher doesn't know which group is treated until after the data have been analyzed. In health studies, such as tests of new drugs, **double-blind experiments** are used, in which neither the subject (who receives a drug or a placebo) nor the researcher knows who is in the treatment group and who is in the control group.

In each of these studies there is one **dependent variable** and one, or perhaps more, **independent variables**. The dependent variable, also known as a response variable, is affected by the independent variables. In a graph, the dependent variable is on the vertical (Y) axis, by convention. Independent variables are rarely really independent (they may be affected by the same environmental conditions as the dependent variable, for example). Many people prefer to call them **explanatory variables**, because we hope they will explain differences in the dependent variable.

## Science is a cumulative process

The scientific method outlined in figure 1.13 is the process used to carry out individual studies. Larger-scale accumulation of scientific knowledge involves cooperation and contributions from countless people. Good science is rarely carried out by a single individual working in isolation. Instead, a community of scientists collaborates in a cumulative, self-correcting process. You often hear about big breakthroughs and dramatic discoveries that change our understanding overnight, but in reality these changes are usually the culmination of the labor of many people, each working on different aspects of a common problem, each adding small insights to solve a problem. Ideas and information are exchanged, debated, tested, and retested to arrive at **scientific consensus**, or general agreement among informed scholars.

The idea of consensus is important. For those not deeply involved in a subject, the multitude of contradictory results can be bewildering: Are coral reefs declining, and does it matter? Is climate changing, and how much? Among those who have done many studies and read many reports, there tends to emerge a general agreement about the state of a problem. Scientific consensus now holds that many coral reefs are in danger, though opinions vary on how severe the problem is. Consensus is that global climates are changing, though models differ somewhat on how rapidly they will change under different policy scenarios.

Sometimes new ideas emerge that cause major shifts in scientific consensus. These great changes in explanatory frameworks were termed **paradigm shifts** by Thomas Kuhn (1967), who studied revolutions in scientific thought. According to Kuhn, paradigm shifts occur when a majority of scientists accept that the old explanation no longer explains new observations very well. For example, two centuries ago, geologists explained many earth features in terms of Noah's flood. The best scientists held that the flood created beaches well above modern sea level, scattered boulders erratically across the landscape, and gouged enormous valleys where there is no water now (fig. 1.16). Then the Swiss glaciologist Louis Agassiz and others suggested that the earth had once been much colder and that glaciers had covered large areas. Periodic ice ages proved to be a more durable explanation for geologic features than did a flood, and this new idea completely altered the way geologists explained their subject. Similarly, the idea of tectonic plate movement, in which continents shift slowly around the earth's surface (chapter 11), revolutionized the ways geologists, biogeographers, ecologists, and others explained the development of the earth and its life-forms.

**Figure 1.16** Paradigm shifts change the ways we explain our world. Geologists now attribute Yosemite's valleys to glaciers, where once they believed catastrophes like Noah's flood carved its walls.

# EXPLORING Science

## Why Do Scientists Answer Questions with a Number?

For many people, a little bit of evidence is convincing. Suppose you lived in Apo Island (opening story), and you had a good day fishing. You might conclude that fisheries were doing really well. But how can you be sure your observation was right? Or that it represented something larger than one person's lucky day of fishing? Scientists try to be cautious and avoid jumping to conclusions, so they usually rely on *trends in data*, rather than *anecdotal observations*, when they evaluate the evidence.

Finding a trend in data requires collecting many observations, and usually we can see trends better by plotting those observations on graphs. Graphs are one of our easiest and most useful ways to see patterns and changes in something we care about. Here are a few ways we use graphs and data to increase our confidence in our conclusions.

1. ***A mean describes the middle of the group.*** To understand what's really going on with fishing rates, you can examine the number of fish caught per day. Of course, some days are unlucky, and fishers vary in their fishing abilities. One way to describe the overall fishing rate by calculating the **mean** (average) for a number of several people: Count all the fish caught in a day, and divide that count by the number of person-hours spent fishing. Try this for the four hypothetical fishing boats listed in the following table.

### Fishing Rate

| Boat | Number of Fish | Hours |
|---|---|---|
| 1 | 10 | 1 |
| 2 | 15 | 4 |
| 3 | 5 | 2 |
| 4 | 20 | 3 |
| Sum: | _____ | _____ |

Number of fish per hour = _____

Is this rate high or low? Suppose your records show that 10 years ago the mean was 12 fish per hour spent fishing. If you calculated a mean of 5 fish per hour earlier, you know the fishing rate has fallen.

2. ***Histograms show a group at a glance.*** You would know still more about the general situation if you examined more than just one village. After all, your village might be an *outlier*, or an unusual case. Records from 10 villages, or 50, would tell a much more complete story. In science, more observations always increase confidence in our conclusions.

   You can't survey each of the thousands of villages in the Philippines, but you could examine a random subset, or sample, of them. The sample should be random to avoid biasing your results: if you just pick villages nearest a big city, for example, they might have especially poor fisheries. This might make your village fishery look great, but it might not tell you much that's useful. Once you have your sample, you can sort the observations and create a **histogram** to show the number of villages with small catches and large catches (fig. 1). The histogram here has many villages with about 6–11 fish per hour and just a few with 2 or 20. A bell-shaped distribution like this is known as a **normal distribution** because large sets of randomly selected observations tend to have this distribution.

3. ***Graphs show relationships.*** Suppose you suspect that the size of marine reserves tends to improve fishing rates. You can test this hypothesis by plotting your two variables against each other. Here the explanatory variable is the size of marine reserves (plotted on the horizontal axis, fig. 2) and fishing rates are the dependent variable (plotted on the vertical axis). Here the pattern of dots shows that fishing does increase as preserve size increases, for this set of villages. Now you can say with good confidence that there is a positive relationship between preserve size and fishing success.

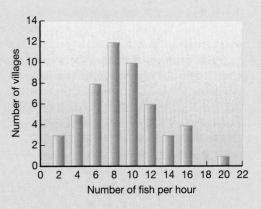

**Figure 1** A bar graph shows values for classes or groups.

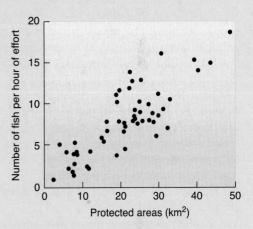

**Figure 2** A scatter plot shows the relationship of *x* and *y* for many observations. Here each observation is a village.

Answering a question with numbers can give you confidence that you're drawing reasonable conclusions about your data. As a critical thinker, you can also examine the numbers in news reports and in public policies. Are policy positions based on anecdotal evidence or on trends among many observations? Are samples selective and biased, or are they random? Asking these sorts of questions as you hear the news is a good practice for being a well-informed voter. Asking these questions may even help you do well in this course.

## What is sound science?

Environmental science often deals with questions that are emotionally or politically charged. Scientific studies of climate change may be threatening to companies that sell coal; studies of health costs of pesticides might worry people who use or sell these chemicals. When controversy surrounds science, claims about **sound science** and accusations of "junk science" often arise. What do these terms mean, and how can you evaluate who is right?

When you hear arguments about whose science is valid, you need to remember the basic principles of science: Are the disputed studies reproducible? Are conclusions drawn with caution and skepticism? Are samples large and random? Are conclusions supported by a majority of scholars who have studied the problem? Do any of the experts have an economic interest in the outcome?

Often media figures on television or radio will take a position contrary to the scientific majority. A contrarian position gains them publicity and political allies (and sometimes money). This strategy has been especially popular around large issues such as climate change. For decades now, almost all climate scientists have agreed that human activities, such as fossil fuel burning and land clearing, are contributing to climate change. But it is always possible to find a contrarian scientist who is happy to contradict the majority of evidence. Especially when political favors, publicity, or money are involved, it is always possible to find "expert" witnesses who will testify on opposite sides of a case.

Scientific uncertainty is frequently invoked as a reason to postpone or reverse policies that a vast majority of informed scientists consider to be prudent. In questions of chemical safety, energy conservation, climate change, or air pollution control, opponents of change may charge that the evidence doesn't constitute absolute proof, so that no action needs to be taken. You will see examples of this in chapter 8 (environmental health), chapter 9 (air quality and climate), and elsewhere in this book.

Similarly, disputes over evolution often hinge on the concept of uncertainty and proof in science. Opponents of teaching evolution in public schools often charge that because scientists call evolution a theory, evolution is just a matter of conjecture. This is a confused use of terminology. The theory of evolution is supported by overwhelming amounts of evidence, but we still call it a theory because scientists prefer to be cautious about proof.

If you see claims of sound science and junk science, how can you evaluate them? How can you identify bogus analysis that is dressed up in quasi-scientific jargon but that has no objectivity? This is such an important question that astronomer Carl Sagan has proposed a "Baloney Detection Kit" (table 1.3) to help you out.

### Is environmental science the same as environmentalism?

Environmental science is the use of scientific methods to study processes and systems in the environment in which we live. Environmentalism is working to influence attitudes and policies that affect our environment. The two are often separate goals. Petroleum geologists, for example, are environmental scientists who study geology in order to find oil resources. They work to

| Table 1.3 | Questions for Baloney Detection |
| --- |
| 1. How reliable are the sources of this claim? Is there reason to believe that they might have an agenda to pursue in this case? |
| 2. Have the claims been verified by other sources? What data are presented in support of this opinion? |
| 3. What position does the majority of the scientific community hold in this issue? |
| 4. How does this claim fit with what we know about how the world works? Is this a reasonable assertion or does it contradict established theories? |
| 5. Are the arguments balanced and logical? Have proponents of a particular position considered alternate points of view or only selected supportive evidence for their particular beliefs? |
| 6. What do you know about the sources of funding for a particular position? Are studies financed by groups with partisan goals? |
| 7. Where was evidence for competing theories published? Has it undergone impartial peer review or is it only in proprietary publication? |

*Source:* Carl Sagan.

increase access to resources, to benefit their company, perhaps to benefit our standard of living, but usually not to protect the environment in which they work and live. Other environmental scientists are also environmentalists. Many ecologists actively work to defend the ecosystems they study. Many environmental scientists work in the public interest, to promote public health, for example, without necessarily being interested in nature or other species.

Whether we use science to pursue public health, economic success, environmental quality, or other goals depends on issues outside of science. Many of these issues have to do with worldviews and ethics, which are discussed later in this chapter.

## 1.5 Critical Thinking

Often in science we ask this question: "How do I know that what you just said is true?" Part of the answer lies in evidence, or data. Part of the answer lies in critical evaluation of the evidence.

An ability to think critically, clearly, and analytically about a problem may be the most valuable skill you can learn in any of your classes. As you know by now, many issues in environmental science are hotly disputed, with firm opinions and plenty of evidence on both sides. How do you evaluate contradictory evidence and viewpoints? **Critical thinking** is a term we use to describe logical, orderly, analytical assessment of ideas, evidence, and arguments. Developing this skill is essential for the course you are taking now. Critical thinking is also an extremely important skill for your life in general. You can use it when you evaluate the claims of a car salesman, a credit card offer, or the campaign rhetoric of a political candidate.

An important complication is that prominent authorities can vehemently disagree about a topic. Disagreements may be based on contradictory data, on different interpretations of the same data, or on different priorities. One expert might consider economic health the overriding priority; another might prioritize environmental quality. A third might worry only about company stock prices, which might depend on the outcome of an environmental policy debate. You can examine the validity of contradictory claims by practicing critical thinking.

## Critical thinking helps us analyze information

There are many different aspects of critical thinking. Much of the process is about asking, "what am I trying to accomplish here, and how will I know when I've succeeded?" You also need to ask "what is the source of my information, and how much does that matter?" **Analytical thinking** asks, "How can I break this problem down into its constituent parts?" **Creative thinking** asks, "How might I approach this problem in new and inventive ways?" **Logical thinking** asks, "Does the structure of my argument make sense?" **Reflective thinking** asks, "What does it all mean?"

All these thinking strategies will help you in this class. They challenge us to examine information in a systematic, purposeful, and responsible manner. These approaches help us discover hidden ideas and meanings, develop strategies for evaluating reasons and conclusions in arguments, recognize the differences between facts and values, and avoid jumping to conclusions (table 1.4).

Notice that many critical thinking processes are self-reflective and self-correcting. Critical thinking isn't critical in the sense of finding fault; rather it is about identifying unspoken assumptions, beliefs, priorities, or motives (fig. 1.17). Often uncovering these unspoken factors contributes to honesty and humility in yourself, too: if you ask "How do I know that what *I* just said is true?" then you are practicing critical thinking, and that question is likely to lead you to new and interesting insights.

## What do you need to think critically?

We all use critical or reflective thinking at times. Suppose a television commercial tells you that a new breakfast cereal is tasty and good for you. You may be suspicious and ask

**Figure 1.17** Critical thinking evaluates premises, contradictions, and assumptions. Was this sign, in the middle of a popular beach near Chicago, the only way to reduce human exposure to bacteria? What other strategies might there be? Why was this one chosen? Who might be affected?

yourself a few questions: What do they mean by *good*? Good for whom or what? Does *tasty* simply mean more sugar and salt? Might the sources of this information have other motives besides your health and happiness? You probably practice this kind of critical analysis regularly.

Here are some steps you can use in critical thinking:

1. *Identify and evaluate premises and conclusions in an argument.* What is the basis for the claims made here? What evidence is presented to support these claims, and what conclusions are drawn from this evidence? If the premises and evidence are reasonable, do the conclusions truly follow from them?

2. *Acknowledge and clarify uncertainties, vagueness, equivocation, and contradictions.* Do the terms used have more than one meaning? If so, are all participants in the argument using the same meanings? Is ambiguity or equivocation deliberate? Can all the claims be true simultaneously?

3. *Distinguish between facts and values.* Can claims be tested? (If so, these are statements of fact and should be verifiable by gathering evidence.) Are claims made about the worth or lack of worth of something? (If so, these are value statements or opinions and probably cannot be verified objectively.)

4. *Recognize and assess assumptions.* Given the backgrounds and views of the protagonists, what underlying reasons might there be for the premises, evidence, or conclusions presented? Does anyone have an "axe to grind" or a personal agenda in this issue? What does s/he think you know, need, want, or believe? Is there a hidden message based on race, gender, ethnicity, economics, or some belief system that distorts this discussion?

| Table 1.4 | Steps in Critical Thinking |
| --- |
| 1. What is the purpose of my thinking? |
| 2. What precise question am I trying to answer? |
| 3. Within what point of view am I thinking? |
| 4. What information am I using? |
| 5. How am I interpreting that information? |
| 6. What concepts or ideas are central to my thinking? |
| 7. What conclusions am I aiming toward? |
| 8. What am I taking for granted; what assumptions am I making? |
| 9. If I accept the conclusions, what are the implications? |
| 10. What would the consequences be if I put my thoughts into action? |

*Source:* R. Paul, National Council for Critical Thinking.

5. *Distinguish source reliability or unreliability.* What qualifies the experts on this issue? What special knowledge or information do they have? What evidence do they present? How can we determine whether the information offered is accurate, true, or even plausible?

6. *Recognize and understand conceptual frameworks.* What are the basic beliefs, attitudes, and values that this person, group, or society holds? What dominating philosophy or ethics control their outlooks and actions? How do these beliefs and values affect the way people view themselves and the world around them? If there are conflicting or contradictory beliefs and values, how can these differences be resolved?

## Critical thinking helps you learn environmental science

In this book, you will have many opportunities to practice critical thinking skills. Every chapter includes facts, figures, opinions, and theories. Are all of them true? Probably not. They were the best information available when this text was written, but new evidence is always emerging. Data change constantly, as does our interpretation of data.

When reading this text, hearing the news, or watching television, try to distinguish between statements of fact and opinion. Ask yourself if the premises support the conclusions drawn from them. Although most of us try to be fair and even-handed in presenting controversies, our personal biases and values—some of which we may not even recognize—affect how we see issues and present arguments. Watch for cases in which you need to think for yourself, and use your critical and reflective thinking skills to uncover the truth.

You'll find more on critical thinking, as well as some useful tips on how to study effectively, on our web page at www.mhhe.com/cunningham6e.

## 1.6 Where Do Our Ideas About the Environment Come From?

Historically, many societies have degraded the resources on which they depended, while others have lived in relative harmony with their surroundings. Today our burgeoning population and our technologies that accelerate resource exploitation have given environmental degradation increased urgency.

Many of our current responses to these changes are rooted in the writings of relatively recent environmental thinkers. Their work can be grouped, for the sake of simplicity, into about four distinct stages: 1) resource conservation for optimal use; 2) nature preservation for moral and aesthetic reasons; 3) concern over health and ecological consequences of pollution; 4) global environmental citizenship. These stages are not mutually exclusive. You might embrace them all simultaneously. As you read this section, consider why you agree with those you find most appealing.

### Nature protection has historic roots

Recognizing human misuse of nature is not unique to modern times. Plato complained in the fourth century B.C. that Greece once was blessed with fertile soil and clothed with abundant forests of fine trees. After the trees were cut to build houses and ships, however, heavy rains washed the soil into the sea, leaving only a rocky "skeleton of a body wasted by disease." Springs and rivers dried up, while farming became all but impossible. Despite these early observations, most modern environmental ideas developed in response to resource depletion associated with more recent agricultural and industrial revolutions.

Some of the earliest recorded scientific studies of environmental damage were carried out in the eighteenth century by French or British colonial administrators, many of whom were trained scientists and who observed rapid soil loss and drying wells that resulted from intensive colonial production of sugar and other commodities. Some of these colonial administrators considered responsible environmental stewardship as an aesthetic and moral priority, as well as an economic necessity. These early conservationists observed and understood the connections between deforestation, soil erosion, and local climate change. The pioneering British plant physiologist Stephen Hales, for instance, suggested that conserving green plants preserves rainfall. His ideas were put into practice in 1764 on the Caribbean island of Tobago, where about 20 percent of the land was marked as "reserved in wood for rains."

Pierre Poivre, an early French governor of Mauritius, an island in the Indian Ocean, was appalled at the environmental and social devastation caused by destruction of wildlife (such as the flightless dodo) and the felling of ebony forests on the island by early European settlers. In 1769 Poivre ordered that one-quarter of the island be preserved in forests, particularly on steep mountain slopes and along waterways. Mauritius remains a model for balancing nature and human needs. Its forest reserves shelter a larger percentage of its original flora and fauna than most other human-occupied islands.

### Resource waste triggered pragmatic resource conservation (stage 1)

Many historians consider the publication of *Man and Nature* in 1864 by geographer George Perkins Marsh as the wellspring of environmental protection in North America. Marsh, who also was a lawyer, politician, and diplomat, traveled widely around the Mediterranean as part of his diplomatic duties in Turkey and Italy. He read widely in the classics (including Plato) and personally observed the damage caused by excessive grazing by goats and sheep and by the deforestation of steep hillsides. Alarmed by the wanton destruction and profligate waste of resources still occurring on the American frontier in his lifetime, he warned of its ecological consequences. Largely because of his book, national forest reserves were established in the United States in 1873 to protect dwindling timber supplies and endangered watersheds.

Among those influenced by Marsh's warnings were U.S. President Theodore Roosevelt and his chief conservation adviser, Gifford Pinchot (fig. 1.18 a and b). In 1905 Roosevelt, who was the leader of the populist, progressive movement, moved forest management out of the corruption-filled Interior Department into the Department of Agriculture. Pinchot, who was the first American-born professional forester, became the first chief of the new Forest Service. He put resource management on an honest, rational, and

(a) President Teddy Roosevelt

(b) Gifford Pinchot

(c) John Muir

(d) Aldo Leopold

**Figure 1.18** Some early pioneers of the American conservation movement. (a) President Teddy Roosevelt and his main advisor (b) Gifford Pinchot emphasized pragmatic resource conservation, while (c) John Muir and (d) Aldo Leopold focused on ethical and aesthetic relationships.

**Figure 1.19** A conservationist might say this forest was valuable as a supplier of useful resources, including timber and fresh water. A preservationist might argue that this ecosystem is important for its own sake. Many people are sympathetic with both outlooks.

scientific basis for the first time in American history. Together with naturalists and activists such as John Muir, Roosevelt and Pinchot established the framework of the national forest, park, and wildlife refuge system. They passed game protection laws and tried to stop some of the most flagrant abuses of the public domain. In 1908 Pinchot organized and chaired the White House Conference on Natural Resources, perhaps the most prestigious and influential environmental meeting ever held in the United States. Pinchot also was governor of Pennsylvania and founding head of the Tennessee Valley Authority, which provided inexpensive power to the southeastern United States.

The basis of Roosevelt's and Pinchot's policies was pragmatic **utilitarian conservation**. They argued that the forests should be saved "not because they are beautiful or because they shelter wild creatures of the wilderness, but only to provide homes and jobs for people." Resources should be used "for the greatest good, for the greatest number, for the longest time." "There has been a fundamental misconception," Pinchot wrote, "that conservation means nothing but husbanding of resources for future generations. Nothing could be further from the truth. The first principle of conservation is development and use of the natural resources now existing on this continent for the benefit of the people who live here now. There may be just as much waste in neglecting the development and use of certain natural resources as there is in their destruction." This pragmatic approach still can be seen in the multiple-use policies of the U.S. Forest Service.

## Ethical and aesthetic concerns inspired the preservation movement (stage 2)

John Muir (fig. 1.18c), amateur geologist, popular author, and first president of the Sierra Club, strenuously opposed Pinchot's utilitarian policies. Muir argued that nature deserves to exist for its own sake, regardless of its usefulness to us. Aesthetic and spiritual values formed the core of his philosophy of nature protection. This outlook prioritizes **preservation** because it emphasizes the fundamental right of other organisms—and nature as a whole—to exist and to pursue their own interests (fig. 1.19). Muir wrote, "The world, we are told, was made for man. A presumption that is totally unsupported by the facts. . . . Nature's object in making animals and plants might possibly be first of all the happiness of each one of them. . . . Why ought man to value himself as more than an infinitely small unit of the one great unit of creation?"

Muir, who was an early explorer and interpreter of California's Sierra Nevada range, fought long and hard for establishment of Yosemite and Kings Canyon National Parks. The National Park Service, established in 1916, was first headed by Muir's disciple, Stephen Mather, and has always been oriented toward preservation of nature rather than consumptive uses. Muir's preservationist ideas have often been at odds with Pinchot's utilitarian approach. One of Muir and Pinchot's biggest battles was over the damming of Hetch Hetchy Valley in Yosemite. Muir regarded flooding the valley a sacrilege against nature. Pinchot, who championed publicly owned utilities, viewed the dam as a way to free San Francisco residents from the clutches of greedy water and power monopolies.

In 1935, pioneering wildlife ecologist Aldo Leopold (fig. 1.18d) bought a small, worn-out farm in central Wisconsin. A dilapidated chicken shack, the only remaining building, was remodeled into a rustic cabin. Working together with his children, Leopold planted thousands of trees in a practical experiment in restoring the health and beauty of the land. "Conservation," he wrote, "is the positive

# Sustainable development
## What does it mean? What does it have to do with environmental science?

*Sustainable development is a goal.* The aim is to meet the needs of people today without compromising resources and environmental systems for future generations. In this context, the term "development" refers to improving access to health care, education, and other conditions necessary for a healthy and productive life, especially in regions of extreme poverty. Meeting the needs of people now, while also guarding those resources for their great-great grandchildren, is both a steep challenge and a good idea.

**What parts of it are achievable, and how?** In general, development means equitable economic growth, which supports better education, housing, and health care. Often development involves accelerated extraction of natural resources, such as more mining, forestry, or conversion of forests and wetlands to farmlands. Sometimes development involves more efficient use of resources or growth in parts of the economy that don't depend on resource extraction, such as education, health care, or knowledge-based economic activities.

Some resources can be enhanced, for example, through reforestation, maintaining fish nurseries, or careful management of soil resources, to use them without depletion for future generations.

Here are ten key factors necessary for sustainable development, according to the United Nations agreement on development, Agenda 21.

CL 1.1

1. **Combating poverty** is a central goal because poverty reduces access to health care, education, and other essential components of development. ▶

CL 1.2

2. **Reducing resource consumption** is a global consideration, but wealthy regions are responsible for most of the world's consumption. For example, the United States and Europe have less than 15 percent of the world's population, but these regions consume about half of the world's metals, food, energy, and other resources. ◀

3. **Population growth** leads to ever-greater resource demands, because all people need some resources. Better family planning, ensuring that all children are wanted, is a matter of justice, resource supply, and economic and social stability for states as well as for families.

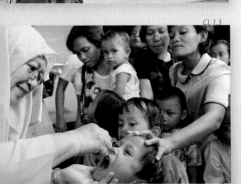

CL 1.3

4. **Health care,** especially for children and mothers (◀), is essential for a productive life. Underdeveloped areas such as that shown above can lead to disease, accidents, respiratory and digestive impairments, and other conditions. Without health, economic security is at risk, and poverty can persist through generations.

5. **Sustainable cities** are key because over half of humanity now lives in cities. Sustainable development involves ensuring that cities are healthy places to live and that they cause minimal environmental impact. ▼

CL 1.4

*Environmental science is essential to sustainable development* because it helps us understand how environmental systems work, how they are degraded, and what factors can help restore them. Studying environmental science can prepare you to aid human development and environmental quality, both at home and abroad, through better policies, resource protection, and planning.

CL 1.5

**10. Agriculture and rural development** affect the lives of the nearly half of humanity who don't live in cities. Improving conditions for billions of rural people, including more sustainable farming systems, soil stewardship to help stabilize yields, and access to land, can help reduce populations in urban slums. ◄

CL 1.6

**9. Combating desertification and drought** through better management of water resources can save farms, ecosystems, and lives. Often removal of vegetation and soil loss make drought worse, and a few bad rainfall years can convert a landscape to desert-like conditions. ►

**8. Combating deforestation and protecting biodiversity** go together because much of the world's biodiversity is in forests. We also depend on forests for water resources, climate regulation, and resources including food, wood, medicines, and building materials. Other key zones of biodiversity include coral reefs, wetlands, and coastal areas. ►

CL 1.7

**7. Protection of the atmosphere** is essential for minimizing the rate of climate change (▼) and for reducing impacts of air pollution on people, plants, and infrastructure.

These ten ideas and others were described in Agenda 21 of the United Nations Conference on Environment and Development (the "Earth Summit") in Rio de Janeiro, Brazil, in 1992. Laying out priorities for stewardship of resources and equity in development, the document known as Agenda 21 was a statement of principles for guiding development policies. This document has no legal power, but it does represent an agreement in principle by the more than 200 countries participating in that 1992 conference.

CL 1.8

**6. Environmental policy** needs to guide decision making in local and national governments, to ensure that environmental quality is protected before it gets damaged, and to set agreed-upon rules for resource use. ▲

## Can You Explain:

1. **What is the relationship between environmental quality and health?**

2. **Why is sustainable development an issue for people in wealthy countries to consider?**

3. **Examine the central photo carefully. What health risks might affect the people you see? What do you suppose the rate of material consumption is here, compared to your neighborhood? Why?**

exercise of skill and insight, not merely a negative exercise of abstinence or caution." The shack became a writing refuge and became the main focus of *A Sand County Almanac,* a much beloved collection of essays about our relation with nature. In it, Leopold wrote, "We abuse land because we regard it as a commodity belonging to us. When we see land as a community to which we belong, we may begin to use it with love and respect." Together with Bob Marshall and two others, Leopold was a founder of the Wilderness Society.

## Rising pollution levels led to the modern environmental movement (stage 3)

The undesirable effects of pollution probably have been recognized as long as people have been building smoky fires. In 1723 the acrid coal smoke in London was so severe that King Edward I threatened to hang anyone who burned coal in the city. In 1661 the English diarist John Evelyn complained about the noxious air pollution caused by coal fires and factories and suggested that sweet-smelling trees be planted to purify city air. Increasingly dangerous smog attacks in Britain led, in 1880, to formation of a national Fog and Smoke Committee to combat this problem. But nearly a century later, London's air (like that of many cities) was still bad. In 1952 an especially bad episode turned midday skies dark and may have caused 12,000 deaths. This event was extreme, but noxious air was common in many large cities.

The tremendous expansion of chemical industries during and after World War II added a new set of concerns to the environmental agenda. *Silent Spring,* written by Rachel Carson (fig. 1.20a) and published in 1962, awakened the public to the threats of pollution and toxic chemicals to humans as well as other species. The movement she engendered might be called **modern environmentalism** because its concerns extended to include both natural resources and environmental pollution.

Two other pioneers of this movement were activist David Brower and scientist Barry Commoner (fig. 1.20b and c). Brower, as executive director of the Sierra Club, Friends of the Earth, and Earth Island Institute, introduced many of the techniques of environmental lobbying and activism, including litigation, testifying at regulatory hearings, book and calendar publishing, and use of mass media for publicity campaigns. Commoner, who was trained as a molecular biologist, has been a leader in analyzing the links between science, technology, and society. Both activism and research remain hallmarks of the modern environmental movement.

Under the leadership of a number of other brilliant and dedicated activists and scientists, the environmental agenda was expanded in the 1970s, to most of the issues addressed in this textbook, such as human population growth, atomic weapons testing and atomic power, fossil fuel extraction and use, recycling, air and water pollution, and wilderness protection. Environmentalism has become well established in the public agenda since the first national Earth Day in 1970. A majority of Americans now consider themselves environmentalists, although there is considerable variation in what that term means.

(a) Rachel Carson

(b) David Brower

(c) Barry Commoner

(d) Wangari Maathai

**Figure 1.20** Among many distinguished environmental leaders in modern times, (a) Rachel Carson, (b) David Brower, (c) Barry Commoner, and (d) Wangari Maathai stand out for their dedication, innovation, and bravery.

## Environmental quality is tied to social progress (stage 4)

Many people today believe that the roots of the environmental movement are elitist—promoting the interests of a wealthy minority, who can afford to vacation in wilderness. In fact, most environmental leaders have seen social justice and environmental equity as closely linked. Gifford Pinchot, Teddy Roosevelt, and John Muir all strove to keep nature accessible to everyone, at a time when public lands, forests, and waterways were increasingly controlled by a few wealthy individuals and private corporations. The idea of national parks, one of our principal strategies for nature conservation, is to provide public access to natural beauty and outdoor recreation. Aldo Leopold, a founder of the Wilderness Society, promoted ideas of land stewardship among farmers, fishers, and hunters. Robert Marshall, also a founder of the Wilderness Society, campaigned all his life for social and economic justice for low-income groups. Both Rachel Carson and Barry Commoner were principally interested in environmental health—an issue that is especially urgent for low-income, minority, and inner-city residents. Many of these individuals grew up in working class families, so their sympathy with social concerns is not surprising.

Increasingly, environmental activists are linking environmental quality and social progress on a global scale (fig. 1.21). One of the core concepts of modern environmental thought is

**Figure 1.21** Environmental scientists increasingly try to address both public health and environmental quality. The poorest populations often suffer most from environmental degradation.

**sustainable development**, the idea that economic improvement for the world's poorest populations is possible without devastating the environment. This idea became widely publicized after the Earth Summit, a United Nations meeting held in Rio de Janeiro, Brazil, in 1992. The Rio meeting was a pivotal event because it brought together many diverse groups. Environmentalists and politicians from wealthy countries, indigenous people and workers struggling for rights and land, and government representatives from developing countries all came together and became more aware of their common needs.

Some of today's leading environmental thinkers come from developing nations, where poverty and environmental degradation together plague hundreds of millions of people. Dr. Wangari Maathai of Kenya is a notable example. In 1977, Dr. Maathai (fig. 1.20d) founded the Green Belt Movement in her native Kenya as a way of both organizing poor rural women and restoring their environment. Beginning at a small, local scale, this organization has grown to more than 600 grassroots networks across Kenya. They have planted more than 30 million trees while mobilizing communities for self-determination, justice, equity, poverty reduction, and environmental conservation. Dr. Maathai was elected to the Kenyan Parliament and served as Assistant Minister for Environment and Natural Resources. Her leadership has helped bring democracy and good government to her country. In 2004, she received the Nobel Peace Prize for her work, the first time a Nobel has been awarded for environmental action. In her acceptance speech, she said, "Working together, we have proven that sustainable development is possible; that reforestation of degraded land is possible; and that exemplary governance is possible when ordinary citizens are informed, sensitized, mobilized and involved in direct action for their environment."

Photographs of the earth from space (see fig. 1.2) provide a powerful icon for the fourth wave of ecological concern,

which might be called **global environmentalism**. Such photos remind us how small, fragile, beautiful, and rare our home planet is. We all share an environment at this global scale. As Ambassador Adlai Stevenson noted, in his 1965 farewell address to the United Nations, we now need to worry about the life-support systems of the planet as a whole. He went on to say in this speech, "We cannot maintain it half fortunate, half miserable, half confident, half despairing, half slave to the ancient enemies of mankind and half free in a liberation of resources undreamed of until this day. No craft, no crew, can travel with such vast contradictions. On their resolution depends the security of us all."

## Conclusion

Environmental science gives us useful tools and ideas for understanding both environmental problems and new solutions to those problems. We face many severe and persistent problems, including human population growth, contaminated water and air, climate change, and biodiversity losses. We can also see many encouraging examples of progress. Human population growth rates have slowed, the extent of habitat preserves has expanded greatly in recent years, we have promising new energy options, and in many regions we have made improvements in air and water quality.

Both poverty and affluence are linked to environmental degradation. Impoverished populations, desperate for cropland, often clear forests and eliminate wildlife habitat. Lacking water treatment, they contaminate water supplies. Illness from contaminated water often leads to a cycle of environmental degradation, illness, and poverty. Affluence also has great environmental costs. Wealthy populations can afford to consume or degrade extraordinary amounts of resources, including energy, water, paper, food, and soil. Differences between the rich and poor can be measured in terms of life expectancy, infant mortality, and other measures of well-being, in addition to income levels.

Science helps us analyze and resolve these problems because it provides an orderly, methodical approach to examining problems. Ideally, scientists are skeptical about evidence and cautious about conclusions. The scientific method provides an approach to doing this: it involves developing a hypothesis and collecting data to test it. Analyzing data often involves statistics, which provide some simple approaches to evaluating and comparing observations.

Critical thinking also provides orderly steps for analyzing the assumptions and logic of arguments. Critical thinking is an essential skill, both in school and in life.

Environmental thought has evolved in response to environmental deterioration. Conservation focuses on maintaining usable resources; preservation focuses on maintaining nature for its own sake. Throughout history, these ideas have been closely tied to concerns for social equity, for the rights of low-income people to have access to resources and to a healthy environment. In recent years these twin concerns have expanded to recognize the possibilities of change in developing countries, and the global interconnections of environmental and social concerns.

1. Describe why fishing has changed at Apo Island, and the direct and indirect effects on people's lives.

2. What are some basic assumptions of science?

3. Distinguish between a hypothesis and a theory.

4. Describe the steps in the scientific method.

5. What is probability? Give an example.

6. In a graph, which axis represents the independent variable? The dependent variable?

7. What's the first step in critical thinking according to table 1.4?

8. Distinguish between utilitarian conservation and biocentric preservation. Name two environmental leaders associated with each of these philosophies.

9. Why do some experts regard water as the most critical natural resource for the twenty-first century?

10. Where in figure 1.6a does the most dramatic warming occur?

11. Describe some signs of hope in overcoming global environmental problems.

12. What is the link between poverty and environmental quality?

13. Define *sustainability* and *sustainable development*.

# Critical Thinking and Discussion Questions

Apply the principles you have learned in this chapter to discuss these questions with other students.

1. How do you think the example of Apo Island's marine sanctuary meets the criteria of being scientifically sound, economically sustainable, and socially acceptable? If you were studying this situation, what information would you look for to support or refute this conclusion?

2. The analytical approaches of science are suitable for answering many questions. Are there some questions that science cannot answer? Why or why not?

3. Many social theorists argue that there is no such thing as objective truth or an impartial observer. If you were researching a controversial topic—perhaps whether marine reserves improve fishing and lead to economic development—what steps would you take to try to maintain objectivity and impartiality?

4. Does the world have enough resources for 8 or 10 billion people to live decent, secure, happy, fulfilling lives? What do those terms mean to you? Try to imagine what they mean to others in our global village.

5. Suppose you wanted to study the environmental impacts of a rich versus a poor country. What factors would you examine, and how would you compare them?

# Data Analysis | Working with Graphs

Do you find it easier to evaluate trends in a graph or in a table of numbers? Many people find the visual presentation of a graph quicker to read than a table. But reading graphs takes practice, and it takes some patience. This exercise asks you to examine different kinds of graphs, as preparation for reading many others that will follow in this book. Solidifying this skill is extremely important for studying environmental science—and many other topics.

### Examining Relationships

Many graphs show the relationship between two variables. Usually we want to know whether changes in one variable are associated with changes in the other. For example, has per capita income gone up or down as time has passed (fig. 1)? Or does fishing tend to be better or worse where there are more marine preserves (fig. 2)?

These two graphs have different styles because they show slightly different kinds of information. In figure 1, lines connect the data points to show that they represent changing values for a place. This graph, of course, shows several places simultaneously. Here, the question the graph answers is *whether there is a change* in income, and how great the change is. In figure 2, on the other hand, the question is *whether there is a relationship* between *x* and *y*.

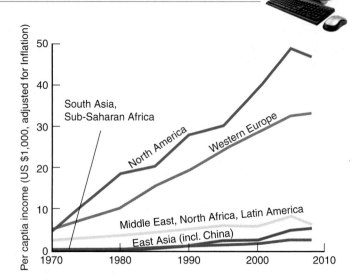

**Figure 1** Per capita income in different regions (in 2008 dollars). Overall income has climbed, but the gap between rich and poor countries as grown faster. *Data Source:* World Bank.

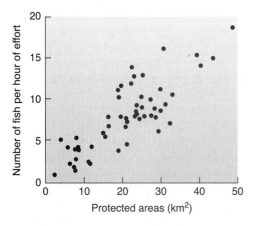

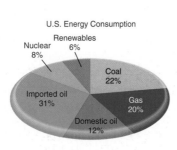

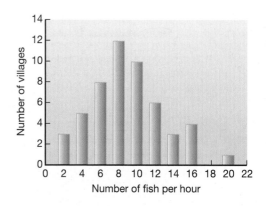

**Figure 2** A scatter plot shows the relationship of *x* and *y* for many observations. Here each observation is a village.

**Figure 3** A pie chart shows proportions.

**Figure 4** A bar graph shows values for classes or groups.

Some graphs ask *what is the relative distribution* of something? A pie chart is a common, easy-to-read method of showing the sizes of portions of a whole, for example, percentages of total energy consumption (fig. 3). Bar charts also show relative amounts of something. For example, figure 4 shows relative amounts of villages with small and large fish catches. Note that we often use the words "graph" and "chart" interchangeably.

### Elements of a Graph

The first step in reading a graph is to look at its elements. By convention, we put the dependent variable on the vertical (Y) axis and the independent (or explanatory) variable on the horizontal (X) axis. Axes are labeled, and tic marks show values along the axes.

Whenever you look at a graph, you should ask yourself a few questions to be sure you understand it. Answer the following questions for figure 1:

1. What is the subject of the graph?
2. What is the independent variable?
3. What is the dependent variable?
4. Does the independent variable really change independently of the other variable?
5. What are the units on the X-axis? What is the magnitude of the values (how small and how big are the numbers)?

6. What are the units on the Y-axis? What is the magnitude of the values?
7. When there are multiple lines, what is the difference in magnitude between the highest and lowest lines (here, in dollars) at the left end of the graph? What is the difference at the right end? Has the difference gotten bigger or smaller?
8. What do the trends in the graph mean? What factors might explain the changes you see?

Answer these questions again, this time using figure 2. Instead of question 7, since there are no lines on this scatter plot, you should ask yourself if the dots form a fairly linear pattern or a loose cloud with no direction. If they form a linear pattern, does the line go upward? Downward? Is it flat? What would those different patterns mean?

9. For review, describe the following:
   • a scatter plot
   • a bar chart
   • a pie chart
   • a line graph
   • a dependent variable
   • the X-axis

# 2 Environmental Systems
## Connections, Cycles, Flows, and Feedback Loops

The Everglades Ecosystem provides critical breeding habitat for many species, including these great egrets.

*Most institutions demand unqualified faith; but the institution of science makes skepticism a virtue.*

— ROBERT KING MERTON

# CASE STUDY

## Working to Rescue an Ecosystem

All living things need nutrients to grow. One of the key nutrients is phosphorus (denoted as P in the periodic table of the elements). Plants use phosphorus for energy transfer in photosynthesis, and the element is an essential part of all proteins, cells, oils, starches, and sugars—many of which we enjoy eating. If you fertilize your house plants or garden, P is one of the three main elements that you're likely to find in your fertilizer (two others are nitrogen, N, and potassium, K). Fertilizer has phosphorus because usually it is in short supply in soil, so shortages of P often slow plant growth, even when plenty of sunshine and moisture are available.

This common chemical element is also costing Florida about half a billion dollars, as the state tries to rescue the Everglades ecosystem and the Everglades National Park from ecological disaster.

The Everglades are one of the United States' most spectacular wetlands. This "river of grass," is a broad, slow-moving sheet of water that starts in springs near Orlando, then flows south through Lake Okeechobee and toward the Gulf of Mexico. Islands of trees hold rookeries of egrets, ibises, storks, and herons. American alligators swim in pools and canals, and endangered Florida panthers lurk in the forest. In the dry season, wading birds easily catch fish and frogs in shrinking pools. In the wet season widespread floods rejuvenate the wetlands.

The Everglades is a jewel among America's national parks, but it is also a struggling ecosystem. The first threat to the area was drainage of the expansive flows that define the region. More than a century ago, sugarcane farmers discovered that the Everglades' rich, black peat was fantastically fertile, with abundant nutrients stored in partly decayed plant matter in the soggy bottom of the wetlands. To aid farmers in the Everglades Agricultural Area, the Army Corps of Engineers dug 1,600 km of drainage canals and built 1,000 km of levees and 200 water control structures to redirect water from the wetlands to the ocean.

Drainage allowed conversion of land to farms and towns. As towns and cities grew, they clamored for more water diversions and flood control. Over time however, those same cities have discovered that they need the precious water that is now sent to the ocean, and they've discovered that the Everglades is dying. Over 90 percent of the wading birds in the Everglades National Park have disappeared, as diminished wetlands provided fewer fish and frogs. For more than a quarter century, politicians, farmers, and ecologists have tried to initiate plans to restore some of the natural flow (fig. 2.1). More than $12 billion in restoration funds have been promised, although little has actually been accomplished in restoring the wetlands, the water supplies, or the ecosystem.

A second consequence of farming in the Everglades is phosphorus loading. Farmers add fertilizers to ensure abundant sugar crops, and tilling has unlocked nitrogen and phosphorus stored in the ancient peat. (Both nutrients matter, but in freshwater systems, phosphorus is usually the limiting nutrient. In marine systems, such as the Gulf of Mexico, nitrogen is usually the limiting nutrient.) Entering the normally nutrient-poor Everglades, excess phosphorus supports invasions of cattails and other weeds. The classic Everglades sawgrass community is being displaced by dense stands of cattails, where the birds have difficulty feeding.

### Progress in Nutrient Control

Dealing with nutrients turns out to be something Florida can readily do to help rescue the Everglades. As a first step, the state has helped sugar farmers reduce excess fertilizer applications and control runoff, and those efforts are producing measurable reductions in phosphorus. As a second step, the state agreed in 2009 to spend over $500 million in federal and state funds to purchase 73,000 acres of land from the U.S. Sugar Corporation, one of several large sugarcane growers in the area. Some of the land will be returned to wetland. Some will be reservoirs or managed wetlands designed to capture nutrients. The ecosystem will also regain some of the original water supply.

The $500 million cost is just part of the $2.2 billion initially proposed to purchase the entire 180,000 acres of U.S. Sugar property. Critics point out that a cheaper strategy would be to eliminate protective sugar import tariffs, which keep cheaper Brazilian and Cuban sugar out of the United States, or to reduce federal sugar subsidies that help keep the sugar growers in the Everglades. Even so, action on nutrient control in the Everglades is an invaluable first step toward restoration of a precious and critical environment.

Understanding the functions of P, N, and other elements is a central theme in environmental science. In this chapter we'll examine some of the common elements used by living things. We'll look at how systems work, and we'll consider how imbalances in key nutrients can cause system instability in this and many other ecosystems.

To view images of the sugar fields, the Everglades, and nearby development, take a look at Google Earth placemarks, which you can find at **EnvironmentalScience-Cunningham.blogspot.com**.

| Historic flow | Current flow |
| --- | --- |

**Figure 2.1** The Everglades was once a vast slowly flowing wetland, but development has redirected and polluted much of the water.

## 2.1 Systems Describe Interactions

Managing nutrients and water in the Everglades is an effort to restore a stable system, one with an equal amount of inputs and outputs and with balanced populations of animals and plants. This balance maintains overall stability and prevents dramatic change or collapse. In general, a **system** is a network of interdependent components and processes, with materials and energy flowing from one component of the system to another. The term "ecosystem" is probably familiar to you. This simple word represents complex assemblages of animals, plants, and their environment, through which materials and energy move. In a sense, you are a system consisting of millions of cells and complex organs, as well as the energy and matter that move through you.

The idea of systems is useful because it helps us organize our thoughts about the inconceivably complex phenomena around us. For example, an ecosystem might consist of countless animals, plants, and their physical surroundings. Keeping track of all the elements and relationships in an ecosystem would probably be an impossible task. But if we step back and think about components in terms of their roles—plants, herbivores, carnivores, and decomposers—and the relationships among them, then we can start to comprehend how the system works (fig. 2.2).

We can use some general terms to describe the components of a system. A simple system consists of state variables (also called compartments), which store resources such as energy, matter, or water; and flows, or the pathways by which those resources move from one state variable to another. In figure 2.2, the plant and animals represent state variables. The plant represents many different plant types, all of which are things that store solar energy and create carbohydrates from carbon, water, and sunlight. The rabbit represents herbivores in general, all of which consume plants, then store energy, water, and carbohydrates until they are used, transformed, or consumed by a carnivore. We can describe the flows in terms of herbivory, predation, or photosynthesis, all processes that transfer energy and matter from one state variable to another.

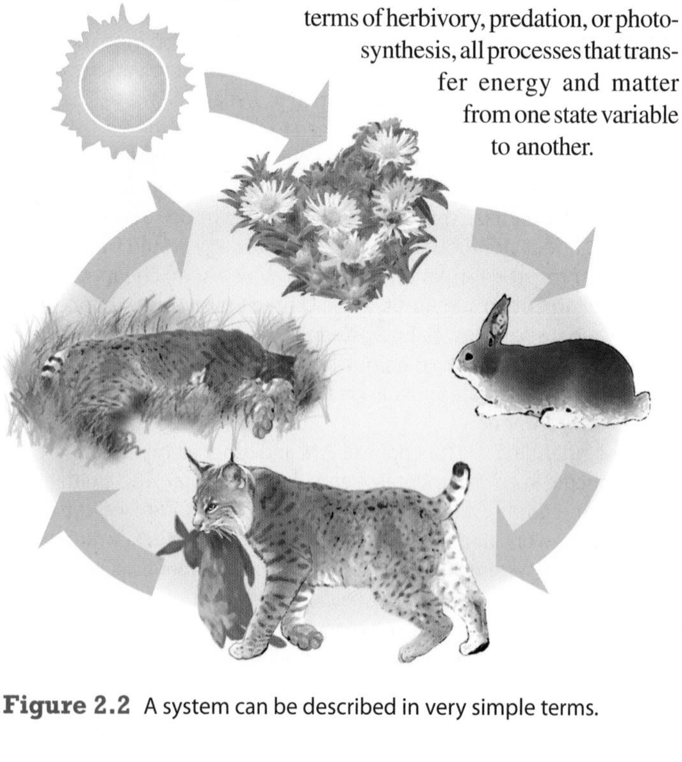

**Figure 2.2** A system can be described in very simple terms.

It may seem cold and analytical to describe a rabbit or a flower as a state variable, but it is also helpful to do so. When we start discussing natural complexity in the simple terms of systems, we can identify common characteristics. Understanding these characteristics can help us diagnose disturbances or changes in the system: for example, if rabbits become too numerous, herbivory can become too rapid for plants to sustain. Overgrazing can lead to widespread collapse of this system. In terms of the Everglades, excess phosphorus has led to explosive plant growth, which interferes with predators (birds catching fish). Let's examine some of the common characteristics we can find in systems.

### Systems can be described in terms of their characteristics

**Open systems** are those that receive inputs from their surroundings and produce outputs that leave the system. Almost all natural systems are open systems. In principle, a **closed system** exchanges no energy or matter with its surroundings, but these are rare. Often we think of pseudo-closed systems, those that exchange only a little energy but no matter with their surroundings. **Throughput** is a term we can use to describe the energy and matter that flow into, through, and out of a system. Larger throughput might expand the size of state variables. For example, you can consider your household economy in terms of throughput. If you get more income, you have the option of enlarging your state variables (bank account, car, television, etc.). Usually an increase in income is also associated with an increase in outflow (the money spent on that new car and TV). Often, a larger system would generally tolerate, or require, larger throughput. A large wetland can absorb and process more nutrients and energy than a small wetland. Thus the Everglades have been absorbing excess nutrients for decades and have not yet utterly collapsed; rather, elements of the system are beginning to disappear. Systems can also have **thresholds** or "tipping points," where rapid change suddenly occurs. Such abrupt changes are a worry for ecologists in the Everglades.

A wetland is an open system, which receives nutrients and water from upstream. Plants and algae transform the nutrients into vegetation, which then become part of a fish, then of a heron that catches the fish. An increase in nutrients can support an increase in plant growth, which allows greater nutrient uptake, which supports greater plant growth, and so on. This increasing response, where an increase in the state variable leads to further increases in the same variable, is called a **positive feedback** (fig. 2.3).

When positive feedbacks accelerate out of control, the system can become unstable and change dramatically. A term for excessive growth in wetlands, in response to abundant nutrients, is eutrophication (chapter 10). The runaway growth of plants leads to biological collapse, or the death of most living things (at least temporarily) of a wetland system. In contrast, a **negative feedback** has a dampening effect: too many fish in a pond leads to food scarcity, which leads to fish mortality (fig. 2.3). Your body is a system with many active negative feedback mechanisms: for example, if you exercise, you become hot, so your skin sweats to keep you from overheating.

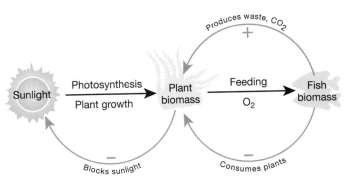

**Figure 2.3** Positive feedbacks (*red*) and negative feedbacks (*blue*) can increase or decrease the size of state variables (or compartments) in a system.

## Systems can exhibit stability

Negative feedback loops tend to maintain stability in a system. We often think of systems exhibiting **homeostasis**, or a tendency to remain more or less stable and unchanging. Your body temperature stays remarkably constant despite dramatic changes in your environment and your activity levels. Changing by just a few degrees is extremely unusual—just think how little temperature change is involved in a serious fever. Natural systems such as wetlands tend to be stable, too, at least on the scale of years or decades. Over long periods of time, they may change quite a bit, though. Systems might also fluctuate: the population of a species in a wetland might rise and fall repeatedly, or in a cycle, and that cycle might be part of the system's normal functioning.

**Disturbances**, events that destabilize or change the system, might cause these population fluctuations. Seasonal drought in a wetland, for example, will periodically reduce some populations and increase others. Disturbances might also be large enough to cause more dramatic and persistent change. Drought could lead to fires, which could remove trees but encourage undergrowth for years, decades, or longer. A flush of nutrient inputs, a hurricane, or drainage canals are all disturbances.

Sometimes ecosystems show **resilience**, or an ability to return to their previous condition after disturbance. Other times ecosystems undergo a **state shift**, where conditions do not return to "normal." For example, rising sea levels could change a freshwater coastal swamp (with standing trees) into a tidal salt marsh. State shifts are a concern in many situations: when a forest is logged, does it return to its original conditions? Or does it transform into something entirely new? That depends on many factors.

**Emergent properties** are another interesting aspect of systems. Sometimes a system is more than the sum of its parts. A wetland has complex varieties of living organisms, colorful dragonflies, intricate webs of relationships that can reinforce each other through their complexity. This system has larger influences beyond its borders—helping to stabilize local temperatures and humidity, producing biodiversity that spills over into surrounding areas, or supporting migrant waterfowl. A wetland also has beautiful sights and sounds that may be irrelevant to its functioning as a system, but that we appreciate nonetheless (fig. 2.4). In a similar way, you are a system made up of component parts, but you have many emergent properties, including your ability to think, share ideas, build relationships, sing, and dance.

**Figure 2.4** Emergent properties of systems, including beautiful sights and sounds, make them exciting to study.

# 2.2 Elements of Life

What exactly are the materials that flow through a system like the Everglades wetlands? If a principal concern in such a wetland system is the control of nutrients, such as $NO_3$ and $PO_4$, as well as maintaining $O_2$ levels, just what exactly are these elements, and why are they important? What does "$O_2$" or "$NO_3$" mean? In this section we will examine matter and the elements and compounds on which all life depends. In the sections that follow, you'll consider how organisms use those elements and compounds to capture and store solar energy, and how materials cycle through global systems, as well as ecosystems.

To understand how these compounds form and move, we need to begin with some of the fundamental properties of matter and energy.

## Matter is recycled but doesn't disappear

Everything that takes up space and has mass is **matter**. Matter exists in three distinct states—solid, liquid, and gas—due to differences in the arrangement of its constitutive particles. Water, for example, can exist as ice (solid), as liquid water, or as water vapor (gas).

Matter also behaves according to the principle of **conservation of matter**: Under ordinary circumstances, matter is neither created nor destroyed but rather is recycled over and over again. It can be tranformed or recombined, but it doesn't disappear; everything goes somewhere. Some of the molecules that make up your body probably contain atoms that once made up the body of a dinosaur and most certainly were part of many smaller prehistoric organisms, as chemical elements have been used and reused by living organisms.

How does this principle apply to human relationships with the biosphere? Particularly in affluent societies, we use natural resources to produce an incredible amount of "disposable" consumer goods. If everything goes somewhere, where do the things we dispose of go after the garbage truck leaves? As the sheer amount of "disposed-of stuff" increases, we are having greater problems finding places to put it. Ultimately, there is no "away" where we can throw things we don't want any more.

| Table 2.1 | Functions of Some Common Elements | |
|---|---|---|
| Function | Elements | Comments |
| Fertilizers | N nitrogen<br>P phosphorus<br>K potassium | Essential components of proteins, cells, other biological compounds; essential fertilizers for plants. |
| Organic compounds | C carbon<br>O oxygen<br>H hydrogen | Form the basic structure of cells and other components of living things, in combination with many other elements. |
| Metals | Fe iron<br>Al aluminum<br>Au gold | Generally malleable; most (not all) react readily with other elements |
| Toxic elements | Pb lead<br>Hg mercury<br>As arsenic | Many are metals that can interfere with processes in nervous systems |

## Elements have predictable characteristics

Matter consists of **elements** such as P (phosphorus) or N (nitrogen), which are substances that cannot be broken down into simpler forms by ordinary chemical reactions. Each of the 115 known elements (92 natural, plus 23 created under special conditions) has distinct chemical characteristics.

Just four elements—oxygen, carbon, hydrogen, and nitrogen (symbolized as O, C, H, and N)—make up more than 96 percent of the mass of most living organisms. Water is composed of two H atoms and one O atom (written $H_2O$). All the elements are listed in the Periodic Table of the Elements, which you can find on the fold out map in the back of this book. Often, though, it's enough to pay attention to just a few (table 2.1).

**Atoms** are the smallest particles that exhibit the characteristics of an element. Atoms are composed of a nucleus, made of positively charged protons and electrically neutral neutrons, circled constantly by negatively charged electrons (fig. 2.5). Electrons, which are tiny in comparison to the other particles, orbit the nucleus at the speed of light.

Each element is listed in the periodic table according to the number of protons per atom, called its **atomic number**. The number of neutrons in the atoms of an element can vary slightly. Thus, the atomic mass, which is the sum of the protons and neutrons in each nucleus, also can vary. We call forms of a single element that differ in atomic mass **isotopes**. For example, hydrogen, the lightest element, normally has only one proton (and no neutrons) in its

nucleus. A small percentage of hydrogen atoms have one proton and one neutron. We call this isotope deuterium ($^2H$). An even smaller percentage of natural hydrogen called tritium ($^3H$) has one proton plus two neutrons. The heavy form of nitrogen ($^{15}N$) has one more neutron in its nucleus than does the more common $^{14}N$. Both these nitrogen isotopes are stable but some isotopes are unstable—that is, they may spontaneously emit electromagnetic energy, or subatomic particles, or both. Radioactive waste and nuclear energy result from unstable isotopes of elements such as uranium and plutonium.

Why should you know about isotopes? Although you might not often think of it this way, both stable and unstable types are in the news every day. Unstable, radioactive isotopes are distributed in the environment by both radioactive waste (potentially from nuclear power plants) and nuclear bombs. Every time you hear debates about nuclear power plants—which might produce the energy that powers the lights you are using right now—or about nuclear weapons in international politics, the core issue is radioactive isotopes. Understanding why they are dangerous, because emitted particles damage living cells, is important as you decide your opinions about these policy issues.

Stable isotopes—those that do not change mass by losing neutrons—are important because they help us understand climate history and many other environmental processes. This is because lightweight isotopes move differently than heavier ones. For example, oxygen occurs as both $^{16}O$ (a lighter isotope) and $^{18}O$ (a heavier isotope). Some water molecules ($H_2O$) contain the lightweight oxygen isotopes. These lightweight molecules evaporate, and turn into rain or snowfall, *slightly* more easily than heavier water molecules, especially in cool weather. Consequently, ice stored in glaciers during cool periods in the earth's history will contain slightly higher proportions of light-isotope water, with $^{16}O$. Ice from warm periods contains relatively higher proportions of $^{18}O$. By examining the proportions of isotopes in ancient ice layers, climate scientists can deduce the earth's temperature from hundreds of thousands of years ago (chapter 9).

So while atoms, elements, and isotopes may seem a little arcane, they actually are fundamental to understanding climate change, nuclear weapons, and energy policy—all issues you can read about in the news almost any day of the week.

 6 protons

6 neutrons

 6 electrons

**Figure 2.5** As difficult as it may be to imagine when you look at a solid object, all matter is composed of tiny, moving particles, separated by space and held together by energy. This model represents a carbon-12 atom, with a nucleus containing six protons and six neutrons; the six electrons are represented as a fuzzy cloud of potential locations, rather than as individual particles.

## Electric charges keep atoms together

Atoms frequently gain or lose electrons, acquiring a negative or positive electrical charge. Charged atoms (or combinations of atoms) are called **ions**. Negatively charged ions (with one or more extra electrons) are *anions*. Positively charged ions are *cations*. A sodium (Na) atom, for example, can give up an electron to become a sodium ion ($Na^+$). Chlorine (Cl) readily gains electrons, forming chlorine ions ($Cl^-$).

Atoms often join to form **compounds**, or substances composed of different kinds of atoms (fig. 2.6). A pair or group of atoms that can exist as a single unit is known as a **molecule**. Some elements commonly occur as molecules, such as molecular oxygen ($O_2$) or molecular nitrogen ($N_2$), and some compounds can exist as molecules, such as glucose ($C_6H_{12}O_6$). In contrast to

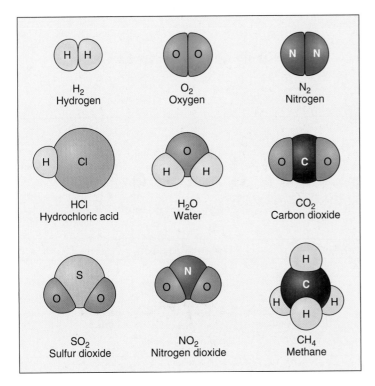

**Figure 2.6** These common molecules, with atoms held together by covalent bonds, are important components of the atmosphere or important pollutants.

these molecules, sodium chloride (NaCl, table salt) is a compound that cannot exist as a single pair of atoms. Instead it occurs in a large mass of Na and Cl atoms or as two ions, $Na^+$ and $Cl^-$, in solution. Most molecules consist of only a few atoms. Others, such as proteins, can include millions or even billions of atoms.

When ions with opposite charges form a compound, the electrical attraction holding them together is an *ionic bond*. Sometimes atoms form bonds by *sharing* electrons. For example, two hydrogen atoms can bond by sharing a single electron—it orbits the two hydrogen nuclei equally and holds the atoms together. Such electron-sharing bonds are known as *covalent bonds*. Carbon (C) can form covalent bonds simultaneously with four other atoms, so carbon can create complex structures such as sugars and proteins. Atoms in covalent bonds do not always share electrons evenly. An important example in environmental science is the covalent bonds in water ($H_2O$). The oxygen atom attracts the shared electrons more strongly than do the two hydrogen atoms. Consequently, the hydrogen portion of the molecule has a slight positive charge, while the oxygen has a slight negative charge. These charges create a mild attraction between water molecules, so that water tends to be somewhat cohesive. This fact helps explain some of the remarkable properties of water (see Exploring Science, p. 34).

When an atom gives up one or more electrons, we say it is *oxidized* (because it is very often oxygen that takes the electron, as bonds are formed with this very common and highly reactive element). When an atom gains electrons, we say it is *reduced*. Chemical reactions necessary for life involve oxidation and reduction: Oxidation of sugar and starch molecules, for example, is an important part of how you gain energy from food.

Breaking bonds requires energy, while forming bonds generally releases energy. Burning wood in your fireplace breaks up large molecules, such as cellulose, and forms many smaller ones, such as carbon dioxide and water. The net result is a release of energy (heat). Generally, some energy input (activation energy) is needed to initiate these reactions. In your fireplace, a match might provide the needed activation energy. In your car, a spark from the battery provides activation energy to initiate the oxidation (burning) of gasoline.

## Acids and bases release reactive $H^+$ and $OH^-$

Substances that readily give up hydrogen ions in water are known as **acids**. Hydrochloric acid, for example, dissociates in water to form $H^+$ and $Cl^-$ ions. In later chapters, you may read about acid rain (which has an abundance of $H^+$ ions), acid mine drainage, and many other environmental problems involving acids. In general, acids cause environmental damage because the $H^+$ ions react readily with living tissues (such as your skin or tissues of fish larvae) and with nonliving substances (such as the limestone on buildings, which erodes under acid rain).

Substances that readily bond with $H^+$ ions are called **bases** or alkaline substances. Sodium hydroxide (NaOH), for example, releases hydroxide ions ($OH^-$) that bond with $H^+$ ions in water. Bases can be highly reactive, so they also cause significant environmental problems. Acids and bases can also be essential to living things: The acids in your stomach help you digest food, for example, and acids in soil help make nutrients available to growing plants.

We describe acids and bases in terms of **pH**, the negative logarithm of its concentration of $H^+$ ions (fig. 2.7). Acids have a pH below 7; bases have a pH greater than 7. A solution of exactly pH 7 is "neutral." Because the pH scale is logarithmic, pH 6 represents *ten times* more hydrogen ions in solution than pH 7.

A solution can be neutralized by adding buffers, or substances that accept or release hydrogen ions. In the environment, for example, alkaline rock can buffer acidic precipitation, decreasing its acidity. Lakes with acidic bedrock, such as granite, are especially vulnerable to acid rain because they have little buffering capacity.

## Organic compounds have a carbon backbone

Organisms use some elements in abundance, others in trace amounts, and others not at all. Certain vital substances are concentrated within cells, while others are actively excluded. Carbon is a particularly important element because chains and rings of carbon atoms form the skeletons of **organic compounds**, the material of which biomolecules, and therefore living organisms, are made.

The four major categories of organic compounds in living things ("bio-organic compounds") are lipids, carbohydrates, proteins, and nucleic acids. Lipids (including fats and oils) store energy for cells, and they provide the core of cell membranes and other structures. Many hormones are also lipids. Lipids do not readily dissolve in water, and their structure is a chain of carbon atoms with attached hydrogen atoms. This structure makes them part of the family of hydrocarbons (fig. 2.8a). Carbohydrates (including sugars, starches, and cellulose) also store energy and provide structure to cells. Like

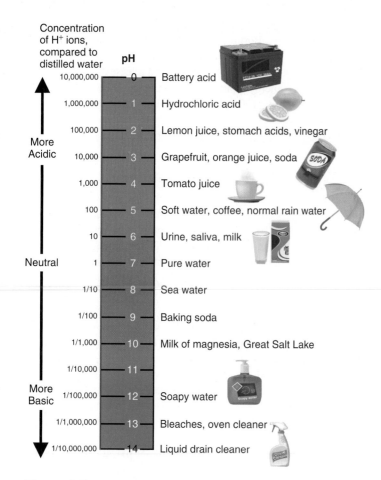

Concentration of H⁺ ions, compared to distilled water | pH

| Concentration | pH | |
|---|---|---|
| 10,000,000 | 0 | Battery acid |
| 1,000,000 | 1 | Hydrochloric acid |
| 100,000 | 2 | Lemon juice, stomach acids, vinegar |
| 10,000 | 3 | Grapefruit, orange juice, soda |
| 1,000 | 4 | Tomato juice |
| 100 | 5 | Soft water, coffee, normal rain water |
| 10 | 6 | Urine, saliva, milk |
| 1 | 7 | Pure water |
| 1/10 | 8 | Sea water |
| 1/100 | 9 | Baking soda |
| 1/1,000 | 10 | Milk of magnesia, Great Salt Lake |
| 1/10,000 | 11 | |
| 1/100,000 | 12 | Soapy water |
| 1/1,000,000 | 13 | Bleaches, oven cleaner |
| 1/10,000,000 | 14 | Liquid drain cleaner |

More Acidic

Neutral

More Basic

**Figure 2.7** The pH scale. The numbers represent the negative logarithm of the hydrogen ion concentration in water. Alkaline (basic) solutions have a pH greater than 7. Acids (pH less than 7) have high concentrations of reactive H⁺ ions.

lipids, carbohydrates have a basic structure of carbon atoms, but hydroxyl (OH) groups replace half the hydrogen atoms in their basic structure, and they usually consist of long chains of simple sugars. Glucose (fig. 2.8b) is an example of a very simple sugar.

Proteins are composed of chains of subunits called amino acids (fig. 2.8c). Folded into complex three-dimensional shapes, proteins provide structure to cells and are used for countless cell functions. Enzymes, such as those that release energy from lipids and carbohydrates, are proteins. Proteins also help identify disease-causing microbes, make muscles move, transport oxygen to cells, and regulate cell activity.

Nucleotides are complex molecules made of a five-carbon sugar (ribose or deoxyribose), one or more phosphate groups, and an organic nitrogen-containing base (fig. 2.8d). Nucleotides are extremely important as signaling molecules (they carry information between cells, tissues, and organs) and as sources of energy within cells. They also form long chains called *ribo*nucleic *a*cid (RNA) or **deoxyribonucleic *a*cid (DNA)** that are essential for storing and expressing genetic information. Only four kinds of nucleotides (adenine, guanine, cytosine, and thyamine) occur in DNA, but DNA contains millions of these molecules arranged in very specific sequences. These sequences of nucleotides provide genetic information, or instructions, for cells. These instructions direct the growth and development of an organism.

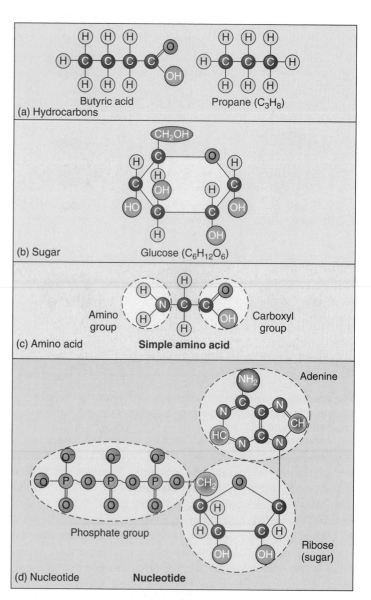

(a) Hydrocarbons — Butyric acid; Propane (C₃H₈)

(b) Sugar — Glucose (C₆H₁₂O₆)

(c) Amino acid — Simple amino acid; Amino group; Carboxyl group

(d) Nucleotide — Nucleotide; Adenine; Phosphate group; Ribose (sugar)

**Figure 2.8** The four major groups of biologically important organic molecules are based on repeating subunits of these carbon-based structures. Basic structures are shown for (a) butyric acid (a building block of lipids) and a hydrocarbon, (b) a simple carbohydrate, (c) a protein, and (d) a nucleic acid.

They also direct the formation of proteins or other compounds, such as those in melanin, a pigment that protects your skin from sunlight.

Long chains of DNA bind together to form a double helix (a two-stranded spiral, fig. 2.9). These chains replicate themselves when cells divide, so that as you grow, your DNA is reproduced in all your cells, from blood cells to hair cells. Since every individual (except identical twins) has a distinctive DNA pattern, DNA has proven useful in identifying individuals in forensics. Since DNA includes records of ancestors' DNA, it has allowed scientists to establish relationships, for example that dinosaurs were more closely related to birds than to lizards. Understanding DNA's structure has also allowed us to combine genes, for example, inserting disease resistant traits into food crops (chapter 7). See the related story "Bar-Coding Life" at **www.mhhe.com/cunningham6e**.

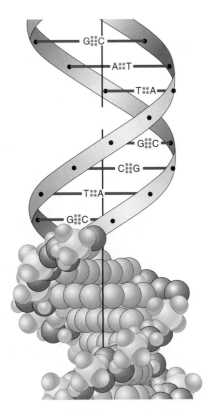

**Figure 2.9** A composite molecular model of DNA. The lower part shows individual atoms, while the upper part has been simplified to show the strands of the double helix held together by hydrogen bonds (small dots) between matching nucleotides (A, T, G, and C). A complete DNA molecule contains millions of nucleotides and carries genetic information for many specific, inheritable traits.

## Cells are the fundamental units of life

All living organisms are composed of **cells**, minute compartments within which the processes of life are carried out (fig. 2.10). Microscopic organisms such as bacteria, some algae, and protozoa are composed of single cells. Most higher organisms are multicellular, usually with many different cell varieties. Your body, for instance, is composed of several trillion cells of about two hundred distinct types. Every cell is surrounded by a thin but dynamic membrane of lipid and protein that receives information about the exterior world and regulates the flow of materials between the cell and its environment. Inside, cells are subdivided into tiny organelles and subcellular particles that provide the machinery for life. Some of these organelles store and release energy. Others manage and distribute information. Still others create the internal structure that gives the cell its shape and allows it to fulfill its role.

## Nitrogen and phosphorus are key nutrients

As you know from the opening case study, nitrogen and phosphorus are key components of ecosystems. These are limiting elements because they are essential for plant and animal growth, but normally they are not abundant in ecosystems.

Notice that in figure 2.8 there are only a few different elements that are especially common. Carbon (C) is captured from air by green plants, and oxygen (O) and hydrogen (H) derive from air or water. The most important additional elements are nitrogen (N) and phosphorus (P), which are essential parts of the complex proteins, lipids, sugars, and nucleic acids that keep you alive. Of course your cells use many other elements, but these are the most abundant. You derive all these elements by consuming molecules produced by green plants. Plants, however, must extract these elements from their environment. Low levels of N and P often limit growth in ecosystems where they are scarce. Abundance of N and P can cause runaway growth. In fertilizers, these elements often occur in the form of nitrate ($NO_3$), ammonium ($NH_4$), and phosphate ($PO_4$). Later in this chapter you will read more about how C, $H_2O$, N, and P circulate in our environment.

## 2.3 Energy

If matter is the material of which things are made, energy provides the force to hold structures together, tear them apart, and move them from one place to another. In this section we will look at some fundamental characteristics of these components of our world.

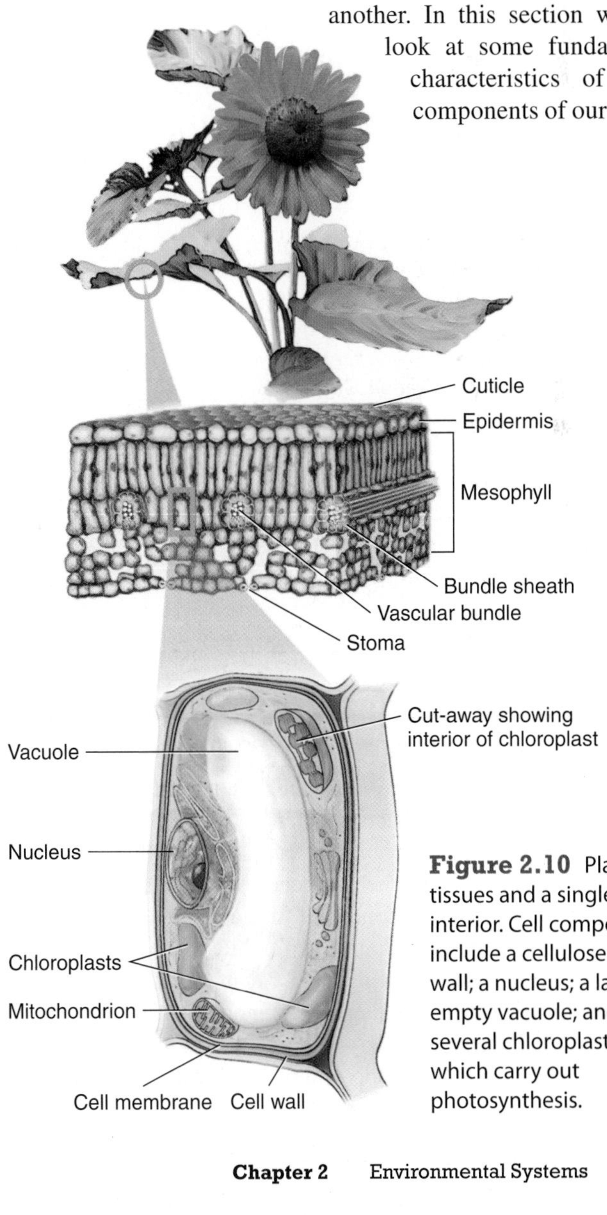

Cuticle

Epidermis

Mesophyll

Bundle sheath

Vascular bundle

Stoma

Cut-away showing interior of chloroplast

Vacuole

Nucleus

Chloroplasts

Mitochondrion

Cell membrane   Cell wall

**Figure 2.10** Plant tissues and a single cell's interior. Cell components include a cellulose cell wall; a nucleus; a large, empty vacuole; and several chloroplasts, which carry out photosynthesis.

# A "Water Planet"

If travelers from another solar system were to visit our lovely, cool, blue planet, they might call it Aqua rather than Terra because of its outstanding feature: the abundance of streams, rivers, lakes, and oceans of liquid water. Our planet is the only place we know where water exists as a liquid in any appreciable quantity. Water covers nearly three-fourths of the earth's surface and moves around constantly through evaporation, precipitation, and runoff that distribute nutrients, replenish freshwater supplies, and shape the land. Water makes up 60 to 70 percent of the weight of most living organisms. It fills cells, giving form and support to tissues. Among water's unique, almost magical qualities, are the following:

1. Water molecules are polar, that is, they have a slight positive charge on one side and a slight negative charge on the other side. Therefore, water readily dissolves polar or ionic substances, including sugars and nutrients, and carries materials to and from cells.

2. Water is the only inorganic liquid that occurs in nature under normal conditions at temperatures suitable for life. Most substances exist as either a solid or a gas, with only a very narrow liquid temperature range. Organisms synthesize organic compounds such as oils and alcohols that remain liquid at ambient temperatures and are therefore extremely valuable to life, but the original and predominant liquid in nature is water.

3. Water molecules are cohesive, tending to stick together tenaciously. You have experienced this property if you have ever done a belly flop off a diving board. Water has the highest surface tension of any common, natural liquid. Water also adheres to surfaces. As a result, water is subject to *capillary action*: it can be drawn into small channels. Without capillary action, movement of water and nutrients into groundwater reservoirs and through living organisms might not be possible.

4. Water is unique in that it expands when it crystallizes. Most substances shrink as they change from liquid to solid. Ice floats because it is less dense than liquid water. When temperatures fall below freezing, the surface layers of lakes, rivers, and oceans cool faster and freeze before deeper water. Floating ice then insulates underlying layers, keeping most water bodies liquid (and aquatic organisms alive) throughout the winter in most places. Without this feature, many aquatic systems would freeze solid in winter.

5. Water has a high heat of vaporization, using a great deal of heat to convert from liquid to vapor. Consequently, evaporating water is an effective way for organisms to shed excess heat. Many animals pant or sweat to moisten evaporative cooling surfaces. Why do you feel less comfortable on a hot, humid day than on a hot, dry day? Because the water vapor–laden air inhibits the rate of evaporation from your skin, thereby impairing your ability to shed heat.

6. Water also has a high specific heat; that is, a great deal of heat is absorbed before it changes temperature. The slow response of water to temperature change helps moderate global temperatures, keeping the environment warm in winter and cool in summer. This effect is especially noticeable near the ocean, but it is important globally.

All these properties make water a unique and vitally important component of the ecological cycles that move materials and energy and make life on earth possible.

Surface tension is demonstrated by the resistance of a water surface to penetration, as when it is walked upon by a water strider.

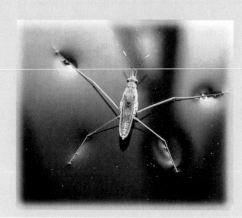

## Energy occurs in different types and qualities

**Energy** is the ability to do work such as moving matter over a distance or causing a heat transfer between two objects at different temperatures. Energy can take many different forms. Heat, light, electricity, and chemical energy are examples that we all experience. The energy contained in moving objects is called **kinetic energy**. A rock rolling down a hill, the wind blowing through the trees, water flowing over a dam (fig. 2.11), or electrons speeding around the nucleus of an atom are all examples of kinetic energy. **Potential energy** is stored energy that is available for use. A rock poised at the top of a hill and water stored behind a dam are examples of potential energy. **Chemical energy** stored in the food that you eat and the gasoline that you put into your car are also examples of potential energy that can be released to do useful work. Energy is often measured in units of heat (calories) or work (joules). One joule (J) is the work done when one kilogram is accelerated at one meter per second per second. One calorie is the amount of energy needed to heat one gram of pure water one degree Celsius. A calorie can also be measured as 4.184 J.

**Heat** describes the energy that can be transferred between objects of different temperature. When a substance absorbs heat, the kinetic energy of its molecules increases, or it may change state: a solid may become a liquid, or a liquid may become a gas. We sense

**Figure 2.11** Water stored behind this dam represents potential energy. Water flowing over the dam has kinetic energy, some of which is converted to heat.

change in heat content as change in temperature (unless the substance changes state).

An object can have a high heat content but a low temperature, such as a lake that freezes slowly in the fall. Other objects, like a burning match, have a high temperature but little heat content. Heat storage in lakes and oceans is essential to moderating climates and maintaining biological communities. Heat absorbed in changing states is also critical. As you will read in chapter 9, evaporation and condensation of water in the atmosphere helps distribute heat around the globe.

Energy that is diffused, dispersed, and low in temperature is considered low-quality energy because it is difficult to gather and use for productive purposes. The heat stored in the oceans, for instance, is immense but hard to capture and use, so it is low quality. Conversely, energy that is intense, concentrated, and high in temperature is high-quality energy because of its usefulness in carrying out work. The intense flames of a very hot fire or high-voltage electrical energy are examples of high-quality forms that are easy to use. Many of our alternative energy sources (such as wind) are diffuse compared to the higher-quality, more concentrated chemical energy in oil, coal, or gas.

## Thermodynamics describes the conservation and degradation of energy

Atoms and molecules cycle endlessly through organisms and their environment, but energy flows in a one-way path. A constant supply of energy—nearly all of it from the sun—is needed to keep biological processes running. Energy can be used repeatedly as it flows through the system, and it can be stored temporarily in the chemical bonds of organic molecules, but eventually it is released and dissipated.

The study of thermodynamics deals with how energy is transferred in natural processes. More specifically, it deals with the rates of flow and the transformation of energy from one form or quality to another. Thermodynamics is a complex, quantitative discipline, but you don't need a great deal of math to understand some of the broad principles that shape our world and our lives.

The **first law of thermodynamics** states that energy is *conserved;* that is, it is neither created nor destroyed under normal conditions. Energy may be transformed, for example, from the energy in a chemical bond to heat energy, but the total amount does not change.

The **second law of thermodynamics** states that, with each successive energy transfer or transformation in a system, less energy is available to do work. That is, energy is degraded to lower-quality forms, or it dissipates and is lost, as it is used. When you drive a car, for example, the chemical energy of the gas is degraded to kinetic energy and heat, which dissipates, eventually, to space. The second law recognizes that disorder, or **entropy**, tends to increase in all natural systems. Consequently, there is always less *useful* energy available when you finish a process than there was before you started. Because of this loss, everything in the universe tends to fall apart, slow down, and get more disorganized.

How does the second law of thermodynamics apply to organisms and biological systems? Organisms are highly organized, both structurally and metabolically. Constant care and maintenance is required to keep up this organization, and a continual supply of energy is required to maintain these processes. Every time some energy is used by a cell to do work, some of that energy is dissipated or lost as heat. If cellular energy supplies are interrupted or depleted, the result—sooner or later—is death.

## 2.4 Energy for Life

Where does the energy needed by living organisms come from? How is it captured and transferred among organisms? For nearly all life on earth, the sun is the ultimate energy source, and the sun's energy is captured by green plants. Green plants are often called **primary producers** because they create carbohydrates and other compounds using just sunlight, air, and water.

There are organisms that get energy in other ways, and these are interesting because they are exceptions to the normal rule. Deep in the earth's crust, or deep on the ocean floor, and in hot springs such as those in Yellowstone National Park, we can find extremophiles, organisms that gain their energy from **chemosynthesis**, or extracting energy from inorganic chemical compounds such as hydrogen sulfide ($H_2S$). Until 30 years ago, we knew almost nothing about these organisms and their ecosystems. Recent deep-sea exploration has shown that an abundance of astonishingly varied and abundant life occurs hundreds of meters deep on the ocean floor. These ecosystems cluster around thermal vents. Thermal vents are cracks where boiling-hot water, heated by magma in the earth's crust, escapes from the ocean floor. Here, microorganisms grow by oxidizing hydrogen sulfide; bacteria support an ecosystem that includes blind shrimp, giant tube worms, crabs, clams, and other organisms (fig. 2.12).

These fascinating systems are exciting and mysterious because we have discovered them so recently. They are also interesting because of their contrast to the incredible profusion of photosynthesis-based life we enjoy here at the earth's surface.

**Figure 2.12** A colony of tube worms and mussels clusters over a cool, deep-sea methane seep in the Gulf of Mexico.

## Green plants get energy from the sun

Our sun is a star, a fiery ball of exploding hydrogen gas. Its thermonuclear reactions emit powerful forms of radiation, including potentially deadly ultraviolet and nuclear radiation (fig. 2.13), yet life here is nurtured by, and dependent upon, this searing energy source.

Solar energy is essential to life for two main reasons. First, the sun provides warmth. Most organisms survive within a relatively narrow temperature range. In fact, each species has its own range of temperatures within which it can function normally. At high temperatures (above 40°C), most biomolecules begin to break down or become distorted and nonfunctional. At low temperatures (near 0°C), some chemical reactions of metabolism occur too slowly to enable organisms to grow and reproduce. Other

planets in our solar system are either too hot or too cold to support life as we know it. The earth's water and atmosphere help to moderate, maintain, and distribute the sun's heat.

Second, nearly all organisms on the earth's surface depend on solar radiation for life-sustaining energy, which is captured by green plants, algae, and some bacteria in a process called **photosynthesis**. Photosynthesis converts radiant energy into useful, high-quality chemical energy in the bonds that hold together organic molecules.

How much of the available solar energy is actually used by organisms? The amount of incoming solar radiation is enormous, about 1,372 watts/m² at the top of the atmosphere (imagine 13 100-watt light bulbs on every square meter of your ceiling). However, more than half of the incoming sunlight is reflected or absorbed by atmospheric clouds, dust, and gases. In particular, harmful, short wavelengths are filtered out by gases (such as ozone) in the upper atmosphere; thus, the atmosphere is a valuable shield, protecting life-forms from harmful doses of ultraviolet and other forms of radiation. Even with these energy reductions, however, the sun provides much more energy than biological systems can harness, and more than enough for all our energy needs if technology could enable us to tap it efficiently.

Of the solar radiation that does reach the earth's surface, about 10 percent is ultraviolet, 45 percent is visible, and 45 percent is infrared. Most of that energy is absorbed by land or water or is reflected into space by water, snow, and land surfaces. (Seen from outer space, Earth shines about as brightly as Venus.)

Of the energy that reaches the earth's surface, photosynthesis uses only certain wavelengths, mainly red and blue light. Most plants reflect green wavelengths, so that is the color they appear to us. Half of the energy plants absorb is used in evaporating water. In the end, only 1 to 2 percent of the sunlight falling on plants is available for photosynthesis. This small percentage represents the energy base for virtually all life in the biosphere!

## How does photosynthesis capture energy?

Photosynthesis occurs in tiny organelles called chloroplasts that reside within plant cells (see fig. 2.10). The most important key to this process is chlorophyll, a unique green molecule that

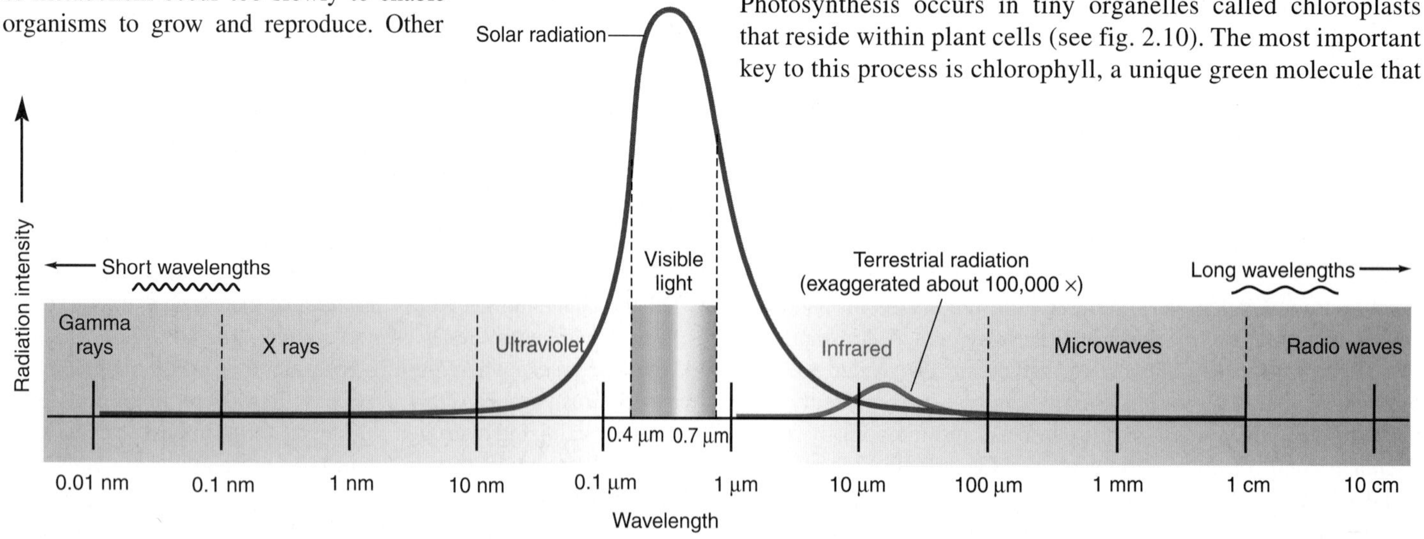

**Figure 2.13** The electromagnetic spectrum. Our eyes are sensitive to visible light wavelengths, which make up nearly half the energy that reaches the earth's surface (represented by the area under the "solar radiation" curve). Photosynthesizing plants use the most abundant solar wavelengths (light and infrared). The earth reemits lower-energy, longer wavelengths (shown by the "terrestrial radiation" curve), mainly the infrared part of the spectrum.

can absorb light energy and use it to create high-energy chemical bonds in compounds that serve as the fuel for all subsequent cellular metabolism. Chlorophyll doesn't do this important job all alone, however. It is assisted by a large group of other lipid, sugar, protein, and nucleotide molecules. Together these components carry out two interconnected cyclic sets of reactions (fig. 2.14).

Photosynthesis begins with a series of steps called light-dependent reactions: These occur only while the chloroplast is receiving light. Enzymes split water molecules and release molecular oxygen ($O_2$). This is the source of nearly all the oxygen in the atmosphere on which all animals, including you, depend for life. The light-dependent reactions also create mobile, high-energy molecules (adenosine triphosphate, or ATP, and nicotinamide adenine dinucleotide phosphate, or NADPH), which provide energy for the next set of processes, the light-independent reactions. As their name implies, these reactions do not use light directly. Here, enzymes extract energy from ATP and NADPH to add carbon atoms (from carbon dioxide) to simple sugar molecules, such as glucose. These molecules provide the building blocks for larger, more complex organic molecules.

In most temperate-zone plants, photosynthesis can be summarized in the following equation:

$$6H_2O + 6CO_2 + \text{solar energy} \xrightarrow[\text{chlorophyll}]{} C_6H_{12}O_6 \text{ (sugar)} + 6O_2$$

We read this equation as "water plus carbon dioxide plus energy produces sugar plus oxygen." The reason the equation uses six

water and six carbon dioxide molecules is that it takes six carbon atoms to make the sugar product. If you look closely, you will see that all the atoms in the reactants balance with those in the products. This is an example of conservation of matter.

You might wonder how making a simple sugar benefits the plant. The answer is that glucose is an energy-rich compound that serves as the central, primary fuel for all metabolic processes of cells. The energy in its chemical bonds—the ones created by photosynthesis—can be released by other enzymes and used to make other molecules (lipids, proteins, nucleic acids, or other carbohydrates), or it can drive kinetic processes such as movement of ions across membranes, transmission of messages, changes in cellular shape or structure, or movement of the cell itself in some cases. This process of releasing chemical energy, called **cellular respiration**, involves splitting carbon and hydrogen atoms from the sugar molecule and recombining them with oxygen to recreate carbon dioxide and water. The net chemical reaction, then, is the reverse of photosynthesis:

$$C_6H_{12}O_6 + 6O_2 \longrightarrow 6H_2O + 6CO_2 + \text{released energy}$$

Note that in photosynthesis, energy is *captured*, while in respiration, energy is *released*. Similarly, photosynthesis *uses* water and carbon dioxide to *produce* sugar and oxygen, while respiration does just the opposite. In both sets of reactions, energy is stored temporarily in chemical bonds, which constitute a kind of energy currency for the cell. Plants carry out both photosynthesis and respiration, but during the day, if light, water, and $CO_2$ are available, they have a net production of $O_2$ and carbohydrates.

We animals don't have chlorophyll and can't carry out photosynthetic food production. We do have the components for cellular respiration, however. In fact, this is how we get all our energy for life. We eat plants—or other animals that have eaten plants—and break down the organic molecules in our food through cellular respiration to obtain energy (fig. 2.15). In the process, we also consume oxygen and release carbon dioxide, thus completing the cycle of photosynthesis and respiration. Later in this chapter we will see how these feeding relationships work.

## 2.5 From Species to Ecosystems

While many biologists study life at the cellular and molecular level, ecologists study interactions at the species, population, biotic community, or ecosystem level. In Latin, *species* literally means *kind*. In biology, **species** refers to all organisms of the same kind that are genetically similar enough to breed in nature and produce live, fertile offspring. There are several qualifications and some important exceptions to this definition of species (especially among bacteria and plants), but for our purposes this is a useful working definition.

### Organisms occur in populations, communities, and ecosystems

A **population** consists of all the members of a species living in a given area at the same time. Chapter 4 deals further with population growth and dynamics. All of the populations

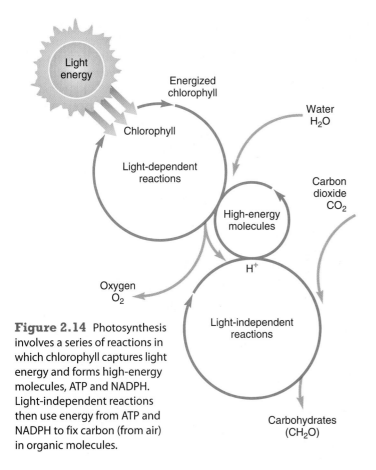

**Figure 2.14** Photosynthesis involves a series of reactions in which chlorophyll captures light energy and forms high-energy molecules, ATP and NADPH. Light-independent reactions then use energy from ATP and NADPH to fix carbon (from air) in organic molecules.

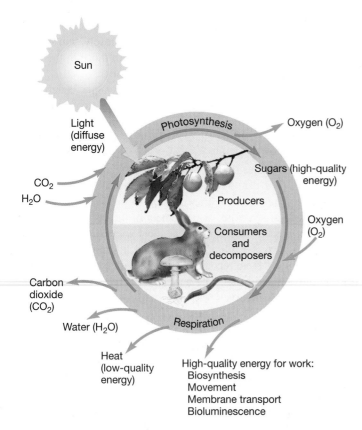

Sun

Light (diffuse energy)

Photosynthesis

Oxygen ($O_2$)

$CO_2$
$H_2O$

Sugars (high-quality energy)

Producers

Oxygen ($O_2$)

Consumers and decomposers

Carbon dioxide ($CO_2$)

Water ($H_2O$)

Respiration

Heat (low-quality energy)

High-quality energy for work:
Biosynthesis
Movement
Membrane transport
Bioluminescence

**Figure 2.15** Energy exchange in ecosystems. Plants use sunlight, water, and carbon dioxide to produce sugars and other organic molecules. Consumers use oxygen and break down sugars during cellular respiration. Plants also carry out respiration, but during the day, if light, water, and $CO_2$ are available, they have a net production of $O_2$ and carbohydrates.

of organisms living and interacting in a particular area make up a **biological community**. What populations make up the biological community of which you are a part? The population sign marking your city limits announces only the number of humans who live there, disregarding the other populations of animals, plants, fungi, and microorganisms that are part of the biological community within the city's boundaries. Characteristics of biological communities are discussed in more detail in chapter 3.

# Active Learning

## Food Webs

To what food webs do you belong? Make a list of what you have eaten today, and trace the energy it contained back to its photosynthetic source. Are you at the same trophic level in all the food webs in which you participate? Are there ways that you could change your ecological role? Might that make more food available for other people? Why, or why not?

An ecological system, or **ecosystem**, is composed of a biological community and its physical environment. The Everglades ecosystem, for example, is a complex community of different species that rely on water, sunlight, and nutrients from the surrounding environment. It is useful to think about the biological community and its environment together, because energy and matter flow through both. Understanding how those flows work is a major theme in ecology.

## Food chains, food webs, and trophic levels link species

Photosynthesis (and rarely chemosynthesis) is the base of all ecosystems. Organisms that produce organic material by photosynthesis, mainly green plants and algae, are therefore known as **producers**. One of the most important properties of an ecosystem is its **productivity**, the amount of **biomass** (biological material) produced in a given area during a given period of time. Photosynthesis is described as *primary productivity* because it is the basis for almost all other growth in an ecosystem. Manufacture of biomass by organisms that eat plants is termed *secondary productivity*. A given ecosystem may have very high total productivity, but if decomposers decompose organic material as rapidly as it is formed, the *net primary productivity* will be low. Remote sensing from aircraft or satellites allows us to measure productivity in large systems (see Exploring Science, p. 39).

In ecosystems, some consumers feed on a single species, but most consumers have multiple food sources. Similarly, some species are prey to a single kind of predator, but many species in an ecosystem are beset by several types of predators and parasites. In this way, individual food chains become interconnected to form a **food web**. Figure 2.16 shows feeding relationships among some of the larger organisms in a woodland and lake community. If we were to add all the insects, worms, and microscopic organisms that belong in this picture, however, we would have overwhelming complexity. Perhaps you can imagine the challenge ecologists face in trying to quantify and interpret the precise matter and energy transfers that occur in a natural ecosystem!

An organism's feeding status in an ecosystem can be expressed as its **trophic level** (from the Greek *trophe*, food). In our first example, the corn plant is at the producer level; it transforms solar energy into chemical energy, producing food molecules. Other organisms in the ecosystem are **consumers** of the chemical energy harnessed by the producers. An organism that eats producers is a primary consumer. An organism that eats primary consumers is a secondary consumer, which may, in turn, be eaten by a tertiary consumer, and so on. Most terrestrial food chains are relatively short (seeds ⟶ mouse ⟶ owl), but aquatic food chains may be quite long (microscopic algae ⟶ copepod ⟶ minnow ⟶ crayfish ⟶ bass ⟶ osprey). The length of a food chain also may reflect the physical characteristics of a particular ecosystem. A harsh arctic landscape generally has a much shorter food chain than a temperate or tropical one.

# Remote Sensing, Photosynthesis, and Material Cycles

Measuring primary productivity is important for understanding individual plants and local environments. Understanding the rates of primary productivity is also key to understanding global processes, such as material cycling, and biological activity:

- In global carbon cycles, how much carbon is stored by plants, how quickly is it stored, and how does carbon storage compare in contrasting environments, such as the Arctic and the tropics?
- How does this carbon storage affect global climates (chapter 9)?
- In global nutrient cycles, how much nitrogen and phosphorus wash offshore, and where?

How can environmental scientists measure primary production (photosynthesis) at a global scale? In a small, relatively closed ecosystem, such as a pond, ecologists can collect and analyze samples of all trophic levels. But that method is impossible for large ecosystems, especially for oceans, which cover 70 percent of the earth's surface. One of the newest methods of quantifying biological productivity involves remote sensing, or using data collected from satellite sensors that observe the energy reflected from the earth's surface.

As you have read in this chapter, chlorophyll in green plants *absorbs* red and blue wavelengths of light and *reflects* green wavelengths. Your eye receives, or senses, these green wavelengths. A white-sand beach, on the other hand, reflects approximately equal amounts of all light wavelengths that reach it from the sun, so it looks white (and bright!) to your eye. In a similar way, different surfaces of the earth reflect characteristic wavelengths. Snow-covered surfaces reflect light wavelengths; dark green forests with abundant chlorophyll-rich leaves—and ocean surfaces rich in photosynthetic algae and plants—reflect greens and near-infrared wavelengths. Dry, brown forests with little active chlorophyll reflect more red and less infrared energy than do dark green forests (fig. 1).

To detect land cover patterns on the earth's surface, we can put a sensor on a satellite that orbits the earth. As the satellite travels, the sensor receives and transmits to earth a series of "snapshots." One of the best known earth-imaging satellites, *Landsat 7*, produces images that cover an area 185 km (115 mi) wide, and each pixel represents an area of just 30 × 30 m on the ground. *Landsat* orbits approximately from pole to pole, so as the earth spins below the satellite, it captures images of the entire surface every 16 days. Another satellite, *SeaWiFS*, was designed mainly for monitoring biological activity in oceans (fig. 2). *SeaWiFS* follows a path similar to *Landsat*'s but it revisits each point on the earth every day and produces images with a pixel resolution of just over 1 km.

Since satellites detect a much greater range of wavelengths than our eyes can, they are able to monitor and map chlorophyll abundance. In oceans, this is a useful measure of ecosystem health, as well as carbon dioxide uptake. By quantifying and mapping primary production in oceans, climatologists are working to estimate the role of ocean ecosystems in moderating climate change: for example, they can estimate the extent of biomass production in the cold, oxygen-rich waters of the North Atlantic (fig. 2). Oceanographers can also detect near-shore areas where nutrients washing off the land surface fertilize marine ecosystems and stimulate high productivity, such as near the mouth of the Amazon or Mississippi River. Monitoring and mapping these patterns helps us estimate human impacts on nutrient flows from land to sea.

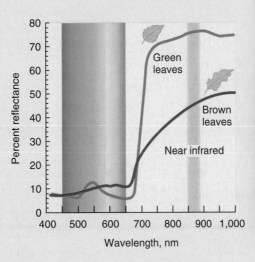

**Figure 1** Energy wavelengths reflected by green and brown leaves.

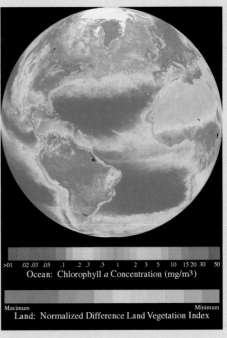

Ocean: Chlorophyll *a* Concentration (mg/m³)
>01  .02 .03 .05   .1   .2 .3   .5   1   2   3   5   10  15 20 30  50

Maximum    Minimum
Land: Normalized Difference Land Vegetation Index

**Figure 2** *SeaWiFS* image showing chlorophyll abundance in oceans and plant growth on land (normalized difference vegetation index).

Organisms can be identified both by the trophic level at which they feed and by the *kinds* of food they eat (fig. 2.17). **Herbivores** are plant eaters, **carnivores** are flesh eaters, and **omnivores** eat both plant and animal matter. What are humans? We are natural omnivores. You can see this because we have teeth for tearing (like a cat) and for grinding (like a horse).

One of the most important trophic levels is occupied by the many kinds of organisms that remove and recycle the dead bodies

**Figure 2.16** Each time an organism feeds, it becomes a link in a food chain. In an ecosystem, food chains become interconnected when predators feed on more than one kind of prey, thus forming a food web. The arrows in this diagram indicate the direction in which matter and energy are transferred through feeding relationships.

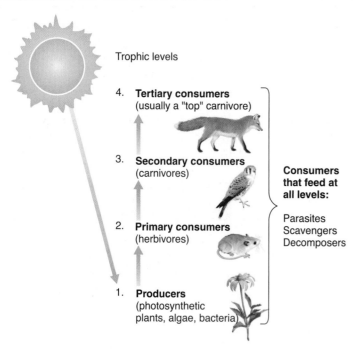

**Figure 2.17** Trophic levels describe an organism's position in a food chain. Some consumers feed on all trophic levels.

and waste products of others. **Scavengers** such as crows, jackals, and vultures clean up dead carcasses of larger animals. **Detritivores** such as ants and beetles consume litter, debris, and dung, while **decomposer** organisms such as fungi and bacteria complete the final break-

down and recycling of organic materials. It could be argued that these microorganisms are second in importance only to producers, because without their activity nutrients would remain locked up in the organic compounds of dead organisms and discarded body wastes, rather than being made available to successive generations of organisms.

### Ecological pyramids describe trophic levels

If we consider organisms according to trophic levels, they often form a pyramid, with a broad base of primary producers and only a few individuals in the highest trophic levels. While there is endless variation in the organization of ecosystems, the pyramid idea helps us describe generally how energy and matter move through ecosystems (see A Closer Look, p. 42).

## 2.6 Biogeochemical Cycles and Life Processes

The elements and compounds that sustain us are cycled endlessly through living things and through the environment. As the great naturalist John Muir said, "When one tugs at a single thing in nature, he finds it attached to the rest of the world." On a global scale, this movement is referred to as biogeochemical cycling. Substances can move quickly or slowly: Carbon might reside in a plant for days or weeks, in the atmosphere for days or months, in your body for hours, days, or years. The earth stores carbon (in coal or oil, for example) for millions of years. When human activities increase flow rates or reduce storage time, these materials can become pollutants. Here we will explore some of the pathways

**Figure 2.18** The hydrologic cycle. Most exchange occurs with evaporation from oceans and precipitation back to oceans. About one-tenth of water evaporated from oceans falls over land, is recycled through terrestrial systems, and eventually drains back to oceans in rivers.

involved in cycling several important substances: water, carbon, nitrogen, sulfur, and phosphorus.

## The hydrologic cycle

The path of water through our environment is perhaps the most familiar material cycle, and it is discussed in greater detail in chapter 10 (fig. 2.18). Most of the earth's water is stored in the oceans, but solar energy continually evaporates this water, and winds distribute water vapor around the globe. Water that condenses over land surfaces, in the form of rain, snow, or fog, supports all terrestrial (land-based) ecosystems. Living organisms emit the moisture they have consumed through respiration and perspiration. Eventually this moisture reenters the atmosphere or enters lakes and streams, from which it ultimately returns to the ocean again.

As it moves through living things and through the atmosphere, water is responsible for metabolic processes within cells, for maintaining the flows of key nutrients through ecosystems, and for global-scale distribution of heat and energy (chapter 9). Water performs countless services because of its unusual properties (see Exploring Science, p. 32). Water is so important that, when astronomers look for signs of life on distant planets, traces of water are the key evidence they seek.

## The carbon cycle

Carbon serves a dual purpose for organisms: (1) it is a structural component of organic molecules, and (2) chemical bonds in carbon compounds provide metabolic energy. The **carbon cycle** begins

with photosynthetic organisms taking up carbon dioxide ($CO_2$) (fig. 2.19). This is called carbon-fixation because carbon is changed from gaseous $CO_2$ to less mobile organic molecules. Once a carbon atom is incorporated into organic compounds, its path to recycling may be very quick or extremely slow. Imagine for a moment what happens to a simple sugar molecule you swallow in a glass of fruit juice. The sugar molecule is absorbed into your bloodstream, where it is made available to your cells for cellular respiration or the production of more complex biomolecules. If it is used in respiration, you may exhale the same carbon atom as $CO_2$ in an hour or less, and a plant could take up that exhaled $CO_2$ the same afternoon.

Alternatively, your body may use that sugar molecule to make larger organic molecules that become part of your cellular structure. The carbon atoms in the sugar molecule could remain a part of your body until it decays after death. Similarly, carbon in the wood of a thousand-year-old tree will be released only when fungi and bacteria digest the wood and release carbon dioxide as a by-product of their respiration.

Sometimes recycling takes a very long time. Coal and oil are the compressed, chemically altered remains of plants and microorganisms that lived millions of years ago. Their carbon atoms (and hydrogen, oxygen, nitrogen, sulfur, etc.) are not released until the coal and oil are burned. Enormous amounts of carbon also are locked up as calcium carbonate ($CaCO_3$), used to build shells and skeletons of marine organisms from tiny protozoans to corals. The world's extensive surface limestone deposits are biologically formed calcium carbonate from ancient oceans, exposed by geological events. The carbon in limestone has been locked away for millennia, which is probably the fate of carbon currently being

# How do energy and matter move through systems?

**Movement of energy and matter unites the parts of a system.** in the Everglades (opening case study), movement of water and nutrients supports photosynthesis, which supports the ecosystem. Recently the Everglades ecosystem has been destabilized by increased nutrient input, which increases photosynthesis and the accumulation of biomass (in invasive cattails).

For ecosystems in general, it is helpful to group organisms by **trophic levels** (feeding levels). In general, *primary producers* (organisms that produce organic matter, mainly green plants) are consumed by *herbivores* (plant eaters), which are consumed by *primary carnivores* (meat eaters), which are consumed by *secondary carnivores*. *Decomposers* consume at all levels and provide energy and matter to producers.

## Why do we find a pyramid of biomass?

Each trophic level requires a great deal of biomass at lower levels because energy is lost through growth, heat, respiration, and movement. This inefficiency is consistent with the second principle of thermodynamics, that energy dissipates and degrades to lower levels as it moves through a system.

A **general rule of thumb** is that only about 10 percent of the energy in one trophic level is represented in the next higher level. For example, it takes roughly 100 kg of clover to make 10 kg of rabbit, and 10 kg of rabbit to make 1 kg of fox.

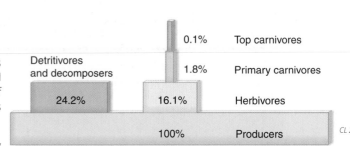

| | |
|---|---|
| | 0.1% Top carnivores |
| Detritivores and decomposers | 1.8% Primary carnivores |
| 24.2% | 16.1% Herbivores |
| 100% | Producers |

*CL 2.1*

In this example, numbers show the percentage of energy that is incorporated into biomass at the next level. Here, decomposers are grouped with producers. ▲

*CL 2.2*

## Why is there so much less energy in each successive trophic level?

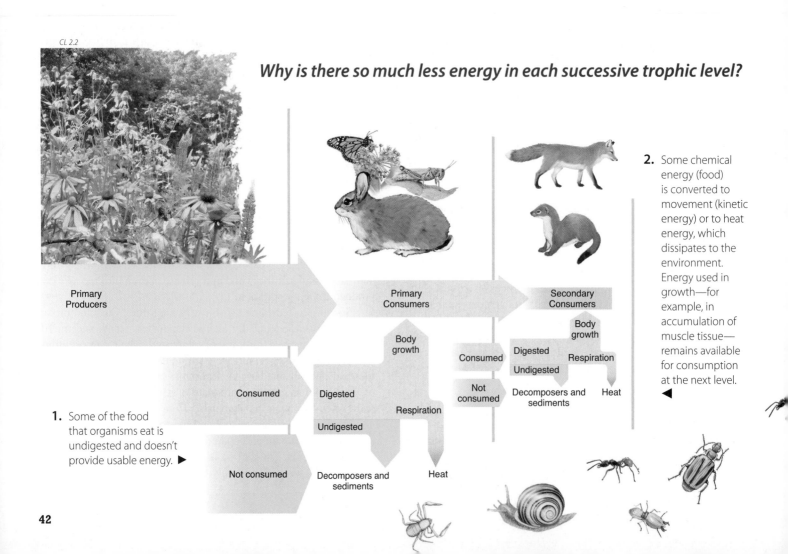

Primary Producers

Consumed

**1.** Some of the food that organisms eat is undigested and doesn't provide usable energy. ▶

Not consumed

Digested

Undigested

Decomposers and sediments

Primary Consumers

Body growth

Respiration

Heat

Consumed

Not consumed

Secondary Consumers

Digested

Undigested

Body growth

Respiration

Decomposers and sediments

Heat

**2.** Some chemical energy (food) is converted to movement (kinetic energy) or to heat energy, which dissipates to the environment. Energy used in growth—for example, in accumulation of muscle tissue—remains available for consumption at the next level. ◀

42

## What happens if the pyramid is disrupted?

Ecosystems undergo many types of disturbances and disruptions. Often ecosystems recover in time; sometimes they shift to a new type of system structure. Forest fire (▼) is a disturbance that eliminates primary production for a short time. Fire also accelerates movement of nutrients through the system, so that nutrients once locked up in standing trees become available to support a burst of new growth.

CL 2.3

Removal of other trophic levels also disturbs an ecosystem. If there are too many predators, prey species will decline or disappear. An overabundance of foxes, for example, may eliminate the rabbit population. With too few rabbits, the foxes may die off, or they may find alternate prey, which can further destabilize the system.

On the other hand, removal of a higher trophic level can also destabilize a system: if foxes were removed, rabbits might become overabundant and overgraze the primary producers (plants).

Sometimes a pyramid can be temporarily inverted. The biomass pyramid, for instance, can be inverted by periodic fluctuations in producer populations. For example, low plant and algal biomass are present during winter in temperate aquatic ecosystems.

### By the numbers

We often think of a pyramid in terms of the number of organisms, rather than amount of biomass in each level. The pyramid at right is a general model. In this pyramid, many smaller organisms support one organism at the next trophic level. So 1,000 m² of grassland might contain 1,500,000 producers (plants), which support 200,000 herbivores, which support 90,000 primary carnivores, which support one top carnivore. ▶

**Don't forget the little things.** A single gram of soil can contain hundreds of millions of bacteria, algae, fungi, and insects.

CL 2.5

CL 2.4

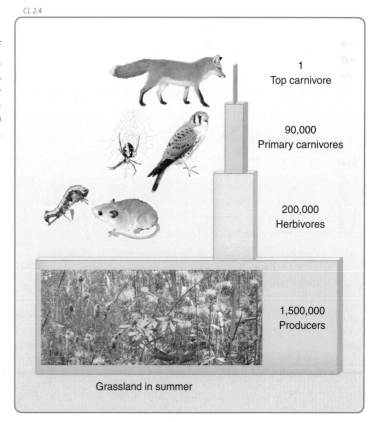

1
Top carnivore

90,000
Primary carnivores

200,000
Herbivores

1,500,000
Producers

Grassland in summer

---

### Can You Explain:

1. **At mainly how many trophic levels do you eat? Is your food pyramid large or small?**

2. **Does your trophic level matter in terms of the structure and stability of the ecosystems you occupy?**

3. **Explain the food pyramid in terms of the two principles of thermodynamics.**

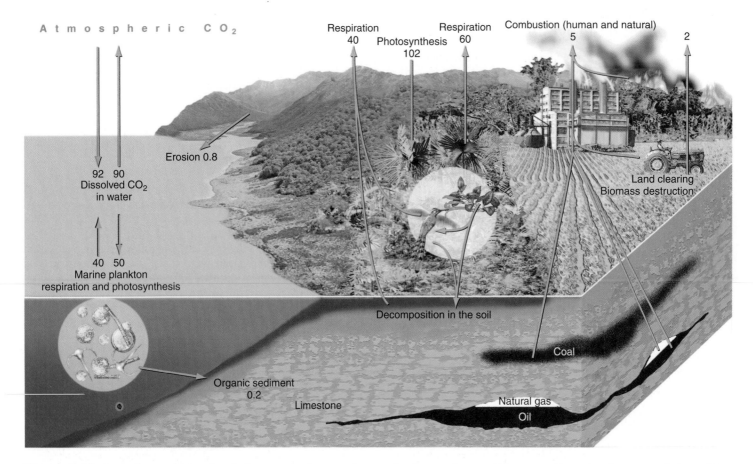

**Figure 2.19** The carbon cycle. Numbers indicate approximate exchange of carbon in gigatons (Gt) per year. Natural exchanges are balanced, but human sources produce a net increase of $CO_2$ in the atmosphere.

deposited in ocean sediments. Eventually, even the deep ocean deposits are recycled as they are drawn into deep molten layers and released via volcanic activity. Geologists estimate that every carbon atom on the earth has made about 30 such round trips over the past 4 billion years.

Materials that store carbon, including geologic formations and standing forests, are known as carbon sinks. When carbon is released from these sinks, as when we burn fossil fuels and inject $CO_2$ into the atmosphere, or when we clear extensive forests, natural recycling systems may not be able to keep up. This is the root of the global warming problem, discussed in chapter 9. Alternatively, extra atmospheric $CO_2$ could support faster plant growth, speeding some of the recycling processes.

## The nitrogen cycle

Organisms cannot exist without amino acids, peptides, and proteins, all of which are organic molecules that contain nitrogen. Nitrogen is therefore an extremely important nutrient for living things. This is why nitrogen is a primary component of household and agricultural fertilizers. Nitrogen makes up about 78 percent of the air around us.

Plants cannot use $N_2$, the stable two-atom form most common in air. But bacteria can. So plants acquire nitrogen from nitrogen-fixing bacteria (including some blue-green algae or cyanobacteria) that live in and around their roots. These bacteria can "fix" nitrogen, or combine gaseous $N_2$ with hydrogen to make ammonia ($NH_3$) and ammonium ($NH_4^+$). Nitrogen fixing by bacteria is a key part of the **nitrogen cycle** (fig. 2.20).

Other bacteria then combine ammonia with oxygen to form nitrite ($NO_2^-$). Another group of bacteria converts nitrites to nitrate ($NO_3^-$), which green plants can absorb and use. Plant cells reduce nitrate to ammonium ($NH_4^+$), which is used to build amino acids that become the building blocks for peptides and proteins.

Members of the bean family (legumes) and a few other kinds of plants are especially useful in agriculture because nitrogen-fixing bacteria actually live in their root tissues (fig. 2.21). Legumes and their associated bacteria add nitrogen to the soil, so interplanting and rotating legumes with crops, such as corn, that use but cannot replace soil nitrates are beneficial farming practices that take practical advantage of this relationship.

Nitrogen reenters the environment in several ways. The most obvious path is through the death of organisms. Fungi and bacteria decompose dead organisms, releasing ammonia and ammonium ions, which then are available for nitrate formation. Organisms don't have to die to donate proteins to the environment, however. Plants shed their leaves, needles, flowers, fruits, and cones; animals shed hair, feathers, skin, exoskeletons, pupal cases, and silk. Animals also produce excrement and urinary wastes that contain nitrogenous compounds. Urine is

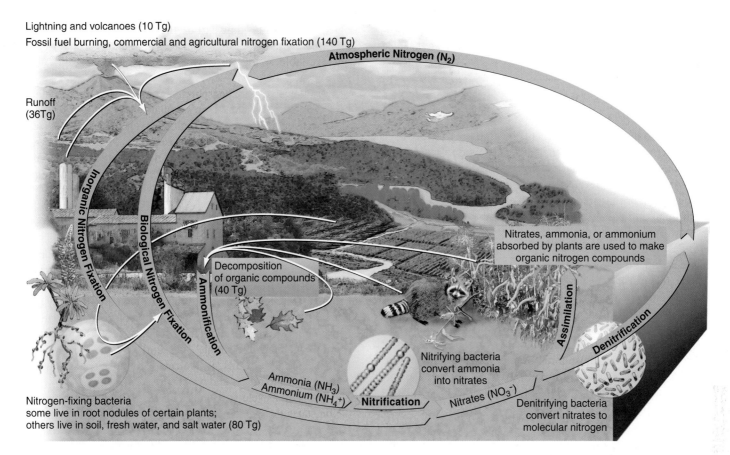

Lightning and volcanoes (10 Tg)

Fossil fuel burning, commercial and agricultural nitrogen fixation (140 Tg)

Atmospheric Nitrogen (N₂)

Runoff
(36Tg)

Inorganic Nitrogen Fixation

Biological Nitrogen Fixation

Ammonification

Decomposition
of organic compounds
(40 Tg)

Nitrates, ammonia, or ammonium
absorbed by plants are used to make
organic nitrogen compounds

Assimilation

Denitrification

Ammonia (NH₃)
Ammonium (NH₄⁺)

Nitrification

Nitrifying bacteria
convert ammonia
into nitrates

Nitrates (NO₃⁻)

Denitrifying bacteria
convert nitrates to
molecular nitrogen

Nitrogen-fixing bacteria
some live in root nodules of certain plants;
others live in soil, fresh water, and salt water (80 Tg)

**Figure 2.20** The nitrozen cycle. Human sources of nitrogen fixation (conversion of molecular nitrogen to ammonia or ammonium) are now about 50 percent greater than natural sources. Bacteria convert ammonia to nitrates, which plants use to create organic nitrogen. Eventually, nitrogen is stored in sediments or converted back to molecular nitrogen (1 Tg = $10^{12}$ g).

**Figure 2.21** Nitrogen molecules (N₂) are converted to useable forms in the bumps (nodules) on the roots of this bean plant. Each nodule is a mass of root tissue containing many bacteria that help convert nitrogen in the soil to a form that the bean plant can assimilate and use to manufacture amino acids.

especially high in nitrogen because it contains the detoxified wastes of protein metabolism. All of these by-products of living organisms decompose, replenishing soil fertility (see related Case Study, "Why Trees Need Salmon," at **www.mhhe.com/cunningham6e**).

How does nitrogen reenter the atmosphere, completing the cycle? Denitrifying bacteria break down nitrates ($NO_3^-$) into $N_2$ and nitrous oxide ($N_2O$), gases that return to the atmosphere. Thus denitrifying bacteria compete with plant roots for available nitrates. Denitrification occurs mainly in waterlogged soils that have low oxygen availability and a large amount of decomposable organic matter. These are suitable growing conditions for many wild plant species in swamps and marshes, but not for most cultivated crop species, except for rice, a domesticated wetland grass.

In recent years, humans have profoundly altered the nitrogen cycle. By using synthetic fertilizers, cultivating nitrogen-fixing crops, and burning fossil fuels, we now convert more nitrogen to ammonia and nitrates than all natural land processes combined. This excess nitrogen input causes algal blooms and excess plant growth in water bodies, called eutrophication, which we will discuss in more detail in chapter 10. Excess nitrogen also causes serious loss of soil nutrients such as calcium and potassium; acidification of rivers and lakes; and rising atmospheric concentrations of nitrous oxide, a greenhouse gas. It also encourages the spread of weeds into areas such as prairies, where native plants are adapted to nitrogen-poor environments.

## The phosphorus cycle takes millions of years

Minerals become available to organisms after they are released from rocks or salts (which are ancient sea deposits). Two mineral cycles of particular significance to organisms are phosphorus and sulfur. At the cellular level, energy-rich phosphorus-containing compounds are primary participants in energy-transfer reactions.

Phosphorus is usually transported in water. Producer organisms take in inorganic phosphorus, incorporate it into organic molecules, and then pass it on to consumers. In this way, phosphorus cycles through ecosystems (fig. 2.22).

The release of phosphorus from rocks and mineral compounds is normally very slow, but mining of fertilizers has greatly speeded the use and movement of phosphorus in the environment. Most phosphate ores used for detergents and inorganic fertilizers come from salt deposits from ancient, shallow sea beds. Most of the phosphorus used in agriculture winds up in the ocean again, from field runoff or through human and animal waste that is released to rivers. Over millions of years, this phosphorus will become part of mineral deposits, but on shorter time scales, many earth scientists worry that we could use up our available sources of phosphorus, putting our agricultural systems at risk.

As you have read, phosphorus is an important water pollutant because excess phosphates can stimulate explosive growth of algae and photosynthetic bacteria populations (algae blooms), upsetting ecosystem stability (see related Case Study, "The Environmental Chemistry of Phosphorus," at www.mhhe.com/cunningham6e). Can you think of ways we could reduce the amount of phosphorus we put into our environment?

## The sulfur cycle

Sulfur plays a vital role in organisms, especially as a minor but essential component of proteins. Sulfur compounds are important determinants of the acidity of rainfall, surface water, and soil. In addition, sulfur in particles and tiny airborne droplets may act as critical regulators of global climate. Most of the earth's sulfur is tied up underground in rocks and minerals, such as iron disulfide (pyrite) and calcium sulfate (gypsum). Weathering, emissions from deep seafloor vents, and volcanic eruptions release this inorganic sulfur into the air and water (fig. 2.23).

The sulfur cycle is complicated by the large number of oxidation states the element can assume, producing hydrogen sulfide ($H_2S$), sulfur dioxide ($SO_2$), sulfate ion ($SO_4^{2-}$), and others. Inorganic processes are responsible for many of these transformations, but living organisms, especially bacteria, also sequester sulfur in biogenic deposits or release it into the environment. Which of the several kinds of sulfur bacteria prevails in any given situation depends on oxygen concentrations, pH level, and light level.

Human activities also release large quantities of sulfur, primarily through burning fossil fuels. Total yearly anthropogenic sulfur emissions rival those of natural processes, and acid rain (caused by sulfuric acid produced as a result of fossil fuel use) is a serious problem in many areas (see chapter 9). Sulfur dioxide and sulfate aerosols cause human health problems, damage buildings and vegetation, and reduce visibility. They also absorb ultraviolet (UV) radiation and create cloud cover that cools cities and may be offsetting greenhouse effects of rising $CO_2$ concentrations.

Interestingly, the biogenic sulfur emissions of oceanic phytoplankton may play a role in global climate

**Figure 2.22** The phosphorus cycle. Natural movement of phosphorus is slight, involving recycling within ecosystems and some erosion and sedimentation of phosphorus-bearing rock. Use of phosphate ($PO_4^{-3}$) fertilizers and cleaning agents increases phosphorus in aquatic systems, causing eutrophication. Units are teragrams (Tg) phosphorus per year.

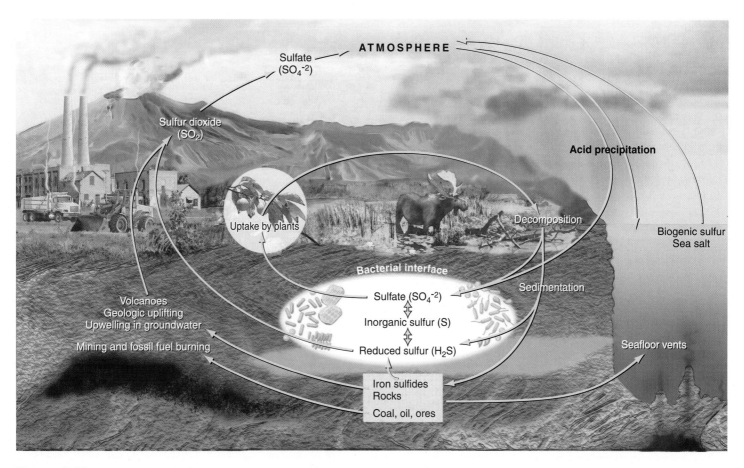

**Figure 2.23** The sulfur cycle. Sulfur is present mainly in rocks, soil, and water. It cycles through ecosystems when it is taken in by organisms. Combustion of fossil fuels causes increased levels of atmospheric sulfur compounds, which create problems related to acid precipitation.

regulation. When ocean water is warm, tiny, single-celled organisms release dimethylsulfide (DMS), which is oxidized to $SO_2$ and then $SO_4^{2-}$ in the atmosphere. Acting as cloud droplet condensation nuclei, these sulfate aerosols increase the earth's albedo (reflectivity) and cool the earth. As ocean temperatures drop because less sunlight gets through, phytoplankton activity decreases, DMS production falls, and clouds disappear. Thus, DMS, which may account for half of all biogenic sulfur emissions, could be a feedback mechanism that keeps temperature within a suitable range for all life.

## Conclusion

The movement of matter and energy through systems, as in the Everglades, maintains the world's living environments. Matter consists of atoms, which make up molecules or compounds. Among the principal substances we consider in ecosystems are water, carbon, nitrogen, phosphorus, and sulfur. Nitrogen and phosphorus, especially, are key nutrients for living things. Energy also moves through systems. The laws of thermodynamics tell us that energy is neither created nor destroyed (first law), but it is degraded and dissipates as it moves through

ecosystems (second law). For example, the chemical energy in food molecules is concentrated potential energy that degrades to less concentrated forms such as heat or kinetic energy as we use it. Matter, similarly, is neither created nor destroyed; it is reused continually.

Primary producers provide the energy and matter in an ecosystem. Nearly all ecosystems rely on green plants, which photosynthesize and create organic compounds that store energy, nutrients, and carbon. Excessive amounts of nutrients can create a positive feedback in plant or algae reproduction and growth, and positive feedbacks can destabilize a system. Negative feedbacks tend to maintain system stability. Cellular respiration is the reverse of photosynthesis: this is how organisms extract energy and nutrients from organic molecules.

Primary producers support smaller numbers of consumers in an ecosystem. Thus, the everglades wetland plants support hundreds of bird, fish, and insect species. Top level predators, such as Florida Panthers, are normally rare because large numbers of organisms are needed at each lower trophic level that supports them. We can think about this pyramid structure of trophic levels in terms of energy, biomass, or numbers of individuals. We can also understand these organisms as components of a system, through which carbon, water, and nutrients move.

1. What are three primary nutrients in fertilizers?

2. What are systems and how do feedback loops regulate them?

3. Your body contains vast numbers of carbon atoms. How is it possible that some of these carbons may have been part of the body of a prehistoric creature?

4. List six unique properties of water. Describe, briefly, how each of these properties makes water essential to life as we know it.

5. What is DNA, and why is it important?

6. The oceans store a vast amount of heat, but this huge reservoir of energy is of little use to humans. Explain the difference between high-quality and low-quality energy.

7. In the biosphere, matter follows circular pathways, while energy flows in a linear fashion. Explain.

8. Which wavelengths do our eyes respond to, and why? (Refer to fig. 2.13.) About how long are short ultraviolet wavelengths to microwave lengths?

9. Where do extremophiles live? How do they get the energy they need for survival?

10. Ecosystems require energy to function. From where does this energy come? Where does it go?

11. How do green plants capture energy, and what do they do with it?

12. Define the terms *species*, *population*, and *biological community*.

13. Why are big fierce animals rare?

14. Most ecosystems can be visualized as a pyramid with many organisms in the lowest trophic levels and only a few individuals at the top. Give an example of an inverted numbers pyramid.

15. What is the ratio of human-caused carbon releases into the atmosphere shown in figure 2.19 compared to the amount released by terrestrial respiration?

# Critical Thinking and Discussion Questions

Apply the principles you have learned in this chapter to discuss these questions with other students.

1. Ecosystems are often defined as a matter of convenience because we can't study everything at once. How would you describe the characteristics and boundaries of the ecosystem in which you live? In what respects is your ecosystem an open one?

2. Think of some practical examples of increasing entropy in everyday life. Is a messy room really evidence of thermodynamics at work, or merely personal preference?

3. Some chemical bonds are weak and have a very short half-life (fractions of a second, in some cases); others are strong and stable, lasting for years or even centuries. What would our world be like if all chemical bonds were either very weak or extremely strong?

4. If you had to design a research project to evaluate the relative biomass of producers and consumers in an ecosystem, what would you measure? (*Note:* This could be a natural system or a human-made one.)

5. Understanding storage compartments is essential to understanding material cycles, such as the carbon cycle. If you look around your backyard, how many carbon storage compartments are there? Which ones are the biggest? Which ones are the longest lasting?

# Data Analysis | Examining Nutrients in a Wetland System

As you have read, movements of nitrogen and phosphorus are among the most important considerations in many wetland systems, because high levels of these nutrients can cause excessive algae and bacteria growth. This is a topic of great interest, and many studies have examined how nutrients move in a wetland, and in other ecosystems. Taking a little time to examine these nutrient cycles in detail will draw on your knowledge of atoms, compounds, systems, cycles, and other ideas in this chapter. Understanding nutrient cycling will also help you in later chapters of this book.

One excellent overview was produced by the Environmental Protection Agency. Go to this website and download a PDF document of the study: http://www.epa.gov/waterscience/criteria/nutrient/guidance/wetlands/index.html. If you prefer, you can also look at just one chapter at a time on this website.

Find chapter 2, An Overview of Wetland Science, and answer the following questions:

1. Look first at the page numbered 28 (section 2.1). How many nutrients are discussed in this chapter? Why are iron (Fe), aluminum (Al), and calcium of interest in understanding phosphorus?

2. Now look at the next page, with the photograph. What are the sources from which nutrients enter a wetland? Think of at least three ways in which human activities can increase these sources.

3. Proceed to page 30, figure 2.5. Study the online figure and fill in the boxes on figure 1 on the next page. How many different forms of nitrogen, or compounds containing nitrogen, are there? List them.

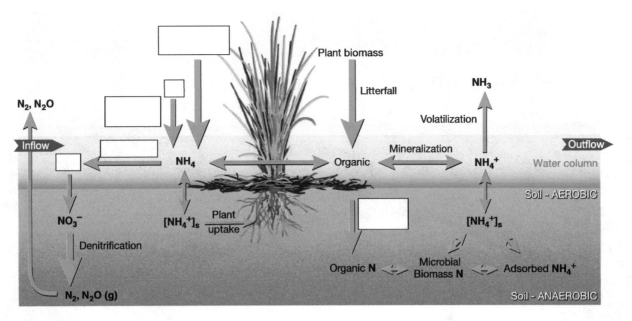

**N₂, N₂O** $N_2, N_2O$

Inflow

Plant biomass

Litterfall

**NH₃** $NH_3$

Volatilization

Outflow

$NH_4$ ⟷ Organic ⟷ Mineralization ⟷ $NH_4^+$

Water column

Soil - AEROBIC

$NO_3^-$

Denitrification

$[NH_4^+]_s$ — Plant uptake

$[NH_4^+]_s$

$N_2, N_2O$ (g)

Organic **N** ⟷ Microbial Biomass **N** ⟷ Adsorbed $NH_4^+$

Soil - ANAEROBIC

**Figure 1** A detailed schematic diagram of the nitrogen cycle in a wetland. Study the online original to fill in the boxes. *Source:* EPA Nutrient Criteria Technical Guidance Manual www.epa.gov/waterscience/criteria/nutrient/guidance/.

4. What is meant by "organic N"? (Think about what the term *organic* means in this chapter.) In what form does the plant take up N? How does N return from a living plant to the floor of the wetland?

5. Two important processes in the nitrogen cycle are nitrification (making nitrate, $NO_3$) and denitrification (breaking up nitrate). One of these processes *increases* the number of O atoms per N; the other *decreases* the number of O atoms per N. Which one decreases the number of O atoms?

6. If you look at the figure 2.6, page 31, you will see that phosphorus compounds are described mainly in terms of whether the P atoms are in an organic (carbon-based) molecule. Which form does the plant take up: dissolved *organic* phosphorus (DOP), or dissolved *inorganic* phosphorus (DIP)? Is a phosphate molecule ($PO_4$) organic or inorganic? Should it be taken up easily by plants?

This EPA document contains a great deal of additional information. Peruse it briefly to see what other questions scientists have in studying wetland systems.

For Additional Help in Studying This Chapter, please visit our website at www.mhhe.com/cunningham6e. You will find practice quizzes, key terms, answers to end of chapter questions, additional case studies, an extensive reading list, and Google Earth™ mapping quizzes.

**connect**

|ENVIRONMENTAL SCIENCE

# 6 Environmental Conservation
## Forests, Grasslands, Parks, and Nature Preserves

British Columbia's Great Bear Rainforest will preserve the home for rare, white-phase black (or spirit) bears along with salmon streams, misty fjords, rich tidal estuaries, and the largest remaining area of old-growth, coastal, temperate rainforest in the world.

*What a country chooses to save is what a country chooses to say about itself.*

— MOLLIE BEATTY, FORMER DIRECTOR,
U.S. FISH AND WILDLIFE SERVICE

## Learning Outcomes

*After studying this chapter, you should be able to answer the following questions:*

- What portion of the world's original forests remain?
- What activities threaten global forests? What steps can be taken to preserve them?
- Why is road construction a challenge to forest conservation?
- Where are the world's most extensive grasslands?
- How are the world's grasslands distributed, and what activities degrade grasslands?
- What are the original purposes of parks and nature preserves in North America?
- What are some steps to help restore natural areas?

# CASE STUDY

## Saving the Great Bear Rainforest

The wild, rugged coast of British Columbia is home to one of the world's most productive natural communities: the temperate rainforest. Nurtured by abundant rainfall and mild year-round temperatures, forests in the deep, misty fjords shelter giant cedar, spruce, and fir trees. Since this cool, moist forest rarely burns, trees often live for 1,000 years or more, and can be 5 m (16 ft) in diameter and 70 m tall. In addition to huge, moss-draped trees, the forest is home to an abundance of wildlife. One animal, in particular, has come to symbolize this beautiful landscape: it's a rare, white or cream-colored black bear. Called a Kermode bear by scientists, these animals are more popularly known as "spirit bears," the name given to them by native Gitga'at people.

The wetlands and adjacent coastal areas also are biologically rich. Whales and dolphins feed in the sheltered fjords and interisland channels. Sea otters float on the rich offshore kelp forests. It's estimated that 20 percent of the world's remaining wild salmon migrate up the wild rivers of this coastline.

In 2006, officials from the provincial government, Native Canadian nations, logging companies, and environmental groups announced a historic agreement for managing the world's largest remaining intact temperate coastal rainforest. This Great Bear Rainforest encompasses about 6 million ha (15.5 million acres) or about the size of Switzerland (fig. 6.1). One-third of the area will be entirely protected from logging. In the rest of the land, only selective, sustainable logging will be allowed rather than the more destructive clear-cutting that has devastated surrounding forests. At least $120 million will be provided for conservation projects and ecologically sustainable business ventures, such as eco-tourism lodges and an oyster farm.

A series of factors contributed to preserving this unique area. The largest environmental protest in Canadian history took place at Clayoquot Sound on nearby Vancouver Island in the 1980s, when logging companies attempted to clear-cut land claimed by First Nations people. This alerted the public to the values of and threats to the coastal temperate rainforest. As a result of the lawsuits and publicity generated by this controversy, most of the largest logging companies have agreed to stop clear-cutting in the remaining virgin forest. The rarity of the spirit bears also caught the public imagination. Tens of thousands of schoolchildren across Canada wrote to the provincial government begging them to set aside a sanctuary for this unique animal. And a growing recognition of the rights of native people also helped convince public officials that traditional lands and ways of living need to be preserved.

More than 60 percent of the world's temperate rainforest has already been logged or developed. The Great Bear Rainforest contains one-quarter of what's left. It also contains about half the estuaries, coastal wetlands, and healthy, salmon-bearing streams in British Columbia.

How did planners choose the areas to be within the protected area? One of the first steps was a biological survey. Where were the biggest and oldest trees? Which areas are especially valuable for wildlife? Protecting water quality in streams and coastal regions was also a high priority. Keeping logging and roads out of riparian habitats is particularly important. Interestingly, native knowledge of the area was also consulted in drawing boundaries. Which places are mentioned in oral histories? What are the traditional uses of the forest? While commercial logging is prohibited in the protected areas, First Nations people will be allowed to continue their customary harvest of selected logs for totem poles, longhouses, and canoes. They also will be allowed to harvest berries, catch fish, and hunt wildlife for their own consumption.

Because it's so remote, few people will ever visit the Great Bear Rainforest, yet many of us like knowing that some special places like this continue to exist. Although we depend on wildlands for many products and services, perhaps we don't need to exploit every place on the planet. Which areas we choose to set aside, and how we protect and manage those special places says a lot about who we are. In chapter 5, we looked at efforts to save individual endangered species. Many biologists believe that we should focus instead on saving habitat and representative biological communities. In this chapter, we'll look at how we use and preserve landscapes.

**Figure 6.1** The Great Bear Rainforest stretches along the British Columbia coast (including the Queen Charlotte Islands) from Victoria Island to the Alaska border. The area will be managed as a unit with some pristine wilderness, some First Nations lands, and some commercial production.

# 6.1 World Forests

Forests and grasslands together occupy almost 60 percent of global land cover (fig. 6.2). These ecosystems provide many of our essential resources, such as lumber, paper pulp, and grazing lands for livestock. They also provide essential ecological services, including regulating climate, controlling water runoff, providing wildlife habitat, purifying air and water, and supporting rainfall. Forests and grasslands also have scenic, cultural, and historic values that deserve protection. But these are also among the most heavily disturbed ecosystems (chapter 5).

As the opening case study for this chapter shows, balancing competing land uses and needs can be complicated. Many conservation debates have concerned protection or use of forests, prairies, and rangelands. This chapter examines the ways we use and abuse these biological communities, as well as some of the ways we can protect them and conserve their resources. We discuss forests first, followed by grasslands and then strategies for conservation, restoration, and preservation.

## Boreal and tropical forests are most abundant

Forests are widely distributed, but most remaining forests are in the cold boreal ("northern") or taiga regions and the humid tropics (fig. 6.3). Assessing forest distribution is tricky, because forests vary in density and height, and many are inaccessible. The UN Food and Agriculture Organization (FAO) defines "forest" as any area where trees cover more than 10 percent of the land. This definition includes woodlands ranging from open **savannas**, whose trees occupy less than 20 percent of the area, to **closed-canopy forests**, in which tree crowns cover most of the ground. The largest tropical forest is in the Amazon River basin. The highest rates of forest loss are in Africa (fig. 6.4). Some of the world's most biologically diverse regions are undergoing rapid deforestation, including Southeast Asia and Central America (see related stories "Saving an African Eden" and "Protecting Forests to Preserve Rain" at **www.mhhe.com/cunningham6e**).

Forests are a huge carbon sink, storing some 422 billion metric tons of carbon in standing biomass. Clearing and burning of forests releases much of this carbon into the atmosphere (chapter 9) and contributes significantly to global climate change. Moisture released from forests affects rainfall not only locally, but sometimes far away. For example, recent climate studies suggest that deforestation of the Amazon could reduce precipitation in the American Midwest.

Among the forests of greatest ecological importance are the remnants of primeval forests that are home to much of the world's biodiversity, endangered species, and indigenous human cultures.

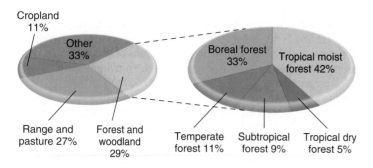

**Figure 6.2** World land use and forest types. The "other" category includes tundra, desert, wetlands, and urban areas. *Source:* UN Food and Agriculture Organization (FAO).

**Figure 6.3** A tropical rainforest in Queensland, Australia. Primary, or old-growth forests, such as this, aren't necessarily composed entirely of huge, old trees. Instead, they have trees of many sizes and species that contribute to complex ecological cycles and relationships.

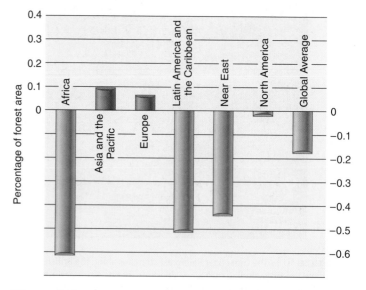

**Figure 6.4** Annual net change in forest area, 2000–2005. The largest annual net deforestation rate in the world is in Africa. Largely because China has planted 50 billion trees in the past decade, Asia has a net increase in forest area. Europe, also, is gaining forest. *Source:* Data from FAO, 2008.

# Active Learning

## Calculating Forest Area

Examine figure 6.4, which shows forest losses between 2000 and 2005. This graph shows only percentage losses. How would you evaluate the total losses from these data? To do so, you'd need some additional information about the forest area at the beginning of this period. The following table will help you in these calculations.

Changes in Forest Area: Years 2000 and 2005

| | 2000 (millions of ha) | 2005 (millions of ha) |
|---|---|---|
| Region | | |
| Africa | 2,200 | 700 |
| Asia/Pacific | 2,300 | 800 |
| Europe | 2,200 | 1,000 |
| Latin America | 1,400 | 900 |
| Near East | 400 | 200 |
| North America | 600 | 550 |
| World | 8,700 | 5,950 |

Now read the relative losses from figure 6.4. For example, Africa lost slightly more than 0.6 percent of the existing forest between 2000 and 2005. How much forest area was lost during this time? ($700 \times 0.006 = 4.2$ million ha.) What percentage of the original forest does this represent? ($4.2/2200 = 0.0019$, or about 0.2 percent).

1. Which region has lost the greatest total forest area in this period and how much was that?

2. Which region has gained the most forest and how much was that?

3. Which region has lost the greatest amount of its original forest?

4. How much global forest was lost between 2000 and 2005?

5. Working with round numbers makes comparison easy. How important are the details lost when you read approximate numbers from the graph? What kinds of generalization might have gone into producing the FAO's original data? What kinds of generalization might have been unavoidable?

*Answers:*
1. Latin America lost 4.5 million ha.
2. Asia gained 8 million ha.
3. Africa has lost about 68 percent of its original forest.
4. The world lost about 10.7 million ha of forest during this period.
5. Usually approximate numbers provide a quick, useful comparison, and additional detail isn't needed until further analysis is done. Defining forests and forest types, or determining extent of either "original" or "current" forest all involve considerable, usually unavoidable generalization.

---

Sometimes called frontier forests, **old-growth forests** are those that cover a relatively large area and have been undisturbed by human activities long enough that trees can live out a natural life cycle and ecological processes can occur in fairly normal fashion.

That doesn't mean that all trees need be enormous or thousands of years old. In some old-growth forests, most trees live less than a century before being killed by disease or some natural disturbance, such as a fire. Nor does it mean that humans have never been present. Where human occupation entails relatively little impact, an old-growth forest may have been inhabited by people for a very long time. Even forests that have been logged or converted to cropland often can revert to old-growth characteristics if allowed to undergo normal successional processes.

While forests still cover about half the area they once did worldwide, only one-quarter of those forests retain old-growth features. The largest remaining areas of old-growth forest are in Russia, Canada, Brazil, Indonesia, and Papua New Guinea. Together, these five countries account for more than three-quarters of all relatively undisturbed forests in the world. In general, remoteness rather than laws protect those forests. Although official data describe only about one-fifth of Russian old-growth forest as threatened, rapid deforestation—both legal and illegal—especially in the Russian Far East, probably put a much greater area at risk.

## Forests provide many valuable products

Wood plays a part in more activities of the modern economy than does any other commodity. There is hardly any industry that does not use wood or wood products somewhere in its manufacturing and marketing processes. Think about the amount of junk mail, newspapers, photocopies, and other paper products that each of us in developed countries handles, stores, and disposes of in a single day. Total annual world wood consumption is about 4 billion $m^3$. This is more than steel and plastic consumption combined. International trade in wood and wood products amounts to more than $100 billion each year. Developed countries produce less than half of all industrial wood but account for about 80 percent of its consumption. Less-developed countries, mainly in the tropics, produce more than half of all industrial wood but use only 20 percent.

Paper pulp, the fastest growing forest product, accounts for nearly a fifth of all wood consumption. Most of the world's paper is used in the wealthier countries of North America, Europe, and Asia. Global demand for paper is increasing rapidly, however, as other countries develop. The United States, Russia, and Canada are the largest producers of both paper pulp and industrial wood (lumber and panels). Much industrial logging in Europe and North America occurs on managed plantations, rather than in untouched old-growth forest. However, paper production is increasingly blamed for deforestation in Southeast Asia, West Africa, and other regions.

Fuelwood accounts for nearly half of global wood use. At least two billion people depend on firewood or charcoal as a principal source of heating and cooking fuel (fig. 6.5). The average amount of fuelwood used in less-developed countries is about 1 $m^3$ per person per year, roughly equal to the amount that each American consumes each year as paper products alone. Demand for fuelwood, which is increasing at slightly less than the global population growth rate, is causing severe fuelwood shortages and depleting forests in some developing areas, especially around growing cities. About 1.5 billion people have less fuelwood than they need, and many experts expect shortages to worsen as poor urban areas grow. In some countries, firewood harvesting is a major cause of deforestation, but foresters argue that biomass energy could be produced sustainably in most developing countries, with careful management.

Approximately one-quarter of the world's forests are managed for wood production. Ideally, forest management involves scientific planning for sustainable harvests, with particular attention paid to forest regeneration. In temperate regions, according to the UN Food and Agriculture Organization, more land is being replanted or allowed to regenerate naturally than is being permanently deforested. Much of this reforestation, however, is in large plantations of single-species, single-use, intensive cropping called **monoculture forestry**. Although this produces rapid growth and easier harvesting than a more diverse forest, a dense, single-species stand often supports little biodiversity and does poorly in providing the ecological services, such as soil erosion control and clean water production, that may be the greatest value of native forests (fig 6.6).

Some of the countries with the most successful reforestation programs are in Asia. China, for instance, cut down most of its forests 1,000 years ago and has suffered centuries of erosion and terrible floods as a consequence. Recently, however, timber cutting in the headwaters of major rivers has been outlawed, and a massive reforestation project has begun. In the past 20 years, China planted some 50 billion trees,

**Figure 6.5** Firewood accounts for almost half of all wood harvested worldwide and is the main energy source for nearly half of all humans.

**Figure 6.6** Monoculture foresty, such as this Wisconsin tree farm, produces valuable timber and pulpwood, but has little biodiversity.

mainly in Xinjiang Province, to stop the spread of deserts. Korea and Japan also have had very successful forest restoration programs. After being almost totally denuded during World War II, both countries are now about 70 percent forested.

## Tropical forests are being cleared rapidly

Tropical forests are among the richest and most diverse terrestrial systems. Although they now occupy less than 10 percent of the earth's land surface, these forests are thought to contain more than two-thirds of all higher plant biomass and at least half of all the plant, animal, and microbial species in the world.

A century ago, an estimated 12.5 million $km^2$ (an area larger than the entire United States) of the tropics were covered with closed-canopy forest. The FAO estimates that only about 40 percent of that forest remains in its original condition, and that about 10 million ha, or about 0.6 percent, of exising tropical forests are cleared each year (fig. 6.7).

There is considerable debate about current rates of deforestation in the tropics. In 2003, satellite data showed more than 30,000 fires in a single month in Brazil. Remote sensing experts calculate that 3 million ha per year are now being cut and burned in the Amazon basin alone. However, there are different definitions of **deforestation**. Some scientists insist that it means a complete change from forest to agriculture, urban areas, or desert. Others include any area that has been logged, even if the cut was selective and regrowth will be rapid. Furthermore, savannas, open woodlands, and succession following natural disturbance are hard to distinguish from logged areas. Consequently, estimates for total tropical forest losses range from about 5 million to more than 20 million ha per year. The FAO estimates of 10 million ha deforested per

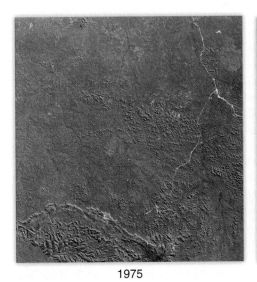

1975         1989         2001

**Figure 6.7** Forest destruction in Rondomia, Brazil, between 1975 and 2001. Construction of logging roads creates a feather-like pattern that opens forests to settlement by farmers.

year are generally the most widely accepted. To put that figure in perspective, it means that about 1 acre—or the area of a football field—is cleared every second, on average, around the clock.

In 2004, Brazil was reported to have lost 2.7 million ha (6.6 million acres) of forest to clearing and fires. This was the highest rate in the world, but Brazil also has by far the largest tropical forests. In 2009, Brazil claimed its deforestation rate had fallen below 1 million ha. It remains to be seen if this is truly progress or merely an anomaly. Indonesia appears to be the current deforestation leader. The FAO estimates that Indonesia is losing about 2 million ha, or about 2 percent of its remaining forest each year. Logging, clearing for oil palm plantations, and fires set to cover up illegal activities account for much of this destruction.

In Africa, the coastal forests of Senegal, Sierra Leone, Ghana, Madagascar, Cameroon, and Liberia already have been mostly demolished. Haiti was once 80 percent forested; today, essentially all that forest has been destroyed, and the land lies barren and eroded. India, Burma, Kampuchea (Cambodia), Thailand, and Vietnam all have little old-growth lowland forest left. In Central America, nearly two-thirds of the original moist tropical forest has been destroyed, mostly within the past 30 years and primarily due to logging and conversion of forest to cattle range. (See related story on "Disappearing Butterfly Forests" at www.mhhe.com/cunningham6e.)

**Causes of Deforestation** A variety of factors contribute to deforestation, and different forces predominate in various parts of the world. Logging for valuable tropical hardwoods, such as teak and mahogany, is generally the first step (fig 6.8). Although loggers may take only one or two of the largest trees per hectare, the canopy of tropical forests is usually so strongly linked by vines and interlocking branches that felling one tree can bring down a dozen others. Building roads to remove logs kills more trees, but even more important, it allows entry to the forest by farmers, miners, hunters, and others who cause further damage.

In Africa, conversion of forest into small-scale agriculture accounts for nearly two-thirds of all tropical forest destruction. In Latin America, poor, landless farmers often start the deforestation but are bought out—or driven out—after a few years by large-scale farmers or ranchers.

Shifting cultivation (sometimes called "slash and burn" or milpa farming) is often blamed for forest destruction. But in many countries, indigenous people have discovered sustainable ways to use complex cycles of mixed polyculture and soil ammendment practices (see the discussion of terra preta soils in chapter 7) to improve soil fertility. Invasion of nonindigenous people and industrial logging and farming into the forest change these traditional practices, however.

As forests are cleared, rainfall patterns can change. A computer model created by Pennsylvania State University scientists suggests this phenomenon might create a kind of chain reaction. As forests are cut down, plant transpiration and rainfall decrease. Drought kills more vegetation, and fires become more numerous and extensive. In a worst-case scenario, an area as large as the entire Amazonian forest might be permanently damaged in just a few decades.

**Forest Protection** What can be done to stop this destruction and encourage tropical forest protection? While much of the news is discouraging, there are some hopeful signs for forest conservation in the tropics. Many countries now recognize that forests are valuable resources.

About 14 percent of all world forests are in some form of conservation status, but the effectiveness of that protection varies greatly. Costa Rica has one of the best plans for forest guardianship in the world. Attempts are being made there not only to rehabilitate the land (make an area useful to humans) but also to restore the ecosystems to naturally occurring associations. One of the best-known of these projects is Dan Janzen's work in Guanacaste National Park. Like many dry, tropical forests, the northwestern part of Costa Rica had been almost completely converted to ranchland. By controlling fires, however, Janzen and his coworkers are

**Figure 6.8** Logging for valuable hardwoods is generally the first step in tropical forest destruction. Although loggers may take only one or two large trees per hectare, the damage caused by extracting logs exposes the forest to invasive species, poachers, and fires.

bringing back the forest. One of the keys to this success is involving local people in the project. Janzen also advocates grazing in the park. The original forest evolved, he reasons, together with ancient grazing animals that are now extinct. Horses and cows can play a valuable role as seed dispersers.

How can we finance forest protection and restoration in developing countries? One of the few positive things to come out of the 2009 Copenhagen Climate Conference was an agreement in principle to fund the REDD program (Reducing Emissions from Deforestation and Degradation) in developing countries. This idea was first proposed by Papua New Guinea and Costa Rica at international climate talks in 2005. It aims to protect existing forests and restore degraded tropical land (see A Closer Look, p. 136). Administered by the United Nations Environment Program, this mechanism, if it succeeds, will represent a massive transfer of money from rich countries to poor ones as part of a commitment to reduce the impacts of greenhouse gas emissions.

Protecting forests is an important step in stabilizing our global climate. According to the Intergovernmental Panel on Climate Change (IPCC), tropical deforestation is now responsible for more

than 17 percent of carbon emissions caused by humans. And lost forests represent a serious reduction of nature's capacity to take up the carbon we release. In addition to their value in carbon storage, forests provide important ecological services. REDD proponents argue that recognizing the value of these services both ecologically and socially is wise. More than 1.2 billion people depend on the forest for their livelihoods. Often these forest guardians are members of marginalized communities. Supplementing their income will allow them to avoid destructive practices and yet remain on the land where their traditional knowledge and stewardship are valuable resources.

The agreement at Copenhagen to fund REDD projects represents a breakthrough in the standoff between rich countries and developing ones about who is responsible for the damages caused by industrialization and the burning of fossil fuels. It could lead not only to forest conservation, but may also allow progress in other areas.

Full implementation of REDD won't occur until 2013, but some projects are already underway. A good example is the Para Project in Brazil. The first phase of this venture is already paying 350 poor landowners not to deforest their property. Payments start at only US$16 per year—not much, but enough to make a difference for marginal families. Over 10 years—the life of this particular project—the payments will increase to $350 per year. Eventually, it's hoped that 10,000 frontier families will join this venture and that emissions of 3.1 million tons of $CO_2$ per year will be avoided. This would be equivalent to taking half a million cars off the road. The total cost will be about $5 (U.S.) per ton, or about one-quarter the price for most carbon offsets.

Reducing deforestation isn't the only way to mitigate climate change. It's expected that a program called REDD-plus will pay for reforestation efforts in many countries. Replanting 300 million ha of degraded forest should result in enough carbon storage to make up one of the climate wedges we discuss in chapter 9—that is it should remove about 1 billion tons of $CO_2$ over 50 years as well as maintaining ecological services and sustaining livelihoods for indigenous and local communities.

Of course there are complications in administering a program as large as this. The United Nations estimates that fully funding REDD will cost between $20 billion and $30 billion per year. It will take careful monitoring and good governance (something often lacking now in developing countries) to ensure that the money is spent wisely and that the projects are successful and sustainable. Nevertheless, this could be the largest experiment in tropical conservation in world history.

## Temperate forests also are at risk

Tropical countries aren't unique in harvesting forests at an unsustainable rate. Northern countries, such as the United States and Canada, also have allowed controversial forest management practices in many areas. For many years, the official policy of the U.S. Forest Service was "multiple use," which implied that the forests could be used for everything that we might want to do there simultaneously. Some uses are incompatible, however. Bird-watching, for example, isn't very enjoyable in an open-pit mine. And protecting species that need unbroken old-growth forest isn't easy when you cut down the forest.

**Figure 6.9** The huge trees of the old-growth temperate rainforest accumulate more total biomass in standing vegetation per unit area than any other ecosystem on earth. They provide habitat to many rare and endagered species, but they also are converted by loggers who can sell a single tree for thousands of dollars.

**Old-growth Forests** Some of the most contentious forestry issues in the United States and Canada in recent years have centered on logging in old-growth temperate rainforests in the Pacific Northwest. As you've learned in the opening case study for this chapter, these forests have incredibly high levels of biodiversity, and they can accumulate five times as much standing biomass per hectare as a tropical rainforest (fig. 6.9). Many endemic species, such as the northern spotted owl (see What Do You Think? p. 138), Vaux's swift, and the marbled murrelet, are so highly adapted to the unique conditions of these ancient forests that they live nowhere else.

The U.S. Northwest forest management plan established in 1994 is a model for integrating scientific study, local needs, and best practices in land use. This plan attempts to integrate human and economic dimensions of issues while also protecting long-term health of forests, wildlife, and waterways. It focuses on scientifically sound, ecologically credible, and legally responsible strategies and implementation. It aims to produce predictable and sustainable level of timber sales and non-timber resources. And it tries to ensure that federal agencies work together. It may not

**Figure 6.10** Large clear-cuts, such as this, threaten species dependent on old-growth forest and expose steep slopes to soil erosion. Restoring something like the original forest will take hundreds of years.

be enough protection, however, to ensure survival of endangered salmon and trout populations in some rivers. Several salmon and steelhead trout populations have been listed as endangered and more are under consideration. What do you think? How would you balance logging, farming, and cheap hydropower against fishing, native rights, and wildlife protection?

**Harvesting Methods** Most lumber and pulpwood in the United States and Canada currently are harvested by **clear-cutting**, in which every tree in a given area is cut, regardless of size (fig. 6.10). This method is effective for producing even-age stands of sun-loving species, such as aspen or some pines, but often increases soil erosion and eliminates habitat for many forest species when carried out on large blocks. It was once thought that good forest management required immediate removal of all dead trees and logging residue. Research has shown, however, that standing snags and coarse woody debris play important ecological roles, including soil protection, habitat for a variety of organisms, and nutrient recycling.

Some alternatives to clear-cutting include **shelterwood harvesting**, in which mature trees are removed in a series of two or more cuts, and **strip-cutting**, in which all the trees in a narrow corridor are harvested. For many forest types, the least disruptive harvest method is **selective cutting**, in which only a small percentage of the mature trees are taken in each 10- or 20-year rotation. Ponderosa pine, for example, are usually selectively cut to thin stands and improve growth of the remaining trees. A forest managed by selective cutting can retain many of the characteristics of age distribution and groundcover of a mature old-growth forest. (See related story "Forestry for the Seventh Generation" at www. mhhe.com/cunningham6e.)

**Roads and Logging** An increasing number of people in the United States are calling for an end to all logging on federal lands. They argue that ecological services, such as maintaining water supplies and recreation, generate more revenue at lower costs. Many remote communities depend on logging jobs, but these jobs

# Save a tree, save the climate?

Forest destruction and land conversion produce about 17 percent of all human-caused $CO_2$ emissions—more than all global transportation emissions. REDD (Reducing Emissions from Deforestation and Forest Degradation) aims to reduce those emissions and help avert a climate catastrophe. Reducing deforestation could accomplish about half of global emission reduction goals. Billions of dollars' worth of ecosystem services, and precious biological diversity, can be saved at the same time. Every day over 30,000 hectares of tropical forest are destroyed by logging and burning; another 30,000 ha are degraded. Each year this adds up to an area twice the size of Alabama.

CL 6.1

### How do deforestation and degradation release carbon?

- Trees are burned, releasing carbon (C) stored in wood and leaves.
- Fallen vegetation decays, releasing stored C (see chapter 2)
- Accumulation of C in soil litter declines; exposed soils dry, and C in soil oxidizes to $CO_2$.
- The forest ecosystem is no longer available to store C.

### What drives deforestation?

- Industrial-scale agriculture (soy and palm oil production, cattle ranching)
- Industrial logging driven by international demand for timber
- Poverty and population pressure as people seek farmland and fuelwood
- Road development, oil development, mining, and dams

CL 6.2

### Products from deforested lands

Oil and gasoline

Food, cosmetics containing palm oil

Paper products

Aluminum (from bauxite ore)

Metals, gems, electronic components

Many, many others

CL6.3

CL 6.10

NASA landsat image reveals parallel clearings on either side of a road near the Amazon River.

5 mi (11 km)

## What ecological services would be protected under REDD?

We rely on forests for countless goods and services; here are some primary examples:

- Water supplies are maintained by forested areas, which store moisture and release it slowly during a dry season.
- Biodiversity, which provides for wild foods, medicines, building materials, migratory species, and tourism.
- Climate and weather regulation: forested areas have less volatile temperature and humidity changes than do cleared areas.

CL 6.4

CL 6.5a

CL 6.5b

CL 6.6

The world's remaining forest area is about 4 billion hectares. Nearly half of these forests are boreal (northern) forest (purple); about half are tropical forest (green). ▼

CL 6.7

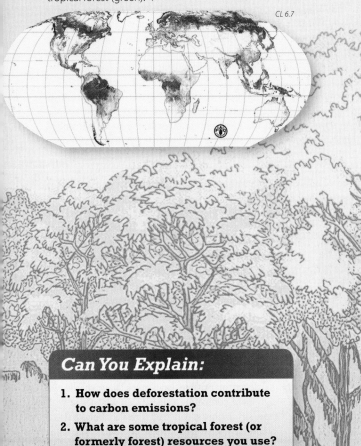

### Would REDD cost money?

Yes. Many developing countries rely on exporting tropical timber, or conversion to oil palm and soy farms, for most of their income. To cooperate with REDD, they would want this income replaced to some extent.

Wealthier countries rely on resources and ecosystem services from developing areas. Paying for the timber, oil, paper, and food products is easy, but REDD suggests that now we should also pay to protect some ecosystem services we rely on, including global climate stabilization, biodiversity, and water resources.

The United Nations REDD program estimates it will take $20-30 billion annually from developed countries to pay for forest protection, carbon offsets, and alternative development strategies.

### What about human rights?

Some 1.2 billion people rely on forests for their livelihoods. More than 2 billion–a third of the world's population–use firewood to cook and to heat their homes.

REDD efforts must recognize the rights of native people and local communities. Channeling money to urban central governments could worsen threats to these communities.

### How can we be sure that REDD projects are sustainable and enduring?

Monitoring, good government, and working at the local level are essential for REDD to succeed. A fascinating and successful example of local involvement is that of the Amazon Conservation Team (ACT), which has been partnering with indigenous peoples to map, monitor, and protect their ancestral lands using Google Earth and GPS. http://www.amazonteam.org

### Can You Explain:

1. **How does deforestation contribute to carbon emissions?**
2. **What are some tropical forest (or formerly forest) resources you use?**

137

# What Do YOU Think?

## Northern Spotted Owls

What's the most controversial bird in the world? If you count the number of scientists, lawyers, journalists, and activists who have debated its protection, as well as the amount of money, time, and effort spent on research and recovery, the answer must be the northern spotted owl (*Strix occidentalis caurina*). This brown, medium-size owl lives in the complex, old-growth forests of North America's Pacific Northwest. Before European settlement, it's thought that northern spotted owls occurred throughout the Coastal Ranges and Cascade Mountains from southern British Columbia to the San Francisco Bay.

Spotted owls nest in cavities in the huge, old-growth trees of the ancient forest. They depend on flying squirrels and wood rats as their primary prey, but they'll also eat voles, mice, gophers, hares, birds, and occasionally insects. With 90 percent of their preferred habitat destroyed or degraded, northern spotted owl populations are declining throughout their former range. When the U.S. Congress established the Endangered Species Act (ESA) in 1973, the northern spotted owl was identified as potentially endangered. After decades of study—but little action to protect them—northern spotted owls were listed as threatened in 1990 by the U.S. Fish and Wildlife Service. At that time, the population was estimated to contain 5,431 breeding pairs.

Several environmental organizations sued the federal government for its failure to do more to protect the owls. In 1991 a federal district judge agreed that the government wasn't following the requirements of the ESA, and temporarily shut down all logging in old-growth habitat in the Pacific Northwest. Timber sales dropped precipitously, and thousands of loggers and mill workers lost their jobs. Although mechanization and export of whole logs to foreign countries accounted for much of these job losses, many people blamed the owls for the economic woes across the region. Fierce debates broke out between loggers, who hung owls in effigy, and conservationists, who regarded them as protectors of the forest along with the whole biological community that lives in it.

In an effort to protect the remaining old-growth while still providing timber jobs, President Clinton started a broad planning process for the whole area. After a great deal of study and consultation, a comprehensive Northwest Forest Plan was adopted in 1994

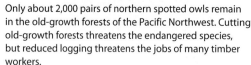

Only about 2,000 pairs of northern spotted owls remain in the old-growth forests of the Pacific Northwest. Cutting old-growth forests threatens the endangered species, but reduced logging threatens the jobs of many timber workers.

as a management guide for about 9.9 million hectares (24.5 million acres) of federal lands in Oregon, Washington, and northern California. The plan was based on the latest science of ecosystem management and represented compromises on all sides. Nevertheless, loggers complained that this plan locked up forests on which their jobs depended, while environmentalists lamented the fact that millions of hectares of old-growth would still be vulnerable to logging.

In spite of the habitat protection provided by the forest plan, northern spotted owl populations continued to decline. By 2004, researchers could find only 1,044 breeding pairs. They reported that 80 percent of the nesting areas occupied two decades earlier no longer had spotted owls, and that 9 of the 13 geographic populations were declining. The courts ordered the Fish and Wildlife Service to establish a recovery plan as required by the ESA. After four more years of study and deliberation, a recovery plan was published in 2008. The plan identified 133 owl conservation areas encompassing 2.6 million hectares (6.4 million acres) of federal lands that will be managed to protect old-growth habitat and, hopefully, stabilize owl populations. Again, both sides complained about the compromise. Loggers accused the government of caring more for owls than people. Conservationists deplored the fact that although less than 10 percent of the original old-growth is left, nearly a third of that remnant is still open to harvesting.

Recently, barred owls (*Strix varia*) have been moving into the Pacific Northwest. These larger and more aggressive cousins of the spotted owl have a wider habitat and prey tolerance, giving them a competitive advantage. When barred owls move in, spotted owls generally move out. In addition, barred owls sometimes interbreed with spotted owls further diluting the endangered spotted owl gene pool. Some wildlife managers suggest that the only way to rebuild spotted owl populations is to kill barred owls, which are common across most of the middle of North America.

As you can see, there are a number of thorny ethical issues here. Is it right to kill one species to protect another? And where there are tradeoffs between jobs, local economies, and homes for people versus habitat for wildlife and the existence of pristine landscapes, how should we weigh these competing values? Can we coexist with these shy, highly specialized forest creatures? There aren't easy answers for these dilemmas. The solutions depend on your values and worldviews. How would you answer these questions?

rely on subsidies. The federal government builds roads, manages forests, fights fires, and sells timber for less than the administrative costs of the sales. How should we weigh these different costs and benefits?

Some argue that logging should be restricted to privately owned lands. Just 4 percent of the nation's timber comes from national forests, and this harvest adds only about $4 billion to the American economy per year. In contrast, recreation, fish and wildlife, clean

water, and other ecological services provided by the forest, by their calculations, are worth at least $224 billion each year. Timber industry officials, on the other hand, dispute these claims, arguing that logging not only provides jobs and supports rural communities but also keeps forests healthy. What do you think? Could we make up for decreased timber production from public lands by more intensive management of private holdings and by substitution or recycling of wood products? Are there alternative ways you could suggest to support communities now dependent on timber harvesting?

Roads on public lands are another controversy. Over the past 40 years, the Forest Service has expanded its system of logging roads more than tenfold, to a current total of nearly 550,000 km (343,000 mi), or more than ten times the length of the interstate highway system. Government economists regard road building as a benefit because it opens up the country to motorized recreation and industrial uses. Wilderness enthusiasts and wildlife supporters, however, see this as an expensive and disruptive program. In 2001 President Clinton established a plan to protect 23.7 million ha (58.5 million acres) of de facto wilderness from roads. Land developers, logging, mining, and energy companies protested this "roadless rule." President G. W. Bush, supported by industry-friendly western judges, overturned the rule and ordered resource managers to expedite logging, mining, and motorized recreation. In 2009, President Obama ordered the rule reinstated. He noted that this measure protects habitat for 1,600 endangered species (including bears and owls) and watersheds for 60 million people. What do you think? How much of the remaining old-growth should be protected as ecological reserves?

**Fire Management** Following a series of disastrous fire years in the 1930s, in which hundreds of millions of hectares of forest were destroyed, whole towns burned to the ground, and hundreds of people died, the U.S. Forest Service adopted a policy of aggressive fire control in which every blaze on public land was to be out before 10 A.M. Smokey Bear was adopted as the forest mascot and warned us that "only you can prevent forest fires." Recent studies, however, of fire's ecological role suggest that our attempts to suppress all fires may have been misguided. Many biological communities are fire-adapted and require periodic burning for regeneration. Furthermore, eliminating fire from these forests has allowed woody debris to accumulate, greatly increasing the chances of a very big fire (fig. 6.11).

Forests that once were characterized by 50 to 100 mature, fire-resistant trees per hectare and an open understory now have a thick tangle of up to 2,000 small, spindly, mostly dead saplings in the same area. The U.S. Forest Service estimates that 33 million ha (73 million acres), or about 40 percent of all federal forestlands, are at risk of severe fires. To make matters worse, Americans increasingly live in remote areas where wildfires are highly likely. Because there haven't been fires in many of these places in living memory, many people assume there is no danger, but by some estimates, 40 million U.S. residents now live in areas with high wildfire risk.

## What Can YOU Do?

### Lowering Your Forest Impacts

For most urban residents, forests—especially tropical forests—seem far away and disconnected from everyday life. There are things that each of us can do, however, to protect forests.

- Reuse and recycle paper. Make double-sided copies. Save office paper, and use the back for scratch paper.

- Use email. Store information in digital form, rather than making hard copies of everything.

- If you build, conserve wood. Use wafer board, particle board, laminated beams, or other composites, rather than plywood and timbers made from old-growth trees.

- Buy products made from "good wood" or other certified sustainably harvested wood.

- Don't buy products made from tropical hardwoods, such as ebony, mahogany, rosewood, or teak, unless the manufacturer can guarantee that the hardwoods were harvested from agroforestry plantations or sustainable-harvest programs.

- Don't patronize fast-food restaurants that purchase beef from cattle grazing on deforested rainforest land. Don't buy coffee, bananas, pineapples, or other cash crops if their production contributes to forest destruction.

- Do buy Brazil nuts, cashews, mushrooms, rattan furniture, and other nontimber forest products harvested sustainably by local people from intact forests. Remember that tropical rainforest is not the only biome under attack. Contact the Taiga Rescue Network (www.taigarescue.org) for information about boreal forests.

- If you hike or camp in forested areas, practice minimum-impact camping. Stay on existing trails, and don't build more or bigger fires than you absolutely need. Use only downed wood for fires. Don't carve on trees or drive nails into them.

- Write to your congressional representatives, and ask them to support forest protection and environmentally responsible government policies. Contact the U.S. Forest Service, and voice your support for recreation and nontimber forest values.

A recent prolonged drought in the western United States has heightened fire danger. In 2007 nearly 80,000 wildfires burned 3.6 million ha (8.9 million acres) of forests and grasslands in the United States. Federal agencies spent almost $2 billion to fight these fires, nearly four times the previous ten-year average.

The dilemma is how to undo years of fire suppression and fuel buildup. Fire ecologists favor small, prescribed burns to clean out debris. Loggers decry this approach as a waste of valuable timber, and local residents of fire-prone areas fear that prescribed fires will escape and threaten them. Recently the Forest Service proposed a massive new program of forest thinning and emergency salvage operations (removing trees and flammable material from mature or recently burned forests) on 16 million ha (40 million acres) of national forest. Carried out over a 20-year period, this program could cost as much as $12 billion and would open up much roadless, de facto wilderness to invasive species and industrial-scale logging. Field evidence shows, moreover, that salvage logging impedes regeneration on burned forest land.

**Figure 6.11** By suppressing fires and allowing fuel to accumulate, we make major fires such as this more likely. The safest and most ecologically sound management policy for some forests may be to allow natural or prescribed fires, which don't threaten property or human life, to burn periodically.

Proponents nevertheless argue that the only way to save the forest is to log it.

**Ecosystem Management** In the 1990s many federal agencies began to shift their policies from a strictly economic focus to **ecosystem management**, which is very similar to the Northwest Forest Plan in its unified, systems approach. Some of its principles include:

- Manage across whole landscapes, watersheds, or regions over ecological time scales.
- Depend on scientifically sound, ecologically credible data for decision making.
- Consider human needs and promote sustainable economic development and communities.
- Maintain biological diversity and essential ecosystem processes.
- Utilize cooperative institutional arrangements.
- Generate meaningful stakeholder and public involvement and facilitate collective decision making.
- Adapt management over time, based on conscious experimentation and routine monitoring.

Some critics argue that we don't understand ecosystems well enough to make practical land management decisions using this system. They argue we should simply set aside large blocks of untrammeled nature to allow for chaotic, catastrophic, and unpredictable events. Others see this approach as a threat to industry and customary ways of doing things. Still, elements of ecosystem management appear in the *National Report on Sustainable Forests* prepared by the U.S. Forest Service. Based on the Montreal Working Group criteria and indicators for forest health, this report suggests goals for sustainable forest management (table 6.1).

| Table 6.1 \| Draft Criteria for Sustainable Forestry |
| --- |
| 1. Conservation of biological diversity |
| 2. Maintenance of productive capacity of forest ecosystems |
| 3. Maintenance of forest ecosystem health and vitality |
| 4. Maintenance of soil and water resources |
| 5. Maintenance of forest contribution to global carbon cycles |
| 6. Maintenance and enhancement of long-term socioeconomic benefits to meet the needs of legal, institutional, and economic framework for forest conservation and sustainable management |

*Source:* Data from USFS, 2002.

## 6.2 Grasslands

After forests, grasslands are among the biomes most heavily used by humans. Prairies, savannas, steppes, open woodlands, and other grasslands occupy about one-quarter of the world's land surface. Much of the U.S. Great Plains and the Prairie Provinces of Canada fall in this category (fig. 6.12). The 3.8 billion ha (12 million mi$^2$) of pastures and grazing lands in this biome make up about twice the area of all agricultural crops. When you add to this about 4 billion ha of other lands (forest, desert, tundra, marsh, and thorn scrub) used for raising livestock, more than half of all land is used at least occasionally for grazing. More than 3 billion cattle, sheep, goats, camels, buffalo, and other domestic animals on these lands make a valuable contribution to human nutrition. Sustainable pastoralism can increase productivity while maintaining biodiversity in a grassland ecosystem.

Because grasslands, chaparral, and open woodlands are attractive for human occupation, they frequently are converted to cropland, urban areas, or other human-dominated landscapes. Worldwide the rate of grassland disturbance each year is three times that of tropical forest. Although they may appear to be uniform and monotonous to the untrained eye, native prairies can be highly productive and species-rich. According to the U.S. Department of Agriculture, more threatened plant species occur in rangelands than in any other major American biome.

### Grazing can be sustainable or damaging

By carefully monitoring the numbers of animals and the condition of the range, ranchers and **pastoralists** (people who live by herding animals) can adjust to variations in rainfall, seasonal plant conditions, and the nutritional quality of forage to keep livestock healthy and avoid overusing any particular area. Conscientious management can actually improve the quality of the range.

When land is abused by overgrazing—especially in arid areas—rain runs off quickly before it can soak into the soil to nourish plants or replenish groundwater. Springs and wells dry up. Seeds can't germinate in the dry, overheated soil. The barren ground reflects more of the sun's heat, changing wind patterns, driving away moisture-laden clouds, and leading to further desiccation. This process of conversion of once fertile land to desert is called **desertification**.

**Figure 6.12** This short-grass prairie in northern Montana is too dry for trees but, nevertheless, supports a diverse biological community.

**Figure 6.14** More than half of all publicly owned grazing land in the United States is in poor or very poor condition. Overgrazing and invasive weeds are the biggest problems.

This process is ancient, but in recent years it has been accelerated by expanding populations and the political conditions that force people to overuse fragile lands. According to the International Soil Reference and Information Centre in the Netherlands, nearly three-quarters of all rangelands in the world show signs of either degraded vegetation or soil erosion. Overgrazing is responsible for about one-third of that degradation (fig. 6.13). The highest percentage of moderate, severe, and extreme land degradation is in Mexico and Central America, while the largest total area is in Asia, where the world's most extensive grass-

lands occur. Can we reverse this process? In some places, people are reclaiming deserts and repairing the effects of neglect and misuse.

## Overgrazing threatens many rangelands

As is the case in many countries, the health of most public grazing lands in the United States is not good. Political and economic pressures encourage managers to increase grazing allotments beyond the carrying capacity of the range. Lack of enforcement of existing regulations and limited funds for range improvement have resulted in **overgrazing**, damage to vegetation and soil including loss of native forage species and erosion. The Natural Resources Defense Council claims that only 30 percent of public rangelands are in fair condition, and 55 percent are poor or very poor (fig. 6.14).

Overgrazing has allowed populations of unpalatable or inedible species, such as sage, mesquite, cheatgrass, and cactus, to build up on both public and private rangelands. Wildlife conservation groups regard cattle grazing as the most ubiquitous form of ecosystem degradation and the greatest threat to endangered species in the southwestern United States. They call for a ban on cattle and sheep grazing on all public lands, noting that it provides only 2 percent of the total forage consumed by beef cattle and supports only 2 percent of all livestock producers.

Like federal timber management policy, grazing fees charged for use of public lands often are far below market value and represent an enormous hidden subsidy to western ranchers. Holders of grazing permits generally pay the government less than 25 percent the amount of leasing comparable private land. The 31,000 permits on federal range bring in only $11 million in grazing fees but cost $47 million per year for administration and maintenance. The $36 million difference amounts to a massive "cow welfare" system of which few people are aware.

On the other hand, ranchers defend their way of life as an important part of western culture and history. Although few

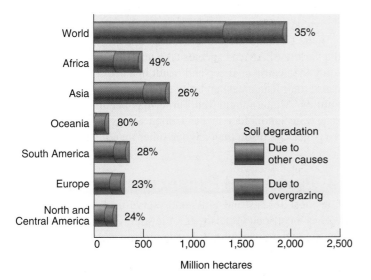

**Figure 6.13** Rangeland soil degradation due to overgrazing and other causes. Notice that, in Europe, Asia, and the Americas, farming, logging, mining, urbanization, and so on are responsible for about three-quarters of all soil degradation. In Africa and Oceania, where more grazing occurs and desert or semiarid scrub make up much of the range, grazing damage is higher.
*Source:* Data from World Resources Institute.

**Figure 6.15** Intensive, rotational grazing encloses livestock in a small area for a short time (often only one day) within a movable electric fence to force them to eat vegetation evenly and fertilize the area heavily.

**Figure 6.16** Red deer (*Cervus elaphus*) are raised in New Zealand for antlers and venison.

cattle go directly to market from their ranches, they produce almost all the beef calves subsequently shipped to feedlots. And without a viable ranch economy, they claim, even more of the western landscape would be subdivided into small ranchettes to the detriment of both wildlife and environmental quality. What do you think? How much should we subsidize extractive industries to preserve rural communities and traditional occupations?

## Ranchers are experimenting with new methods

Where a small number of livestock are free to roam a large area, they generally eat the tender, best-tasting grasses and forbs first, leaving the tough, unpalatable species to flourish and gradually dominate the vegetation. In some places, farmers and ranchers find that short-term, intensive grazing helps maintain forage quality. As South African range specialist Allan Savory observed, wild ungulates (hoofed animals), such as gnus or zebras in Africa or bison (buffalo) in America, often tend to form dense herds that graze briefly but intensively in a particular location before moving on to the next area. Rest alone doesn't necessarily improve pastures and rangelands. Short-duration, **rotational grazing**—confining animals to a small area for a short time (often only a day or two) before shifting them to a new location—simulates the effects of wild herds (fig. 6.15). Forcing livestock to eat everything equally, to trample the ground thoroughly, and to fertilize heavily with manure before moving on helps keep weeds in check and encourages the growth of more desirable forage species. This approach doesn't work everywhere, however. Many plant communities in the U.S. desert Southwest, for example, apparently evolved in the absence of large, hoofed animals and can't withstand intensive grazing.

Restoring fire can be as beneficial to grasslands as it is to forests. In some cases, ranchers are cooperating with environmental

groups in range management and preservation of a ranching economy (see Exploring Science, p. 143).

Another approach to ranching in some areas is to raise wild species, such as impala, wildebeest, oryx, or elk (fig. 6.16). These animals forage more efficiently, resist harsh climates, often are more pest- and disease-resistant, and fend off predators better than usual domestic livestock. Native species also may have different feeding preferences and needs for water and shelter than cows, goats, or sheep. The African Sahel, for instance, can provide only enough grass to raise about 20 to 30 kg (44 to 66 lbs) of beef per hectare. Ranchers can produce three times as much meat with wild native species in the same area because these animals browse on a wider variety of plant materials.

In the United States, ranchers find that elk, American bison, and a variety of African species take less care and supplemental feeding than cattle or sheep and result in a better financial return because their lean meat can bring a better market price than beef or mutton. Media mogul Ted Turner has become both the biggest private landholder in the United States and the owner of more American bison than anyone other than the government.

## 6.3 Parks and Preserves

While most forests and grasslands serve useful, or utilitarian, purposes most societies also set aside some natural areas for aesthetic or recreational purposes. Natural preserves have existed for thousands of years. Ancient Greeks protected sacred groves for religious purposes. Royal hunting grounds have preserved forests in Europe for centuries. Although these areas were usually reserved for elite classes in society, they have maintained biodiversity and natural landscapes in regions where most lands are heavily used.

The first public parks open to ordinary citizens may have been the tree-sheltered agoras in planned Greek cities. But the idea of providing natural space for recreation, and to preserve natural

Protecting biodiversity-rich tropical forests often is difficult because information is so elusive. Deep, remote, swampy, tropical jungles are difficult to enter, map, and assess for their ecological value. Yet without information about their ecological importance, most people have little reason to care about these remote, trackless forests. How can you conserve ecosystems if you don't know what's there?

For most of history, understanding the extent and conditions of a remote area required an arduous trek to see the place in person. Even on publicly owned lands, only those who could afford the time, or who could afford to pay surveyors, might understand the resources. Over time, maps improved, but maps usually show only a few features, such as roads, rivers, and some boundaries.

In recent years, details about public lands and resources have suddenly burst into public view through the use of geographic information systems (**GIS**). A GIS consists of spatial data, such as boundaries or road networks, and software to display and analyze the data. Spatial data can include variables that are hard to see on the ground—watershed boundaries, annual rainfall, land ownership, or historical land use. Data can also represent phenomena much larger than we can readily see—land surface slopes and elevation, forested regions, river networks, and so on. By overlaying these data displays, GIS analysts can investigate completely new questions about conservation, planning, and restoration.

You have probably used a GIS. Online mapping programs such as MapQuest or Google Earth organize and display spatial data. They let you turn layers on and off, or zoom in and out to display different scales. You can also use an online mapping program to calculate distances and driving directions between

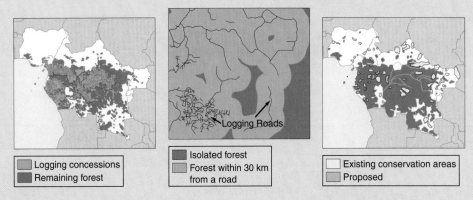

Figure 2 A few GIS layers used to identify priority conservation areas. *Source*: Wildlife Conservation Society.

- Logging concessions
- Remaining forest
- Isolated forest
- Forest within 30 km from a road
- Existing conservation areas
- Proposed

places. An ecologist, meanwhile, might use a GIS to calculate the extent of habitat areas, to monitor changes in area, to calculate the size of habitat fragments, or to calculate the length of waterways in a watershed.

### Identifying Priority Areas

Recently, a joint effort of several conservation organizations has used GIS and spatial data to identify priority areas for conservation in Central Africa. The project was initiated because new data, including emerging GIS data, were showing dramatic increases in planned logging, in a region that contains the world's second greatest extent of tropical forest (fig. 1).

Researchers from the Wildlife Conservation Society, Worldwide Fund for Nature, World Resources Institute, USGS, and other agencies and groups, began collecting GIS data on a variety of variables. They identified the range of great apes and other rare or threatened species. They identified areas of extreme plant diversity. They calculated the sizes of forest fragments to identify concentrations of intact, ancient forests. Using maps of logging roads, they calculated the area within a 30 km "buffer" around these routes, since loggers, settlers, and hunters usually threaten biodiversity near roads. They also mapped existing and planned conservation areas (fig. 2).

By overlaying these and other layers, analysts identified priority conservation areas of extensive original forest, which have high biodiversity and

rare species. Overlaying these priority areas with a map of protected lands and a map of timber concessions, they identified *threatened* priority areas (fig. 3).

Most of the unprotected priority areas may never be protected, but having this map provides two important guides for future conservation. First, it assesses the state of the problem. With this map, we know that most of the forest is unprotected but also that the region's primary forest is extensive. Second, this map provides priorities for conservation planning. In addition, maps are very effective tools for publicizing an issue. When a map like this is published, more people become enthusiastic about joining the conservation effort.

GIS has become an essential tool for conserving forests, grasslands, ecosystems, and nature preserves. GIS has revolutionized the science of planning and conservation—examining problems using quantitative data—just as it may have revolutionized the way you plan a driving trip.

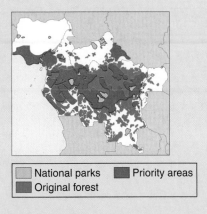

- National parks
- Original forest
- Priority areas

Figure 3 Priority areas outside of national parks. *Source*: Wildlife Conservation Society.

Gabon

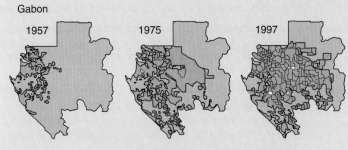

1957 1975 1997

**Figure 1** Gabon, Central Africa, has seen a steady increase in logging concessions. *Source*: Wildlife Conservation Society.

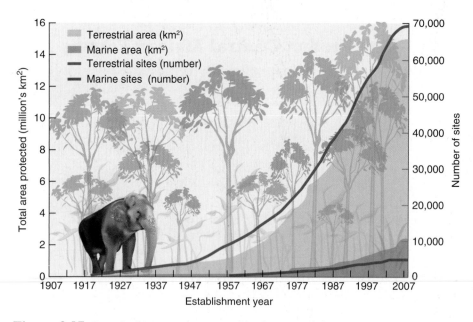

**Figure 6.17** Growth of protected areas worldwide, 1907–2007.

environments, has really developed in the past 50 years (fig. 6.17). While the first parks were intended mainly for the recreation of growing urban populations, parks have taken on many additional purposes. Today we see our national parks as playgrounds for rest and recreation, as havens for wildlife, as places to experiment with ecological management, and as opportunities to restore ecosystems.

Currently, nearly 14 percent of the land area of the earth is protected in some sort of park, preserve, or wildlife management area. This represents about 21 million ha (52 million acres) in 122,000 different preserves. This is an encouraging environmental success story.

## Many countries have created nature preserves

Different levels of protection are found in nature preserves. The World Conservation Union divides protected areas into five categories depending on the intended level of allowed human use (table 6.2). In the most stringent category (ecological reserves and wilderness areas) little or no human impacts are allowed. In some

| Table 6.2 | IUCN Categories of Protected Areas | |
|---|---|
| **Category** | **Allowed Human Impact or Intervention** |
| 1. Ecological reserves and wilderness areas | Little or none |
| 2. National parks | Low |
| 3. Natural monuments and archaeological sites | Low to medium |
| 4. Habitat and wildlife management areas | Medium |
| 5. Cultural or scenic landscapes, recreation areas | Medium to high |

*Source:* Data from World Conservation Union, 1990.

strict nature preserves, where particularly sensitive wildlife or natural features are located, human entry may be limited only to scientific research groups that visit on rare occasions. In some wildlife sanctuaries, for example, only a few people per year are allowed to visit to avoid introducing invasive species or disrupting native species. In the least restrictive categories (national forests and other natural resource management areas), on the other hand, there may be a high level of human use.

Venezuela claims to have the highest proportion of its land area protected (66 percent) of any country in the world. About half this land is designated as preserves for indigenous people or for sustainable resource harvesting. With little formal management, however, protection from poaching by hunters, loggers, and illegal gold hunters is minimal. Unfortunately, it's not uncommon in the developing world to have "paper parks" that exist only as a line drawn on a map with no budget for staff, management, or infrastructure. The United States, by contrast, has only about 22 percent of its land area in protected status, and less than one-third of that amount is in IUCN categories I or II (nature reserves, wilderness areas, national parks). The rest is in national forests or wildlife management zones that are designated for sustainable use. With hundreds of thousands of state and federal employees, billions of dollars in public funding, and a high level of public interest and visibility, U.S. public lands are generally well managed.

Brazil, with more than one-quarter of all the world's tropical rainforest, is especially important in biodiversity protection. Currently, Brazil has the largest total area in protected status of any country. More than 2.5 million km² or 29 percent of the nation's land—mostly in the Amazon basin—is in some protected status. In 2006, the northern Brazilian state of Para, in collaboration with Conservation International (CI) and other nongovernmental organizations, announced the establishment of nine new protected areas along the border with Suriname and Guyana. These new areas, about half of which will be strictly protected nature preserves, will link together several existing indigenous areas and nature preserves to create the largest tropical forest reserve in the world. More than 90 percent of the new 15 million ha (58,000 mi², or about the size of Illinois) Guyana Shield Corridor is in pristine natural state. CI president Russ Mittermeir says, "If any tropical rainforest on earth remains intact a century from now, it will be this portion of northern Amazonia." In contrast to this dramatic success, the Pantanal, the world's largest wetland/savanna complex, which lies in southern Brazil and is richer in some biodiversity categories than the Amazon, is almost entirely privately owned. There are efforts to set aside some of this important wetland, but so far, little is in protected status.

Some other countries with very large reserved areas include Greenland (with a 980,000 km² national park that covers most of the northern part of the island), and Saudi Arabia (with a 825,000 km² wildlife management area in its Empty Quarter). These areas

**Figure 6.18** Canada's Quttinirpaaq National Park at the north end of Ellesmere Island has plenty of solitude and pristine landscapes, but little biodiversity.

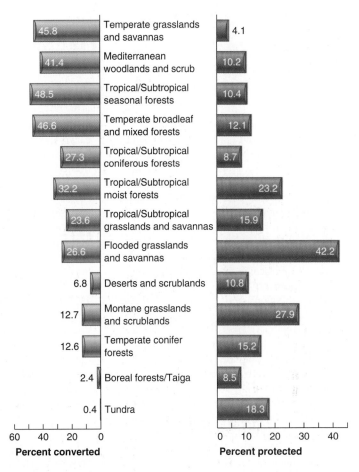

| Percent converted | Biome | Percent protected |
|---|---|---|
| 45.8 | Temperate grasslands and savannas | 4.1 |
| 41.4 | Mediterranean woodlands and scrub | 10.2 |
| 48.5 | Tropical/Subtropical seasonal forests | 10.4 |
| 46.6 | Temperate broadleaf and mixed forests | 12.1 |
| 27.3 | Tropical/Subtropical coniferous forests | 8.7 |
| 32.2 | Tropical/Subtropical moist forests | 23.2 |
| 23.6 | Tropical/Subtropical grasslands and savannas | 15.9 |
| 26.6 | Flooded grasslands and savannas | 42.2 |
| 6.8 | Deserts and scrublands | 10.8 |
| 12.7 | Montane grasslands and scrublands | 27.9 |
| 12.6 | Temperate conifer forests | 15.2 |
| 2.4 | Boreal forests/Taiga | 8.5 |
| 0.4 | Tundra | 18.3 |

**Figure 6.19** With few exceptions, the percent of each biome converted to human use is roughly inverse to the percent protected in parks and preserves. Rock and ice, lakes, and Antarctic ecoregions are excluded. World Database on Protected Areas, 2009.

are relatively easy to set aside, however, being mostly ice covered (Greenland) or desert (Saudi Arabia). Canada's Quttinirpaaq National Park on Ellesmere Island is an example of a preserve with high wilderness values but little biodiversity. Only 800 km (500 miles) from the North Pole, this remote park gets fewer than 100 human visitors per year during its brief, three-week summer season (fig. 6.18). With little evidence of human occupation, it has abundant solitude and stark beauty, but very little wildlife and almost no vegetation. By contrast, the Great Bear Rainforest management area described in the opening case study for this chapter has a rich diversity of both marine and terrestrial life, but the valuable timber, mineral, and wildlife resources in the area make protecting it expensive and controversial. In other places, scientific principles also are being used to identify the best remaining natural areas (see Exploring Science, p. 146).

Figure 6.19 shows a comparison between the percent of each major biome in protected status. Not surprisingly, there's an inverse relationship between the percentage converted to human use (and where people live) and the percentage protected. Temperate grasslands and savannas (such as the American Midwest) and Mediterranean woodlands and scrub (such as the French Riviera or the coast of southern California) are highly domesticated, and, therefore, expensive to set aside in large areas. Temperate conifer forests (think of Siberia, or Canada's vast expanse of boreal forest) are relatively uninhabited, and therefore easy to put into some protected category.

## Not all preserves are preserved

Even parks and preserves designated with a high level of protection aren't always safe from exploitation or changes in political priorities. Serious problems threaten natural resources and environmental quality in many countries. In Greece, the Pindus National Park is threatened by plans to build a hydroelectric dam in the center of the park. Furthermore, excessive stock grazing and forestry exploitation

in the peripheral zone are causing erosion and loss of wildlife habitat. In Columbia, dam building also threatens the Paramillo National Park. Ecuador's largest nature preserve, Yasuni National Park, which contains one of the world's most megadiverse regions of lowland Amazonian forest, has been opened to oil drilling, while miners and loggers in Peru have invaded portions of Huascaran National Park. In Palau, coral reefs identified as a potential biosphere reserve are damaged by dynamite fishing, while on some beaches in Indonesia, almost every egg laid by endangered sea turtles is taken by egg hunters. These are just a few of the many problems faced by parks and preserves around the world. Often countries with the most important biomes lack funds, trained personnel, and experience to manage the areas under their control.

Even in rich countries, such as the United States, some of the "crown jewels" of the National Park System suffer from overuse and degradation. Yellowstone and Grand Canyon National Parks, for example, have large budgets and are highly regulated, but are being "loved to death" because they are so popular. When the U.S. National Park Service was established in 1916, Stephen Mather, the first director, reasoned that he needed to make the parks comfortable and entertaining for tourists as a way of building public support. He created an extensive network

# Finding Common Ground on the Range

For decades, environmentalists have tried to limit grazing on public lands, where ranchers lease pastures from the government. Now some scientists and conservationists are saying that cattle ranches may be the last best hope for preserving habitat for many native species. Maintaining ranches may also be the only way to restore the periodic fires that keep brush and cactus from taking over western grasslands. In a number of places in the United States, ranchers are forming alliances with environmental organizations and government officials to find new ways to protect and manage rangelands.

One of the pressures driving this new model of collaboration is the growing popularity of western hobby ranches and rural homesteads for city folk. Falling commodity prices, drought, taxes, and other forces are causing many ranchers to consider selling their land. Why continue to struggle to make a living with ranching when you can make millions by cutting up your land into 40-acre ranchettes? But when the land is subdivided, invasive species move in along with people and their pets, and fewer native species can survive. Furthermore, it becomes much harder, if not impossible, to let fires burn across the land periodically, a process that is now thought to be essential in the southwestern landscape.

Some grazing practices clearly have been detrimental. Studies have found extensive damage from grazing in and around streams in the desert West, for instance. But few studies have compared the alternatives to ranching on these lands, which are home not only to ranchers but to many native animal and plant species. Recent research has found that ranches have at least as many species of birds, carnivores, and plants as similar areas protected as wildlife refuges. Ranches also have fewer invasive weeds.

An outstanding example of new cooperative relationships between ranchers, conservationists, and government agencies is the Malpai Borderlands Group (MBG). This community-based ecosystem management effort was created by landowners in a region called the "boot heel," where New Mexico, Arizona, and Mexico meet. Malpai is derived from the Spanish word for badlands. The craggy mountains, grassy plains, and scrub-covered desert hills of this region are home to more than 20 threatened species. Nearly 400,000 ha (about 1 million acres) are part of the collaboration, including private property, state trust lands, national forest, and Bureau of Land Management acreage.

This pioneering collaboration began in 1993 in an effort to address threats to ranching. Thirty-five neighbors got together to discuss common problems. They agreed that excluding wildfire from the range was contributing to increasing brush and declining grass cover, resulting in the loss of watershed stability, wildlife habitat, and livestock forage.

Early on, community leaders approached The Nature Conservancy (TNC) for assistance. TNC, in turn, brought in ecologists familiar with the borderlands ecosystems to aid in organizing a science program. This input from scientists was crucial in giving the MBG efforts a systems-based approach to range management. This approach emphasized conservation of natural processes rather than just a focus on the management of single species or particular resources as is typical of many conservation programs. Since 1993, the MBG and collaborators have established more than 200 monitoring plots to assess ecosystem health.

Using range science as a starting point, the MBG's goal has evolved to a comprehensive natural resource management and rural development agenda. Their stated goal is "To preserve and maintain the natural processes that create and protect a healthy, unfragmented landscape to support a diverse, flourishing community of human, plant, and animal life in the borderlands region." One of the key features of this plan is to restore fire as a management tool.

With a large, contiguous area under common management, it's now possible to set prescribed fires that have a significant effect on vegetation. Before formation of the MBG coalition, the patchwork of ownership and management in the area made large-scale operations all but impossible. A key to MBG success was purchase of the 120,000-hectare Gray Ranch by TNC. This large landholding in the heart of the Malpai borderlands makes it possible to carry out an innovative program called "grass banking." If a neighbor rancher has a bad season (perhaps due to prolonged drought), he can move his cattle onto Gray Ranch until his own ranchland is able to recover. The rancher grants a conservation easement of equal value over to the MBG that prohibits future subdivision.

The MBG isn't the only innovative initiative in ranching country. The Quivira Coalition, also based in New Mexico, brings together ranchers, conservationists, and land managers from throughout the West to foster scientifically guided ranch management and riparian restoration. TNC-owned Matador Ranch in Montana also has a grass-banking program. Perhaps the success of these programs will inspire similar cooperation rather than confrontation and litigation, not only on rangeland problems, but also on other contentious environmental issues.

The Malpai border lands are in the boot heel of New Mexico, where it meets Arizona and Mexico. Ranchers in this area have joined with government agents and conservation organizations to restore fire, protect wildlife habitat, and regenerate grasslands.

**Figure 6.20** Wild animals have always been one of the main attractions in national parks. Many people lose all common sense when interacting with big, dangerous animals. This is not a petting zoo.

**Figure 6.21** Thousands of people wait for an eruption of Old Faithful geyser in Yellowstone National Park. Can you find the ranger who's giving a geology lecture?

of roads in the largest parks so that visitors could view famous sights from the windows of their automobiles, and he encouraged construction of grand lodges in which guests could stay in luxury.

His plan was successful; the National Park System is cherished and supported by many American citizens. But sometimes entertainment has trumped over nature protection. Visitors were allowed—in some cases even encouraged—to feed wildlife. Bears lost their fear of humans and became dependent on an unhealthy diet of garbage and handouts (fig. 6.20). In Yellowstone and the Grand Teton National Parks, the elk herd was allowed to grow to 25,000 animals, or about twice the carrying capacity of the habitat. The excess population overgrazed the vegetation to the detriment of many smaller species and the biological community in general. As we discussed earlier in this chapter, 70 years of fire suppression resulted in changes of forest composition and fuel buildup that made huge fires all but inevitable. In Yosemite, you can stay in a world-class hotel, buy a pizza, play video games, do laundry, play golf or tennis, and shop for curios, but you may find it difficult to experience the solitude or enjoy the natural beauty extolled by John Muir as a prime reason for creating the park.

In many of the most famous parks, traffic congestion and crowds of people stress park resources and detract from the experience of unspoiled nature (fig. 6.21). Some parks, such as Yosemite, and Zion National Park, have banned private automobiles from the most congested areas. Visitors must park in remote lots and take clean, quiet electric or natural gas-burning buses to popular sites. Other parks are considering limits on the number of visitors admitted each day. How would you feel about a lottery system that might allow you to visit some famous parks only once in your lifetime, but to have an uncrowded, peaceful experience on your one

allowed visit? Or would you prefer to be able to visit whenever you wish even if it means fighting crowds and congestion?

Originally, the great wilderness parks of Canada and the United States were distant from development and isolated from most human impacts. This has changed in many cases. Forests are clear-cut right up to some park boundaries. Mine drainage contaminates streams and groundwater. At least 13 U.S. National Monuments are open to oil and gas drilling, including Texas's Padre Island, the only breeding ground for endangered Kemps Ridley sea turtles. Even in the dry desert air of the Grand Canyon, where visibility was once up to 150 km, it's often too smoggy now to see across the canyon due to air pollution from power plants just outside the park. Snowmobiles and off-road vehicles (ORV) create pollution and noise and cause erosion while disrupting wildlife in many parks (fig. 6.22).

**Figure 6.22** Off-road vehicles cause severe, long-lasting environmental damage when driven through wetlands.

**Figure 6.23** Coral reefs are among both the most biologically rich and endangered ecosystems in the world. Marine reserves are being established in many places to preserve and protect these irreplaceable resources.

Chronically underfunded, the U.S. National Park System now has a maintenance backlog estimated to be at least $5 billion. Politicians from both major political parties vow to repair park facilities during election campaigns, but then find other uses for public funds once in office. Ironically, a recent study found that, on average, parks generate $4 in user fees for every $1 they receive in federal subsidies. In other words, they more than pay their own way, and should have a healthy surplus if they were allowed to retain all the money they generate.

In recent years, the U.S. National Park System has begun to emphasize nature protection and environmental education over entertainment. This new agenda is being adopted by other countries as well. The IUCN has developed a **world conservation strategy** for protecting natural resources that includes the following three objectives: (1) to maintain essential ecological processes and life-support systems (such as soil regeneration and protection, nutrient recycling, and water purification) on which human survival and development depend; (2) to preserve genetic diversity essential for breeding programs to improve cultivated plants and domestic animals; and (3) to ensure that any utilization of wild species and ecosystems is sustainable.

## Marine ecosystems need greater protection

As ocean fish stocks become increasingly depleted globally, biologists are calling for protected areas where marine organisms are sheltered from destructive harvest methods. Although about 14 percent of land area is in some conservation status, only about 5 percent of nearshore marine biomes are protected. As the opening case study for chapter 1 describes, limiting the amount and kind of fishing in marine reserves can quickly replenish fish stocks in surrounding areas. In a study of 100 marine refuges around the world, researchers found that, on average, the number of organisms inside no-take preserves was twice as high as surrounding areas where fishing was allowed. In addition, the biomass of organisms was three times as great and individual animals were, on average, 30 percent larger inside the refuge compared to outside. Recent research has shown that closing reserves to fishing even for a few months can have beneficial results in restoring marine populations. The size necessary for a safe haven to protect flora and fauna depends on the species involved, but some marine biologists call on nations to protect at least 20 percent of their nearshore territory as marine refuges.

Coral reefs are among the most threatened marine ecosystems in the world. Surveys show that, worldwide, living coral reefs have declined by about half in the past century, and 90 percent of all reefs face threats from rising sea temperatures, destructive fishing methods, coral mining, sediment runoff, and other human disturbance. In many ways, coral reefs are the old-growth rainforests of the ocean (fig. 6.23). Biologically rich, these sensitive communities can take a century or more to recover from damage. If current trends continue, some researchers predict that in 50 years there will be no viable coral reefs anywhere in the world.

What can be done to reverse this trend? Some countries are establishing large marine reserves specifically to protect coral reefs. Australia has one of the largest marine reserves in the world in its 344,000 km² Great Barrier Reef (a large portion of which is open ocean). In his final days in office, President G. W. Bush declared more than 505,000 km² (195,000 mi²) of ocean including the Mariana trench, and atolls around Samoa and some other uninhabited Pacific islands as national monuments. Altogether, however, aquatic reserves make up less than one-tenth of all the world's protected areas despite the fact that nearly three-quarters of the earth's surface is water. A survey of marine biological resources identified the ten richest and most threatened "hot spots," including the Philippines, the Gulf of Guinea and Cape Verde Islands (off the west coast of Africa), Indonesia's Sunda Islands, the Mascarene Islands in the Indian Ocean, South Africa's coast, southern Japan and the east China Sea, the western Caribbean, and the Red Sea and Gulf of Aden. We urgently need more no-take preserves to protect marine resources.

## Conservation and economic development can work together

Many of the most biologically rich communities in the world are in developing countries, especially in the tropics. These countries are the guardians of biological resources important to all of us. Unfortunately, where political and economic systems fail to provide residents with land, jobs, food, and other necessities of life, people do whatever is necessary to meet their own needs. Immediate survival takes precedence over long-term environmental goals. Clearly the struggle to save species and ecosystems can't be divorced from the broader struggle to meet human needs.

People in some developing countries are beginning to realize that their biological resources may be their most valuable assets, and that their preservation is vital for sustainable development. **Ecotourism** (tourism that is ecologically and socially sustainable) can be more beneficial in many places over the long term than extractive industries, such as logging and mining. The What Can You Do? box (p. 149) suggests some ways to ensure that your vacations are ecologically responsible.

## Native people can play important roles in nature protection

The American ideal of wilderness parks untouched by humans is unrealistic in many parts of the world. As we mentioned earlier, some biological communities are so fragile that human intrusions have to be strictly limited to protect delicate natural features or particularly sensitive wildlife. In many important biomes, however, aboriginal people have been present for thousands of years and have a legitimate right to pursue traditional ways of life. Furthermore, many of the approximately 5,000 indigenous or native cultures that remain today possess ecological knowledge about their ancestral homelands that can be valuable in ecosystem management. According to author Alan Durning, "encoded in indigenous languages, customs, and practices may be as much understanding of nature as is stored in the libraries of modern science."

Some countries have adopted draconian policies to remove native people from parks (fig. 6.24). In South Africa's Kruger National Park, for example, heavily armed soldiers keep intruders out with orders to shoot to kill. This is very effective in protecting wildlife. In all fairness, before this policy was instituted there was a great deal of poaching by mercenaries armed with automatic weapons. But it also means that people who were forcibly displaced from the park could be killed on sight merely for returning to their former homes to collect firewood or to hunt for small game. Similarly, in 2006, thousands of peasant farmers on the edge of the vast Mau Forest in Kenya's Rift Valley were forced from their homes at

gun point by police who claimed that the land needed to be cleared to protect the country's natural resources. Critics claimed that the forced removal amounted to "ethnic cleansing" and was based on tribal politics rather than nature protection.

Other countries recognize that finding ways to integrate local human needs with those of nature is essential for successful conservation. In 1986, UNESCO (United Nations Educational, Scientific, and Cultural Organization) initiated its **Man and Biosphere (MAB) program**, which encourages the designation of **biosphere reserves**, protected areas divided into zones with different purposes. Critical ecosystem functions and endangered wildlife are protected in a central core region, where limited scientific study is the only human access allowed. Ecotourism and research facilities are located in a relatively pristine buffer zone around the core, while sustainable resource harvesting and permanent habitation are allowed in multiple-use peripheral regions (fig. 6.25).

While not yet given a formal MAB designation, the Great Bear Rainforest described in the opening case study for this chapter is organized along this general plan. A well established example of a biosphere reserve is Mexico's 545,000 ha (2,100 mi$^2$) Sian Ka'an Reserve on the Tulum Coast of the Yucatán. The core area includes 528,000 ha (1.3 million acres) of coral reefs, bays, wetlands, and lowland tropical forest. More than 335 bird species have been observed within the reserve, along with endangered manatees, five types of jungle cats, spider and howler monkeys, and four species of increasingly rare sea turtles. Approximately 25,000 people (about the same number who live in the Great Bear Rainforest)

**Figure 6.24** Some parks take draconian measures to expel residents and prohibit trespassing. How can we reconcile the rights of local or indigenous people with the need to protect nature?

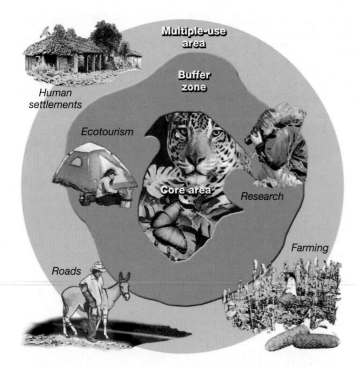

**Figure 6.25** A model biosphere reserve. Traditional parks and wildlife refuges have well-defined boundaries to keep wildlife in and people out. Biosphere reserves, by contrast, recognize the need for people to have access to resources. Critical ecosystem is preserved in the core. Research and tourism are allowed in the buffer zone, while sustainable resource harvesting and permanent habitations are situated in the multiple-use area around the perimeter.

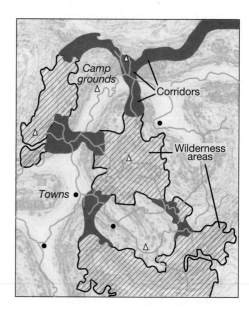

**Figure 6.26** Corridors serve as routes of migration, linking isolated populations of plants and animals in scattered nature preserves. Although individual preserves may be too small to sustain viable populations, connecting them through river valleys and coastal corridors can facilitate interbreeding and provide an escape route if local conditions become unfavorable.

reside in communities and the countryside around Sian Ka'an. In addition to tourism, the economic base of the area includes lobster fishing, small-scale farming, and coconut cultivation.

The Amigos de Sian Ka'an, a local community organization, played a central role in establishing the reserve and is working to protect natural resources while also improving living standards for local people. New intensive farming techniques and sustainable harvesting of forest products enable residents to make a living without harming their ecological base. Better lobster harvesting techniques developed at the reserve have improved the catch without depleting native stocks. Local people now see the reserve as a benefit rather than an imposition from the outside. Similar success stories from many parts of the world show how we can support local people and recognize indigenous rights while still protecting important environmental features.

## Species survival can depend on preserve size and shape

Many natural parks and preserves are increasingly isolated, remnant fragments of ecosystems that once extended over large areas. As park ecosystems are shrinking, however, they are also becoming more and more important for maintaining biological diversity. Principles of landscape design and landscape structure become important in managing and restoring these shrinking islands of habitat.

For years, conservation biologists have disputed whether it is better to have a *single large* or *several small* reserves (the SLOSS debate). Ideally, a reserve should be large enough to support viable populations of endangered species, keep ecosystems intact, and isolate critical core areas from damaging external forces. For some species with small territories, several small, isolated refuges can support viables populations, and having several small reserves provides insurance against a disease, habitat destruction, or other calamities that might wipe out a single population. But small preserves can't support species such as elephants or tigers, which need large amounts of space. Given human needs and pressures, however, big preserves aren't always possible. One proposed solution has been to create **corridors** of natural habitat that can connect to smaller habitat areas (fig. 6.26). Corridors could effectively create a large preserve from several small ones. Corridors could also allow populations to maintain genetic diversity or expand into new breeding territory. The effectiveness of corridors probably depends on how long and wide they are, and on how readily a species will use them.

One of the reasons large preserves are considered better than small preserves is that they have more **core habitat**, areas deep in the interior of a habitat area, and that core habitat has better conditions for specialized species than do edges. **Edge effects** is a term generally used to describe habitat edges: for example, a forest edge is usually more open, bright, and windy than a forest interior, and temperatures and humidity are more varied. For a grassland, on the other hand, edges may be wooded, with more shade, and perhaps more predators, than in the core of the grassland area. As human

**Figure 6.27** How small can a nature preserve be? In an ambitious research project, scientists in the Brazilian rainforest are carefully tracking wildlife in plots of various sizes, either connected to existing forests or surrounded by clear-cuts. As you might expect, the largest and most highly specialized species are the first to disappear.

disturbance fragments an ecosystem, habitat is broken into increasingly isolated islands, with less core and more edge. Small, isolated fragments of habitat often support fewer species, especially fewer rare species, than do extensive, uninterrupted ecosystems. The size and isolation of a wildlife preserve, then, may be critical to the survival of rare species.

A dramatic experiment in reserve size, shape, and isolation is being carried out in the Brazilian rainforest. In a project funded by the World Wildlife Fund and the Smithsonian Institution, loggers left 23 test sites when they clear-cut a forest. Test sites range from 1 ha (2.47 acres) to 10,000 ha. Clear-cuts surround some, and newly created pasture surrounds others (fig. 6.27); others remain connected to the surrounding forest. Selected species are regularly inventoried to monitor their survival after disturbance. As expected, some species disappear very quickly, especially from small areas. Sun-loving species flourish in the newly created forest edges, but deep-forest, shade-loving species disappear, particularly when the size or shape of a reserve reduces availability of core habitat. This experiment demonstrates the importance of maintaining core habitat in preserves.

## Conclusion

Forests and grasslands cover nearly 60 percent of global land area. The vast majority of humans live in these biomes, and we obtain many valuable materials from them. And yet, these biomes also are the source of much of the world's biodiversity on which we depend for life-supporting ecological services. How we can live sustainably on our natural resources while also preserving enough nature so those resources can be replenished represents one of the most important questions in environmental science.

There is some good news in our search for a balance between exploitation and preservation. Although deforestation and land degradation are continuing at unacceptable rates—particularly in some developing countries—many countries are more densely forested now than they were two centuries ago. Protection of the Great Bear Rainforest in Canada and Australia's Great Barrier Reef shows that we can choose to protect some biodiverse areas in spite of forces that want to exploit them. Overall, nearly 14 percent of the earth's land area is now in some sort of protected status. While the level of protection in these preserves varies, the rapid recent increase in number and area in protected status exceeds the goals of the United Nations Millennium Project.

While we haven't settled the debate between focusing on individual endangered species versus setting aside representative samples of habitat, pursuing both strategies seems to be working. Protecting charismatic umbrella organisms, such as the "spirit bears" of the Great Bear Rainforest can result in preservation of innumerable unseen species. At the same time, protecting whole landscapes for aesthetic or recreational purposes can also achieve the same end.

## Practice Quiz

1. What do we mean by *closed-canopy* forest and *old-growth* forest?
2. What continent is experiencing the greatest forest losses?
3. What is REDD, and how might it work?
4. Why is fire suppression a controversial strategy?
5. What portion of the United States' public rangelands are in poor or very poor condition due to overgrazing? Why do some groups say grazing fees amount to a "hidden subsidy"?
6. What is *rotational grazing*, and how does it mimic natural processes?
7. How do the size and design of nature preserves influence their effectiveness? What do landscape ecologists mean by *interior habitat* and *edge effects*?
8. What percentage of the earth's land area has some sort of protected status? How has the amount of protected areas changed globally?
9. What is *ecotourism*, and why is it important?
10. What is a *biosphere reserve*, and how does it differ from a wilderness area or wildlife preserve?

# Critical Thinking and Discussion Questions

Apply the principles you have learned in this chapter to discuss these questions with other students.

1. Conservationists argue that watershed protection and other ecological functions of forests are more economically valuable than timber. Timber companies argue that continued production supports stable jobs and local economies. If you were a judge attempting to decide which group was right, what evidence would you need on both sides? How would you gather this evidence?

2. Divide your class into a ranching group, a conservation group, and a suburban home-builders group, and debate the merits of subsidized grazing in the American West. What is the best use of the land? What landscapes are most desirable? Why? How do you propose to maintain these landscapes?

3. Calculating forest area and forest losses is complicated by the difficulty of defining exactly what constitutes a forest. Outline a definition for what counts as forest in your area, in terms of size, density, height, or other characteristics. Compare your definition to those of your colleagues. Is it easy to agree? Would your definition change if you lived in a different region?

4. There is considerable uncertainty about the extent of degradation on grazing lands. Suppose you were a range management scientist, and it was your job to evaluate degradation for the state of Montana. What data would you need? With an infinite budget, how would you gather the data you need? How would you proceed if you had a very small budget?

5. Why do you suppose dry tropical forest and tundra are well represented in protected areas, while grasslands and wetlands are protected relatively rarely? Consider social, cultural, geographic, and economic reasons in your answer.

6. Oil and gas companies want to drill in several parks, monuments, and wildlife refuges. Do you think this should be allowed? Why or why not? Under what conditions would drilling be allowable?

# Data Analysis | Detecting Edge Effects

Edge effects are a fundamental consideration in nature preserves. We usually expect to find dramatic edge effects in pristine habitat with many specialized species. But you may be able to find interior-edge differences on your own college campus, or in a park or other unbuilt area near you. Here are three testable questions you can examine using your own local patch of habitat: (1) Can an edge effect be detected or not? (2) Which species will indicate the difference between edge and interior conditions? (3) At what distance can you detect a difference between edge and interior conditions? To answer these questions, you can form a hypothesis and test it as follows:

1. Choose a study area. Find a distinct patch of habitat, such as woods, unmowed grass, or marshy but walkable wetland, about 50 m wide or larger. With other students, list some local, familiar plant species that you would expect to find in your study area. If possible, make this list on a visit to your site.

2. Form a hypothesis. Examine your list, and predict which species will occur most on edges, and (if you can) which you think will occur more in the interior. Form a hypothesis, or a testable statement, based on one of the three questions above. For example, "I will be able to detect an edge effect in my patch," or "I think an edge effect will be indicated by these species: _____," or "I think changes in species abundance will indicate an edge-interior change at _____ m from the edge of the patch."

3. Gather data. Get a meter tape and lay it along the ground from the edge of your habitat patch toward the interior. (You can also use a string and pace distances: treat one pace as a meter.) This line is your *transect*. At the edge end of the tape (or string), count the number of different species you can see within 1 m$^2$ on either side of your line. Repeat this count at each 5 m interval, up to 25 m. Thus you will create a list of species at 0, 5, 10, 15, 20, and 25 m in from the edge.

4. Examine your lists, and determine whether your hypothesis was correct. Can you see a change in species presence/absence from 0 to 25 m? Were you correct in your prediction of which species disappeared with distance from the edge? If you can identify an edge effect, at what distance did it occur?

5. Consider ways that your test could be improved. Should you take more frequent samples? Larger samples? Should you compare abundance rather than presence/absence? Might you have gotten different results if you had chosen a different study site? Or if your class had examined many sites and averaged the results? How else might you modify your test to improve the quality of your results?

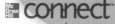

# 7 Food and Agriculture

Enormous farms have been carved out of Brazil's Cerrado (savanna), which once was the most biodiverse grassland and open tropical forest complex in the world.

*We can't solve problems by using the same kind of thinking we used when we created them.*

— ALBERT EINSTEIN

# CASE STUDY

## Farming the Cerrado

A soybean boom is sweeping across South America. Inexpensive land, availability of new crop varieties, and government policies that favor agricultural expansion have made South America the fastest growing agricultural area in the world. The center of this rapid expansion is the Cerrado, a huge area of grassland and tropical forest stretching from Bolivia and Paraguay across the center of Brazil almost to the Atlantic Ocean (fig. 7.1). Biologically, this rolling expanse of grasslands and tropical woodland is the richest savanna in the world, with at least 130,000 different plant and animal species, many of which are threatened by agricultural expansion.

Until recently, the Cerrado, which is roughly equal in size to the American Midwest, was thought to be unsuitable for cultivation. Its red iron-rich soils are highly acidic and poor in essential plant nutrients. Furthermore, the warm, humid climate harbors many destructive pests and pathogens. For hundreds of years, the Cerrado was primarily cattle country with many poor-quality pastures producing low livestock yields.

In the past few decades, however, Brazilian farmers have learned that modest applications of lime and phosphorus can quadruple yields of soybeans, maize, cotton, and other valuable crops. Researchers have developed more than 40 varieties of soybeans—mostly through conventional breeding, but some created with molecular techniques—specially adapted for the soils and climate of the Cerrado. Until about 30 years ago, soybeans were a relatively minor crop in Brazil. Since 1975, however, the area planted with soy has quadrupled, reaching more than 22 million ha (56 million acres) in 2010. Although that's a large area, it represents only one-eighth of the Cerrado, more than half of which is still occupied by pasture.

Brazil is now the world's top soy exporter, shipping some 27 million metric tons per year, or about 10 percent more than the United States. With two crops per year, cheap land, low labor costs, favorable tax rates, and yields per hectare equal to those in the American Midwest, Brazilian farmers can produce soybeans for less than half the cost in America. Agricultural economists predict that, by 2020, the global soy crop will double from the current 160 million metric tons per year, and that South America could be responsible for most of that growth. In addition to soy, Brazil now leads the world in beef, corn (maize), oranges, and coffee exports. This dramatic increase in South American agriculture helps answer the question of how the world may feed a growing human population.

A major factor in Brazil's current soy expansion is rising income in China. With more money to spend, the Chinese are consuming more soy, both directly as tofu and other soy products, and indirectly as animal feed. Between 2002 and 2004, China's soy imports doubled to more than 21 million metric tons, or about one-third of total global soy shipments. The outbreak of mad cow disease (or BSE, see chapter 8) in Europe,

Canada, and Japan also fueled increased world-wide demand for soybeans. Rather than feed livestock meat-processing wastes that may convey mad cow disease, producers are turning to protein- and lipid-rich soy meal. With 175 million free-range, grass-fed (and presumably BSE-free) cattle, Brazil has become the world's largest beef exporter.

Increasing demand for both soybeans and beef create land conflicts in Brazil. The pressure for more cropland and pasture is a leading cause of deforestation and habitat loss, most of which is occurring in the "arc of destruction" between the Cerrado and the Amazon. Small family farms are being gobbled up, and farm workers, displaced by mechanization, often migrate either to the big cities or to frontier forest areas. Increasing conflicts between poor farmers and big landowners have led to violent confrontations. The Landless Workers Movement claims that 1,237 rural workers died in Brazil between 1985 and 2000 as a result of assassinations and clashes over land rights. In 2005, a 74-year-old Catholic nun, Sister Dorothy Stang, was shot by gunmen hired by ranchers who resented her advocacy for native people, workers, and environmental protection. Over the past 20 years, Brazil claims to have resettled 600,000 families from the Cerrado. Still, tens of thousands of landless farm workers and displaced families live in unauthorized squatter camps and shantytowns across the country awaiting relocation.

**Figure 7.1** Brazil's Cerrado, 2 million ha of savanna (grassland) and open woodland is the site of the world's fastest growing soybean production. Cattle ranchers and agricultural workers, displaced by mechanized crop production, are moving northward into the "arc of destruction" at the edge of the Amazon rainforest, where the continent's highest rate of forest clearing is occurring.

As you can see, rapid growth of beef and soy production in Brazil have both positive and negative aspects. On one hand, more high-quality food is now available to feed the world. The 2 million km² of the Cerrado represents one of the world's last opportunities to open a large area of new, highly productive cropland. On the other hand, the rapid expansion and mechanization of agriculture in Brazil is destroying biodiversity and creating social conflicts as people move into formerly pristine lands. The issues raised in this case study illustrate many of the major themes in this chapter. Will there be enough food for everyone in the world? What will be the environmental and social consequences of producing the nutrition we need? In this chapter, we'll look at world food supplies, agricultural inputs, and sustainable approaches that can help solve some of the difficult questions we face.

# 7.1 Global Trends in Food and Nutrition

Brazilian agriculture is one of the most dramatic cases of environmental change today. The Cerrado is a long way from Iowa and Illinois, in the heart of the U.S. corn belt, but if you live in an agricultural state you might recognize some of the changes in the soy fields of South America. Food production has been transformed from small-scale, diversified operations to vast operations of thousands of hectares, growing one or two genetically modified crops, with abundant inputs of fuel and fertilizer, for a competitive global market.

These changes have dramatically increased production, lowered food prices, and provided affordable meat protein in developing countries from Brazil to China. Food production has increased so dramatically that we now use edible corn and sugar to run our cars (chapter 12). According to the International Monetary Fund, 2005 global food costs (in inflation-adjusted dollars) were the lowest ever recorded, less than one-quarter of the cost in the mid-1970s. In the United States and Europe, overproduction has driven prices low enough that we pay farmers billions of dollars each year to take land out of production.

Despite these changes, food costs have risen in many areas, especially for the poorest populations. In general, global food supply problems have more to do with distribution than with supplies. We continue to produce surpluses, but hunger remains an urgent problem.

Revolutions in production have also profoundly altered our environment and our diets. In this chapter we'll examine these changes, as well as the ways farmers have managed to feed more and more of the world's growing population. We'll also consider some of the strategies needed for long-term sustainability in food production.

## Food security is unevenly distributed

Fifty years ago, hunger was one of the world's most prominent, persistent problems. In 1960, nearly 60 percent of people in developing countries were chronically undernourished, and the world's population was increasing by more than 2 percent every year. Today, some conditions have changed dramatically; others have changed very little. The world's population has risen from 3 billion to about 7 billion, but food production has increased even faster. While the average population growth in the past 45 years has been 1.7 percent per year, food production has increased by an average of 2.2 percent per year. Food availability has increased in most countries to well over 2,200 kilocalories, the amount generally considered necessary for a healthy and productive life (fig. 7.2a).

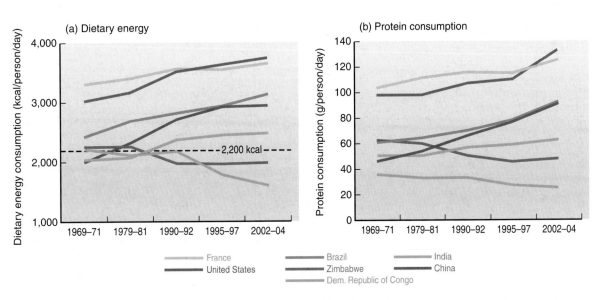

**Figure 7.2** Changes in dietary energy (kcal) and protein consumption in selected countries. *Source:* Data from Food and Agriculture Organization (FAO), 2008.

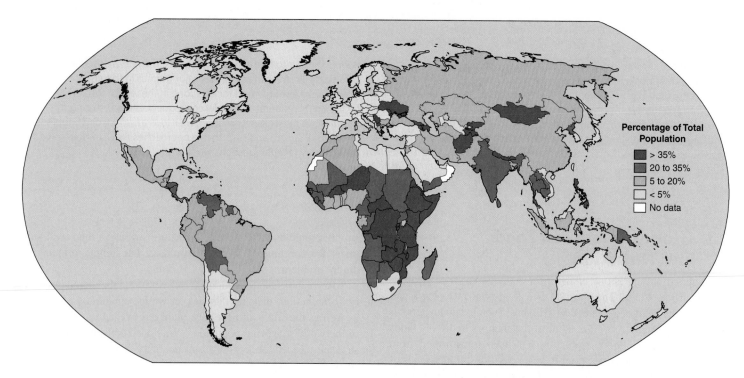

**Figure 7.3** Hunger around the world. In 2007, the United Nations reported that 854 million people—815 million of them in developing countries—suffered from chronic hunger and malnutrition. Africa has the largest number of countries with food shortages. Source: Hunger map from Food and Agriculture Organization of the United Nations website. Used by permission.

Protein intake has also increased in most countries, including China and India, the two most populous countries (fig. 7.2b). Less than 20 percent of people in developing countries now face chronic food shortages, as compared to 60 percent just 50 years ago.

But hunger is still with us. An estimated 854 million people— almost one in every eight people on earth—suffer chronic hunger (fig. 7.3). This number is up slightly from a few years ago, but because of population growth, the *percentage* of malnourished people is still falling (fig. 7.4).

About 95 percent of hungry people are in developing countries. Hunger is especially serious in sub-Saharan Africa, a region plagued by political instability (figs. 7.2, 7.3). Increasingly, we are coming to understand that **food security**, or the ability to obtain sufficient, healthy food on a day-to-day basis, is a combined problem of economic, environmental, and social conditions. Even in wealthy countries such as the United States, millions lack a sufficient, healthy diet. Poverty, job losses, lack of social services, and other factors lead to persistent hunger—and

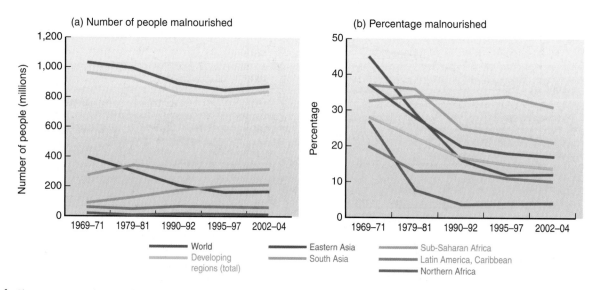

**Figure 7.4** Changes in numbers and rates of malnourishment, by region. *Source:* Data from UN Food and Agriculture Organization, 2008.

http://www.mhhe.com/cunningham6e

even more to persistent poor diets—despite the fact that we have more, cheaper food (in terms of the work needed to acquire it) than almost any society in history.

Food security is important at multiple scales. In the poorest countries, entire national economies can suffer from a severe drought, flood, or insect outbreak. Individual villages also suffer from a lack of food security. In extremely poor areas, a single bad crop can devastate a family or a village, and local economies can collapse if farmers cannot produce a crop to eat and sell. Even within families there can be unequal food security. Males often get both the largest share and the most nutritious food, while women and children—who need food most—all too often get the poorest diet. At least 6 million children under 5 years old die every year of diseases exacerbated by hunger and malnutrition. Providing a healthy diet might eliminate as much as 60 percent of all child deaths worldwide.

Hungry people can't work their way out of poverty. Nobel Prize-winning economist Robert Fogel estimates that in 1790, 20 percent of the population of England and France were effectively excluded from the labor force because they were too weak and hungry to work. Fogel calculates that improved nutrition can account for about half of all European economic growth during the nineteenth century. This analysis suggests that reducing hunger in today's poor countries could yield more than $120 billion (U.S.) in economic growth, by producing a healthier, longer-lived, and more productive work force.

## Famines usually have political and social roots

Globally, widespread hunger arises when political instability, war, and conflict displace populations, removing villagers from their farms or making farming too dangerous to carry on. Economic disparities may drive peasants from the land, for example when landowners find it more profitable to raise commercial soybeans than to collect rent from peasant farmers. This has occurred in Brazil (opening case study) and countless other countries. Landlessness is a desperate problem in many areas. Displaced farmers often have no choice but to migrate to the already overcrowded slums of major cities when they lose their land (chapter 14).

# Active Learning

### Mapping Poverty and Plenty

Examine the map in figure 7.3. Using the map of political boundaries at the end of your book, identify ten of the hungriest countries. Then identify ten of the countries with less than 5 percent of people facing chronic undernourishment (yellow areas). The world's five most populous countries are China, India, United States, Indonesia, and Brazil. Which classes do these five belong to?

*Answers:* China, Indonesia, and Brazil have 5–20 percent malnourished; India has 20–35 percent; the United States has <5 percent.

**Figure 7.5** Children wait for their daily ration of porridge at a feeding station in Somalia. When people are driven from their homes by hunger or war, social systems collapse, diseases spread rapidly, and the situation quickly becomes desperate.

**Famines** are large-scale food shortages, with widespread starvation, social disruption, and economic chaos. Starving people are forced to eat their seed grain and slaughter breeding livestock in a desperate attempt to keep themselves and their families alive. Even when better conditions return, they have often sacrificed their productive capacity and will take a long time to recover. Famines often trigger mass migrations to relief camps, where people survive but cannot maintain a healthy and productive life (fig. 7.5).

Economist Amartya K. Sen, of Harvard, has shown that, while natural disasters often precipitate famines, farmers have almost always managed to survive these events if they aren't thwarted by inept or corrupt governments or greedy elites. Professor Sen points out that armed conflict and political oppression are almost always at the root of famine. No democratic country with a relatively free press, he says, has ever had a major famine.

China's recovery from the famines of the 1960s is a dramatic example of this relationship (see trends in fig. 7.2). Misguided policies from the central government destabilized farming economies all across China. Two years of bad crops in 1959–60 precipitated famines that may have killed 30 million people. In recent years, political and economic changes have transformed access to food, even while the population has doubled, from 650 million in 1960 to 1.37 billion in 2010. China now consumes almost twice as much meat (pork, chicken, and beef) as the United States—increasingly this meat comes from livestock fed on soybeans bought from Brazil.

## 7.2 How Much Food Do We Need?

A good diet is essential to keep you healthy. You need a balance of foods to provide the right nutrients, as well as enough calories for a productive and energetic lifestyle. The United Nations Food and Agriculture Organization (FAO) estimates that nearly 3 billion people (almost half the world's population) suffer from vitamin, mineral, or protein deficiencies. These shortages result in devastating illnesses and death, as well as reduced mental capacity, developmental abnormalities, and stunted growth.

## A healthy diet includes the right nutrients

**Malnourishment** is a general term for nutritional imbalances caused by a lack of specific nutrients. In conditions of extreme food shortages, a lack of protein in young children can cause kwashiorkor, which is characterized by a bloated belly and discolored hair and skin. *Kwashiorkor* is a West African word meaning "displaced child." (A young child is displaced—and deprived of nutritious breast milk—when a new baby is born.) Marasmus (from Greek, "to waste away") is another severe condition in children who lack both protein and calories. A child suffering from severe marasmus is generally thin and shriveled, like a tiny, very old, starving person (fig. 7.6a). Children with these deficiencies have low resistance to disease and infections, and they may suffer permanent debilities in mental, as well as physical, development.

Deficiencies in vitamin A, folic acid, and iodine are more widespread problems. Both are found in vegetables, especially dark green leafy vegetables. Deficiencies in folic acid have been linked to neurological problems in babies. Effects of vitamin A shortages cause an estimated 350,000 people to go blind every year. Dr. Alfred Sommer, an ophthalmologist from Johns Hopkins University, has shown that giving children just two cents' worth of vitamin A twice a year could prevent almost all cases of childhood blindness and premature death associated with shortages of vitamin A. Vitamin supplements also reduced maternal mortality by nearly 40 percent in one study in Nepal.

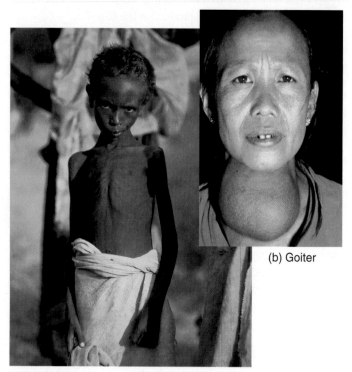

(a) Marasmus

**Figure 7.6** Dietary deficiencies can cause serious illness. (a) Marasmus results from protein and calorie deficiency and gives children a wizened look and dry, flaky skin. (b) Goiter, a swelling of the thyroid gland, results from an iodine deficiency.

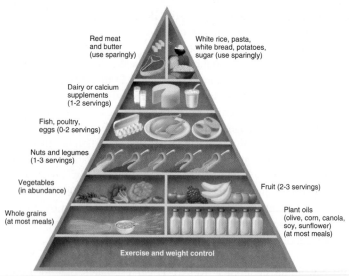

Harvard food pyramid

**Figure 7.7** The Harvard food pyramid emphasizes fruits, vegetables, and whole grains as the basis of a healthy diet. Red meat, white rice, pasta, and potatoes should be consumed sparingly. *Source:* Data from Willett and Stampfer, 2002.

Iodine deficiencies can cause goiter (fig. 7.6b), a swelling of the thyroid gland. Iodine is essential for synthesis of thyroxin, an endocrine hormone that regulates metabolism and brain development, among other things. The FAO estimates that 740 million people, mostly in Southeast Asia, suffer from iodine deficiency, including 177 million children whose development and growth have been stunted. Developed countries have largely eliminated this problem by adding a few pennies' worth of iodine to our salt.

Starchy foods, such as maize, polished rice, and manioc (tapioca), form the bulk of the diet for many poor people, but these foods are low in several essential vitamins and minerals. One celebrated effort to deliver crucial nutrients has been through genetic engineering of common foods, such as "golden rice," developed by Monsanto to include a gene for producing vitamin A. This strategy has shown promise, but it also has critics, who argue that genetically modified rice is too expensive for poor peasants. In addition, the herbicides needed to grow the golden rice kill the greens that villagers rely on to provide their essential nutrients. (See the related story "Golden Rice" at www.mhhe.com/cunningham6e.)

The best way to stay healthy is to eat lots of vegetables and grains, moderate amounts of eggs and dairy products, and sparing amounts of meat, oils, and processed foods. A solid base of regular exercise underpins an ideal diet outlined by Harvard dieticians (fig. 7.7) Modest amounts of fats are essential for healthy skin, cell function, and metabolism. But your body is not designed to process excessive amounts of fats (or sugars). Unsaturated plant-based oils, such as olive oil, are recommended by dietitians; trans fats (found in hydrogenated margarine) are not recommended.

## Overeating is a growing world problem

For the first time in history, there are probably more overweight people (more than 1 billion) than underweight people (about 850 million). This trend isn't limited to richer countries. Obesity

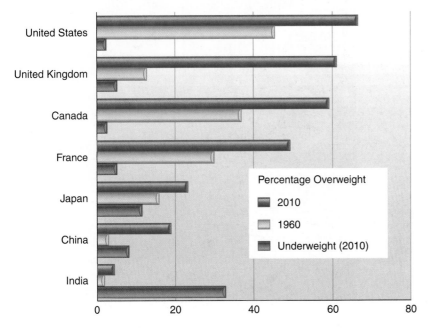

**Figure 7.8** Chronic obesity is a growing problem worldwide. In wealthier countries and many developing areas, the number overweight vastly exceeds the number underweight. *Data Source:* World Health Organization, 2010.

is spreading around the world (fig. 7.8). Diseases once thought to afflict only wealthy nations, such as heart attack, stroke, and diabetes, are now becoming the most prevalent causes of death and disability everywhere (chapter 8).

In the U.S., and increasingly in Europe, China, and developing countries, highly processed foods rich in sugars and fats have become a large part of our diet. Some 64 percent of adult Americans are overweight, up from 40 percent only a decade ago. About one-third of us are seriously overweight, or **obese**—generally considered to mean more than 20 percent over the ideal weight for a person's height and sex.

Being overweight increases your risk of hypertension, diabetes, heart attacks, stroke, gallbladder disease, osteoarthritis, respiratory problems, and some cancers. Every year, about 400,000 people in the United States die from illnesses related to obesity. This number is approaching the number related to smoking (435,000 annually). Paradoxically, food insecurity and poverty can contribute to obesity. In one study, more than half the women who reported not having enough to eat were overweight, compared with one-third of the food-secure women. Lack of good quality food may contribute to a craving for carbohydrates in people with a poor diet. A lack of time for cooking, limited access to healthy food choices, and ready availability of fast-food snacks and calorie-laden soft drinks, also lead to dangerous dietary imbalances for many people.

## More production doesn't necessarily reduce hunger

Most strategies for reducing world hunger have to do with increasing efficiency of farm production, expanding use of fertilizers and improved seeds, and converting more unused land or forest to agriculture. But the prevalence of obesity, and the instability of farm income, suggest that lack of supply is not necessarily the principal cause of world hunger. An overabundance of food supplies in much

of the world suggests that answers to global hunger may lie in better distribution of food resources.

For most farmers in the developed world, overproduction constantly threatens prices for farm products. To reduce food supplies and stabilize prices in the United States, Canada, and Europe, we send millions of tons of food aid to developing areas every year. Often, however, these shipments of free food destabilize farm economies in receiving areas. Prices for local farm products collapse and political corruption can expand if war lords control distribution. Even in developing areas, lack of food production is not always the cause of hunger.

There are also many inefficiencies in food use. Americans throw away some 40 percent of prepared food, sending it to landfills or incinerators rather than consuming it. A vegetable-rich diet like that in fig. 7.7 requires much less land and energy than does the meat-rich diet that is more common in wealthier countries. In developing countries, production of soy, palm oil, and other products for export often displaces food production.

Biofuels can also reduce food supplies. Using crops such as soy, corn, and palm oil to drive our cars is an important strategy for supporting farm economies, especially in the United States, where federal ethanol subsidies have led to sharp improvements in corn prices. But many questions remain regarding the efficiency of this land use for fuel production.

## 7.3 What Do We Eat?

Of the thousands of edible plants and animals in the world, only a few provide almost all our food. About a dozen types of grasses, three root crops, twenty or so fruits and vegetables, six mammals, two domestic fowl, and a few fish species make up almost all the food we eat (table 7.1). Two grasses, wheat and rice, are especially

| Table 7.1 | Key Global Food Sources | |
| --- | --- |
| **Crop** | **2004 Yield (Million Metric Tons)** |
| Wheat | 620 |
| Rice (paddy) | 610 |
| Maize (corn) | 643 |
| Potatoes | 310 |
| Coarse grains* | 1,013 |
| Soybeans | 221 |
| Cassava and sweet potatoes | 449 |
| Sugar (cane and beet) | 144 |
| Pulses (beans, peas) | 55 |
| Oil seeds | 375 |
| Vegetables and fruits | 1,206 |
| Meat and milk | 870 |
| Fish and seafood | 140 |

*Barley, oats, sorghum, rye, millet.
*Source:* Data from Food and Agriculture Organization (FAO), 2005.

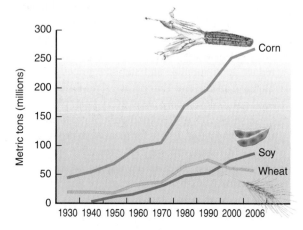

**Figure 7.9** United States production of our three dominant crops, corn, soybeans, and wheat. *Source: Data from USDA and UN FAO, 2008.*

**Figure 7.10** Meat and dairy consumption has quadrupled in the past 40 years, and China represents about 40 percent of that increased demand.

important because they are the staple foods for most of the 5 billion people in developing countries.

In the United States, corn (another grass, also known as maize) and soybeans have become our primary staples. We rarely eat either corn or soybeans directly, but corn provides the corn sweeteners, corn oil, and the livestock feed for producing our beef, chicken, and pork, as well as industrial starches and many synthetic vitamins. Soybeans are also fed to livestock, and soy provides protein and oils for processed foods. Because we have developed so many uses for corn, it now accounts for nearly two-thirds of our bulk commodity crops (corn, soy, wheat, rice). Together, corn and soy make up about 85 percent of these crops, with an annual production of 268 million tons of corn and 88 million tons of soy (fig. 7.9).

## Rising meat production is a sign of wealth

Because of dramatic increases in corn and soy production, meat consumption has grown in both developed and developing countries. In developing countries, meat consumption has risen from just 10 kg per person per year in the 1960s to over 26 kg today (fig. 7.10). In the United States, our meat consumption has risen from 90 kg to 136 kg per person per year in the same interval. Meat is a concentrated, high-value source of protein, iron, fats, and other nutrients that give us the energy to lead productive lives. Dairy products are also a key protein source: globally we consume more than twice as much dairy as meat. But dairy production per capita has declined slightly while global meat production has doubled in the past 45 years.

Meat is a good indicator of wealth because it is expensive to produce in terms of the resources needed to grow an animal (fig. 7.11). As discussed in chapter 2, herbivores use most of the energy they consume in growing muscle and bone, moving around, staying warm, and metabolizing (digesting) food. Only a little food energy is stored for consumption by carnivores, at the next level of the food pyramid. It takes over 8 kilos of grain fed to a beef cow to produce a single kilo of meat. (Actually, we raise mainly steers, or neutered males, for beef.) Pigs, being smaller, are more efficient. Just three pounds of pig feed are needed to produce a kilo of pork. Chickens and herbivorous fish (such as catfish) are still more efficient. Globally, some 660 million metric tons of cereals are used as livestock feed each year. This represents just

over a third of the world cereal use. As figure 7.11 suggests, we could feed at least 8 times as many people by eating those cereals directly. What differences do you suppose it would make if we did so?

A number of technological and breeding innovations have made this increased production possible. One of the most important is the **confined animal feeding operation (CAFO)**, where animals are housed and fed—mainly soy and corn—for rapid growth (fig. 7.12). These operations dominate livestock raising in the U.S., Europe, and increasingly in China and other countries. Animals are housed in giant enclosures, with up to 10,000 hogs or a million chickens in an enormous barn complex, or 100,000 cattle in a feed lot (fig. 7.13). Operators feed the animals specially prepared mixes of corn, soy, and animal protein that maximizes their growth rate. New breeds of livestock have been developed that produce meat rapidly, rather than simply getting fat. The turn-around time is getting shorter, too. A U.S. chicken producer can turn baby chicks into chicken nuggets after just 8 weeks of growth. Steers reach full size by just 18 months

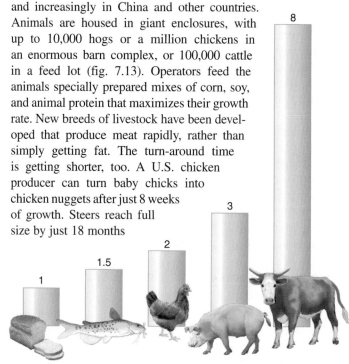

**Figure 7.11** Number of kilograms of grain needed to produce 1 kg of bread or 1 kg live weight gain.

(a)

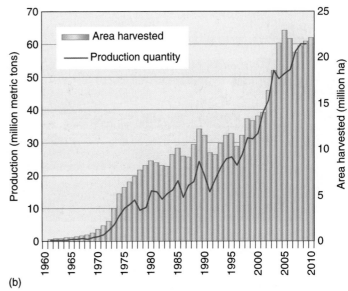

(b)

**Figure 7.12** (a) Confined animal feeding operations have expanded the global market for corn and soybeans. (b) Brazil's soy production has grown from near zero to being the country's dominant agricultural product. *Source:* Data from UN Food and Agriculture Organization.

**Figure 7.13** Most livestock grown in the United States are raised in large-scale, concentrated animal-feeding operations. Up to a million animals can be held in a single facility. High population densities require heavy use of antibiotics and can cause severe local air and water pollution.

of age. Increased use of antibiotics, which are mixed in daily feed, make it possible to raise large numbers of animals in close quarters. Nearly 90 percent of U.S. hogs receive antibiotics in their feed.

## Seafood is both wild and farmed, but nearly all depends on wild-source inputs

The 140 million metric tons of seafood we eat every year is an important part of our diet. Seafood provides about 15 percent of all animal protein eaten by humans, and it is the main animal protein source for about 1 billion people in developing countries. Unfortunately, overharvesting and habitat destruction threaten most of the world's wild fisheries. Annual catches of ocean fish rose by about

4 percent annually between 1950 and 1988. Since 1989, however, 13 of 17 major marine fisheries have declined dramatically or become commercially unsustainable. According to the United Nations, three-quarters of the world's edible ocean fish, crustaceans, and mollusks are declining and in urgent need of managed conservation.

The problem is too many boats using efficient but destructive technology to exploit a dwindling resource base. Boats as big as ocean liners travel thousands of kilometers and drag nets large enough to scoop up a dozen jumbo jets, sweeping a large patch of ocean clean of fish in a few hours. Long-line fishing boats set cables up to 10 km long with hooks every 2 meters that catch birds, turtles, and other unwanted "by-catch" along with targeted species. Trawlers drag heavy nets across the bottom, scooping up everything indiscriminately and reducing broad swaths of habitat to rubble. One marine biologist compared the technique to harvesting forest mushrooms with a bulldozer. In some operations, up to 15 kg of dead and dying by-catch are dumped back into the ocean for every kilogram of marketable food. The FAO estimates that operating costs for the 4 million boats now harvesting wild fish exceed sales by $50 billion (U.S.) per year. Countries subsidize fishing fleets to preserve jobs and to ensure access to this valuable resource.

The best solution, according to a United Nations study on ecosystem services, is to establish better international agreements on fisheries. Instead of a free-for-all race to exploit fish first, nations could manage fisheries for long-term, sustained production. Just as with hunting laws within a single country, agreement to international fishery rules could improve total food production, fishery employment, and ecosystem stability.

Aquaculture is providing an increasing share of the world's seafood. Fish can be grown in farm ponds that take relatively little space but are highly productive. For cultivation of plant-eating fish such as tilapia, these systems can be very sustainable. Cultivation of high-value carnivorous species such as salmon, however, threatens

**Figure 7.14** Pens for fish-rearing in Thailand.

wild fish populations, which are caught to feed captive fish. Coastal fish-rearing ponds have replaced hundreds of thousands of hectares of mangrove forests and wetlands, which serve as irreplaceable nurseries for marine species. Net pens anchored in nearshore areas encourage spread of diseases, as they release feces, uneaten food, antibiotics, and other pollutants into surrounding ecosystems (fig. 7.14).

## Biohazards can arise in industrial production

Increasingly efficient production can have externalized (unaccounted for) costs in terms of public health. Land conversion to crop fields increases soil erosion, which degrades water quality. Bacteria in the manure in the feedlots, or liquid wastes in manure storage lagoons (holding tanks) around hog farms, can escape into the environment—from airborne dust around feedlots or from breaches in the walls of a manure tank. When Hurricane Floyd hit North Carolina's coastal hog production region in 1999, some 10 million $m^3$ of hog and poultry waste overflowed into local rivers, creating a dead zone in Pamlico Sound. Could this happen again?

Constant use of antibiotics may be producing antibiotic-resistant diseases. More than half of all antibiotics used in the United States are administered to livestock. This massive and constant exposure produces antibiotic-resistant pathogens, strains that have adapted to survive antibiotics. This use, then, is slowly rendering our standard antibiotics useless for human health care. Next time you are prescribed an antibiotic by your doctor, you might ask whether she or he worries about antibiotic resistance, and you might think about how you would feel if your prescription was ineffective against your illness.

Although the public is increasingly aware of these environmental and health risks of concentrated meat production, we seem to be willing to accept these risks because this production system has made our favorite foods cheaper, bigger, and more available. A fast-food hamburger today is more than twice the size it was in 1960, especially if you buy the kind with multiple patties and special sauce, and Americans love to eat them. At the same time, this larger burger costs less per pound, in constant dollars, than it did in 1960. As a consequence, for much of the world, consumption of protein and calories has climbed beyond what we really need to be healthy (figs. 7.2, 7.8).

As environmental scientists, we are faced with a conundrum, then. Improved efficiency has great environmental costs; it has also given us the abundant, inexpensive foods that we love. We have more protein, but also more obesity, heart disease, and diabetes than we ever had before. What do you think? Do the environmental risks balance a globally improved quality of life? Or should we consider reducing our consumption to reduce environmental costs? How might we go about making changes, if you think any are needed?

## 7.4 Living Soil Is a Precious Resource

Understanding the environmental science of food production requires some understanding of the soil that supports us. Most of us think of soil as just dirt. But healthy soil is a marvelous substance with astonishing complexity. Soil contains mineral grains weathered from rocks, partially decomposed organic molecules, and a host of living organisms. The complex community of bacteria and fungi are primarily responsible for providing nutrients that plants need to grow. Soil can be considered a living ecosystem by itself. How can we manage our soils to maintain and build these precious systems?

Building a few millimeters of soil can take anything from a few years (in a healthy grassland) to a few thousand years (in a desert or tundra). Under the best circumstances, topsoil accumulates at about 1 mm per year. With careful husbandry that prevents erosion and adds organic material, soil can be replenished and renewed indefinitely (fig. 7.15). But many farming techniques deplete soil. Crops consume the nutrients; plowing exposes the soil to erosion by wind or water. Severe erosion can carry away 25 mm or more of soil per year, far more than can accumulate under the best of conditions.

### What is soil?

Soil is a complex mixture of six components:

1. *sand and gravel* (mineral particles from bedrock, either in place or moved from elsewhere, as in wind-blown sand)
2. *silts and clays* (extremely small mineral particles; many clays are sticky and hold water because of their flat surfaces and ionic charges; others give red color to soil)
3. *dead organic material* (decaying plant matter stores nutrients and gives soils a black or brown color)
4. *soil fauna and flora* (living organisms, including soil bacteria, worms, fungi, roots of plants, and insects, recycle organic compounds and nutrients)

## Active Learning

### Where in the World Did You Eat Today?

Make a list of every food you ate today or yesterday. From this list, make a graph of the number of items in the following categories: grains, vegetables, dairy, meat, other. Which food type was most abundant? With other students, try to identify the location or region where each food was grown. How many come from a region more than half-way across the country? From another country?

5. *water* (moisture from rainfall or groundwater, essential for soil fauna and plants)

6. *air* (tiny pockets of air help soil bacteria and other organisms survive)

Variations in these six components produce almost infinite variety in the world's soils. Abundant clays make soil sticky and wet. Abundant organic material and sand make the soil soft and easy to dig. Sandy soils drain quickly, often depriving plants of moisture. Silt particles are larger than clays and smaller than sand, so they aren't sticky and soggy, and they don't drain too quickly. Thus silty soils are ideal for growing crops, but they are also light and blow away easily when exposed to wind. Soils with abundant soil fauna quickly decay dead leaves and roots, making nutrients available for new plant growth. Compacted soils have few air spaces, making soil fauna and plants grow poorly. You can see some of these differences just looking at soil. Reddish soils are colored by iron-rich, rust-colored clays, the kind that store few nutrients for plants. Deep black soils are rich in decayed organic material, and thus are rich in nutrients.

## Healthy soil fauna can determine soil fertility

Soil bacteria, algae, and fungi decompose and recycle leaf litter into plant-available nutrients, as well as helping to give soils structure and loose texture (fig. 7.16). Microscopic worms and nematodes process organic matter and create air spaces as they burrow through soil. These organisms mostly stay near the

**Figure 7.15** Terracing, as in these Balinese rice paddies, can control erosion and make steep hillsides productive. These terraced rice paddies have produced two or three crops a year for centuries because the soils are carefully managed and organic nutrients are maintained.

**Figure 7.16** Soil ecosystems include numerous consumer organisms, as depicted here: (1) snail, (2) termite, (3) nematode and nematode-killing constricting fungus, (4) earthworm, (5) wood roach, (6) centipede, (7) carabid (ground) beetle, (8) slug, (9) soil fungus, (10) wireworm (click beetle larva), (11) soil protozoan, (12) sow bug, (13) ant, (14) mite, (15) springtail, (16) pseudoscorpion, and (17) cicada nymph.

surface, often within the top few centimeters. The sweet aroma of freshly turned soil is caused by actinomycetes, bacteria that grow in fungus-like strands and give us the antibiotics streptomycin and tetracycline.

The health of the soil ecosystem depends on environmental conditions, including climate, topography, and parent material (the mineral grains or bedrock on which soil is built), and frequency of disturbance. Too much rain washes away nutrients and organic matter, but soil fauna cannot survive with too little rain. In extreme cold, soil fauna recycle nutrients extremely slowly; in extreme heat they may work so fast that leaf litter on the forest floor is taken up by plants in just weeks or months—so that the soil retains little organic matter. Frequent disturbance prevents the development of a healthy soil ecosystem, as does steep topography that allows rain to wash away soils. In the United States, the best farming soils tend to occur where the climate is not too wet or dry, on glacial silt deposits such as those in the upper Midwest, and on silt and clay-rich flood deposits, like those along the Mississippi River.

Most soil fauna occur in the uppermost layers of a soil, where they consume leaf litter. This layer is known as the "O" (organic) horizon. Just below the O horizon is a layer of mixed organic and mineral soil material, the A horizon (fig. 7.17), or **surface soil**.

The B horizon, or **subsoil**, lies below most organic activity, and it tends to have more clays than the A layer. The B layer accumulates clays that seep downward from the A horizon with rainwater that percolates through the soil. If you dig a hole, you may be able to tell where the B horizon begins because the soil tends to become slightly sticky. If you squeeze a handful of B soil, it should hold its shape better than a handful of A soil.

Sometimes an E (eluviated, or washed-out) layer lies between the A and B horizons. The E layer is loose and light-colored because most of its clays and organic material have been washed down to the B horizon. The C horizon, below the subsoil, is mainly decomposed rock fragments. Parent materials underlie the C layer. Parent material is the sand, wind-blown silt, bedrock, or other mineral material on which the soil is built. About 70 percent of the parent material in the United States was transported to its present site by glaciers, wind, and water, and is not related to the bedrock formations below it.

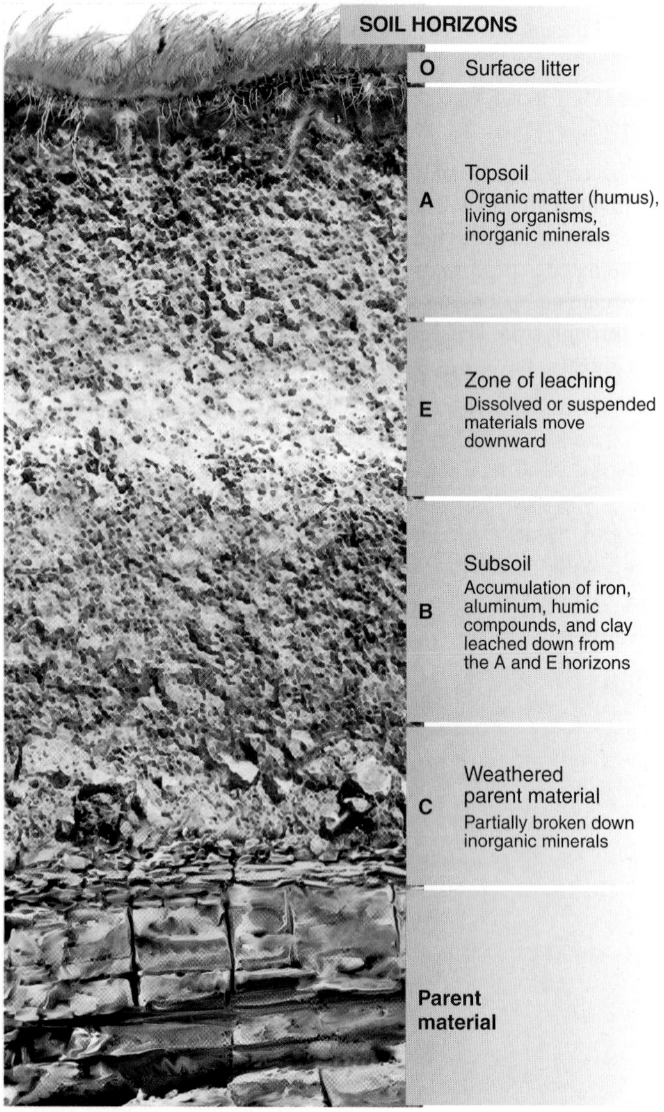

## Your food comes mostly from the A horizon

Ideal farming soils have a thick, organic-rich A horizon. The soils that support the corn belt farm states of the U.S. Midwest have rich, black A horizon that can be over two meters thick, although a century of farming has washed much of this soil down the Mississippi River to the Gulf of Mexico. Most soils have less than half a meter of A horizon. Desert soils, with slow rates of organic activity, might have almost no O or A horizons (fig. 7.18).

Because topsoil is so important to our survival, we differentiate soils largely according to the thickness and composition of their upper layers. The U.S. Department of Agriculture

**Figure 7.17** Idealized soil profile showing possible soil horizons. The actual number, composition, and thickness of these layers vary in different soil types.

**SOIL HORIZONS**

O  Surface litter

A  Topsoil
Organic matter (humus), living organisms, inorganic minerals

E  Zone of leaching
Dissolved or suspended materials move downward

B  Subsoil
Accumulation of iron, aluminum, humic compounds, and clay leached down from the A and E horizons

C  Weathered parent material
Partially broken down inorganic minerals

Parent material

**Figure 7.18** In many areas, soil or climate constraints limit soil development and agricultural production. These hungry goats in Sudan feed on a solitary Acacia shrub.

Each green dot represents 10,000 ha (25,000 ac) of cropland.
Total acres: 376,997,900.

**Figure 7.19** Distribution of cropland in the United States. Glacial deposits and floodplain sediments make especially rich farmland.
*Source:* USDA Natural Resource Conservation Service.

classifies the thousands of different soil types into 11 soil orders (**http://soils.usda.gov/technical/classification/orders/**). Mollisols (*mollic* = soft, *sol* = soil), for example, have a thick, organic-rich A horizon that develops from the deep, dense roots of prairie grasses. Alfisols (*alfa* = first) have a slightly thinner A horizon, with slightly less organic matter. Alfisols develop in deciduous forests, where leaf litter is abundant. In contrast, the aridisols (*arid* = dry) of the desert Southwest have little organic matter, and they often have accumulations of mineral salts. Mollisols and alfisols dominate most of the farming regions of the United States (fig. 7.19).

## 7.5 Ways We Use and Abuse Soil

Only about 11 percent of the earth's land area (14.66 million km² out of a total of 132.4 million km²) is currently in agricultural production. Perhaps four times as much land could be converted to cropland, but much of this land serves as a refuge for cultural or biological diversity or suffers from constraints, such as steep slopes, shallow soils, poor drainage, tillage problems, low nutrient levels, metal toxicity, or excess soluble salts or acidity, that limit the types of crops that can be grown there.

### Arable land is unevenly distributed

In parts of Canada and the United States, temperate climates, abundant water, and high soil fertility produce high crop yields that contribute to high standards of living. Other countries, although rich in land area, lack suitable soil, topography, water, or climate to sustain our levels of productivity.

Chiefly because of population growth, the world's arable land per person shrank from 0.38 ha (0.94 acre) in 1970 to 0.23 ha (0.56 acre) per person in 2000 (1 ha = 100 m × 100 m). If current population projections are correct, the amount of cropland per person will decline to 0.15 ha (0.37 acre) by 2050. In Asia, cropland will be even more scarce—0.09 ha (0.22 acre) per person—in 50 years. If you live on a typical quarter-acre suburban lot, look at your yard and imagine feeding yourself for a year on what you could produce there.

Many developing countries are reaching the limit of lands that can be exploited for agriculture. Others still have considerable potential for opening new agricultural lands, although there are social and environmental costs in converting forests and wetlands, and other ecosystems to agriculture, as noted in the opening case study. The largest increases in cropland over the past 30 years have occurred in South America, where forests and grazing lands are rapidly being converted to farms. East Asia, for instance, uses about three-quarters of its potentially arable land. Most remaining land is too dry, wet, or steep for farming. Latin America, by contrast, uses only about one-fifth of its potential land, and Africa uses only about one-fourth of the land that theoretically could grow crops. Further increases in crop production will probably have to come from higher yields per hectare, or from rehabilitating degraded lands.

Land surveys tell us that much more land in the world could be cultivated, but not all of that land necessarily should be farmed. Much of it is more valuable in its natural state. Forests and wetlands provide ecological services that farmers depend on—regulating water supplies, providing insect pollinators, moderating extreme temperature shifts. Meanwhile, most tropical soils in Asia, Africa, and South America are deeply weathered and generally infertile, so they make poor farmland. Clearing land for agriculture in the tropics has often resulted in tragic losses of biodiversity and ecological services, and much of this land has turned into useless scrub or semidesert.

### Soil degradation reduces crop yields

Agriculture both causes and suffers from environmental degradation. The International Soil Reference and Information Centre in the Netherlands estimates that, every year, 3 million ha (7.4 million acres) of cropland are ruined by erosion, 4 million ha are turned into deserts, and 8 million ha are converted to nonagricultural uses, such as homes, highways, shopping centers, factories, and reservoirs. Over the past 50 years, some 1.9 billion ha of agricultural land (an area greater than that now in production) have been degraded to some extent. About 300 million ha of this land are strongly degraded (meaning that the soil has deep gullies, severe nutrient depletion, or poor crop growth, or that restoration is difficult and expensive). Some 910 million ha—about the size of China—are moderately degraded. Nearly 9 million ha of former croplands are so degraded that they no longer support any crops at all. The causes of this extreme degradation vary: in Ethiopia, it is water erosion; in Somalia, it is wind; and in Uzbekistan, salt and toxic chemicals

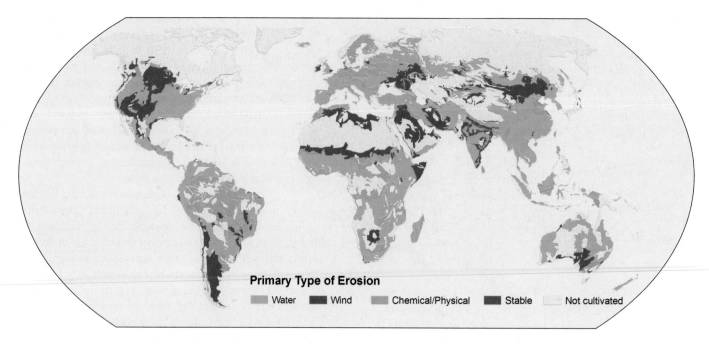

**Figure 7.20** Global causes of soil erosion and degradation. Globally, 62 percent of eroded land is mainly affected by water; 20 percent is mainly affected by wind. *Source:* ISRIC Global Assessment of Human-induced Soil Degradation, 2008.

are responsible. In Sweden and Finland, fallout from the Chernobyl nuclear reaction explosion has contaminated large amounts of grazing land and farmland.

Water and wind erosion provide the motive force for the vast majority of all soil degradation worldwide (fig. 7.20). Chemical degradation includes nutrient depletion, salt accumulation, acidification, and pollution. Physical degradation includes compaction by heavy machinery or trampling by cattle, water accumulation from excess irrigation and poor drainage, and laterization (solidification of iron and aluminum-rich tropical soil when exposed to sun and rain).

## Farming accelerates erosion

Erosion is an important natural process, resulting in the redistribution of the products of geologic weathering, and it is part of both soil formation and soil loss. The world's landscapes have been sculpted by erosion. When the results are spectacular enough, we enshrine them in national parks, as we did with the Grand Canyon.

Where erosion has worn down mountains and spread soil over the plains or deposited rich alluvial silt in river bottoms, we farm it. Erosion is a disaster only when it occurs in the wrong place at the wrong time.

Some erosion occurs so rapidly that you can watch it happen. Deep gullies are created where water scours away the soil, leaving fenceposts and trees sitting on tall pedestals as the land erodes away around them. In most places, however, erosion is more subtle. It is a creeping disaster that occurs in small increments. A thin layer of topsoil washes off of fields year after year until, eventually, nothing is left but poor-quality subsoil that requires more and more fertilizer and water to produce any crop at all.

An estimated 25 billion metric tons of soil are lost from croplands every year due to wind and water erosion. The net effect, worldwide, of this widespread topsoil erosion is a reduction in crop production equivalent to removing about 1 percent of the world's cropland *each year*. Many farmers are able to compensate for this loss by applying more fertilizer and by bringing new land into cultivation. Continuation of current erosion rates, however, could reduce agricultural production by 25 percent in Central America and Africa and by 20 percent in South America by 2020. The total annual soil loss from croplands is thought to be 25 billion metric tons. About twice that much soil is lost from rangelands, forests, and urban construction sites each year.

In addition to reduced land fertility, erosion results in sediment loading of rivers and lakes, siltation of reservoirs and harbors, smothering of wetlands and coral reefs, creation of "dead zones" in coastal regions, and clogging of water intakes and waterpower turbines.

## Wind and water move soil

Wind and water are the main agents that move soil around. Water flowing across a gently sloping, bare field removes a thin, uniform layer of soil in what is known as **sheet erosion**. When little rivulets of running water gather together and cut small channels in the soil, the process is called **rill erosion** (fig. 7.21a). If rills enlarge to form bigger channels or ravines that are too large to be removed by normal tillage operations, we call the process **gully erosion** (fig. 7.21b). Streambank erosion is the washing away of soil from the banks of established streams, creeks, or rivers, often as a result of removing trees and brush along streambanks and of cattle damaging the banks.

(a) Sheet and rill erosion

(b) Gullying

(c) Wind erosion and desertification

**Figure 7.21** Land degradation affects more than 1 billion ha yearly, or about two-thirds of all global cropland. (a and b) Water erosion account for about half that total. (c) Wind erosion affects a nearly equal area.

Most soil erosion on agricultural land is rill erosion. Large amounts of soil can be transported a little bit at a time without being very noticeable. A farm field can lose 20 metric tons of soil per hectare during winter and spring runoff in rills so small that they are erased by the first spring cultivation. That loss represents only a few millimeters of soil over the whole surface of the field, hardly apparent to any but the most discerning eye, but it doesn't take much mathematical skill to see that if you lose soil twice as fast as it is being replaced, it eventually will run out.

Wind can equal or exceed water in erosive force, especially in a dry climate and on relatively flat land. When plant cover and surface litter are removed from the land by agriculture or grazing, wind lifts loose soil particles and sweeps them away. In extreme conditions, windblown dunes encroach on useful land and cover roads and buildings (fig. 7.21c). Over the past 30 years, China has lost 93,000 km² (about the size of Indiana) to **desertification**, or conversion of productive land to desert. Advancing dunes from the Gobi desert are now only 160 km (100 mi) from Beijing. Every year more than 1 million tons of sand and dust blow from Chinese drylands, often traveling across the Pacific Ocean to the West Coast of North America. Since 1985, China has planted more than 40 billion trees to try to stabilize the soil and hold back deserts.

Many areas of the United States and Canada have very high erosion rates. The U.S. Department of Agriculture reports that 69 million ha (170 million acres) of U.S. farmland and range are eroding faster than 1 mm per year (10 tons/ha/year), the rate at which soil accumulates in the best conditions. These erosion rates steadily deplete long-term productivity.

Intensive farming practices are largely responsible for this situation. Row crops, such as corn and soybeans, leave soil exposed for much of the growing season. Deep plowing and heavy herbicide applications create weed-free fields that look neat but are subject to erosion. Farmers sometimes plow through grass-lined watercourses (low areas where water runs off after a rain) and pull out windbreaks and fencerows to accommodate the large machines and to get every last square meter into production.

## 7.6 Agricultural Inputs

Soil is only part of the agricultural resource picture. Agriculture is also dependent upon water, nutrients, favorable climates to grow crops, productive crop varieties, and the mechanical energy to tend and harvest the crops.

### Irrigation is often needed for high yields

Agriculture accounts for the largest single share of global water use. At least two-thirds of all fresh water withdrawn from rivers, lakes, and groundwater supplies is used for irrigation (chapter 10). Irrigation increases yields of most crops by 100 to 400 percent. Although estimates vary widely (as do definitions of irrigated land), about 15 percent of all cropland, worldwide, is irrigated.

Some countries are water rich and can readily afford to irrigate farmland, while other countries are water poor and must use water very carefully. The efficiency of irrigation water use varies greatly. High evaporative and seepage losses from unlined and uncovered canals in some places can mean that as much as 80 percent of water withdrawn for irrigation never reaches its intended destination. Poor farmers may overirrigate because they lack the technology to meter water and distribute just the amount needed. In wealthier countries, farmers can afford sometimes-extravagant uses of water; they can also afford water-saving technologies such as drip irrigation or downward-facing sprinklers (fig. 7.22).

Excessive use not only wastes water but also often results in **waterlogging**. Waterlogged soil is saturated with water, and plant roots die from lack of oxygen. **Salinization**, in which mineral salts accumulate in the soil, is often a problem when irrigation water dissolves and mobilizes salts in the soil. As the water evaporates, it leaves behind a salty crust on the soil surface that is lethal to most plants. Flushing with excess water can wash away this salt accumulation, but the result is even more saline water for downstream users.

The FAO estimates that 20 percent of all irrigated land is damaged to some extent by waterlogging or salinity. Water conservation techniques can greatly reduce problems arising from excess water use.

**Figure 7.22** Downward-facing sprinklers on this center-pivot irrigation system deliver water more efficiently than upward-facing sprinklers.

## Fertilizer boosts production

Plants require small amounts of inorganic nutrients from soil. In large-scale farming, fertilizers are used to ensure a sufficient supply of these nutrients. The major elements required by most plants are nitrogen, potassium, phosphorus, calcium, magnesium, and sulfur. Nitrogen, a component of all living cells, is the most common limiting factor for plant growth. Phosphorus and potassium can also be limited in supply, so nitrogen, phosphorus, and potassium are our primary fertilizers. In rainy regions such as Brazil, calcium and magnesium often are washed away and must be supplied in the form of lime. Much of the doubling in worldwide crop production since 1950 has come from increased inorganic fertilizer use. In 1950 the average amount of fertilizer used was 20 kg per hectare. In 2000 this had increased to an average of 90 kg per hectare worldwide.

There is considerable potential for increasing the world's food supply by increasing fertilizer use in low-production countries if ways can be found to apply fertilizer more effectively and to reduce pollution. Africa, for instance, uses an average of only 19 kg of fertilizer per hectare (17 lbs per acre), or about one-fourth of the world average. It has been estimated that the developing world could at least triple its crop production by raising fertilizer use to the world average.

Overfertilizing is also a common problem. While European farmers use more than twice as much fertilizer per hectare as do North American farmers, their yields are not proportionally higher. Phosphates and nitrates from farm fields and cattle feedlots are a major cause of aquatic ecosystem pollution. Nitrate levels in groundwater have risen to dangerous levels in many areas where intensive farming is practiced. Young children are especially sensitive to the presence of nitrates. Using nitrate-contaminated water to mix infant formula can be fatal for newborns.

Enriching organic material in soils is an alternative way to fertilize crops. Manure is an important natural source of soil nutrients. Cover crops also can be grown and then plowed into the soil. Nitrogen-fixing bacteria living symbiotically in root nodules of legumes are valuable for making nitrogen available as a plant nutrient (chapter 2). Interplanting and rotating beans or some other leguminous crop with such crops as corn and wheat are traditional ways of increasing nitrogen availability.

## Modern agriculture runs on oil

The food system in the United States consumes about 16 percent of the total energy we use. Most of our foods require more energy to produce, process, and get to market than they yield when we eat them. Reliance on fossil fuels began in the 1920s, with the adoption of tractors. Energy use increased sharply after World War II, with the invention of nitrogen fertilizer produced from natural gas. Reliance on diesel and gasoline to run tractors, combines, irrigation pumps, and other equipment has continued to grow since then. David Pimentel, of Cornell University, has calculated that each hectare of corn (an area 100 m × 100 m) produced in the Unted States consumes the equivalent of 800 liters of oil (5 barrels of oil). One third of this energy is used in producing nitrogen fertilizers from natural gas. Another third is inputs for machinery and fuel. The remaining third is used for irrigation, synthetic herbicides, and other fertilizers.

After crops leave the farm, additional energy is used in food processing, distribution, and storage. It has been estimated that the average food item in the American diet travels 2,000 km (1,250 mi) between the farm that grew it and the person who consumes it. The energy required for this complex processing and distribution system may be five times as much as is used directly in farming.

Farmers also produce energy in the form of ethanol and biodiesel. There has been much debate about the environmental and economic costs and benefits of this production. The balance of energy inputs and outputs is difficult to calculate, and in the United States and Europe, biofuel production, especially ethanol, has not been economically viable without heavy subsidies for growing and processing crops. On the other hand, plant oils from sunflowers, soybeans, corn, and other oil seed crops can be burned directly in most diesel engines, and may be closer than ethanol to a net energy gain (chapter 12). Brazil produces ethanol more efficiently for its tropical sugarcane crops. Annual output of more than 16 billion liters of ethanol is a major contribution to Brazil's energy budget.

## Pesticides save crops but have health risks

Biological pests reduce crop yields and spoil as much as half of the crops harvested every year in some areas. Modern agriculture depends on toxic chemicals to kill these pests. There are concerns about the types and amounts of pesticides we use, but our reliance on them has grown steadily over the years (fig. 7.23).

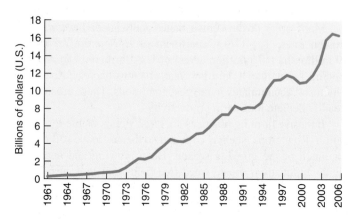

**Figure 7.23** Value of global trade in pesticides (imports).
*Source:* Data from the UN Food and Agriculture Organization, 2009.

**Figure 7.24** Spraying pesticides by air is quick and cheap, but toxins often drift to nearby fields.

Traditional strategies for evading pest damage often involved mixed crops and crop rotation. With many small patches of multiple crops, pests populations tend to remain relatively small. Reliance on a suite of different food sources can also reduce people's vulnerability to a particular crop pest. Rotating crops from one year to another reduces pests' ability to build up populations over time, and traditional crops often include varieties selected for pest resistance.

Modern agriculture, however, involves vast expanses of a single crop, often with little genetic variation, which increases the need for new methods of pest control. The invention of synthetic organic chemicals, such as DDT (dichlorodiphenyltrichloroethane) transformed our approach to pest control. These chemicals have been an important part of our increased crop production and have helped control many disease-causing organisms. It's estimated that up to half our current crop yields might be lost if we had no pesticides to protect them. Indiscriminate and profligate pesticide use, however, also has caused many problems, such as killing nontarget species, creating new pests of organisms that previously were not a problem, and causing widespread pesticide resistance among pest species (fig. 7.24). Often highly persistent and mobile in the environment, many pesticides have moved through air, water, and soil and bioaccumulated or bioconcentrated in food chains, nearly exterminating several top predators, such as peregrine falcons.

What are our pimary types of inorganic pesticides? **Organophosphates** are the most abundantly used synthetic pesticsides. These can be designed to prevent growth of broadleaf weeds or to attack the nervous systems of insect pests. Glyphosate, the single most heavily used herbicide in the United States, is also known by the trade name Roundup. Glyphosate is applied to 90 percent of U.S. soybeans. "Roundup-ready" soybeans (see discussion below) are one of the most commonly used type of genetically modified crop. **Chlorinated hydrocarbons**, also called organochlorines, are persistant and highly toxic to sensitive organisms. Atrazine, which is applied to 96 percent of all U.S. corn, was the most abundantly used pesticide until about 1998 (see A Closer Look, p. 170).

Other important pesticides include fumigants, highly toxic gases such as methylene bromide, which is used to kill fungus on strawberries and other low-growing crops; inorganic pesticides, such as arsenic and copper; and natural "botanical" pesticides derived from plants, such as nicotinoid alkaloids derived from tobacco.

Your exposure to pesticides is probably higher than you suspect. A study by the U.S. Department of Agriculture found that 73 percent of conventionally grown foods (out of 94,000 samples assayed) had residues from at least one pesticide. By contrast, only 23 percent of the organic samples of the same food groups had any residues.

In 2002 Swiss researchers published results of a two-decades-long comparison of organic and conventional farming. Crops grown without synthetic fertilizers or pesticides produced, on average, about a 20 percent lower yield than similar crops grown by conventional methods, but they more than made up the difference with lower operating costs, premium crop prices, less ecological damage, and healthier farm families.

Alternatives for reducing our dependence on chemical pesticides include management changes, such as using cover crops and mechanical cultivation, and planting mixed polycultures rather than vast monoculture fields. Biological controls, such as insect predators or pathogens, can help reduce chemical use. Genetic breeding and biotechnology can produce pest-resistant crop and livestock strains as well. Integrated pest management (IPM) combines all of these alternative methods, together with judicious use of synthetic pesticides under precisely controlled conditions. Consumers can also learn to accept less than perfect fruits and vegetables. For ways you can minimize pesticides in your diet, see What Can You Do? (below).

## What Can YOU Do?

### Reducing the Pesticides in Your Food

If you want to reduce the amount of pesticide residues and other toxic chemicals in your diet, follow these simple rules.

- Wash and scrub all fresh fruits and vegetables thoroughly under running water.
- Peel fruits and vegetables when possible. Throw away the outer leaves of leafy vegetables, such as lettuce and cabbage.
- Cook foods that you suspect have been treated with pesticides to break down chemical residues.
- Trim the fat from meat, chicken, and fish. Eat lower on the food chain when possible to reduce bioaccumulated chemicals.
- Don't pick and eat berries or other wild foods that grow on the edges of roadsides where pesticides may have been sprayed.
- Grow your own fruits and vegetables without using pesticides or with minimal use of dangerous chemicals.
- Ask for organically grown food at your local grocery store, or shop at a farmer's market or co-op where you can get such food.

# How can we feed the world?

The world's population has climbed from 3 billion to 7 billion in about two generations (since 1960). Despite this growth, the proportion of chronically hungry people has declined from 60 percent to about 20 percent in developing countries, where most population growth has occurred. How have we managed to increase food production so rapidly? What are the pros and cons of these strategies? What additional choices do we have? Presented here are three main strategies in food production.

*CL 7.1*

Circular green fields, irrigated by center-pivot sprinklers, produce the corn, soybeans, and other crops that are the backbone of our food system.

*Background image source:* NAIP, 2009.

***The Green Revolution*** involved development of high responders—crops that grow and yield well with increased use of fertilizer, irrigation, and pesticides.

### Benefits

- Yields have grown dramatically with increased inputs.
- Efficiency is high for large-scale production, which aids in feeding billions.
- Development of pesticides has improved yields by eliminating competition with other plants or predation by insects.
- Labor costs are low: one farmer can work a huge area.

### Problems

- Dependence on pesticides and fertilizers has grown; pesticides have sometimes lost effectiveness through overuse.
- Agricultural chemicals have unintended ecological consequences, including lost biodiversity, probable loss of pollinating insects, and contamination of drinking water.
- New varieties can be hard for poor farmers to afford, so that wealthier farmers and wealthier regions gain a relative advantage.
- Increased use of nitrogen fertilizer is an important source of greenhouse gases and consumer of fossil fuels.

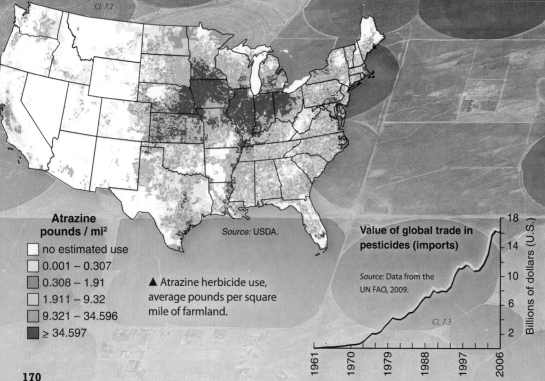

*CL 7.2*

**Atrazine pounds / mi²**

- ☐ no estimated use
- ☐ 0.001 – 0.307
- ☐ 0.308 – 1.91
- ☐ 1.911 – 9.32
- ☐ 9.321 – 34.596
- ☐ ≥ 34.597

*Source:* USDA.

▲ Atrazine herbicide use, average pounds per square mile of farmland.

**Value of global trade in pesticides (imports)**

*Source:* Data from the UN FAO, 2009.

*CL 7.3*

Billions of dollars (U.S.)

18 — 14 — 10 — 6 — 2

1961  1970  1979  1988  1997  2006

## Can You Explain:

1. What was the Green Revolution?

2. Which are our top three pesticides? Which of these have you heard of previously?

3. Think of what you've eaten today. Which of the three agricultural strategies on this page contributed to your food?

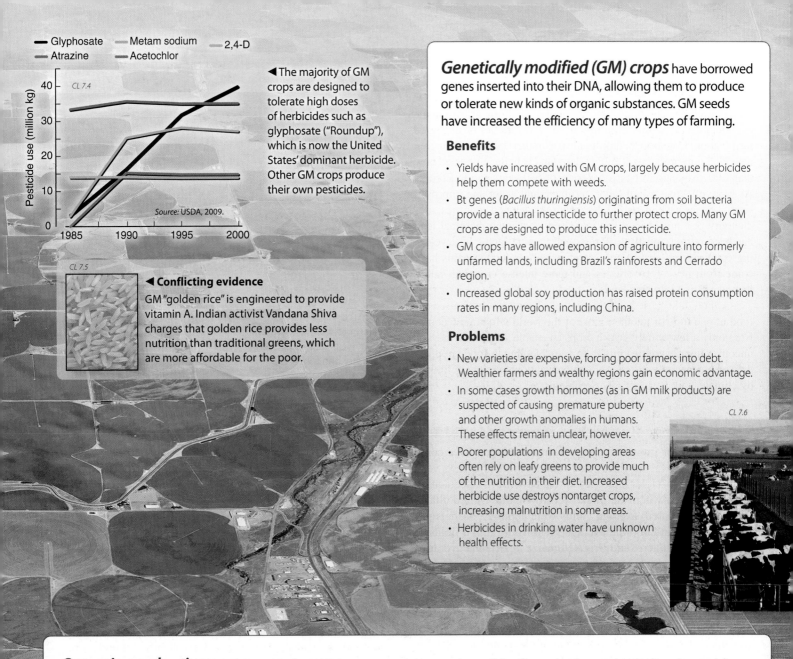

CL 7.4

Pesticide use (million kg)

- Glyphosate
- Atrazine
- Metam sodium
- Acetochlor
- 2,4-D

40
30
20
10
0

1985  1990  1995  2000

*Source: USDA, 2009.*

◀ The majority of GM crops are designed to tolerate high doses of herbicides such as glyphosate ("Roundup"), which is now the United States' dominant herbicide. Other GM crops produce their own pesticides.

CL 7.5

◀ **Conflicting evidence**

GM "golden rice" is engineered to provide vitamin A. Indian activist Vandana Shiva charges that golden rice provides less nutrition than traditional greens, which are more affordable for the poor.

## *Genetically modified (GM) crops* have borrowed genes inserted into their DNA, allowing them to produce or tolerate new kinds of organic substances. GM seeds have increased the efficiency of many types of farming.

### Benefits

- Yields have increased with GM crops, largely because herbicides help them compete with weeds.
- Bt genes (*Bacillus thuringiensis*) originating from soil bacteria provide a natural insecticide to further protect crops. Many GM crops are designed to produce this insecticide.
- GM crops have allowed expansion of agriculture into formerly unfarmed lands, including Brazil's rainforests and Cerrado region.
- Increased global soy production has raised protein consumption rates in many regions, including China.

### Problems

- New varieties are expensive, forcing poor farmers into debt. Wealthier farmers and wealthy regions gain economic advantage.
- In some cases growth hormones (as in GM milk products) are suspected of causing premature puberty and other growth anomalies in humans. These effects remain unclear, however.
- Poorer populations in developing areas often rely on leafy greens to provide much of the nutrition in their diet. Increased herbicide use destroys nontarget crops, increasing malnutrition in some areas.
- Herbicides in drinking water have unknown health effects.

CL 7.6

## *Organic production* involves mixed strategies: crop rotation retains soil fertility; mixed cropping reduces pest risk; organic fertilizers and pesticides reduce costs of commercial inputs. Organic methods are more sustainable but don't lend themselves to the industrial-scale production of conventional farming, which involves vast expanses of a single crop, such as soy or corn.

### Benefits

- Input costs (fertilizers, pesticides, fuel) are minimal.
- Can be sustainable as it preserves or even improves soil, water quality, and biodiversity.
- Crop varieties are usually more mixed, which contributes to healthier diets and more stable farm ecosystems.
- Organic methods are traditional in most areas, and low costs make this approach appropriate for poor farmers, especially in developing regions.
- Integrated pest management (small amounts of pesticides together with other strategies), can protect yields.

### Problems

- Labor costs can be high for weed and pest control.
- Careful planning and management may be necessary to ensure good crop management: Creative and innovative problem solving is needed, not simple solutions such as spraying fields.
- Organically farmed food can be more expensive in the United States because it lacks the large-scale distribution networks of conventional products and because conventional methods receive abundant subsidies in tax breaks and price-support payments.
- These methods are unfamiliar to many farmers and can be less efficient in terms of volume of production per unit labor.

CL 7.7

CL 7.8

## 7.7 How Have We Managed to Feed Billions?

In the developed countries, 95 percent of agricultural growth in the twentieth century came from improved crop varieties or increased fertilization, irrigation, and pesticide use, rather than from bringing new land into production. In fact, less land is being cultivated now than 100 years ago in North America, or 600 years ago in Europe. As more effective use of labor, fertilizer, and water and improved seed varieties have increased in the more-developed countries, productivity per unit of land has increased, and much marginal land has been retired, mostly to forests and grazing lands. In developing countries, at least two-thirds of recent production gains have come from new crop varieties and more intense cropping, rather than expansion into new lands.

Although at least 3,000 species of plants have been used for food at one time or another, most of the world's food now comes from only a few widely grown crops (see table 7.1). Many new or unconventional varieties might be valuable human food supplies, however, especially in areas where conventional crops are limited by climate, soil, pests, or other problems.

**Figure 7.25** Semidwarf wheat (*right*), bred by Norman Borlaug, has shorter, stiffer stems and is less likely to lodge (fall over) when wet than its conventional cousin (*left*). This "miracle" wheat responds better to water and fertilizer and has played a vital role in feeding a growing human population.

### The green revolution has increased yields

So far, the major improvements in farm production have come from technological advances and modification of a few well-known species. Yield increases often have been spectacular. A century ago, when all maize (corn) in the United States was open pollinated, average yields were about 25 bushels per acre (bu/acre). In 2000 the average yield from rainfed fields in Iowa was 138 bu/acre, and irrigated maize in Arizona averaged 208 bu/acre. The highest yield ever recorded in field production was 370 bu/acre on an Illinois farm, but theoretical calculations suggest that 500 bu/acre (32 metric tons per hectare) could be possible. Most of this gain was accomplished by use of synthetic fertilizers along with conventional plant breeding: geneticists laboriously hand-pollinating plants and looking for desired characteristics in the progeny.

Starting about 50 years ago, agricultural research stations began to breed tropical wheat and rice varieties that would provide food for growing populations in developing countries. The first of the "miracle" varieties was a dwarf, high-yielding wheat developed by Norman Borlaug (who received a Nobel Peace Prize for his work) at a research center in Mexico (fig. 7.25). At about the same time, the International Rice Institute in the Philippines developed dwarf rice strains with three or four times the production of varieties in use at the time. The spread of these new high-yield varieties around the world has been called the **green revolution**. It is one of the main reasons that world food supplies have more than kept pace with the growing human population over the past few decades.

Most green revolution breeds really are "high responders," meaning that they yield well in response to optimal inputs of fertilizer, water, and chemical protection from pests and diseases (fig. 7.26). With fewer inputs, on the other hand, high responders may not produce as well as traditional varieties. Poor farmers

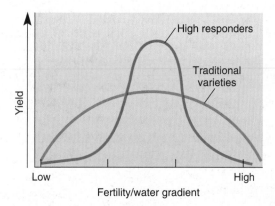

**Figure 7.26** Green revolution miracle crops are really high responders, meaning that they have excellent yields under optimum conditions. For poor farmers who can't afford the fertilizer and water needed by high responders, traditional varieties may produce better yields.

who can't afford the expensive seed, fertilizer, and water required to become part of this movement usually are left out of the green revolution. In fact, they may be driven out of farming altogether as rising land values and falling commodity prices squeeze them from both sides.

### Genetic engineering could have benefits and costs

**Genetic engineering**, splicing a gene from one organism into the chromosome of another, has the potential to greatly increase both the quantity and the quality of our food supply. It is now possible to build entirely new genes, and even new organisms, often called "transgenic" organisms or **genetically modified organisms (GMOs)**, by taking a bit of DNA from here, a bit

**Figure 7.27** A researcher measures growth of genetically engineered rice plants. Superior growth and yield, pest resistance, and other useful traits can be moved from one species to another by molecular biotechnology.

from there, and even synthesizing artificial sequences to create desired characteristics in engineered organisms (fig. 7.27).

Proponents predict dramatic benefits from this new technology. Research is now underway to improve yields and create crops that resist drought, frost, or diseases. Other strains are being developed to tolerate salty, waterlogged, or low-nutrient soils, allowing degraded or marginal farmland to become productive. All of these could be important for reducing hunger in developing countries. Plants that produce their own pesticides might reduce the need for toxic chemicals, while engineering for improved protein or vitamin content could make our food more nutritious. Crops such as bananas and tomatoes have been altered to contain oral vaccines that can be grown in developing countries where refrigeration and sterile needles are unavailable. Plants have been engineered to make industrial oils and plastics. Animals, too, are being genetically modified to grow faster, gain weight on less food, and produce pharmaceuticals, such as insulin, in their milk. Pigs are now being engineered to produce omega-3 fatty acids for a "heart healthy" diet. It may even be possible to create animals with human cell-recognition factors that could serve as organ donors.

Opponents worry that moving genes willy-nilly also could create problems we can't even imagine. GMOs themselves might escape and become pests, or they might interbreed with wild relatives. In either case, we may create superweeds or reduce native biodiversity. Constant presence of pesticides in plants could accelerate pesticide resistance in insects or leave toxic residues in soil or our food. Genes for toxicity or allergies could be transferred along with desirable genes, or novel toxins could be created as genes are mixed together.

Both the number of GMO crops and the acreage devoted to growing them is increasing rapidly (fig. 7.28). Worldwide, over 25 percent of all cropland (72 million ha) were planted with GMO crops in 2009. The United States accounted for 63 percent of that acreage, followed by Argentina with 21 percent. Canada, Brazil, and China together make up 22 percent of all transgenic cropland.

Some transgenic crops have reached mainstream status. About 82 percent of all soybeans, one-quarter of all maize (corn), and 71 percent of all cotton grown in the United States are now GMOs. You've already probably eaten some genetically modified food. Estimates are that at least 60 percent of all processed food in America contains GMO ingredients, chiefly from corn or soy.

## Most GMOs are engineered for pesticide production or pesticide tolerance

Biotechnologists have created plants with genes for endogenous insecticides. *Bacillus thuringiensis* (Bt), a bacterium, makes toxins lethal to Lepidoptera (butterfly family) and Coleoptera (beetle family). The genes for some of these toxins have been transferred into crops such as maize (to protect against European cutworms), potatoes (to fight potato beetles), and cotton (to protect against boll weevils). This allows farmers to reduce insecticide spraying. Arizona cotton farmers, for example, report reducing their use of chemical insecticides by 75 percent.

Entomologists worry that Bt plants churn out toxin throughout the growing season, regardless of the level of infestation, creating perfect conditions for selection of Bt resistance in pests. Already 500 species of insect, mite, or tick are resistant to one or more pesticides. Having Bt constantly available can only aggravate this dilemma.

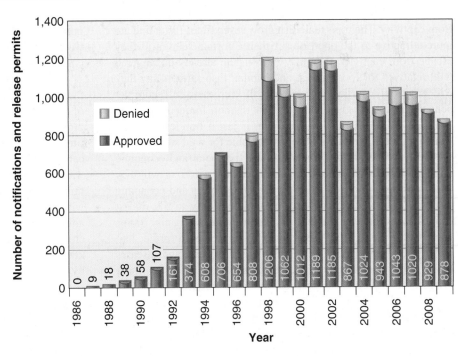

**Figure 7.28** Transgenic crop field releases in the United States, 1990 to 2005. *Source:* Data from Information Systems for Biotechnology, Virginia Tech University.

The other major group of transgenic crops is engineered to tolerate high doses of herbicides. The two dominant products in this category are Monsanto's "Roundup Ready" crops—so-called because they can withstand treatment with Monsanto's best-selling herbicide, Roundup (glyphosate)—and AgrEvo's "Liberty Link" crops, which resist that company's Liberty (glufosinate) herbicide. Because crops with these genes can grow in spite of high herbicide doses, farmers can spray fields heavily to exterminate weeds. This allows for conservation tillage and leaving more crop residue on fields to protect topsoil from erosion—both good ideas—but it also can mean using more herbicide in higher doses than might otherwise be used.

## Is genetic engineering safe?

Consumers have long been worried about unknown health effects of GM foods, but the U.S. Food and Drug Administration has declined to require labeling of foods containing GMOs. The agency argues that these new varieties are "substantially equivalent" to related varieties bred via traditional practices. After all, proponents say, we have been moving genes around for centuries through plant and animal breeding. All domesticated organisms should be classified as genetically modified, some people argue. Biotechnology may be a more precise way of creating novel organisms than normal breeding procedures, its supporters suggest.

The first genetically modified animal designed to be eaten by humans is an Atlantic salmon (*Salmo salar*) containing extra growth hormone genes from an oceanic pout (*Macrozoarces americanus*). The greatest worry from this fish is not that it will introduce extra hormones into our diet—that's already being done by chickens and beef that get extra growth hormone via injections or their diet—but, rather, the ecological effects if the fish escape from captivity. The transgenic fish grow seven times faster and are more attractive to the opposite sex than a normal salmon. If they escape from captivity, they may outcompete already endangered wild relatives for food, mates, and habitat. Fish farmers say they will grow only sterile females and will keep them in secure net pens. Marine ecologists point out that salmon frequently escape from aquaculture operations and that, if just a few fertile transgenic fish break out, it could be catastrophic for wild stocks.

Perhaps the greatest unknowns are the social and economic implications of GMOs. Will they help feed the world, or will they lead to a greater consolidation of corporate power and economic disparity? This technology may be available only to the richest countries or the wealthiest corporations, making family farms uncompetitive and driving developing countries even further into poverty. Or higher yields and fewer losses to pests and diseases might allow poor farmers in developing countries to stop using marginal land. Critics suggest that there are simpler and cheaper ways other than high-tech crop varieties to provide vitamin A to children in developing countries or to increase the income of poor rural families. Adding a cow or a fishpond or training people in water harvesting or regenerative farming techniques (as we'll discuss in the next section) may have a longer-lasting impact than selling them expensive new seeds.

On the other hand, if we hope to reduce malnutrition and feed 8 billion people in 50 years, maybe we need all the tools we can get. Where do you stand in this debate? What additional information would you need to reach a reasoned judgment about the risks and benefits of this new technology?

# 7.8 Sustainable Farming Strategies

Innovations in farming have changed the ways we eat and live. Can we ensure that farming and food production also are sustainable and equitable? These are the goals of **sustainable agriculture**, or **regenerative farming**, which aim to reduce or repair the damage caused by destructive practices. Some alternative methods are developed through scientific research; others are discovered in traditional cultures and practices nearly forgotten in our mechanization and industrialization of agriculture.

## Soil conservation is essential

With careful husbandry, soil is a renewable resource that can be replenished and renewed indefinitely. Since agriculture is the area in which soil is most essential and most often lost through erosion, agriculture offers the greatest potential for soil conservation and rebuilding. Some rice paddies in Southeast Asia, for instance, have been farmed continuously for a thousand years without any apparent loss of fertility. The rice-growing cultures that depend on these fields have developed management practices that return organic material to the paddies and carefully nurture the soil's ability to sustain life.

While American agriculture hasn't reached that level of sustainability, there is evidence that soil conservation programs are having a positive effect. In one Wisconsin study, erosion rates in one small watershed were 90 percent less in 1975–1993 than they were in the 1930s. Among the most important elements in soil conservation are terracing, ground cover, and reduced tillage.

Most erosion happens because water runs downhill. The faster it runs, the more soil it carries off the fields. Comparisons of erosion rates in Africa have shown that a 5 percent slope in a plowed field has three times the water runoff volume and eight times the soil erosion rate of a comparable field with a 1 percent slope. Water runoff can be reduced by grass strips in waterways and by **contour plowing**—that is, plowing across the hill rather than up and down. Contour plowing is often combined with **strip-farming**, the planting of different kinds of crops in alternating strips along the land contours (fig. 7.29). When one crop is harvested, the other is still present to protect the soil and keep water from running straight downhill. The ridges created by cultivation make little dams that trap water and allow it to seep into the soil, rather than running off. In areas where rainfall is very heavy, tied ridges are often useful. This method involves a series of ridges running at right angles to each other, so that water runoff is blocked in all directions and is encouraged to soak into the soil.

**Terracing** involves shaping the land to create level shelves of earth to hold water and soil. The edges of the terrace are planted

**Table 7.2 | Soil Cover and Soil Erosion**

| Cropping System | Average Annual Soil Loss (Tons/Hectare) | Percent Rainfall Runoff |
|---|---|---|
| Bare soil (no crop) | 41.0 | 30 |
| Continuous corn | 19.7 | 29 |
| Continuous wheat | 10.1 | 23 |
| Rotation: corn, wheat, clover | 2.7 | 14 |
| Continuous bluegrass | 0.3 | 12 |

*Source:* Based on 14 years of data from Missouri Experiment Station, Columbia, Missouri.

**Figure 7.29** Contour plowing and strip cropping help prevent soil erosion on hilly terrain, as well as create a beautiful landscape.

with soil-anchoring plant species. This is an expensive procedure, requiring either much hand labor or expensive machinery, but it makes farming of very steep hillsides possible. The rice terraces in the Chico River Valley in the Philippines rise as much as 300 m (1,000 ft) above the valley floor. They are considered one of the wonders of the world. Some of these terraces have been farmed for 1,000 years without any apparent fertility loss. Will we be able to say the same thing a millenium from now?

## Groundcover protects the soil

Annual row crops, such as corn or beans, generally cause the highest erosion rates because they leave soil bare for much of the year (table 7.2). Often the easiest way to provide cover that protects soil from erosion is to leave crop residues on the land after harvest. They not only cover the surface to break the erosive effects of wind and water but also reduce evaporation and soil temperature in hot climates and protect ground organisms that help aerate and rebuild soil. In some experiments, 1 ton of crop residue per acre (0.4 ha) increased water infiltration 99 percent, reduced runoff 99 percent, and reduced erosion 98 percent. Leaving crop residues on the field also can increase disease and pest problems, however, and may require increased use of pesticides and herbicides.

Where crop residues are not adequate to protect the soil or are inappropriate for subsequent crops or farming methods, such **cover crops** as rye, alfalfa, and clover can be planted immediately after harvest to hold and protect the soil. These cover crops can be plowed under at planting time to provide green manure. Another method is to flatten cover crops with a roller and drill seeds through the residue to provide a continuous protective cover during early stages of crop growth.

In some cases, interplanting of two different crops in the same field not only protects the soil but also is a more efficient use of the land, providing double harvests. Native Americans and pioneer farmers, for instance, planted beans or pumpkins between the corn rows. The beans provided nitrogen needed by the corn, the pumpkins crowded out weeds, and both crops provided foods that nutritionally balance corn. Traditional swidden (slash-and-burn) cultivators in Africa and South America often plant as many as 20 different crops together in small plots. The crops mature at different times, so that there is always something to eat, and the soil is never exposed to erosion for very long. Shade-grown coffee and cocoa can play important roles in conserving biodiversity (see What Do You Think? p. 176).

## Reduced tillage cuts erosion

Farmers have traditionally used a moldboard plow to till the soil, digging a deep trench and turning the topsoil upside down. In the 1800s it was shown that tilling a field fully—until it was "clean"—increased crop production. It helped control weeds and pests, reducing competition; it brought fresh nutrients to the surface, providing a good seedbed; and it improved surface drainage and aerated the soil. This is still true for many crops and many soil types, but it is not always the best way to grow crops. Less plowing and cultivation often improves water management, preserves soil, saves energy, and increases crop yields.

There are three major **reduced tillage systems**. *Minimum till* involves reducing the number of times a farmer disturbs the soil by plowing, cultivating, and so on. This often involves a disc or chisel plow rather than a traditional moldboard plow. A chisel plow is a curved, chisel-like blade that doesn't turn the soil over but creates ridges on which seeds can be planted. It leaves up to 75 percent of plant debris on the surface between the rows, preventing erosion. *Conserv-till* farming uses a coulter (a sharp disc, like a pizza cutter), which slices through the soil, opening up a furrow, or slot, just wide enough to insert seeds. This disturbs the soil very little and leaves almost all

## Shade-Grown Coffee and Cocoa

Has it ever occurred to you that your purchases of coffee and chocolate may be contributing to the protection or destruction of tropical forests? Both coffee and cocoa are examples of food products grown exclusively in developing countries but consumed almost entirely in the wealthier, developed nations (vanilla and bananas are some other examples). Coffee grows in cool, mountain areas of the tropics, while cocoa is native to the warm, moist lowlands. Both are small trees of the forest understory, adapted to low light levels.

Until a few decades ago, most of the world's coffee and cocoa were **shade-grown** under a canopy of large forest trees. Recently, however, new varieties of both crops have been developed that can be grown in full sun. Because more coffee or cocoa trees can be crowded into these fields, and they get more solar energy than in a shaded plantation, yields for sun-grown crops are higher.

There are costs, however, in this new technology. Sun-grown trees die earlier from the stress and diseases common in these fields. Furthermore, ornithologists have found that the number of bird species can be cut in half in full-sun plantations, and the number of individual birds may be reduced by 90 percent. Shade-grown coffee and cocoa generally require fewer pesticides (or sometimes none) because the birds and insects residing in the forest canopy eat many of the pests. Shade-grown plantations also need less chemical fertilizer because many of the plants in these complex forests add nutrients to the soil. In addition, shade-grown crops rarely need to be irrigated because heavy leaf fall protects the soil, while forest cover reduces evaporation.

Currently, about 40 percent of the world's coffee and cocoa plantations have been converted to full-sun varieties and another 25 percent are in process. Traditional techniques for coffee and cocoa production are worth preserving. Thirteen of the world's 25 biodiversity hot spots occur in coffee or cocoa regions. If all the 20 million ha (49 million acres) of coffee and cocoa plantations in these areas are converted to monocultures, an incalculable number of species will be lost.

The Brazilian state of Bahia is a good example of both the ecological importance of these crops and how they might help preserve forest species. At one time, Brazil produced much of the world's cocoa, but in the early 1900s, the crop was introduced into West Africa. Now Côte d'Ivoire alone grows more than 40 percent of the world total, and the value of Brazil's harvest has dropped by 90 percent. Côte d'Ivoire is aided in this competition by a labor system that reportedly includes widespread child slavery. Even adult workers in Côte d'Ivoire get only about $165 (U.S.) per year (if they get paid at all), compared with a minimum wage of $850 (U.S.) per year in Brazil. As African cocoa production ratchets up, Brazilian landowners are converting their plantations to pastures or other crops.

Cocoa pods grow directly on the trunk and large branches of cocoa trees.

The area of Bahia where cocoa was once king is part of Brazil's Atlantic Forest, one of the most threatened forest biomes in the world. Only 8 percent of this forest remains undisturbed. Although cocoa plantations don't represent the full diversity of intact forests, they protect a surprisingly large sample of what once was there. And shade-grown cocoa can provide an economic rationale for preserving that biodiversity. Brazilian cocoa will probably never compete with that from other areas for lowest cost. There is room in the market, however, for specialty products. If consumers were willing to pay a small premium for organic, fair-trade, shade-grown chocolate and coffee, it might provide the incentive needed to preserve biodiversity. Wouldn't you like to know that your chocolate or coffee wasn't grown with child slavery and is helping protect plants and animal species that might otherwise go extinct?

plant debris on the surface. *No-till* planting is accomplished by drilling seeds into the ground directly through mulch and groundcover. This allows a cover crop to be interseeded with a subsequent crop (fig. 7.30).

Farmers who use these conservation tillage techniques often must depend on pesticides (insecticides, fungicides, and herbicides) to control insects and weeds. Increased use of toxic agricultural chemicals is a matter of great concern. Massive use of pesticides is not, however, a necessary corollary of soil conservation. It is possible to combat pests and diseases with integrated pest management that combines crop rotation, trap crops, natural repellents, and biological controls.

**Figure 7.30** No-till planting involves drilling seeds through debris from last year's crops. Here, soybeans grow through corn mulch. Debris keeps weeds down, reduces wind and water erosion, and keeps moisture in the soil.

**Figure 7.31** On the Minar family's 230-acre dairy farm near New Prague, Minnesota, cows and calves spend the winter outdoors in the snow, bedding down on hay. Dave Minar is part of a growing counterculture that is seeking to keep farmers on the land and bring prosperity to rural areas. ©2004 Star Tribune/Minneapolis-St. Paul.

## Low-input sustainable agriculture can benefit farmers, consumers, and the environment

In contrast to the trend toward industrialization and dependence on chemical fertilizers, pesticides, antibiotics, and artificial growth factors common in conventional agriculture, some farmers are going back to a more natural, agroecological farming style. Finding that they can't—or don't want to—compete with factory farms, these folks are making money and staying in farming by returning to small-scale, low-input agriculture. The Minar family, for instance, operates a highly successful 150-cow dairy operation on 97 ha (230 acres) near New Prague, Minnesota. No synthetic chemicals are used on their farm. Cows are rotated every day between 45 pastures or paddocks to reduce erosion and maintain healthy grass. Even in the winter, livestock remain outdoors to avoid the spread of diseases common in confinement (fig. 7.31). Antibiotics are used only to fight diseases. Milk and meat from this operation are marketed through co-ops and a community-supported agriculture (CSA) program. Sand Creek, which flows across the Minar land, has been shown to be cleaner when leaving the farm than when it enters.

Similarly, the Franzen family, who raise livestock on their organic farm near Alta Vista, Iowa, allow their pigs to roam in lush pastures, where they can supplement their diet of corn and soybeans with grasses and legumes. Housing for these happy hogs is in spacious, open-ended hoop structures. As fresh layers of straw are added to the bedding, layers of manure beneath are composted, breaking down into odorless organic fertilizer.

Low-input farms such as these typically don't turn out the quantity of meat or milk that their intensive agriculture neighbors do, but their production costs are lower, and they get higher prices for their crops, so that the all-important net gain is often higher. The Franzens, for example, calculate that they pay 30 percent less for animal feed, 70 percent less for veterinary bills, and half as much for buildings and equipment as their neighboring confinement operations. And on the Minar's farm, erosion after an especially heavy rain was measured to be 400 times lower than on a conventional farm nearby.

Preserving small-scale family farms also helps preserve rural culture. As Marty Strange of the Center for Rural Affairs in Nebraska asks, "Which is better for the enrollment in rural schools, the membership of rural churches, and the fellowship of rural communities—two farms milking 1,000 cows each or twenty farms milking 100 cows each?" Family farms help keep rural towns alive by purchasing machinery at the local implement dealer, gasoline at the neighborhood filling station, and groceries at the mom-and-pop grocery store.

## 7.9 Consumers Help Shape Farming

Since the 1960s, U.S. farm policy and agricultural research has focused on developing large-scale production methods that use fertilizer, pesticides, breeding, and genetic engineering to provide abundant, inexpensive grain, meat, and milk. As a consequence we can afford to eat more calories and more meat than ever before. Hunger still plagues many regions, but increasing nutrition has reached most of the world's population, not just wealthy countries. We now worry about weight-associated illnesses as a cause of mortality, possibly a first in human history.

Cheap-food policies have raised production dramatically to feed growing populations both in the United States and abroad. Farm commodity prices have fallen so low, that we now spend billions of dollars every year to support prices or repay farmers whose production expenses are greater than the value of their crops. The United States buys millions of tons of surplus food every year, often using it as food aid to famine-stricken regions. This social good is also problematic, as cheap or free food donations undermine small farmers in other countries, who cannot compete with free or nearly free food on the local market.

These policies are deeply entrenched in our way of life, politics, and food systems. But there may be some steps that consumers can take to support the beneficial changes in farming methods and farm policies, while reducing their negative effects.

## You can be a locavore

A "locavore" is a person who consumes locally produced food. Supporting local farmers can have a variety of benefits, from keeping money in the local economy to ensuring a fresh and healthy diet. Maintaining a viable farm economy can also help slow the conversion of farmland into expanding suburban subdivisions. As many farmers point out, you don't need to eat 100 percent local. Converting just part of your shopping activity to locally produced goods can make a big difference to farmers.

**Figure 7.32** Your local farmer's market is a good source of locally grown and organic produce.

Farmers' markets are usually the easiest way to eat locally (fig. 7.32). The produce is fresh, and profits go directly to the farmer who grows the crop. "Pick your own" farms also let you buy fresh fruit and other products—and they make a fun, social outing. Many conventional grocery stores also now offer locally produced, organic, and pesticide-free foods. Buying these products may (or may not) cost a little more than nonorganic and nonlocal produce, but they can be better for you and they can help keep farming and fresh, local food in the community.

Many colleges and universities have adopted policies to buy as much locally grown food as possible. Because schools purchase a lot of vegetables, meat, eggs, and milk, this can mean a large amount of income for local and regional farm economies. Although this policy can take more effort and creativity than ordering from centralized, national distributors, many college food service administrators are happy to try to buy locally, if they see that students are interested. If your school doesn't have such a policy, perhaps you could talk to administrators about starting one.

Many areas also have "community supported agriculture" (CSA) projects, farms supported by local residents who pay ahead of time for shares of the farm's products, which can vary from vegetables to flowers to meat and eggs. While CSAs require a lump payment early in the season, the net cost of food by the end of the season is often less than you would have paid at the grocery store. You also get to meet interesting people and learn more about your local area by participating in a CSA. Usually you can find local CSA networks by searching online.

## You can eat low on the food chain

Since there is less energy involved in producing food from plants than producing it from animals, one way you can reduce your impact on the world's soil and water is to eat a little more grains, vegetables, and dairy and a little less meat. This doesn't mean turning vegetarian—unless you choose to do so. Just returning

to the level of protein and fat consumption your grandparents had could make a big difference for the environment and for your health.

Low-input, organic foods also reduce the environmental impact of your food choices. When you buy organic food, you support farmers who use no pesticides or artificial fertilizers. Often these farmers use crop rotations to preserve soil nutrients and manage erosion carefully, to prevent loss of their topsoil. Sometimes these farmers preserve diverse varieties of crops, helping to maintain genetic diversity and pest resistance in crops.

Grass-fed beef and free-range poultry or pork can also be excellent low-input foods. By converting grass to protein, they can be an efficient food source where soils or steep hillsides are unsuitable for cropping. With good management, pastures have minimal soil erosion, since vegetation keeps the soil covered year-round.

## Conclusion

Food production has grown faster than the human population in recent decades, and the percentage of people facing chronic hunger has declined, although the number has increased. Most of us consume more calories and protein than we need, but some 854 million people still are malnourished. Much, or perhaps most, hunger results from political instability, which displaces farmers, inhibits food distribution, and undermines local farming economies.

Increases in food production result from many innovations in agricultural production. The green revolution produced new varieties that yield more crops per hectare, although these crops often require extra inputs such as fertilizers, irrigation, or pesticides. Genetically modified organisms have also increased yields. Most GMOs are designed to tolerate herbicides, and many produce their own pesticides. Confined animal feeding operations, made possible by large-scale corn and soy production, have greatly increased the efficiency of producing meat. The rise of soy in Brazil, and of meat consumption in the United States, China, and elsewhere, result from these innovations.

These changes bring about important environmental effects, such as soil erosion and degradation, and water contamination from pesticide and fertilizer applications. Health effects are also a concern, including weight-related diseases, such as diabetes, exposure to agricultural chemicals, and antibiotic resistance.

Consumers can influence farm production by eating locally, eating low on the food chain, shopping at farmers' markets, and buying organic foods or grass-fed meat.

# Practice Quiz

1. What is Brazil's Cerrado, and how is agriculture affecting it?
2. Explain how soybeans grown in Brazil are improving diets in China.
3. What does it mean to be chronically undernourished? How many people in the world currently suffer from this condition?
4. Why do nutritionists worry about food security? Who is most likely to suffer from food insecurity?
5. Describe the conditions that constitute a famine. Why does Amartya Sen say that famines are caused more by politics and economics than by natural disasters?
6. Define *malnutrition* and *obesity*. How many Americans are now considered obese?
7. What three crops provide most human caloric intake?
8. What are confined animal feeding operations, and why are they controversial?
9. What is *soil*? Why are soil organisms so important?
10. What are four dominant types of soil degradation? What is the primary cause of soil erosion?
11. What do we mean by the *green revolution*?
12. What is *genetic engineering*, and how can it help or hurt agriculture?
13. What is *sustainable agriculture*?
14. How could your choices of coffee or cocoa help preserve forests, biodiversity, and local economies in tropical countries?
15. What are the economic advantages of low-input farming?

# Critical Thinking and Discussion Questions

Apply the principles you have learned in this chapter to discuss these questions with other students.

1. Suppose that you were engaged in biotechnology, or genetic engineering; what environmental safeguards would you impose on your own research? Are there experiments that would be ethically off-limits for you?
2. Debate the claim that famines are caused more by human actions (or inactions) than by environmental forces. What scientific evidence would you need to have to settle this question? What hypotheses could you test to help resolve the debate?
3. Should farmers be forced to use ecologically sound techniques that serve farmers' best interests in the long run, regardless of short-term consequences? How could we mitigate hardships brought about by such policies?
4. How would you provide assurance to consumers, government officials, and other interested parties that new genetically engineered products were environmentally and socially safe? What experiments would you set up to test for unknown unknowns?
5. Former U.S. President Jimmy Carter said, "Responsible biotechnology is not the enemy; starvation is." What did he mean? Do you agree?

# Data Analysis | Mapping Your Food Supply

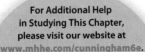

Understanding where your food comes from helps you understand the environmental issues involved with producing the food you eat. Because this information is so important, culturally and economically, the United States Department of Agriculture (USDA) maintains a Natural Resources Inventory (NRI) that includes maps of our major crops. While these maps are updated only at long intervals, they describe large trends—the details change only a little from year to year, and the patterns you see in the maps are still current. Find this website and explore the maps to answer the following questions:
http://www.nrcs.usda.gov/technical/NRI/maps/cropland.html

1. This page lists maps that show the use and erodibility of soils in the United States. Click on one or two map titles to see the maps that are available. List five topics that the USDA thinks are important to map.
2. Near the bottom of the list of maps, you can find the "Percent of Cultivated Cropland in Corn, 1997." This is the first of several crop maps. *Percentage* here means the fraction of watersheds planted in that crop. Click on that title, then click on the map image to see a larger version of the map. What do the two brownest shades mean? What are seven Midwestern states that have the most dark brown (greater than 50 percent of land in corn)?

3. Locate the Mississippi River. Also locate the Missouri and Ohio rivers, which enter the Mississippi as it passes between Missouri and Illinois. How does corn production differ on the Missouri and the Ohio? What factors might explain this difference?
4. Return to the page listing map topics. Find the map of "Cultivated Cropland in Soybeans." Is the distribution of soybeans similar to corn, or very different?
5. Most Americans consume more potatoes than any other vegetable. Have you eaten a potato this week? Make a list of three states that you think may have produced the potatoes you eat.
6. Now find the map of land in potatoes. Note that the map shows *intensity* of potato production, in terms of percentage of cultivable land. List five of the states that have the most land in yellow and brown colors. Did your lists match?
7. Return to the list of maps again, and identify two crops that you think should grow in your state. Look at their maps. Were you correct in your guess? Does your state produce more of those two crops than other states do? Why or why not?

# 8 Environmental Health and Toxicology

A public health worker explains to villagers that guinea worm is a parasitic disease, not the result of bad behavior or sorcery. Once the most guinea-worm-plagued region in the world, West Africa is now almost free of this terrible disease.

*To wish to become well is a part of becoming well.*

— SENECA

## Learning Outcomes

*After studying this chapter, you should be able to answer the following questions:*

- What is environmental health?
- What health risks should worry us most?
- Emergent diseases seem to be more frequent now. What human factors may be involved in this trend?
- Are there connections between ecology and our health?
- When Paracelsus said, "The dose makes the poison," what did he mean?
- What makes some chemicals dangerous and others harmless?
- How much risk is acceptable, and to whom?

# CASE STUDY

## Defeating the Fiery Serpent

Fighting back tears, an African child cradles her swollen foot as a thin, white worm emerges from an oozing sore. The unfortunate youngster has been infected by a guinea worm (*Dracunculus mediensis*). The pain is intense. Her whole leg feels like it's on fire. It's difficult to walk or work when you're afflicted with one of these terrible invaders. The disease is known in Africa as "empty granary," because the worms usually erupt during harvest season, making it impossible to work in the fields and harvest crops on which the whole family depends.

The infection cycle starts when someone suffering from the pain of an emerging worm (fig. 8.1) bathes their wound in a local lake or pond. The worm, sensing water, emerges to release thousands of larvae, which are ingested by freshwater copepods ("water fleas"). Inside the water fleas, the larvae develop into the infective stage in about two weeks. When villagers drink the contaminated water, the copepods are digested, but the worms survive and penetrate the wall of the intestine and move to the abdominal cavity. Over the next year, the worm grows to about a meter long (3 feet) and as thick as a spaghetti noodle. When fully grown, the worm migrates to the site where it will erupt, usually in the legs or feet—or even eye sockets—of victims. It takes several weeks for the worm to emerge completely. If you pull too hard on it, the worm breaks, and the part left in your body festers and decays. If the suffering host soaks the lesion in water to soothe the pain, the cycle begins again.

This terrible parasite has plagued tropical countries for thousands of years. It has been found in Egyptian mummies and is thought to be the "fiery serpent" described in the Old Testament as torturing the Israelites in the desert. As recently as 1986, at least 3 million people in 16 countries suffered from this affliction, and more than 100 million people were at risk worldwide. But there's a happy ending to this story. In 1988, the world health community, led by former U.S. President Jimmy Carter, began a campaign to eliminate guinea worms.

Eradicating the parasite is fairly simple and relatively inexpensive. There is no medicine to cure the infection once the worm is inside your body, but wells can be drilled to prevent patients from contaminating drinking-water sources. And local ponds can be treated with pesticides that are safe for human consumption but kill the worm larvae and copepods. Furthermore, families can be taught to pour their drinking water through a fine cloth filter to remove any remaining water fleas. The problem is simply to get the proper materials and information to remote villages. Having the prestige of a former American president has been a powerful tool in convincing local officials that the world cares, and that a cure is possible.

Progress has been spectacular. Only a few countries still are afflicted by this horrendous disease. Nigeria is an example of this remarkable success. In 1986, the country was the most Guinea-worm-plagued country in the world, with more than 650,000 cases in 36 states. By 2006, more than 99.9 percent of the infections had been eliminated, and only 120 people still suffered from infections. Worldwide, there now are fewer than 12,000 cases, mostly in Sudan, where civil war has made public health intervention difficult. When guinea worms are finally eradicated, it will be only the second disease ever completely eliminated (smallpox, which was abolished in 1977 was first), and the only human parasite totally exterminated worldwide.

An encouraging outcome of this crusade is the demonstration that public health education and community organization can be effective, even in some of the poorest and most remote areas. Once people understand how the disease spreads and what they need to do to protect themselves and their families, they do change their behavior. And when the campaign is completed and guinea worms are completely vanquished, the health workers and volunteers will be available for further community development projects.

This case study reminds us of the importance of public health and how susceptible humans have always been to diseases and contaminants. In this chapter we'll look at the principles of environmental health to help you understand some of the risks we face and what we might do about them.

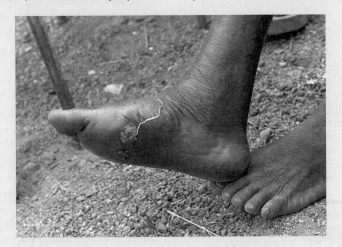

**Figure 8.1** A guinea worm emerges from a patient's foot.

## 8.1 Environmental Health

What is health? The World Health Organization (WHO) defines **health** as a state of complete physical, mental, and social well-being, not merely the absence of disease or infirmity. By that definition, we all are ill to some extent. Likewise, we all can improve our health to live happier, longer, more productive, and more satisfying lives if we think about what we do.

What is disease? A **disease** is an abnormal change in the body's condition that impairs important physical or psychological functions. Diet and nutrition, infectious agents, toxic substances, genetics, trauma, and stress all play roles in **morbidity** (illness) and **mortality** (death). **Environmental health** focuses on factors that cause disease, including elements of the natural, social, cultural, and technological worlds in which we live. The WHO estimates that 24 percent of all global disease burden and 23 percent of premature mortality are due to environmental factors. Among children (0 to 14 years) deaths attributable to environmental factors may be as high as 36 percent. Figure 8.2 shows some of these environmental risk factors as well as the media through which we encounter them.

In ecological terms, your body is an ecosystem. Of the approximately 100 trillion cells that make up each of us, only about 10 percent are actually human. The others are bacteria, fungi, protozoans, arthropods, and other species. Ideally, the various organisms in this complex system maintain a harmonious balance. Beneficial species help regulate the dangerous ones. The health challenge shouldn't be to try to totally eradicate all these other species; we couldn't live without them. Rather, we need to find ways to live in equilibrium with our environment and our fellow travelers.

Ever since the publication of Rachel Carson's *Silent Spring* in 1962, the discharge, movement, fate, and effects of synthetic chemical toxins have been a special focus of environmental health, but, as the opening case study shows, infectious diseases remain a grave threat. In this chapter, we'll study these topics in detail. First, however, let's look at some of the major causes of illness worldwide.

### Global disease burden is changing

In the past, health organizations have focused on the leading causes of death as the best summary of world health. Mortality data, however, fail to capture the impacts of nonfatal outcomes of disease and injury, such as dementia or blindness, on human well-being. When people are ill, work isn't done, crops aren't planted or harvested, meals aren't cooked, and children can't study and learn. Health agencies now calculate **disability-adjusted life years (DALYs)** as a measure of disease burden. DALYs combine premature deaths and loss of a healthy life resulting from illness or disability. This is an attempt to evaluate the total cost of disease, not simply how many people die. Clearly, many more years of expected life are lost when a child dies of neonatal tetanus than when an 80 year-old dies of pneumonia. Similarly, a teenager permanently paralyzed by a traffic accident will have many more years of suffering and lost potential than will a senior citizen who has a stroke. According to the WHO, chronic diseases now account for nearly 60 percent of the 56.5 million total deaths worldwide each year and about half of the global disease burden.

The world is now undergoing a dramatic epidemiological transition. Chronic conditions, such as cardiovascular disease and cancer, no longer afflict only wealthy people. Marvelous progress in eliminating communicable diseases, such as smallpox, polio, and malaria, is allowing people nearly everywhere to live longer. As chapter 6 points out, over the past century the average life expectancy worldwide has risen by about two-thirds. In some poorer countries, such as India, life expectancies nearly tripled in the twentieth century. Although the traditional killers in developing countries—infections, maternal and perinatal (birth) complications, and nutritional deficiencies—still take a terrible toll, diseases such as depression and heart attacks that once were thought to occur only in rich countries are rapidly becoming the leading causes of disability and premature death everywhere.

In 2020, the WHO predicts that heart disease, which was fifth in the list of causes of global disease burden a decade ago, will be the leading source of disability and deaths worldwide (table 8.1). Most of that increase will be in the poorer parts of the world where people are rapidly adopting the lifestyles and diet of the richer countries. Similarly, global cancer rates will increase by 50 percent. By 2020 it's expected that 15 million people will have cancer and 9 million will die from it.

Taking disability as well as death into account in our assessment of disease burden reveals the increasing role of mental health as a worldwide problem. WHO projections suggest that psychiatric and neurological conditions could increase their share of the global burden from 10 percent currently to 15 percent of the total load by 2020. Again, this isn't just a problem of the developed world. Depression is expected to be the second largest cause of

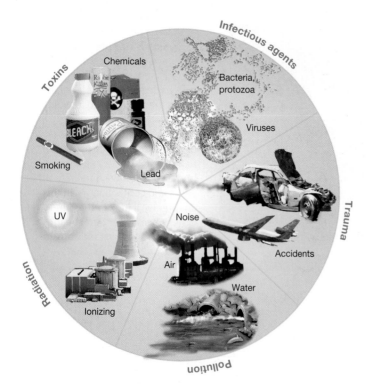

**Figure 8.2** Major sources of environmental health risks.

| Table 8.1 | Leading Causes of Global Disease Burden | | |
|---|---|---|---|
| **Rank** | **1990** | **Rank** | **2020** |
| 1 | Pneumonia | 1 | Heart disease |
| 2 | Diarrhea | 2 | Depression |
| 3 | Perinatal conditions | 3 | Traffic accidents |
| 4 | Depression | 4 | Stroke |
| 5 | Heart disease | 5 | Chronic lung disease |
| 6 | Stroke | 6 | Pneumonia |
| 7 | Tuberculosis | 7 | Tuberculosis |
| 8 | Measles | 8 | War |
| 9 | Traffic accidents | 9 | Diarrhea |
| 10 | Birth defects | 10 | HIV/AIDS |
| 11 | Chronic lung disease | 11 | Perinatal conditions |
| 12 | Malaria | 12 | Violence |
| 13 | Falls | 13 | Birth defects |
| 14 | Iron anemia | 14 | Self-inflicted injuries |
| 15 | Malnutrition | 15 | Respiratory cancer |

*Source:* Data from World Health Organization, 2002.

all years lived with disability worldwide, as well as the cause of 1.4 percent of all deaths. For women in both developing and developed regions, depression is the leading cause of disease burden, while suicide, which often is the result of untreated depression, is the fourth largest cause of female deaths.

Notice in table 8.1 that diarrhea, which was the second leading cause of disease burden in 1990, is expected to be ninth on the list in 2020, while measles and malaria are expected to drop out of the top 15 causes of disability. Tuberculosis, which is becoming resistant to antibiotics and is spreading rapidly in many areas (especially in Russia and South Africa), is the only infectious disease whose ranking is not expected to change over the next 20 years. Traffic accidents are now soaring as more people drive. War, violence, and self-inflicted injuries similarly are becoming much more important health risks than ever before.

Chronic obstructive lung diseases (e.g., emphysema, asthma, and lung cancer) are expected to increase from eleventh to fifth in disease burden by 2020. A large part of the increase is due to rising use of tobacco in developing countries, sometimes called "the tobacco epidemic." Every day about 100,000 young people—most of them in poorer countries—become addicted to tobacco. At least 1.1 billion people now smoke, and this number is expected to increase at least 50 percent by 2020. If current patterns persist, about 500 million people alive today will eventually be killed by tobacco. This is expected to be the biggest single cause of death worldwide (because illnesses such as heart attack and depression

are triggered by multiple factors). In 2003 the World Health Assembly adopted a historic tobacco-control convention that requires countries to impose restrictions on tobacco advertising, establish clean indoor air controls, and clamp down on tobacco smuggling. Dr. Gro Harlem Brundtland, former director-general of the WHO, predicted that the convention, if ratified by enough nations, could save billions of lives.

As chapter 7 points out, the world is now experiencing an epidemic of obesity. Poor diet and lack of exercise are now the second leading underlying cause of death in America, causing at least 400,000 deaths per year. Obesity is expected to overtake tobacco soon as the largest single health risk in many countries.

## Emergent and infectious diseases still kill millions of people

Although the ills of modern life have become the leading killers almost everywhere in the world, communicable diseases still are responsible for about one-third of all disease-related mortality. Diarrhea, acute respiratory illnesses, malaria, measles, tetanus, and a few other infectious diseases kill about 11 million children under age five every year in the developing world. Better nutrition, clean water, improved sanitation, and inexpensive inoculations could eliminate most of those deaths (fig. 8.3).

A wide variety of **pathogens** (disease-causing organisms) afflict humans, including viruses, bacteria, protozoans (single-celled animals), parasitic worms, and flukes (fig. 8.4). The greatest loss of life from an individual disease in a single year was the great influenza pandemic of 1918. Epidemiologists now estimate that at least one-third of all humans living at the time were infected, and that between 50 to 100 million died. Businesses, schools, churches, and sports or

**Figure 8.3** Millions of children die each year from easily prevented childhood diseases. This Guatemalan billboard urges that children be vaccinated against polio, diphtheria, TB, tetanus, pertussis (whooping cough), and scarlet fever (*left to right*).

entertainment events were shut down for months. There were worries that the H1N1 pandemic that spread around the world in 2009 might sicken 2 billion people, kill up to 150 million, and bring the world economy to a standstill. Fortunately, it hasn't been nearly as bad—so far—as the 1918 strain. Influenza is caused by a family of viruses (fig. 8.4a) that mutate rapidly and move from wild and domestic animals to humans, making control of this disease very difficult.

Every year there are 76 million cases of foodborne illnesses in the United States, resulting in 300,000 hospitalizations and 5,000 deaths. Both bacteria and intestinal protozoa cause these illnesses (fig. 8.4b and c). They are spread from feces through food and water. In 2009 about 2.5 million pounds (about 11,000 metric tons) of ground beef were recalled in the United States because of contamination by *E. coli* strain O157:H7. However, this was far less than 2007, when 35 million pounds of beef were recalled.

At any given time, around 2 billion people—nearly one-third of the world population—suffer from worms, flukes, and other internal parasites. Guinea worms (see opening case study) are one example. While people rarely die from parasites, they can be extremely debilitating, and can cause poverty that leads to other, more deadly, diseases.

Malaria is one of the most prevalent remaining infectious diseases. Every year about 500 million new cases of this disease occur, and about one million people die from it. The territory infected by this disease is expanding as global climate change allows mosquito vectors to move into new territory. Simply providing insecticide-treated bed nets and a few dollars worth of anti-malarial pills could prevent tens of millions of cases of this debilitating disease every year. Tragically, some of the countries where malaria is most widespread tax both bed nets and medicine as luxuries, placing them out of reach for ordinary people.

**Emergent diseases** are those not previously known or that have been absent for at least 20 years. The H1N1 flu that spread around the world in 2009 is a good example. There have been at least 40 outbreaks of emergent diseases over the past two decades, including the extremely deadly Ebola and Marburg fevers, which have afflicted Central Africa in at least six different locations in the past decade.

Similarly, cholera, which had been absent from South America for more than a century, reemerged in Peru in 1992 (fig. 8.5). Some other examples include a new drug-resistant form of tuberculosis, now spreading in South Africa; dengue fever, which is spreading through Southeast Asia and the Caribbean; and a new human lymphotropic virus (HTLV), which is thought to have jumped from monkeys into people in Cameroon who handled or ate bushmeat. These HTLV strains are now thought to infect 25 million people.

Growing human populations push people into remote areas where they encounter diseases that may have existed for a long time, but only now are exposed to humans. Rapid international travel makes it possible for these new diseases to spread around the world at jet speed. Epidemiologists warn that the next deadly epidemic is only a plane ride away.

West Nile virus shows how fast new diseases can travel. West Nile belongs to a family of mosquito-transmitted viruses that cause encephalitis (brain inflammation). Although recognized in Africa in 1937, the West Nile virus was absent from North America until 1999, when it apparently was introduced by an imported bird or mosquito. The disease spread rapidly from New York, where it was first reported, throughout the eastern United States in only two years (fig. 8.6). Within five years, it was found almost everywhere in the lower 48 states. The virus infects at least 250 bird species and 18 mammalian species. In 2007, about 4,000 people contracted West Nile and about 100 died.

The largest recent human death toll from an emergent disease is due to HIV/AIDS. Although it was first recognized in the early 1980s, acquired immune deficiency syndrome has now become the fifth greatest cause of contagious deaths. The WHO estimates that about 33 million people are now infected with the human immunodeficiency virus and that 3 million die every year from AIDS complications. Although two-thirds of all current HIV infections are now in sub-Saharan Africa, the disease is spreading rapidly in South and East Asia. Over the next 20 years, there could be an additional 65 million AIDS deaths. In Swaziland, health officials estimate nearly 40 percent of all adults are HIV-positive and that two-thirds of all current 15 year-olds will die of AIDS before age 50. Without AIDS, the life expectancy in Swaziland would be expected to be

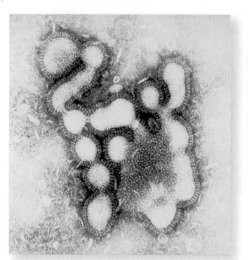

(a) Influenza viruses

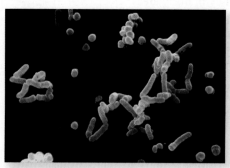

(b) Pathogenic bacteria

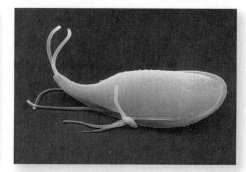

(c) *Giardia*

**Figure 8.4** (a) A group of influenza viruses magnified about 300,000 times. (b) Pathogenic bacteria magnified about 50,000 times. (c) *Giardia*, a parasitic intestinal protozoan, magnified about 10,000 times.

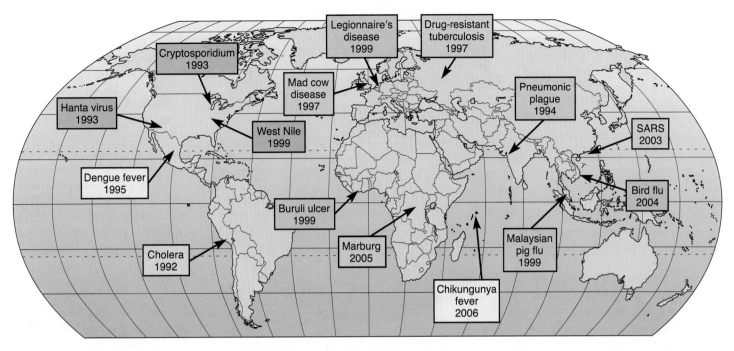

**Figure 8.5** Some recent outbreaks of highly lethal infectious diseases. Why are supercontagious organisms emerging in so many different places? *Source:* Data from U.S. Centers for Disease Control and Prevention.

55.3 years. With AIDS, Swaziland's average life expectancy is now 35.7 years. Worldwide, more than 15 million children—the equivalent of every child under age five in America—have lost one or both parents to AIDS. The economic costs of treating patients and lost productivity from premature deaths resulting from this disease are estimated to be at least $35 billion (U.S.) per year, or about one-tenth of the total GDP of sub-Saharan Africa.

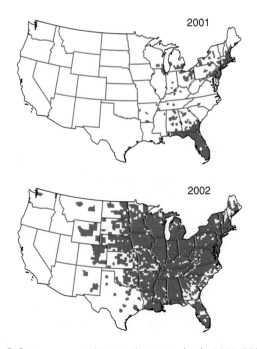

**Figure 8.6** The spread of West Nile virus in birds, 2001–2002. *Source:* Data from U.S. Centers for Disease Control and U.S. Geological Survey.

## Conservation medicine combines ecology and health care

Humans aren't the only ones to suffer from new and devastating diseases. Domestic animals and wildlife also experience sudden and widespread epidemics, which are sometimes called **ecological diseases.** Ebola hemorrhagic fever is one of the most virulent viruses ever seen, killing up to 90 percent of its victims. In 2002, an outbreak of Ebola fever began killing humans along the Gabon-Congo border. A few months later, researchers found that 221 of the 235 western lowland gorillas they had been studying in this area disappeared in just a few months. Many chimpanzees also died. Although the study team could only find a few of the dead gorillas, 75 percent of those tested positive for Ebola. Altogether, researchers estimate that 5,000 gorillas died in this small area of the Congo. Extrapolating to all of central Africa, it's possible that Ebola has killed one-quarter of all the gorillas in the world. It's thought that the spread of this disease in humans resulted from the practice of hunting and eating primates.

Two parasites called Dermo (*Perkinsus marinus*) and MSX (multinucleated sphere X) (*Haplosporidium nelsoni*) have killed billions of oysters in Chesapeake Bay. Dermo, which was first documented in the Gulf of Mexico in the early 1940s, had spread to the Chesapeake by 1949. MSX is thought to have been introduced intentionally via an infected oyster from Japan in 1959. These parasites can kill 90 percent of exposed oysters. Together with excess harvesting, pollution, and sediment, these diseases caused Chesapeake oyster harvests to fall from 20 to 30 million metric tons per year in the 1880s to about 1,000 metric tons today.

Botulism often causes disastrous die-offs among birds, especially when they're concentrated during migration. Over the past decade, large numbers of dead water birds have been discovered in the American Great Lakes (fig. 8.7). The spread of this epidemic from east to west through the lakes seems to be associated with the migration of the round goby, an invasive species from Europe. Algae and aquatic plants grow in lake areas fertilized by excessive nutrient runoff. When this plant matter falls to the lake bottom and decays, it creates anoxic conditions in which the bacteria that produce botulism toxic flourish. Invasive zebra and quagga mussels accumulate the toxic through filter feeding. The mussels are then eaten by round gobies, which are paralyzed by the toxic and easily caught by birds that also die.

Chronic wasting disease (CWD) is spreading through deer and elk populations in North America. Caused by a strange protein called a prion, CWD is one of a family of irreversible, degenerative neurological diseases known as transmissible spongiform encephalopathies (TSE) that include mad cow disease in cattle, scrapie in sheep, and Creutzfeldt-Jakob disease in humans. CWD probably started when elk ranchers fed contaminated animal by-products to their herds. Infected animals were sold to other ranches, and now the disease has spread to wild populations. First recognized in 1967 in Saskatchewan, CWD has been identified in wild deer populations and ranch operations in at least eleven American states.

No humans are known to have contracted TSE from deer or elk, but there is a concern that we might see something like the mad cow disaster that inflicted Europe in the 1990s. At least 100 people died, and nearly 5 million European cattle and sheep were slaughtered in an effort to contain that disease.

One thing that emergent diseases in humans and ecological diseases in natural communities have in common is environmental change that stresses biological systems and upsets normal ecological relationships. We cut down forests and drain wetlands, destroying habitat for native species. Invasive organisms and diseases are accidentally or intentionally introduced into new areas where they can grow explosively. Increasing incursion into former wilderness is spurred by human population growth and ecotourism. In 1950, only about 3 million people per year flew on commercial jets; by 2010, more than 1 billion flew on 20 million flights. Diseases can spread around the globe in mere days as people pass through international travel hubs. In the case of severe acute respiratory syndrome (SARS), which emerged in southern China in 2003, one flight attendant is thought to have spread the virus to 160 people in seven countries before he was diagnosed with the disease (see related stories "The Cough Heard

**Figure 8.7** Hundreds of loons died in 2007 in the American Great Lakes. They were apparently killed by botulism toxin accumulated by zebra and quagga mussels and round gobies, invasive species from Europe currently spreading through the lakes.

Round the World" and "The Next Pandemic" at www.mhhe.com/cunningham6e).

Climate change also facilitates—or forces—expansion of species into new territories. In 2001, a congressionally mandated assessment of climate change predicted greater incidence of malaria, yellow fever, and other tropical diseases in the United States, as mosquitoes, rodents, and other animals expand their range. This phenomenon is occurring worldwide. In the 1970s, only nine countries suffered from dengue fever. Today, dengue has spread to over 100 countries. Other diseases linked to environmental changes include lyme disease, schistosomiasis, tuberculosis, bubonic plague, and cholera.

We are coming to recognize that the delicate ecological balances that we value so highly—and disrupt so frequently—are important to our own health. **Conservation medicine** is an emerging discipline that attempts to understand how our environmental changes threaten our own health as well as that of the natural communities on which we depend for ecological services. While still small, this new field is gaining recognition from mainstream funding sources such as the World Bank, the World Health Organization, and the U.S. National Institutes of Health.

## Resistance to antibiotics and pesticides is increasing

In recent years, health workers have become increasingly alarmed about the rapid spread of methicillin-resistant *Staphylococcus aureus* (MRSA). Staphylococcus (or staph) is very common. Most people have at least some of these bacteria. They are a common cause of sore throats and skin infections, but are usually easily controlled. This new strain, however, is resistant to penicillin and related antibiotics, and can cause deadly infections, especially in people with weak immune systems. MRSA is most frequent in hospitals, nursing homes, correctional facilities, and other places where people are in close contact. It's generally spread through direct skin contact. School locker rooms, gymnasiums, and contact sports also are sources of infections. Several states have closed schools as a result of MRSA contamination. In 2006, the Centers for Disease Control estimated that at least 100,000 MRSA infections in the United States resulted in about 19,000 deaths. Since then a campaign for better hygiene in hospitals and schools appears to have brought infection rates down. A much worse situation is reported in China, where about half of the 5 million annual staph infections are thought to be methicillin-resistant.

(a) Mutation and selection create drug-resistant strains

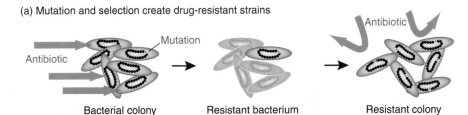

Bacterial colony → Resistant bacterium → Resistant colony

(b) Conjugation transfers drug resistance from one strain to another

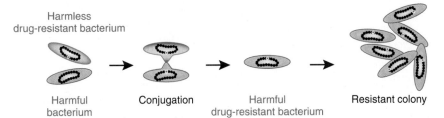

Harmful bacterium → Conjugation → Harmful drug-resistant bacterium → Resistant colony

**Figure 8.8** How microbes acquire antibiotic resistance. (a) Random mutations make a few cells resistant. When challenged by antibiotics, only those cells survive to give rise to a resistant colony. (b) Sexual reproduction (conjugation) or plasmid transfer moves genes from one strain or species to another.

Why have vectors, such as mosquitoes, and pathogens, such as bacteria or the malaria parasite, become resistant to pesticides and antibiotics? Part of the answer is natural selection and the ability of many organisms to evolve rapidly. Another factor is the human tendency to use control measures carelessly. Many doctors prescribe penicillin and other antibiotics just in case they may do some good. Similarly, when we discovered that DDT and other insecticides could control mosquito populations, we spread them everywhere. This not only harmed wildlife and beneficial insects but also created perfect conditions for natural selection.

Many pests and pathogens were exposed only minimally to control measures, allowing those with natural resistance to survive and spread their genes through the population (fig. 8.8). After repeated cycles of exposure and selection, many microorganisms and their vectors have become insensitive to almost all our weapons against them.

Raising huge numbers of cattle, hogs, and poultry in densely packed barns and feedlots is another reason for widespread antibiotic resistance in pathogens. Confined animals are dosed constantly with antibiotics and steroid hormones to keep them disease-free and to make them gain weight faster. More than half of all antibiotics used in the United States each year are fed to livestock. A significant amount of these antibiotics and hormones are excreted in urine and feces, which are spread, untreated, on the land or discharged into surface water, where they contribute further to the evolution of supervirulent pathogens.

At least half of the 100 million antibiotic doses prescribed for humans every year in the United States are unnecessary or are the wrong ones. Furthermore, many people who start a course of antibiotic treatment fail to carry it out for the time prescribed. For your own health and that of the people around you, if you are taking an antibiotic, follow your doctor's orders. Finish your prescribed doses and don't stop taking the medicine as soon as you start feeling better.

## Who should pay for health care?

The heaviest burden of illness is borne by the poorest people, who can afford neither a healthy environment nor adequate health care. Women in sub-Saharan Africa, for example, suffer six times the disease burden of women in most European countries. The WHO estimates that 90 percent of all disease burden occurs in developing countries, where less than one-tenth of all health care dollars is spent. The group Medecins Sans Frontieres (MSF, or Doctors without Borders) calls this the 10/90 gap. While wealthy nations pursue drugs to treat baldness and obesity, depression in dogs, and erectile dysfunction, billions of people are sick or dying from treatable infections and parasitic diseases to which little attention is paid. Worldwide, only 2 percent of the people with AIDS have access to modern medicines. Every year, some 600,000 infants acquire HIV—almost all of them through mother-to-child transmission during birth or breast-feeding. Antiretroviral therapy costing only a few dollars can prevent most of this transmission. The Bill and Melinda Gates Foundation has pledged $200 million for medical aid to developing countries to help fight AIDS, TB, and malaria.

Dr. Jeffrey Sachs of the Columbia University Earth Institute says that disease is as much a cause as a consequence of poverty and political unrest, yet the world's richest countries now spend just $1 per person per year on global health. He predicts that raising our commitment to about $25 billion annually (about 0.1 percent of the annual GDP of the 20 richest countries) would not only save about 8 million lives each year but also would boost the world economy by billions of dollars. There also would be huge social benefits for the rich countries in not living in a world endangered by mass social instability; the spread of pathogens across borders; the spread of other ills, such as terrorism; and drug trafficking caused by social problems. Sachs also argues that reducing disease burden would help reduce population growth. When parents believe their offspring will survive, they have fewer children and invest more in food, health, and education for smaller families.

The United States is among the least generous of the world's rich countries, donating only about 12 cents per $100 of GDP on international development aid. Could this country do better? During this time of fear of terrorism and rising anti-American feelings around the globe, it's difficult to interest legislators in international aid, yet helping reduce disease might win the United States more friends and make the nation safer than buying more bombs and bullets. Improved health care in poorer countries may also help prevent the spread of emergent diseases, such as SARS, in a globally interconnected world.

Epidemiologists note that almost all of the 2.2 billion people expected to be added to the world population in the next 30 years will live in megacities of the developing world. The economic and environmental conditions in those cities will have a profound impact on global disease burden. Many world leaders urge us to address the "lethal disease of poverty." More discussion of urban areas and their problems is presented in chapter 14.

## 8.2 Toxicology

**Toxic** means poisonous. Toxicology is the study of the adverse effects of external factors on an organism or a system. This includes environmental chemicals, drugs, and diet as well as physical factors, such as ionizing radiation, UV light, and electromagnetic forces, In addition to studying agents that cause toxicity, scientists in this field are concerned with movement and fate of poisons in the environment, routes of entry into the body and effects of exposure to these agents. Toxic substances damage or kill living organisms because they react with cellular components to disrupt metabolic functions. Toxins often are harmful even in extremely dilute concentrations. In some cases, billionths, or even trillionths, of a gram can cause irreversible damage.

Many toxicologists limit the term "toxin" to proteins or other molecules synthesized by living organisms. Nonbiological noxious substances are called toxicants (from Latin *toxicum,* or poison). The modes of action of organic or inorganic as well as synthetic or natural materials are so similar, however, that we'll use the generic terms "toxins" and "toxics" for poisons in this chapter regardless of their origin.

Hazardous materials aren't necessarily toxic. Some substances are dangerous because they're flammable, explosive, acidic, caustic, irritants, or sensitizers. Many of these materials must be handled carefully in large doses or high concentrations, but they can be rendered relatively innocuous by dilution, neutralization, or other physical treatment.

Environmental toxicology, or ecotoxicology, specifically deals with the interactions, transformation, fate, and effects of toxic materials in the biosphere, including individual organisms, populations, and whole ecosystems. In aquatic systems the fate of the pollutants is primarily studied in relation to mechanisms and processes at interfaces of the ecosystem components. Special attention is devoted to the sediment/water, water/organisms, and water/air interfaces. In terrestrial environments, the emphasis tends to be on effects of metals on soil fauna community and population characteristics.

Table 8.2 is a list of the top 20 toxic and hazardous substances considered the highest risk by the U.S. Environmental Protection Agency. Compiled from the 275 substances regulated by the Comprehensive Environmental Response, Compensation, and Liability Act (CERCLA), commonly known as the Superfund Act, these materials are listed in order of assessed importance in terms of human and environmental health.

### How do toxics affect us?

**Allergens** are substances that activate the immune system. Some allergens act directly as **antigens**; that is, they are recognized as foreign by white blood cells and stimulate the production of specific antibodies (proteins that recognize and bind to foreign cells or chemicals). Other allergens act indirectly by binding to and changing the chemistry of foreign materials so they become antigenic and cause an immune response.

Formaldehyde is a good example of a widely used chemical that is a powerful sensitizer of the immune system. It is directly allergenic and can trigger reactions to other substances. Widely used in plastics, wood products, insulation, glue, and fabrics, formaldehyde concentrations in indoor air can be thousands of times higher than in normal outdoor air.

Some people suffer from what is called **sick building syndrome**: headaches, allergies, and chronic fatigue caused by poorly vented indoor air contaminated by molds, carbon monoxide, nitrogen oxides, formaldehyde, and other toxic chemicals released by carpets, insulation, plastics, building materials, and other sources. The Environmental Protection Agency estimates that poor indoor air quality may cost the nation $60 billion a year in absenteeism and reduced productivity (see A Closer Look, p. 190).

**Neurotoxins** are a special class of metabolic poisons that specifically attack nerve cells (neurons). The nervous system is so important in regulating body activities that disruption of its activities is especially fast-acting and devastating. Different types of neurotoxics act in different ways. Heavy metals, such as lead and mercury, kill nerve cells and cause permanent neurological damage. Anesthetics (ether, chloroform, halothane, etc.) and chlorinated hydrocarbons (DDT, Dieldrin, Aldrin) disrupt nerve cell

## Table 8.2 | Top 20 Toxic and Hazardous Substances

| Material | Major Sources |
|---|---|
| 1. Arsenic | Treated lumber |
| 2. Lead | Paint, gasoline |
| 3. Mercury | Coal combustion |
| 4. Vinyl chloride | Plastics, industrial uses |
| 5. Polychlorinated biphenyls (PCBs) | Electric insulation |
| 6. Benzene | Gasoline, industrial use |
| 7. Cadmium | Batteries |
| 8. Benzo(a)pyrene | Waste incineration |
| 9. Polycyclic aromatic hydrocarbons | Combustion |
| 10. Benzo(b)fluoranthene | Fuels |
| 11. Chloroform | Water purification, industry |
| 12. DDT | Pesticide use |
| 13. Aroclor 1254 | Plastics |
| 14. Aroclor 1260 | Plastics |
| 15. Trichloroethylene | Solvents |
| 16. Dibenz (a, h)anthracene | Incineration |
| 17. Dieldrin | Pesticides |
| 18. Chromium, hexavalent | Paints, coatings, welding, anticorrosion agents |
| 19. Chlordane | Pesticides |
| 20. Hexachlorobutadiene | Pesticides |

*Source:* Data from U.S. Environmental Protection Agency.

membranes necessary for nerve action. Organophosphates (Malathion, Parathion) and carbamates (carbaryl, zeneb, maneb) inhibit acetylcholinesterase, an enzyme that regulates signal transmission between nerve cells and the tissues or organs they innervate (for example, muscle). Most neurotoxics are both acute and extremely toxic. More than 850 compounds are now recognized as neurotoxics.

**Mutagens** are agents, such as chemicals and radiation, that damage or alter genetic material (DNA) in cells. This can lead to birth defects if the damage occurs during embryonic or fetal growth. Later in life, genetic damage may trigger neoplastic (tumor) growth. When damage occurs in reproductive cells, the results can be passed on to future generations. Cells have repair mechanisms to detect and restore damaged genetic material, but some changes may be hidden, and the repair process itself can be flawed. It is generally accepted that there is no "safe" threshold for exposure to mutagens. Any exposure has some possibility of causing damage.

**Teratogens** are chemicals or other factors that specifically cause abnormalities during embryonic growth and development. Some compounds that are not otherwise harmful can cause tragic problems in these sensitive stages of life. Perhaps the most prevalent teratogen in the world is alcohol. Drinking during pregnancy can lead to **fetal alcohol syndrome**—a cluster of symptoms including craniofacial abnormalities, developmental delays, behavioral problems, and mental defects, that last throughout a child's life. Even one alcoholic drink a day during pregnancy has been associated with decreased birth weight.

**Carcinogens** are substances that cause **cancer**—invasive, out-of-control cell growth that results in malignant tumors. Cancer rates rose in most industrialized countries during the twentieth century, and cancer is now the second leading cause of death in the United States, killing about a half a million people per year. Sixteen of the 20 compounds listed by the U.S. EPA as the greatest risk to human health are probable or possible human carcinogens. More than 200 million Americans live in areas where the combined upper limit lifetime cancer risk from these carcinogens exceeds 10 in 1 million, or 10 times the risk normally considered acceptable.

In 2010, the U.S. President's Cancer Panel warned that exposure to carcinogens and hormone-disrupting environmental chemicals may be a much greater threat than previously recognized. In particular, the panel was concerned about exposure during pregnancy, when the risk seems greatest. Noting that 300 contaminants have been detected in umbilical cord blood, they said that babies are being born "pre-polluted." The panel called for more rigorous regulation of chemicals, noting that only a few hundred of the more than 80,000 chemicals in use in the United States have been tested thoroughly for human toxicity.

## Endocrine hormone disrupters are of special concern

One of the most recently recognized environmental health threats are **endocrine hormone disrupters**, chemicals that interrupt the normal endocrine hormone functions. Hormones are chemicals released into the bloodstream by glands in one part of the body to regulate the development and function of tissues and organs elsewhere in the body (fig. 8.9). You undoubtedly have heard about sex hormones and

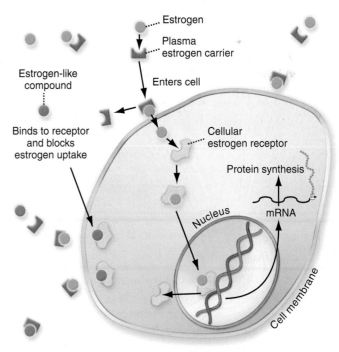

**Figure 8.9** Steroid hormone action. Plasma hormone carriers deliver regulatory molecules to the cell surface, where they cross the cell membrane. Intracellular carriers deliver hormones to the nucleus, where they bind to and regulate expression of DNA.

# What toxins and hazards are present in your home?

The EPA warns that indoor air can be much more polluted than outdoor air. Many illnesses can be linked to poor air quality and exposure to toxins in the home. Since 1950, at least 70,000 new chemical compounds have been invented and dispersed into our environment. Only a fraction of these have been tested for human toxicity, but it's suspected that many may contribute to allergies, birth defects, cancer, and other disorders. Which of the following materials can be found in your home? What toxins and hazards are present in your home?

▼ **Garage**
- Antifreeze
- Automotive polishes and waxes
- Batteries
- Fungicides and herbicides
- Gasoline and solvents
- Insecticides, herbicides, pesticides
- Paints, stains
- Pool supplies
- Rust remover
- Wood preservatives

▼ **Kitchen/Laundry Area**
- Bleach
- Carbon monoxide and fine particulates
- Cleansers, disinfectants
- Laundry detergents
- Drain cleaners
- Floor polishes
- Oven cleaners
- Nonstick by-products
- Window cleaners

**Basement** ▶
- Carbon monoxide from furnace and water heaters
- Epoxy glues
- Gasoline, kerosene, and other flammable solvents
- Lye and other caustics
- Mold, bacteria, and other pathogens or allergens
- Paint and paint remover
- PVC and other plastics
- Radon gas from subsoil

### ▼ Bathroom

- Chloroform from showers and bath
- Leftover drugs and medications
- Fingernail polish and remover
- Makeup
- Mold
- Mouthwash
- Toilet bowl cleaner

### ◀ Attic

- Asbestos
- Fiberglass insulation
- PBDE-treated cellulose

### ◀ Bedroom

- Aerosols
- Bis-phenol A, lead, cadmium in toys and jewelry
- Flame retardants, fungicides and insecticides in carpets and bedding
- Mothballs

### ▲ Living Room

- Asbestos from floor or ceiling tiles
- Benzepyrenes from smoking
- Flame retardants
- Freons from air conditioners
- Furniture and metal polishes
- Lead or cadmium from toys
- Paints, fabrics
- Plastics

### Can You Explain:

1. Which space has the largest number of toxic materials?
2. In which room do you spend the most time?
3. Which space has the greatest number of toxins to which you're likely to be exposed on a regular basis?

their powerful effects on how we look and behave, but these are only one example of the many regulatory hormones that rule our lives.

We now know that some of the most insidious effects of persistent chemicals, such as DDT and PCBs, are that they interfere with normal growth, development, and physiology of a variety of animals—-presumably including humans—at very low doses. In some cases, picogram concentrations (trillionths of a gram per liter) may be enough to cause developmental abnormalities in sensitive organisms. These chemicals are sometimes called environmental estrogens or androgens, because they often cause sexual dysfunction (reproductive health problems in females or feminization of males, for example). They are just as likely, however, to disrupt thyroxin functions or those of other important regulatory molecules as they are to obstruct sex hormones.

## 8.3 Movement, Distribution, and Fate of Toxins

There are many sources of toxic and hazardous chemicals in the environment and many factors related to each chemical itself, its route or method of exposure, and its persistence in the environment, as well as characteristics of the target organism (table 8.3), that determine the danger of the chemical. We can think of both individuals and an ecosystem as sets of interacting compartments between which chemicals move, based on molecular size, solubility, stability, and reactivity (fig. 8.10). The dose (amount), route of entry, timing of exposure, and sensitivity of the organism all play important roles in determining toxicity. In this section, we will consider some of these characteristics and how they affect environmental health.

## Solubility and mobility determine when and where chemicals move

Solubility is one of the most important characteristics in determining how, where, and when a toxic material will move through the environment or through the body to its site of action. Chemicals can be divided into two major groups: those that dissolve more readily in water and those that dissolve more readily in oil. Water-soluble compounds move rapidly and widely through the environment because water is ubiquitous. They also tend to have ready access to most cells in the body because aqueous solutions bathe all our cells. Molecules that are oil- or fat-soluble (usually organic molecules) generally need a carrier to move through the environment and into or within the body. Once inside the

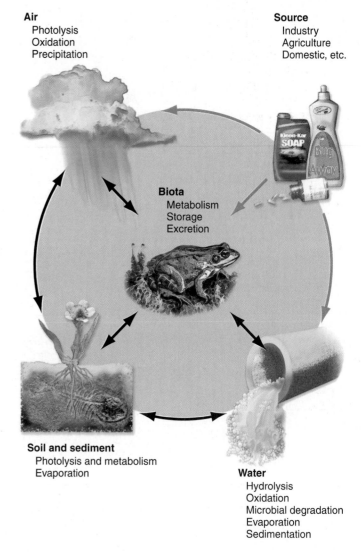

**Figure 8.10** Movement and fate of chemicals in the environment. Processes that modify, remove, or sequester compounds are shown below each compartment. Toxins also move directly from a source to soil and sediment.

| Table 8.3 | Factors in Environmental Toxicity |
|---|---|

**Factors Related to the Toxic Agent**

1. Chemical composition and reactivity
2. Physical characteristics (such as solubility, state)
3. Presence of impurities or contaminants
4. Stability and storage characteristics of toxic agent
5. Availability of vehicle (such as solvent) to carry agent
6. Movement of agent through environment and into cells

**Factors Related to Exposure**

1. Dose (concentration and volume of exposure)
2. Route, rate, and site of exposure
3. Duration and frequency of exposure
4. Time of exposure (time of day, season, year)

**Factors Related to the Organism**

1. Resistance to uptake, storage, or cell permeability of agent
2. Ability to metabolize, inactivate, sequester, or eliminate agent
3. Tendency to activate or alter nontoxic substances so they become toxic
4. Concurrent infections or physical or chemical stress
5. Species and genetic characteristics of organism
6. Nutritional status of subject
7. Age, sex, body weight, immunological status, and maturity

body, however, oil-soluble toxics penetrate readily into tissues and cells because the membranes that enclose cells are themselves made of similar oil-soluble chemicals. Once inside cells, oil-soluble materials are likely to accumulate and to be stored in lipid deposits, where they may be protected from metabolic breakdown and persist for many years.

## Exposure and susceptibility determine how we respond

Just as there are many sources of toxic materials in our environment, there are many routes for entry into our bodies (fig. 8.11). Airborne toxics generally cause more ill health than any other exposure source. We breathe far more air every day than the volume of food we eat or water we drink. Furthermore, the lining of our lungs, which is designed to exchange gases very efficiently, also absorbs toxics very well. Epidemiologists estimate that 3 million people—two-thirds of them children—die each year from diseases caused or exacerbated by air pollution.

But food, water, and skin contact also can expose us to a wide variety of hazards. The largest exposures for many toxics are found in industrial settings, where workers may encounter doses thousands of times higher than would be found anywhere else. The European Agency for Safety and Health at Work warns that 32 million people (20 percent of all employees) in the European Union are exposed to unacceptable levels of carcinogens and other chemicals in their workplace.

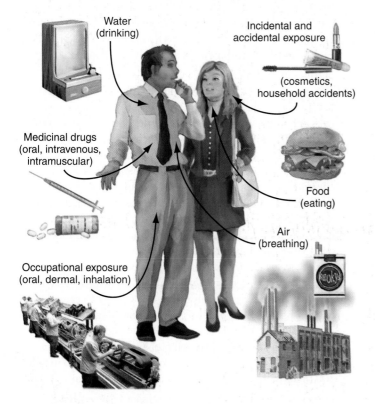

**Figure 8.11** Routes of exposure to toxic and hazardous environmental factors.

Condition of the organism and timing of exposure also have strong influences on toxicity. Healthy adults, for example, may be relatively insensitive to doses that are very dangerous to young children or to someone already weakened by other diseases. Pound for pound, children drink more water, eat more food, and breathe more air than do adults. Putting fingers, toys, and other objects into their mouths increases children's exposure to toxics in dust or soil.

Furthermore, children generally have less-developed immune systems or processes to degrade or excrete toxics. The developing brain is especially sensitive to damage. Obviously, disrupting the complex and sensitive process of brain growth and development can have tragic long-term consequences. Researchers estimate that one in six children in America has a developmental disability, usually involving the nervous system.

The best-known example of an environmental risk for children is lead poisoning. Before lead paint and leaded gasoline were banned in the 1970s, at least 4 million American children had dangerous levels of lead in their blood. Banning these products has been one of the greatest successes in environmental health. Blood lead levels in children have fallen more than 90 percent in the past three decades. Unfortunately, this tremendous success hasn't yet extended to developing countries. In 2009, the *China Daily* reported that 1.1 million children are born in China every year with birth defects attributed to environmental factors.

The notorious teratogen thalidomide is a prime example of differences in sensitivity between species and within stages of fetal development. A single dose of this teratogen taken in the third week of human pregnancy (a time when many women aren't aware they're pregnant) can cause severe abnormalities in fetal limb development. Thalidomide was tested on a number of laboratory animals without showing any deleterious effects. Unfortunately, however, it's a powerful teratogen in humans.

## Bioaccumulation and biomagnification increase chemical concentrations

Cells have mechanisms for **bioaccumulation**, the selective absorption and storage of a great variety of molecules. This allows them to accumulate nutrients and essential minerals, but at the same time, they also may absorb and store harmful substances through the same mechanisms. Materials that are rather dilute in the environment can reach dangerous levels inside cells and tissues through this process of bioaccumulation.

Toxic substances also can be magnified through food webs. **Biomagnification** occurs when the toxic burden of a large number of organisms at a lower trophic level is accumulated and concentrated by a predator in a higher trophic level. Phytoplankton and bacteria in aquatic ecosystems, for instance, take up heavy metals or toxic organic molecules from water or sediments (fig. 8.12). Their predators—zooplankton and small fish—collect and retain the toxics from many prey organisms, building up higher concentrations of toxics. The top carnivores in the food chain—game fish, fish-eating birds, and humans—can accumulate such high toxic levels that they suffer adverse health effects.

One of the first well-known examples of bioaccumulation and biomagnification was DDT, which accumulated through food chains,

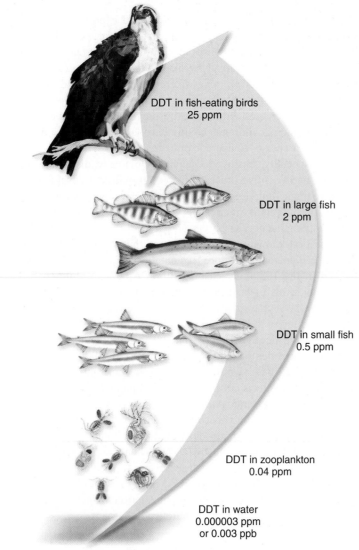

DDT in fish-eating birds
25 ppm

DDT in large fish
2 ppm

DDT in small fish
0.5 ppm

DDT in zooplankton
0.04 ppm

DDT in water
0.000003 ppm
or 0.003 ppb

**Figure 8.12** Bioaccumulation and biomagnification. Organisms lower on the food chain take up and store toxins from the environment. They are eaten by larger predators, who are eaten, in turn, by even larger predators. The highest members of the food chain can accumulate very high levels of the toxin.

so that by the 1960s it was shown to be interfering with reproduction of peregrine falcons, brown pelicans, and other predatory birds at the top of their food chains.

## Persistence makes some materials a greater threat

Many toxic substances degrade when exposed to sun, air, and water. This can destroy them or convert them to inactive forms, but some materials are persistent and can last for years or even centuries as they cycle through ecosytems. Even if released in minute concentrations, they can bioaccumulate in food webs to reach dangerous levels. Heavy metals, such as lead and mercury, are classic examples. Mercury, like lead, can destroy nerve cells and is particularly dangerous to children. The largest source of mercury in the United States is from burning coal. Every year, power plants in the United

States release 48 tons of this toxic metal into the air (see "Controlling Mercury Pollution" at **www.mhhe.com/cunningham6e**). It works its way through food chains and is concentrated to dangerous levels in fish. Mercury contamination is the most common cause of lakes and rivers failing to meet pollution regulation standards. Forty-four states have issued warnings against eating local fish by children and pregnant women. In a nationwide survey of lakes and rivers in 2007, the Environmental Protection Agency found that 55 percent of the 2,500 fish sampled had mercury levels that exceeded dietary recommendations.

Many organic compounds, such as PVC plastics and chlorinated hydrocarbon pesticides, also are highly resistant to degradation. This makes them very useful, but it also allows them to accumulate in the environment and have unexpected effects far from the site of their original use. Some of these **persistent organic pollutants (POPs)** have become extremely widespread, being found now from the tropics to the Arctic. They often accumulate in food webs and reach toxic concentrations in long-living top predators, such as humans, sharks, raptors, swordfish, and bears. These are some of the greatest current concerns:

- Polybrominated diphenyl ethers (PBDE) are widely used as flame-retardants in textiles, foam in upholstery, and plastic in appliances and computers. This compound was first reported accumulating in women's breast milk in Sweden in the 1990s. It was subsequently found in humans and other species everywhere from Canada to Israel. Nearly 150 million metric tons (330 million lbs) of PBDEs are used every year worldwide. The toxicity and environmental persistence of PBDE are much like those of PCBs, to which it is closely related chemically. The dust at ground zero in New York City after September 11 was heavily laden with PBDE. The European Union has already banned this compound.

- Perfluorooctane sulfonate (PFOS) and perfluorooctanoic acid (PFOA, also known as C8) are members of a chemical family used to make nonstick, waterproof, and stain-resistant products such as Teflon, Gortex, Scotchguard, and Stainmaster. Industry makes use of their slippery, heat-stable properties to manufacture everything from airplanes and computers to cosmetics and household cleaners. Now these chemicals—which are reported to be infinitely persistent in the environment—are found throughout the world, even the most remote and seemingly pristine sites. Almost all Americans have one or more perfluorinated compounds in their blood. In one long-term study, workers exposed to high levels of PFOA were twice as likely to die of prostate cancer or stroke than colleagues with little or no exposure to the chemical. Heating some nonstick cooking pans above 260°C (500°F) can release enough PFOA to kill pet birds. This chemical family has been shown to cause liver damage as well as various cancers and reproductive and developmental problems in rats. Exposure may be especially dangerous to women and girls, who may be 100 times more sensitive than men to these chemicals.

- Perchlorate is a waterborne contaminant left over from propellants and rocket fuels. About 12,000 sites in the United States were used by the military for live munition testing and are contaminated with perchlorate. Polluted water used to irrigate crops such as alfalfa and lettuce has introduced the chemical into the human food chain. Tests of cow's milk and human breast milk detected perchlorate in nearly every sample from throughout the United States. Perchlorate can interfere with iodine uptake in the thyroid gland, disrupting adult metabolism and childhood development.

- Phthalates (pronounced *thalates*) are found in cosmetics, deodorants, and many plastics (such as soft polyvinyl chloride, or PVC) used for food packaging, children's toys, and medical devices. Some members of this chemical family are known to be toxic to laboratory animals, causing kidney and liver damage and possibly some cancers. In addition, many phthalates act as endocrine hormone disrupters and have been linked to reproductive abnormalities and decreased fertility. A correlation has been found between phthalate levels in urine and low sperm numbers and decreased sperm motility in men. Nearly everyone in the United States has phthalates in his or her body at levels reported to cause these problems. While not yet conclusive, these results could help explain a 50-year decline in semen quality in most industrialized countries. In 2007, California banned phthalates in products designed for children.

- Bisphenol A (BPA), a prime ingredient in polycarbonate plastic (commonly used for products ranging from water bottles to tooth-protecting sealants), has been widely found in humans. One possible source is canned food, which commonly has BPA in interior linings. So far, there is little direct evidence linking BPA exposure to human health risks, but studies in animals have found that the chemical can cause abnormal chromosome numbers, a condition called aneuploidy, which is the leading cause of miscarriages and several forms of mental retardation. It also is an environmental estrogen and may alter sexual development in both males and females.

- Atrazine is the most widely used herbicide in America. More than 60 million pounds of this compound are applied per year, mainly on corn and cereal grains, but also on golf courses, sugarcane, and Christmas trees. It has long been known to disrupt endocrine hormone functions in mammals, resulting in spontaneous abortions, low birth weights, and neurological disorders. Studies of families in corn-producing areas in the American Midwest have found higher rates of developmental defects among infants, and certain cancers in families with elevated atrazine levels in their drinking water. University of California professor Tyrone Hayes has shown that atrazine levels as low as 0.1 ppb (30 times less than the EPA maximum contaminant level) caused severe reproductive effects in amphibians, including abnormal gonadal development and hermaphroditism. Atrazine now is found in rain and surface waters nearly everywhere in the United States at levels that could cause abnormal development in frogs. In 2003, the European Union withdrew regulatory approval for this herbicide, and several countries banned its use altogether. Some toxicologists have suggested a similar rule in the United States.

## Chemical interactions can increase toxicity

Some materials produce *antagonistic* reactions. That is, they interfere with the effects or stimulate the breakdown of other chemicals. For instance, vitamins E and A can reduce the response to some carcinogens. Other materials are *additive* when they occur together in exposures. Rats exposed to both lead and arsenic show twice the toxicity of only one of these elements. Perhaps the greatest concern is synergistic effects. **Synergism** is an interaction in which one substance exacerbates the effects of another. For example, occupational asbestos exposure increases lung cancer rates 20-fold. Smoking increases lung cancer rates by the same amount. Asbestos workers who also smoke, however, have a 400-fold increase in cancer rates. How many other toxic chemicals are we exposed to that are below threshold limits individually but combine to give toxic results?

# 8.4 Mechanisms for Minimizing Toxic Effects

A fundamental concept in toxicology is that every material can be poisonous under some conditions, but most chemicals have a safe level or threshold below which their effects are undetectable or insignificant. Each of us consumes lethal doses of many chemicals over the course of a lifetime. One hundred cups of strong coffee, for instance, contain a lethal dose of caffeine. Similarly, 100 aspirin tablets, 10 kg (22 lbs) of spinach or rhubarb, or a liter of alcohol would be deadly if consumed all at once. Taken in small doses, however, these materials can be broken down or excreted before they do much harm. Furthermore, the damage they cause can be repaired. Sometimes, however, mechanisms that protect us from a particular toxin at one stage in the life cycle become deleterious with another substance or in another stage of development. Let's look at how these processes help protect us from harmful substances, as well as how they can go awry.

## Metabolic degradation and excretion eliminate toxics

Most organisms have enzymes that process waste products and environmental poisons to reduce their toxicity. In mammals, most of these enzymes are located in the liver, the primary site of detoxification of both natural wastes and introduced poisons. Sometimes, however, these reactions work to our disadvantage. Compounds such as benzepyrene, for example, that aren't toxic in their original form are processed by the same liver enzymes into cancer-causing carcinogens. Why would we have a system that makes a chemical more dangerous? Evolution and natural selection are expressed through reproductive success or failure. Defense mechanisms that protect us from toxins and hazards early in life are "selected for" by evolution. Factors or conditions that affect postreproductive ages (such as cancer or premature senility) usually don't affect reproductive success or exert "selective pressure."

We also reduce the effects of waste products and environmental toxics by eliminating them from the body through excretion. Volatile molecules, such as carbon dioxide, hydrogen cyanide, and ketones, are excreted via breathing. Some excess salts and other substances are excreted in sweat. Primarily, however, excretion is a function of the kidneys, which can eliminate significant amounts of soluble materials through urine formation. Accumulated toxins in the urine can damage this vital system, however. In the same way, the stomach, intestine, and colon often suffer damage from materials concentrated in the digestive system and may be afflicted by diseases and tumors.

## Repair mechanisms mend damage

In the same way that individual cells have enzymes to repair damage to DNA and protein at the molecular level, tissues and organs that are exposed regularly to physical wear-and-tear or to toxic or hazardous materials often have mechanisms for damage repair. Our skin and the epithelial linings of the gastrointestinal tract, blood vessels, lungs, and urogenital system have high cellular reproduction rates to replace injured cells. With each reproduction cycle, however, there is a chance that some cells will lose normal growth controls and run amok, creating a tumor. Thus, any agent, such as smoking or drinking, that irritates tissues is likely to be carcinogenic. And tissues with high cell-replacement rates are among the most likely to develop cancers.

# 8.5 Measuring Toxicity

In 1540 the Swiss scientist Paracelsus said, "The dose makes the poison," by which he meant that almost everything is toxic at very high levels, but can be safe if diluted enough. This remains the most basic principle of toxicology. Sodium chloride (table salt), for instance, is essential for human life in small doses. If you were forced to eat a kilogram of salt all at once, however, it would make you very sick. A similar amount injected into your bloodstream would be lethal. How a material is delivered—at what rate, through which route of entry, and in what medium—plays a vital role in determining toxicity.

This doesn't mean that all toxics are identical, however. Some are so poisonous that a single drop on your skin can kill you. Others require massive amounts injected directly into the blood to be lethal. Measuring and comparing the toxicity of various materials are difficult because species differ in sensitivity, and individuals within a species respond differently to a given exposure. In this section, we will look at methods of toxicity testing and at how results are analyzed and reported.

## We usually test toxic effects on lab animals

The most commonly used and widely accepted toxicity test is to expose a population of laboratory animals to measured doses of a specific substance under controlled conditions. This procedure is expensive, time-consuming, and often painful and debilitating to the animals being tested. It commonly takes hundreds—or even thousands—of animals, several years of hard work, and hundreds of thousands of dollars to thoroughly test the effects of a toxic at very low doses. More humane toxicity tests using computer simulations of model reactions, cell cultures, and other substitutes for whole living animals are being developed. However, conventional

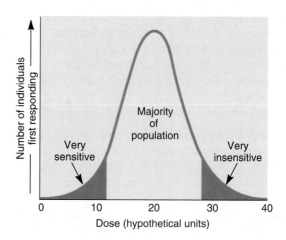

**Figure 8.13** Probable variations in sensitivity to a toxin within a population. Some members of a population may be very sensitive to a given toxin, while others are much less sensitive. The majority of the population falls somewhere between the two extremes.

large-scale animal testing is the method in which scientists have the most confidence and on which most public policies about pollution and environmental or occupational health hazards are based.

In addition to humanitarian concerns, several other problems in laboratory animal testing trouble both toxicologists and policymakers. One problem is differences in toxic sensitivity among the members of a specific population. Figure 8.13 shows a typical dose/response curve for exposure to a hypothetical chemical. Some individuals are very sensitive to the material, while others are insensitive. Most, however, fall in a middle category, forming a bell-shaped curve. The question for regulators and politicians is whether we should set pollution levels that will protect everyone, including the most sensitive people, or only aim to protect the average person. It might cost billions of extra dollars to protect a very small number of individuals at the extreme end of the curve. Is that a good use of resources? Why or why not?

Dose/response curves aren't always symmetrical, making it difficult to compare toxicity of unlike chemicals or different species of organisms. A convenient way to describe toxicity of a chemical is to determine the dose to which 50 percent of the test population is sensitive. In the case of a lethal dose (LD), this is called the **LD50** (fig. 8.14).

Unrelated species can react very differently to the same poison, not only because body sizes vary but also because physiology and metabolism differ. Even closely related species can have very dissimilar reactions to a particular chemical. Hamsters, for instance, are nearly 5,000 times less sensitive to some dioxins than are guinea pigs. Of 226 chemicals found to be carcinogenic in either rats or mice, 95 cause cancer in one species but not the other. These variations make it difficult to estimate the risks for humans, since we don't consider it ethical to perform controlled experiments in which we deliberately expose people to toxins.

Even within a single species, there can be variations in responses between different genetic lines. A current controversy in determining the toxicity of bisphenol A (BPA) concerns the type of rats used for toxicology studies. In most labs, a sturdy strain

# Active Learning

called the Sprague-Dawley rat is standard. It turns out, however, that these animals, which were bred to grow fast and breed prolifically in lab conditions, are thousands of times less sensitive to endocrine disrupters than ordinary rats. Industry reports that declare BPA to be harmless based on Sprague-Dawley rats are highly suspect.

## There is a wide range of toxicity

It's useful to group materials according to their relative toxicity. A moderately harmful substance takes about 1 g per kg of body weight (about 2 oz for an average human) to make a lethal dose. Very toxic materials take about one-tenth that amount, while extremely poisonous materials take one-hundredth as much (only a few drops) to kill most people. Supertoxic chemicals are extremely potent; for some, a few micrograms (millionths of a gram—an amount invisible to the naked eye) make a lethal dose. These materials aren't all synthetic. One of the most toxic chemicals known, for instance, is ricin, a protein found in castor bean seeds. It is so poisonous that 0.3 billionths of a gram given intravenously will kill a mouse. If aspirin were this toxic for humans, a single tablet, divided evenly, could kill 1 million people.

Many carcinogens, mutagens, and teratogens are dangerous at levels far below their direct toxic effect because abnormal cell growth exerts a kind of biological amplification. A single cell,

perhaps altered by a molecular event, such as methylation, can multiply into millions of tumor cells or an entire organism. Just as there are different levels of direct toxicity, however, there are different degrees of carcinogenicity, mutagenicity, and teratogenicity. Methanesulfonic acid, for instance, is highly carcinogenic, while the sweetener saccharin is a possible carcinogen whose effects may be vanishingly small.

## Acute versus chronic doses and effects

Most of the toxic effects that we have discussed so far have been **acute effects**. That is, they are caused by a single exposure to the threat and result in an immediate health crisis. Often, if the individual experiencing an acute reaction survives this immediate crisis, the effects are reversible. **Chronic effects**, on the other hand, are long-lasting, perhaps even permanent. A chronic effect can result from a single dose of a very toxic substance, or it can be the result of a continuous or repeated sublethal exposure.

We also describe long-lasting exposures as chronic, although their effects may or may not persist after the toxic agent is removed. It usually is difficult to assess the specific health risks of chronic exposures because other factors, such as aging or normal diseases, act simultaneously with the factor under study. It often requires very large populations of experimental animals to obtain statistically significant results for low-level chronic exposures. Toxicologists talk about "megarat" experiments in which it might take a million rats to determine the health risks of some supertoxic chemicals at very low doses. Such an experiment would be terribly expensive for even a single chemical, let alone for the thousands of chemicals and factors suspected of being dangerous.

An alternative to enormous studies involving millions of animals is to give massive amounts—usually the maximum tolerable dose—of a compound being studied to a smaller number of individuals and then to extrapolate what the effects of lower doses might have been. This is a controversial approach because it is not clear that responses to toxics are linear or uniform across a wide range of doses.

Figure 8.15 shows three possible results from low doses of a toxic material. Curve (a) shows a baseline level of response in the population, even at zero dose. This suggests that some other factor

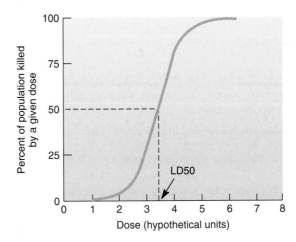

**Figure 8.14** Cumulative population response to increasing doses of a toxin. The LD50 is the dose that is lethal to half the population.

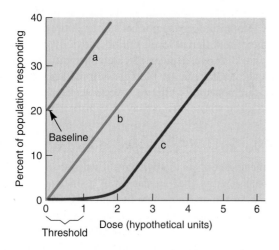

**Figure 8.15** Three possible dose-response curves at low doses. (a) Some individuals respond, even at zero dose, indicating that some other factor must be involved. (b) Response is linear down to the lowest possible dose. (c) Threshold must be passed before any response is seen.

in the environment also causes this response. Curve (b) shows a straight-line relationship from the highest doses to zero exposure. Many carcinogens and mutagens show this kind of response. Any exposure to such agents, no matter how small, carries some risks. Curve (c) shows a threshold for the response where some minimal dose is necessary before any effect can be observed. This generally suggests the presence of a defense mechanism that prevents the toxin from reaching its target in an active form or repairs the damage that the toxic causes. Low levels of exposure to the material in question may have no deleterious effects, and it might not be necessary to try to keep exposures to zero.

Which, if any, environmental health hazards have thresholds is an important but difficult question. The 1958 Delaney Clause to the U.S. Food and Drug Act forbids the addition of any amount of known carcinogens to food and drugs, based on the assumption that any exposure to these substances represents unacceptable risks. This standard was replaced in 1996 by a "no reasonable harm" requirement, defined as less than one cancer for every million people exposed over a lifetime. This change was supported by a report from the National Academy of Sciences concluding that synthetic chemicals in our diet are unlikely to represent an appreciable cancer risk. We'll discuss risk analysis in section 8.6.

## Detectable levels aren't always dangerous

You may have seen or heard dire warnings about toxic materials detected in samples of air, water, or food. A typical headline announced recently that 23 pesticides were found in 16 food samples. What does that mean? The implication seems to be that any amount of dangerous materials is unacceptable and that counting the numbers of compounds detected is a reliable way to establish danger. We have seen, however, that the dose makes the poison. It matters not only what is there but also how much, where it's located, how accessible it is, and who's exposed. At some level, the mere presence of a substance is insignificant.

Noxious materials may seem to be more widespread now than in the past, and this is surely a valid perception for many

substances (fig. 8.16). The daily reports we hear of new chemicals found in new places, however, are also due, in part, to our more sensitive measuring techniques. Twenty years ago, parts per million were generally the limits of detection for most materials. Anything below that amount was often reported as "zero" or "absent," rather than more accurately as "undetected." A decade ago, new machines and techniques were developed to measure parts per billion. Suddenly, substances were found where none had been suspected. Now we can detect parts per trillion or even parts per quadrillion in some cases. Increasingly sophisticated measuring capabilities may lead us to believe that toxic materials have become more prevalent. In fact, our environment may be no more dangerous; we're just better at finding trace amounts.

What accounts for the seemingly enormous increase in conditions, such as asthma, autism, food allergies, and behavioral disorders in American children? Is this evidence for higher levels of environmental pollutants or merely, overdiagnosis or increased public paranoia? Perhaps these conditions always existed but weren't so often given labels. In one surprising study, the only factor that appeared to correlate with increased childhood autism was the educational level of the parents. And how can it be that if asthma is caused by air pollution or other environmental contaminants, the disease is almost unknown in China, where conditions are far worse than in America? One interesting suggestion is that when we aren't exposed to common pathogens early in life, our immune systems began to attack normal tissues and organs. Clearly, humans are complex organisms and we still have much to learn about our interactions with toxins and our environment.

## Low doses can have variable effects

A complication in assessing risk is that the effects of low doses of some toxics and health hazards can be nonlinear. They may be either more or less dangerous than would be predicted from exposure to higher doses. For example, low doses of DHEP suppress activity of an enzyme essential for rat brain development. This is

**Figure 8.16** "Do you want to stop reading those ingredients while we're trying to eat?" *Source:* Reprinted with permission of the *Star-Tribune*, Minneapolis-St. Paul.

surprising because higher doses stimulated this enzyme. Thus, low doses can be more damaging to brain development than expected.

On the other hand, very low amounts of radiation seem to be protective against certain cancers. This is perplexing, because ionizing radiation has long been recognized as a human carcinogen. It's thought now, however, that very low radiation exposure may stimulate DNA repair along with enzymes that destroy free radicals (atoms with unpaired, reactive electrons in their outer shells). Activating these repair mechanisms may defend us from other, unrelated hazards. These nonlinear effects are called **hormesis**.

Another complication is that some substances can have long-lasting effects on genetic expression. For example, researchers found that exposure of pregnant rats to certain chemicals can have effects not only on the exposed rats, but on their daughters and grand-daughters. A single dose given on a specific day in pregnancy can be expressed several generations later, even if those offspring have never been exposed to the chemical (see Exploring Science, below).

# EXPLORING Science

## The Epigenome

Could your diet, behavior, or environment affect the lives of your children or grandchildren? For a century or more, scientists assumed that the genes you receive from your parents irreversibly fix your destiny, and that factors, such as stress, habits, toxic exposure or parenting have no effect on future generations.

Now, however, a series of startling discoveries are making us reexamine those ideas. Scientists are finding that a complex set of chemical markers and genetic switches—called the **epigenome**—consisting of DNA and its associated proteins and other small molecules, regulates gene function in ways that can affect numerous functions simultaneously and persist for multiple generations. "Epi" means above, and the epigenome is above ordinary genes in that it regulate their functions. Understanding how this system works helps us see how many environmental factors affect health, and may become useful in treating a variety of diseases.

One of the most striking epigenetic experiments was carried out a decade ago by researchers at Duke University. They were studying the affects of diet on an a strain of mice carrying a gene called "agouti" that makes them obese, yellow, and prone to cancer and diabetes. Starting just before conception, mother agouti mice were fed a diet rich in B vitamins (folic acid and B12). Amazingly, this simple dietary change resulted in baby mice that were sleek, brown, and healthy. The vitamins somehow had turned off the agouti gene in the offspring.

We know now that B vitamins as well as vegetables, such as onions, garlic, and beets, are methyl donors—that is, they can add a carbon atom and three hydrogens to proteins and nucleic acids. Attaching an extra methyl group can switch genes on or off by changing the way proteins and nucleic acids translate the DNA. Similarly, acetylating DNA (addition of an acetyl group: $CH_3CO$) can also either stimulate or inhibit gene expression. Both of these reactions are key methods of regulating gene expression.

These reactions involve not only the genes themselves, but also a huge set of what we once thought was useless, or junk DNA in chromosomes as well as a large amount of protein that once seemed to be merely packing material. We now know that both this extra DNA and the proteins around which genes are wrapped play vital roles in gene expression. And methylating or acetylating these proteins or nucleic acid sequences can have lasting effects on whole families of genes.

More remarkable is that changes in the epigenome can carry through multiple generations. In 2004, Michael Skinner, a geneticist at Washington State University was studying the effects on rats of exposure to a commonly used fungicide. He found that male rats exposed in utero had lower sperm counts later in life. It only took a single exposure to cause this effect. Amazingly, the effect lasted for at least four generations even though those subsequent offspring were never exposed to the fungicide. Somehow, the changes in the switching system can be passed from one generation to another along with the DNA it controls.

The way a mother rodent nurtures her young also can cause changes in methylation patterns in her babies' brains that are somewhat like the prenatal vitamins and nutrients that affected the agouti gene. It's thought that licking and grooming activate serotonin receptors that turn on genes to reduce stress responses, resulting in profound brain changes. In

Agouti mice (*left*) have a gene that makes them obese, yellow, and prone to cancer and diabetes. If mother agouti mice are given B vitamins during pregnancy, the gene is turned off and their babies are sleek, brown, and healthy (right). Amazingly, this genetic change lasts for several generations before the gene resumes its deleterious effects "sleek, brown, and healthy."

*Continued—*

*Continued—*

another study, rats given extra attention, diet, and mental stimulation (toys) did better at memory tests than did environmentally deprived controls. Altered methylation patterns in the hippocampus—the part of the brain that controls memory—were detected in both these cases. Subsequent generations maintained this methylation pattern.

Epigenetic effects have also been found in humans. One of the most compelling studies involved comparison of two centuries of health records, climate, and food supply in a remote village in northern Sweden. The village of Overkalix was so isolated that when bad weather caused crop failures, famine struck everyone. In good years, on the other hand, there was plenty of food and people stuffed themselves. A remarkable pattern emerged. When other social factors were factored in, grandfathers who were pre-teens during lean years had grandsons who lived an amazing 32 years longer than those whose grandfathers had gorged themselves as pre-teens. Similarly, women whose mothers had an access to a rich diet while they were pregnant were much more likely to have daughters and

granddaughters with health problems and shortened lives.

In an another surprising human health study, researchers found, in a long-term analysis of couples in Bristol, England, that fathers who started smoking before they were eleven years old (just as they were starting puberty and sperm formation was beginning) were much more likely to have sons and grandsons who were overweight and who lived significantly shortened lives than those of non-smokers. Both these results are attributed to epigenetic effects.

A wide variety of factors can cause epigenetic changes. Smoking, for example, leaves a host of persistent methylation markers in your DNA. So does exposure to a number of pesticides, toxics, drugs, and stressors. At the same time, polyphenols in green tea and deeply colored fruit, B vitamins, as well as healthy foods, such as garlic, onions, and turmeric, can help prevent deleterious methylations. Not surprisingly, epigenetic changes are implicated in many cancers, including colon, prostate, breast, and blood. This may

explain many confusing cases in which our environment seems to have long-lasting effects on health and development that can't be explained by ordinary metabolic effects.

Unlike mutations, epigenetic changes aren't permanent. Eventually the epigenome returns to normal if the exposure isn't repeated. This makes them candidates for drug therapy. Currently the U.S. Food and Drug Administration has approved two drugs, Vidaza and Dacogen, that inhibit methylation and are used to treat a precursor to leukemia. Another drug, Zolinza, which enhances acetylation, is approved to treat another form of leukemia. Dozens of other drugs that may treat a variety of diseases including rheumatoid arthritis, neurodegenerative diseases, and diabetes are under development.

So, your diet, behavior, and environment can have a much stronger impact on both your health and that of your descendents than we previously understood. What you ate, drank, smoked, or did last night may have profound effects on future generations.

This effect doesn't require a permanent mutation in genes, but it can result in changes, both positive and negative, in expression of whole groups of critical genes over multiple generations. It also can have different outcomes in variants of the same gene. Thus, exposure to a particular toxin could be very harmful to you but have no detectable effects in someone who has slightly different forms of the same genes. This may explain why, in a group of people exposed to the same carcinogen, some will get cancer while others don't. Or it could explain why a particular diet protects the health of some people but not others. As scientists are increasing our knowledge of this intricate network of switches and controls, they're helping explain much about our environment and health.

# 8.6 Risk Assessment and Acceptance

Even if we know with some certainty how toxic a specific chemical is in laboratory tests, it's still difficult to determine **risk** (the probability of harm multiplied by the probability of exposure) if that chemical is released into the environment. As we have seen, many factors complicate the movement and fate of chemicals both around us and within our bodies. Furthermore, public perception

of relative dangers from environmental hazards can be skewed so that some risks seem much more important than others.

## Our perception of risks isn't always rational

A number of factors influence how we perceive relative risks associated with different situations.

- People with social, political, or economic interests—including environmentalists—tend to downplay certain risks and emphasize others that suit their own agendas. We do this individually as well, building up the dangers of things that don't benefit us, while diminishing or ignoring the negative aspects of activities we enjoy or profit from.

- Most people have difficulty understanding and believing probabilities. We feel that there must be patterns and connections in events, even though statistical theory says otherwise. If the coin turned up heads last time, we feel certain that it will turn up tails next time. In the same way, it is difficult to understand the meaning of a 1-in-10,000 risk of being poisoned by a chemical.

- Our personal experiences often are misleading. When we have not personally experienced a bad outcome, we feel it is more rare and unlikely to occur than it actually may be. Furthermore, the anxieties generated by life's gambles make us want to deny uncertainty and to misjudge many risks (fig. 8.17).

- We have an exaggerated view of our own abilities to control our fate. We generally consider ourselves above-average drivers, safer than most when using appliances or power tools, and less likely than others to suffer medical problems, such as heart attacks. People often feel they can avoid hazards because they are wiser or luckier than others.

- News media give us a biased perspective on the frequency of certain kinds of health hazards, overreporting some accidents or diseases, while downplaying or underreporting others. Sensational, gory, or especially frightful causes of death, such as murders, plane crashes, fires, or terrible accidents, receive a disproportionate amount of attention in the public media. Heart disease, cancer, and stroke kill nearly 15 times as many people in the United States as do accidents and 75 times as many people as do homicides, but the emphasis placed by the media on accidents and homicides is nearly inversely proportional to their relative frequency, compared with either cardiovascular disease or cancer. This gives us an inaccurate picture of the real risks to which we are exposed.

- We tend to have an irrational fear or distrust of certain technologies or activities that leads us to overestimate their dangers. Nuclear power, for instance, is viewed as very risky, while coal-burning power plants seem to be familiar and relatively benign; in fact, coal mining, shipping, and combustion cause an estimated 10,000 deaths each year in the United States, compared with none known so far for nuclear power generation. An old, familiar technology seems safer and more acceptable than does a new, unknown one.

- Alarmist myths and fallacies spread through society, often fueled by xenophobia, politics, or religion. For example, the World Health Organization campaign to eradicate polio worldwide has been thwarted by religious leaders in northern Nigeria—the last country where the disease remains widespread—who claim that oral vaccination is a U.S. plot to spread AIDS or infertility among Muslims.

## How much risk is acceptable?

How much is it worth to minimize and avoid exposure to certain risks? Most people will tolerate a higher probability of occurrence of

**Figure 8.17** How dangerous are the things we choose to do? Many parents regard motorcycles as extremely risky, while many students—especially males—believe the risks (which are about the same as your chances of dying from surgery or other medical care) are acceptable. Perhaps the more important question is whether the benefits outweigh the risks.

an event if the harm caused by that event is low. Conversely, harm of greater severity is acceptable only at low levels of frequency. A 1-in-10,000 chance of being killed might be of more concern to you than a 1-in-100 chance of being injured. For most people, a 1 in 100,000 chance of dying from some event or some factor is a threshold for changing what they do. That is, if the chance of death is less than 1 in 100,000, we are not likely to be worried enough to change our ways. If the risk is greater, we will probably do something about it. The Environmental Protection Agency generally assumes that a risk of 1 in 1 million is acceptable for most environmental hazards. Critics of this policy ask, acceptable to whom?

For activities that we enjoy or find profitable, we are often willing to accept far greater risks than this general threshold. Conversely, for risks that benefit someone else, we demand far higher protection. For instance, your chance of dying in a motor vehicle accident in any given year are about 1 in 5,000, but that doesn't deter many people from riding in automobiles. Your chances of dying from lung cancer if you smoke one pack of cigarettes per day are about 1 in 1,000. By comparison, the risk from drinking water with the EPA limit of trichloroethylene is about 2 in 1 billion. Strangely, many people demand water with zero levels of trichloroethylene while continuing to smoke cigarettes.

More than 1 million Americans are diagnosed with skin cancer each year. Some of these cancers are lethal, and most are disfiguring, yet only one-third of teenagers routinely use sunscreen. Tanning beds more than double your chances of cancer, especially if you're young, but about 10 percent of all teenagers admit regularly using these devices.

Table 8.4 lists lifetime odds of dying from some leading causes. These are statistical averages, of course, and there clearly are differences in where one lives and how one behaves that affect the danger level of these activities. Although the average lifetime chance of dying in an automobile accident is 1 in 100, there are clearly things you can do—such as wearing a seat belt, driving defensively, and avoiding risky situations—to improve your odds. Still, it is interesting how we readily accept some risks while shunning others.

Our perception of relative risks is strongly affected by whether risks are known or unknown, whether we feel in control of the outcome, and how dreadful the results are. Risks that are unknown or unpredictable and results that are particularly gruesome or disgusting seem far worse than those that are familiar and socially acceptable.

Studies of public risk perception show that most people react more to emotion than to statistics. We go to great lengths to avoid some dangers while gladly accepting others. Factors that are involuntary, unfamiliar, undetectable to those exposed or catastrophic; those that have delayed effects; and those that are a threat to future generations are especially feared. Factors that are voluntary, familiar,

| Table 8.4 | Lifetime Chances of Dying in the United States | |
| --- | --- | --- |
| **Source** | **Odds (1 in ×)** | |
| Heart disease | 2 | |
| Cancer | 3 | |
| Smoking | 4 | |
| Lung disease | 15 | |
| Pneumonia | 30 | |
| Automobile accident | 100 | |
| Suicide | 100 | |
| Falls | 200 | |
| Firearms | 200 | |
| Fires | 1,000 | |
| Airplane accident | 5,000 | |
| Jumping from high places | 6,000 | |
| Drowning | 10,000 | |
| Lightning | 56,000 | |
| Hornets, wasps, bees | 76,000 | |
| Dog bite | 230,000 | |
| Poisonous snakes, spiders | 700,000 | |
| Botulism | 1 million | |
| Falling space debris | 5 million | |
| Drinking water with EPA limit of trichloroethylene | 10 million | |

*Source:* Data from U.S. National Safety Council, 2003.

## Active Learning

### Calculating Probabilities

You can calculate the statistical danger of a risky activity by multiplying the probability of danger by the frequency of the activity. For example, in the United States, 1 person in 3 will be injured in a car accident in their lifetime (so the probability of injury is 1 per 3 persons, or $^1/_3$). In a population of 30 car-riding people, the cumulative risk of injury is 30 people × (1 injury/3 people) = 10 injuries over 30 lifetimes.

1. If the average person takes 50,000 trips in a lifetime, and the accident risk is $^1/_3$ per lifetime, what is the probability of an accident per trip?

2. If you have been riding safely for 20 years, what is the probability of an accident during your next trip?

*Answers:* 1. Probability of injury per trip = (1 injury/3 lifetimes) × (1 lifetime/50,000 trips) = 1 injury/150,000 trips. 2. 1 in 150,000. Statistically, you have the same chance each time.

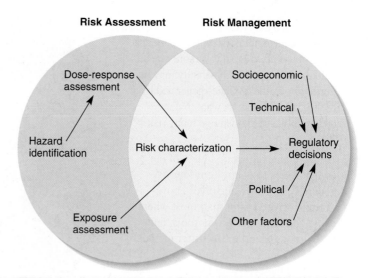

**Figure 8.18** Risk assessment organizes and analyzes data to determine relative risk. Risk management sets priorities and evaluates relevant factors to make regulatory decisions.

nuclear energy, or genetic engineering, the latter group preoccupies us far more than the former.

## 8.7 Establishing Public Policy

Risk management combines principles of environmental health and toxicology with regulatory decisions based on socioeconomic, technical, and political considerations (fig. 8.18). The biggest problem in making regulatory decisions is that we are usually exposed to many sources of harm, often unknowingly. It is difficult to separate the effects of all these different hazards and to evaluate their risks accurately, especially when the exposures are near the threshold of measurement and response. In spite of often vague and contradictory data, public policymakers must make decisions.

The struggle over whether to vaccinate children against common illnesses is a good example of the difficulties in risk assessment. In 1998, a British physician published a paper suggesting that the measles, mumps, and rubella (MMR) vaccine is linked to autism. In 2010 the U.K. General Medical Council found the author of that study guilty of "dishonesty and misleading conduct" for failing to disclose his personal interest in this research and scientific and ethical errors led to retraction of the original paper by the *Lancet*. At least 20 subsequent studies have failed to find any link between vaccines and autism, but none of that scientific evidence is reassuring to thousands of angry and frightened parents who demand answers for why their children are autistic. Many of them remain convinced that vaccines cause this distressing condition and they refuse to allow their children to be vaccinated. Physicians argue that this is a danger not only to the children but also to the population at large, which is at risk from epidemics when there's a large pool of nonimmune children. Nevertheless, the absence of a clear, convincing explanation for what does cause autism simply fuels many people's suspicions. This is a good example of the power of anecdotal evidence and personal bias versus scientific evidence.

detectable, or immediate cause less anxiety. Even though the actual number of deaths from automobile accidents, smoking, or alcohol, for instance, is thousands of times greater than those from pesticides,

In setting standards for environmental toxics, we need to consider (1) combined effects of exposure to many different sources of damage, (2) different sensitivities of members of the population, and (3) effects of chronic as well as acute exposures. Some people argue that pollution levels should be set at the highest amount that does *not* cause measurable effects. Others demand that pollution be reduced to zero if possible, or as low as is technologically feasible. It may not be reasonable to demand that we be protected from every potentially harmful contaminant in our environment, no matter how small the risk. As we have seen, our bodies have mechanisms that enable us to avoid or repair many kinds of damage, so that most of us can withstand a minimal level of exposure without harm.

On the other hand, each challenge to our cells by toxic substances represents stress on our bodies. Although each individual stress may not be life-threatening, the cumulative effects of all the environmental stresses, both natural and human-caused, to which we are exposed may seriously shorten or restrict our lives. Furthermore, some individuals in any population are more susceptible to those stresses than others. Should we set pollution standards so that no one is adversely affected, even the most sensitive individuals, or should the acceptable level of risk be based on the average member of the population?

| Table 8.5 | Relative Risks to Human Welfare |
|---|
| **Relatively High-Risk Problems** |
| Habitat alteration and destruction |
| Species extinction and loss of biological diversity |
| Stratospheric ozone depletion |
| Global climate change |
| **Relatively Medium-Risk Problems** |
| Herbicides/pesticides |
| Toxins and pollutants in surface waters |
| Acid deposition |
| Airborne toxins |
| **Relatively Low-Risk Problems** |
| Oil spills |
| Groundwater pollution |
| Radionuclides |
| Thermal pollution |

*Source:* Data from U.S. Environmental Protection Agency.

Finally, policy decisions about hazardous and toxic materials also need to be based on information about how such materials affect the plants, animals, and other organisms that define and maintain our environment. In some cases, pollution can harm or destroy whole ecosystems with devastating effects on the life-supporting cycles on which we depend. In other cases, only the most sensitive species are threatened. Table 8.5 shows the Environmental Protection Agency's assessment of relative risks to human welfare. This ranking reflects a concern that our exclusive focus on reducing pollution to protect human health has neglected risks to natural ecological systems. While there have been many benefits from a case-by-case approach in which we evaluate the health risks of individual chemicals, we have often missed broader ecological problems that may be of greater ultimate importance.

## Conclusion

We have made marvelous progress in reducing some of the worst diseases that have long plagued humans. Smallpox is the first major disease to be completely eliminated. Guinea worms and polio are nearly eradicated worldwide; typhoid fever, cholera, yellow fever, tuberculosis, mumps, and other highly communicable diseases are rarely encountered in advanced countries. Childhood mortality has decreased 90 percent globally, and people almost everywhere are living twice as long, on average, as they did a century ago.

But the technological innovations and affluence that have diminished many terrible diseases, have also introduced new risks. Chronic conditions, such as cardiovascular disease, cancer, depression, dementia, diabetes, and traffic accidents, that once were confined to richer countries, now have become leading health problems nearly everywhere. Part of this change is that we no longer die at an early age of infectious disease, so we live long enough to develop the infirmities of old age. Another factor is that affluent lifestyles, lack of exercise, and unhealthy diets aggravate these chronic conditions.

New, emergent diseases are appearing at an increasing rate. With increased international travel, diseases can spread around the globe in a few days. Epidemiologists warn that the next deadly epidemic may be only a plane ride away. In addition, modern industry is introducing thousands of new chemical substances every year, most of which aren't studied thoroughly for long-term health effects. Endocrine disrupters, neurotoxics, carcinogens, mutagens, teratogens, and other toxics can have tragic outcomes. The effects of lead on children's mental development is an example of both how we have introduced materials with unintended consequences, and a success story of controlling a serious health risk. Many other industrial chemicals could be having similar harmful effects.

## Practice Quiz

1. Define the terms *health* and *disease*.
2. Name the five leading causes of global disease burden expected by 2020.
3. Define *emergent diseases* and give some recent examples.
4. What is *conservation medicine*?
5. What is the difference between toxic and hazardous? Give some examples of materials in each category.
6. What are *endocrine disrupters*, and why are they of concern?
7. What are *bioaccumulation* and *biomagnification*?
8. Why is atrazine a concern?
9. What is an *LD50*?
10. Distinguish between acute and chronic toxicity.

# Critical Thinking and Discussion Questions

Apply the principles you have learned in this chapter to discuss these questions with other students.

1. Is it ever possible to be completely healthy?

2. How much would be appropriate for wealthy countries to contribute to global health? Why should we do more than we do now? What's in it for us?

3. Why do we spend more money on heart diseases or cancer than childhood diseases?

4. Why do we tend to assume that natural chemicals are safe while industrial chemicals are evil? Is this correct?

5. In the list of reasons why people have a flawed perception of certain risks, do you see things that you or someone you know sometimes do?

6. Do you agree that 1 in 1 million risk of death is an acceptable risk? Notice that almost everything in table 8.4 carries a greater risk than this. Does this make you want to change your habits?

# Data Analysis | Graphing Multiple Variables

Is it possible to show relationships between two dependent variables on the same graph? Sometimes that's desirable when you want to make comparisons between them. The graph on page 204 does just that. It's a description of how people perceive different risks. We judge the severity of risks based on how familiar they are and how much control we have over our exposure.

- Take a look at the different risks in the figure. Make a list of about five that you consider most dangerous. Then list about five that you think are least dangerous.

- Do most of your most dangerous activities/items fall into one quadrant? What are the axes of the graph? Do the ideas on the axes help explain why you consider some activities more dangerous than others?

- Are there other factors that help explain why you consider certain activities dangerous and others relatively safe? What are those other factors? If you compare your list to other peoples' lists, are they similar or different?

On this graph, which represents attitudes of many people, the Y-axis represents how mysterious, unknown, or delayed the risk seems to be. Things that are unobservable, unknown to those exposed, delayed in their effects, and unfamiliar or unknown to science tend to be more greatly feared than those that are observable, known, immediate, familiar, and known to science. The X-axis represents a measure of dread, which combines how much control we feel we have over the risk, how terrible the results could potentially be, and how equitably the risks are distributed. The size of the symbol for each risk indicates the combined effect of these two variables.

Notice that things such as DNA technology or nuclear waste, which have high levels of both mystery and dread, tend to be regarded with the greatest fear, while familiar, voluntary, personally rewarding behaviors such as riding in automobiles or on bicycles, or drinking alcohol are thought to be relatively minor risks. Actuarial experts (statisticians who gather mortality data) would tell you that automobiles, bicycles, and alcohol have killed far more people (so far) than DNA technology or radioactive waste. But this isn't just a question of data. It's a reflection of how much we fear various risks. Notice that this is a kind of scatter plot mapping categories of data that have no temporal sequence. Still, you can draw some useful inferences from this sort of graphic presentation.

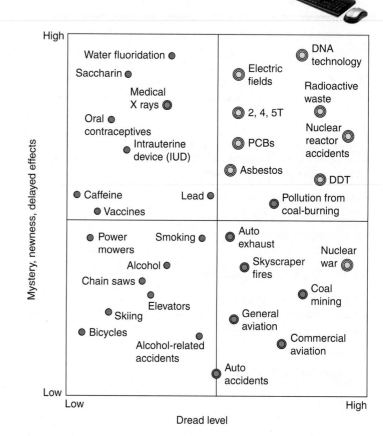

Public perception of risk depending on the familiarity, apparent potential for harm, and personal control over the risk. *Source:* Data from Slovic, Paul. 1987. Perception of Risk, *Science* 236 (4799):286–290.

For Additional Help in Studying This Chapter, please visit our website at www.mhhe.com/cunningham6e. You will find practice quizzes, key terms, answers to end of chapter questions, additional case studies, an extensive reading list, and Google Earth™ mapping quizzes.

# Air: Climate and Pollution

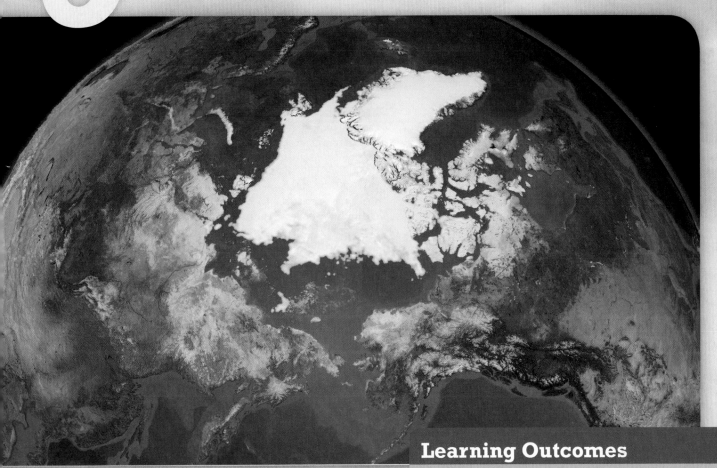

Arctic sea ice is disappearing at an accelerating rate. The 2007 summer extent shown here was the lowest on record at the time. *Source:* NASA.

*The next decade is critical. If emissions do not peak by around 2020, . . . the needed 50% reduction by 2050 will become much more costly. In fact, the opportunity may be lost completely.*

— INTERNATIONAL ENERGY AGENCY, 2010

## Learning Outcomes

*After studying this chapter, you should be able to answer the following questions:*

- What is the difference between the troposphere and stratosphere?
- Explain the greenhouse effect and how it is changing our climate.
- How do we know the cause of recent climate change?
- What are some strategies for minimizing global climate change?
- In what ways can air pollution affect human health?
- What are the main sources and effects of air pollution?
- Has world air quality been getting better or worse? Why?

# CASE STUDY

## When Wedges Do More than Silver Bullets

I f your parents sometimes tell you how much deeper the snow was when they were young or how much longer winters were, you might think they're just telling tales. Increasing volumes of data, however, suggest they're telling the truth. Eleven of the 12 warmest years on record occurred within the past 12 years, and temperatures are about 0.5–1°C higher than they've been in centuries. All this is consistent with observed increases in greenhouse gases since the beginning of the industrial era (fig. 9.1).

An average difference of 1°C or so (about 2°F) might seem trivial, but the difference between the last glacial maximum and today is only about 5°C. A change of 1°C might translate to more crop pests and weeds that survive winters farther north. Slight warming could dry soil enough to force farmers to irrigate crops more, where irrigation is possible, or to abandon farms in poor countries, where migrants to teeming cities already suffer from poverty and violence. Moreover, the conclusion of climate scientists today is that if we don't work in the next few years to reduce our carbon output, melting permafrost and ice caps will set us on a path for irreversible and unavoidable increases of 5–7°C within the coming century, with sea-level rises of 1 m or more by 2100.

Images of shrinking Arctic sea ice and disintegrating Antarctic ice shelves have caught much public attention. In California and other western states where cities rely on snowmelt in the mountains for water, the specter of declining snowpack is sobering up a lot of voters and politicians alike. But still we have a hard time getting around to finding new policies to reduce greenhouse gas emissions.

Among climate scientists, there is no longer any debate about whether humans are causing climate change or whether that change is likely to be extraordinarily costly, in both human and economic terms. Debates do continue about details: how fast sea levels are likely to rise, or where drought will be worst, or about fine-tuning of climate models.

Among policymakers, it's another matter. Politicians are responsible for establishing new rules that will reduce our carbon output, but many still have a hard time connecting the idea of climate change to recent increases in forest fires, drought, water shortages, heat waves, and pest outbreaks. For those that do understand climate change, what policies can they suggest that won't get them thrown out of office? Climate changes are gradual, proceeding over decades, so it's hard to get the public focused on remedies today.

Many politicians have hoped for a silver bullet—a technology that will fix the problem all at once—perhaps nuclear fusion, or space-based solar energy, or giant mirrors that would reflect solar energy away from the earth's surface. While these are intriguing ideas, all are still in the distant future, and climate scientists are warning us that action now is critical to avoid disaster.

### Wedges Can Work Now

To help us out of this quagmire of indecision, a Princeton ecologist and an engineer have proposed a completely different approach to imagining alternatives. Their approach has come to be called wedge analysis, or breaking down a large problem into smaller, bite-size pieces. By calculating the contribution of each wedge, we can add them up, see the magnitude of their collective effect, and decide that it's worth trying to move forward. Stephen Pacala and Robert Socolow, of Princeton University's Climate Mitigation Initiative, introduced the wedge idea in a 2004 article in the journal *Science*. Their core idea was that currently available technologies—efficient vehicles, buildings, power plants, alternative fuels—could solve our problems today, if we just take them seriously. Future technologies, no matter how brilliant, can do nothing for us right now. They have further honed their ideas in subsequent papers, and others have picked up the wedge idea to envision strategies for problems such as reducing transportation energy use, or reducing water consumption.

The *Science* paper focuses on $CO_2$ production, but the authors point out that similar analysis could be done for other greenhouse gases. Pacala and Socolow's paper described three possible trajectories in our carbon emissions. The "business as usual" scenario follows the current pattern of constantly increasing $CO_2$ output. This trajectory heads toward at tripling of $CO_2$ by 2100, accompanied by temperature increases of around 5°C (9°F) and a sea-level rise of 0.5–1 m (fig. 9.2).

A second trajectory is a "stabilization scenario." In this scenario, we prevent further increases in $CO_2$ emissions, and we nearly double $CO_2$ in the atmosphere by 2100. Temperatures increase by about 2–3°C, and sea level rises by about 29–50 cm. A third trajectory is declining $CO_2$ emissions. To achieve stabilization, we need to reduce our annual carbon emissions by about 7 billion tons (or 7 gigatons, GT) per year within 50 years (fig. 9.2). To break down the problem into more

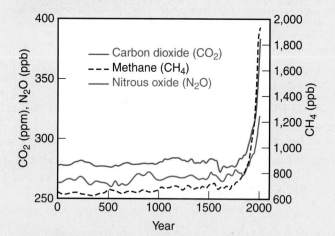

**Figure 9.1** Increases in concentrations of these gases since 1750 are due to human activities in the industrial era. Concentration units are parts per million (ppm) or parts per billion (ppb), indicating the number of molecules of the greenhouse gas per million or billion molecules of air. *Source:* USGS, 2009.

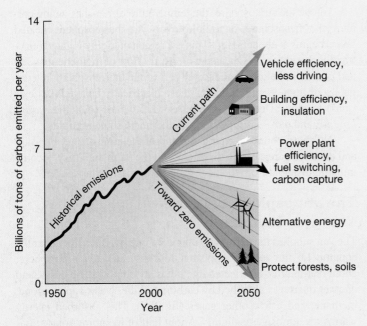

**Figure 9.2** We could stabilize or even reduce carbon emissions now if we focus on multiple modest strategies.

manageable parts, this 7 GT can be subdivided into seven wedges, each representing 1 GT of carbon we need to cut.

Cutting one of those gigatons could be accomplished by increasing fuel economy in our cars from 30 to 60 mpg. Another gigaton could be eliminated if we reduced reliance on cars (with more public transit or less suburban sprawl, for example) and cut driving from an average 10,000 miles to 5,000 miles per year. Better insulation and efficient appliances in our houses and office buildings would equal

another wedge. Increased efficiency in our coal power plants would equal another wedge.

These steps add up to 4/7 of the stabilization triangle, using currently available technologies. The remaining 3/7 can be accomplished by capturing and storing carbon at power plants, by changing the way power plants operate, and by reducing reliance on coal power. Another set of seven wedges, including alternative energy, preventing deforestation, and reducing soil loss, could put us on a trajectory to reduce our $CO_2$ emissions and prevent disastrous rates of climate change. Further details on the wedges are given later in this chapter.

The net effect of these strategies is likely to be economic gain, which contradicts many traditional fears of economists and politicians that we cannot afford climate mitigation. Many of the needed changes involve efficiency, which means long-term cost savings. Employment is likely to increase as new cars and appliances replace old ones, and as we insulate more buildings.

There are other potential benefits, too. Efficient cars will save household income. Cleaner power plants will reduce asthma and other respiratory illnesses, saving health care costs as well as improving quality of life. Less reliance on coal will reduce toxic mercury in our food chain, because coal burning is the largest single source of airborne mercury emissions.

In this chapter we'll examine the evidence for climate change and its consequences, as well as important issues in air pollution. To begin, we'll discuss what our climate is, and how it works.

For related resources, including Google Earth™ place marks that show locations where these issues can be seen, visit http://EnvironmentalScience-Cunningham.blogspot.com.

**Further Reading**

Pacala, S., and Socolow, R. 2004. Stabilization wedges: Solving the climate problem for the next 50 years with current technologies. *Science,* 305 (5686): 968–72.

# 9.1 What Is the Atmosphere?

Earth's atmosphere consists of gas molecules, relatively densely packed near the surface and thinning gradually to about 500 km (300 mi) above the earth's surface. In the lowest layer of the atmosphere, air moves ceaselessly, flowing, swirling, and continually redistributing heat and moisture from one part of the globe to another. The daily temperatures, wind, and precipitation that we call **weather** occur in the troposphere. Long-term temperatures and precipitation trends we refer to as **climate**.

The earliest atmosphere on earth probably consisted mainly of hydrogen and helium. Over billions of years, most of that hydrogen and helium diffused into space. Volcanic emissions added carbon, nitrogen, oxygen, sulfur, and other elements to the atmosphere. Virtually all of the molecular oxygen ($O_2$) we breathe was probably produced by photosynthesis in blue-green bacteria, algae, and green plants.

Clean, dry air is 78 percent nitrogen and almost 21 percent oxygen, with the remaining 1 percent composed of argon, carbon dioxide ($CO_2$), and a variety of other gases. Water vapor ($H_2O$ in gas

form) varies from near 0 to 4 percent, depending on air temperature and available moisture. Minute particles and liquid droplets—collectively called **aerosols**—also are suspended in the air. Atmospheric aerosols and water vapor play important roles in the earth's energy budget and in rain production.

The atmosphere has four distinct zones of contrasting temperature, due to differences in absorption of solar energy (fig. 9.3). The layer immediately adjacent to the earth's surface is called the **troposphere** (*tropein* means to turn or change, in Greek). Within the troposphere, air circulates in great vertical and horizontal **convection currents**, constantly redistributing heat and moisture around the globe (fig. 9.4). The troposphere ranges in depth from about 18 km (11 mi) over the equator to about 8 km (5 mi) over the poles, where air is cold and dense. Because gravity holds most air molecules close to the earth's surface, the troposphere is much denser than the other layers: it contains about 75 percent of the total mass of the atmosphere. Air temperature drops rapidly with increasing altitude in this layer, reaching about –60°C (–76°F) at the top of the troposphere.

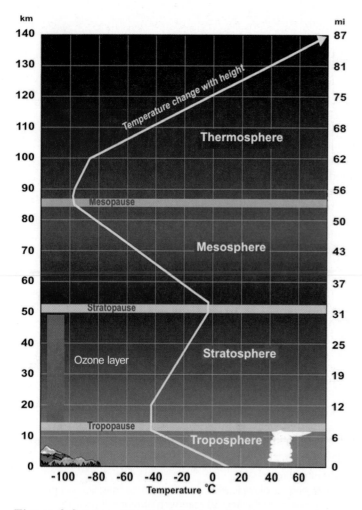

**Figure 9.3** Layers of the atmosphere vary in temperature and composition. Most weather happens in the troposphere. Stratospheric ozone is important for blocking ultraviolet solar energy. *Source:* National Weather Service: http://www.srh.noaa.gov/jetstream/atmos/atmprofile.htm.

A sudden reversal of this temperature gradient creates a boundary called the tropopause. This temperature boundary occurs because **ozone** ($O_3$) molecules in the stratosphere absorb solar energy. In particular, ozone absorbs ultraviolet (UV) radiation (wavelengths of 290–330 nm, see fig. 2.13). This absorbed energy makes the stratosphere warmer than the upper troposphere. Tropospheric air cannot continue to rise when it is cooler than the surrounding air, so there is little mixing across this boundary.

The **stratosphere** extends about 50 km (31 mi) out from the tropopause. It is far more dilute than the troposphere, but it has a similar composition—except that it has almost no water vapor and nearly 1,000 times more ozone.

Since UV radiation damages living tissues, UV absorption in the stratosphere is also essential for life on earth. Depletion of stratospheric ozone by chemical pollutants has been a major public health concern. Increased UV radiation reaching the earth's surface can increase skin cancer rates and damage biological communities. Fortunately, global cooperation to restrict key pollutants is beginning to reduce the loss of stratospheric ozone.

Unlike the troposphere, the stratosphere is relatively calm. There is so little mixing in the stratosphere that volcanic ash and human-caused contaminants can remain in suspension there for many years.

Above the stratosphere, the temperature diminishes again, creating the mesosphere, or middle layer. The thermosphere (heated layer) begins at about 50 km. This is a region of highly ionized (electrically charged) gases, heated by a steady flow of high-energy solar and cosmic radiation. In the lower part of the thermosphere, intense pulses of high-energy radiation cause electrically charged particles (ions) to glow. This phenomenon is what we know as the *aurora borealis* and *aurora australis*, or northern and southern lights.

No sharp boundary marks the end of the atmosphere. Pressure and density decrease with distance from the earth until they become indistinguishable from the near vacuum of interstellar space.

## The atmosphere captures energy selectively

The sun supplies the earth with abundant energy, especially near the equator. Of the solar energy that reaches the outer atmosphere, about one-quarter is reflected by clouds and atmospheric gases, and another quarter is absorbed by carbon dioxide, water vapor, ozone, methane, and a few other gases (fig. 9.5). This absorbed energy warms the atmosphere slightly. About half of incoming solar radiation (insolation) reaches the earth's surface. Most of this energy is in the form of light or infrared (heat) energy.

Some incoming solar energy is reflected by bright surfaces, such as snow, ice, and sand. The rest is absorbed by the earth's surface and by water. Surfaces that *reflect* energy have a high **albedo** (reflectivity). Fresh snow and dense clouds, for instance, can reflect as much as 85 to 90 percent of the light falling on them (table 9.1). Surfaces that absorb energy have a low albedo and generally appear dark. Black soil, asphalt pavement, and water, for example, have low albedo, with reflectivity as low as 3 to 5 percent.

Absorbed energy heats materials (such as an asphalt parking lot in summer), evaporates water, and provides the energy for photosynthesis

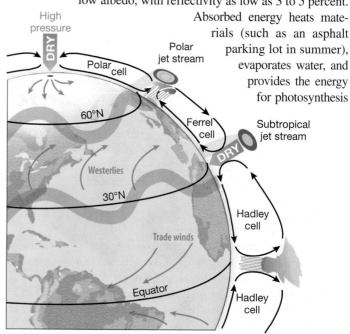

**Figure 9.4** Convection cells circulate air, moisture, and heat around the globe. Jet streams develop where cells meet, and surface winds result from convection. Convection cells expand and shift seasonally.

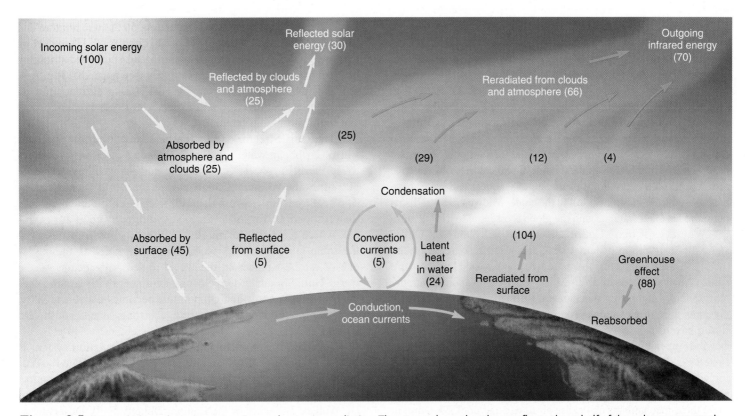

**Figure 9.5** Energy balance between incoming and outgoing radiation. The atmosphere absorbs or reflects about half of the solar energy reaching the earth. Most of the energy reemitted from the earth's surface is long-wave, infrared energy. Most of this infrared energy is absorbed by aerosols and gases in the atmosphere and is re-radiated toward the planet, keeping the surface much warmer than it would otherwise be. This is known as the greenhouse effect.

| Table 9.1 | Albedo (reflecticity) of Earth Surfaces |
|---|---|
| **Surface** | **Albedo (%)** |
| Fresh snow | 80–85 |
| Dense clouds | 70–90 |
| Water (low sun) | 50–80 |
| Sand | 20–30 |
| Forest | 5–10 |
| Water (sun overhead) | 5 |
| Dark soil | 3 |

in plants. Following the second law of thermodynamics, absorbed energy is gradually reemitted as lower-quality heat energy. The walls of a brick building, for example, absorb light (high-intensity energy) and remit that energy as heat (low-intensity energy).

The change in energy intensity is important because the gases that make up our atmosphere let light energy pass through—this is why it's bright during the day—but these gases absorb or reflect the lower-intensity heat energy that is re-emitted from the earth (fig. 9.5). Several trace gases in the atmosphere are especially effective at trapping reradiated heat energy. The most effective and abundant of these gases are water vapor ($H_2O$), carbon dioxide ($CO_2$), methane ($CH_4$), and nitrous oxide ($N_2O$).

If our atmosphere didn't capture all this reemitted heat energy, the earth's average surface temperature would be about 20°C (36°F) colder than it is now. Thus energy capture is necessary for liquid water on earth, and for life as we know it. The **"greenhouse effect"** is a common term to describe the capture of energy by gases in the atmosphere. Something like glass of a greenhouse, the atmosphere transmits sunlight but traps some heat inside. Also like a greenhouse, the atmosphere gradually lets that energy dissipate to space.

The balance of the rate of incoming energy and outgoing energy determines the temperature inside the greenhouse. The policy issue that faces us is that we are slowing the rate of heat loss, thus increasing heat storage in our "greenhouse." We are doing this by adding $CO_2$, $CH_4$, and $N_2O$ to the atmosphere at levels the earth has not seen since before the appearance of humans as a species. The question is whether we will be able to agree on changing this trend.

### Evaporated water stores and redistributes heat

Much of the incoming solar energy is used up in evaporating water. Every gram of evaporating water absorbs 580 calories of energy as it transforms from liquid to gas. Water vapor in the air stores that 580 calories per gram, and we call that stored heat **latent heat**. Later, when the water vapor condenses it releases 580 calories per gram.

Globally, this release produces huge amounts of energy, enough to power thunderstorms, hurricanes, and tornadoes. Imagine the sun shining on the Gulf of Mexico in the winter. Warm sunshine and plenty of water allow continuous evaporation that converts an immense amount of solar (light) energy into latent heat stored in evaporated water. Now imagine a wind blowing the humid air north from the Gulf toward Canada. The air cools as it rises and moves north. Eventually, cooling causes the water vapor to condense. Rain (or snow) falls as a consequence. Note that it is not only water that has moved from the Gulf to the Midwest: 580 calories of heat have also moved with every gram of moisture. The heat and water have now moved from the sunny Gulf to the colder Midwest. This redistribution of heat and water around the globe is essential to life on earth.

Why does it rain? Understanding this will help you understand the distribution of latent heat, and water resources, around the globe. Rain falls when there are two conditions: (1) a moisture source, such as an ocean, from which water can evaporate into the atmosphere; (2) a lifting mechanism. Lifting is important because air cools at high elevations. You may have observed this cooling if you have driven over a mountain pass. Sometimes air is lifted as winds push it over a mountain range; sometimes warm weather systems collide with cooler weather systems, and the warm air is forced up over the cooler air. Sometimes hot air, warmed near the earth's surface on a sunny day, rises in convection currents. Any of these three mechanisms can cause air to rise and cool. Moisture in the cooling air then condenses. We see the moisture falling as rain or snow.

Next time you watch the weather report, see if you can find references to these processes in predicted rain and snowfall.

## Ocean currents also redistribute heat

Warm and cold ocean currents strongly influence climate conditions on land. Surface ocean currents result from wind pushing on the ocean surface. As surface water moves, deep water wells up to replace it, creating deeper ocean currents.

Differences in water density—depending on the temperature and saltiness of the water—also drive ocean circulation. Huge cycling currents called gyres carry water north and south, redistributing heat from low latitudes to high latitudes (see appendix 3, p. A-4, global climate map). For example, the Alaska current, flowing from Alaska southward to California, keeps San Francisco cool and foggy during the summer.

The Gulf Stream, one of the best known currents, carries warm Caribbean water north past Canada's maritime provinces to northern Europe (fig. 9.6). This current is immense, some 800 times the volume of the Amazon, the world's largest river. The heat transported from the Gulf keeps Europe much warmer than it should be for its latitude. Stockholm, Sweden, for example, where temperatures rarely fall much below freezing, is at the same latitude as Churchill, Manitoba, which is famous as one of the best places in the world to see polar bears. As the warm Gulf Stream passes Scandinavia and swirls around Iceland, the water cools and evaporates, becomes dense and salty, and plunges downward, creating a strong, deep, southward current.

Together, this surface and deep-water circulation system is called the **thermohaline** (temperature and salinity-related) circulation, because both temperature and salt concentrations control the density of water, and contrasts in density drive its movement. Dr. Wallace Broecker of the Lamont Doherty Earth Observatory, who first described this great conveyor system, also found it can shut down suddenly. About 11,000 years ago, as the earth was warming at the end of the last ice age, cold glacial meltwater surged into the North Atlantic and interrupted the thermohaline circulation cycle. Europe was plunged into a cold period that lasted for 1,300 years. Temperatures may have changed dramatically in just a few years.

Could this happen again? Some climatologists suggest that melting of the Greenland ice sheet, which contains 10 percent of the globe's glacial ice, could cause sudden changes in ocean circulation.

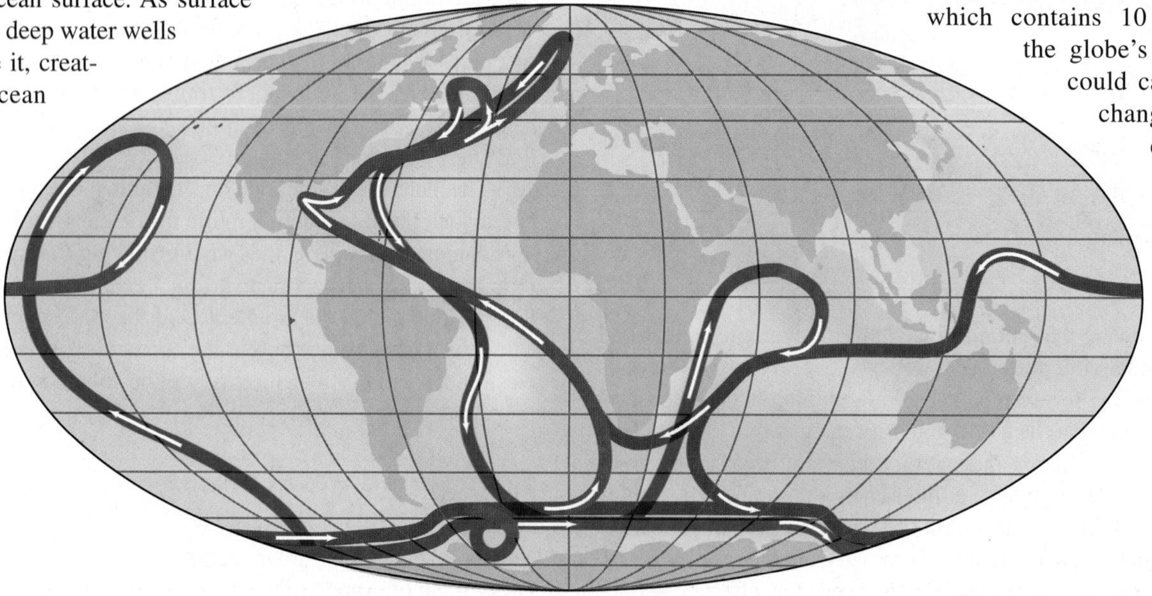

**Figure 9.6** Ocean currents act as a global conveyor system, redistributing warm and cold water around the globe. These currents moderate our climate. For example, the Gulf Stream keeps northern Europe much warmer than northern Canada. Ocean colors show salinity variation from low (*blue*) to high (*yellow*). *Source:* NASA.

# 9.2 Climate Changes Over Time

Climatologist Wallace Broeker has said that "climate is an angry beast, and we are poking it with sticks." He meant that we assume our climate is stable, but our thoughtless actions may be stirring it to sudden and dramatic changes. How stable is climate? That depends upon the time frame you consider. Over centuries and millennia, we know that climate shifts somewhat, but usually we expect little change on the scale of a human lifetime. The question now is whether that is a reasonable expectation. If climate does shift, how fast might it change, and what will those changes mean for the environmental systems on which we depend?

## Ice cores tell us about climate history

Every time it snows, small amounts of air are trapped in the snow layers. In Greenland and Antarctica and other places where cold is persistent, yearly snows slowly accumulate over the centuries. New layers compress lower layers into ice, but still tiny air bubbles remain, even thousands of meters deep into glacial ice. Each bubble is a tiny sample of the atmosphere at the time that snow fell.

Climatologists have discovered that by drilling deep into an ice sheet, they can extract ice cores, from which they can collect air-bubble samples. Samples taken every few centimeters show how the atmosphere has changed over time. Ice core records have revolutionized our understanding of climate history (fig. 9.7). We can now see how concentrations of atmospheric $CO_2$ have varied. We can detect ash layers and spikes in sulfate concentrations that record volcanic eruptions. Most important, we can look at isotopes of oxygen. In cold years, water molecules with slightly lighter oxygen atoms evaporate more easily than water with slightly heavier isotopes. Consequently, by looking at the proportions of heavier and lighter oxygen atoms, climatologists can reconstruct temperatures over time,

and plot temperature changes against $CO_2$ concentrations and other atmospheric components.

The first very long record was from the Vostok ice core, which reached 3,100 m into the Antarctic ice and which gives us a record of temperatures and atmospheric $CO_2$ over the past 420,000 years. A team of Russian scientists worked for 37 years at the Vostok site, about 1,000 km from the South Pole to extract this ice core. A similar core has been drilled from the Greenland ice sheet. More recently the European Project for Ice Coring in Antarctica (EPICA) has produced a record reaching back over 800,000 years (fig. 9.8). All these cores show that climate has varied dramatically over time but that there is a close correlation between atmospheric temperatures and $CO_2$ concentrations.

From these ice cores, we know that $CO_2$ concentrations have varied between 180 to 300 ppm (parts per million) in the past 800,000 years. Therefore we know that today's concentrations of approximately 390 ppm are about one-third higher than the earth has seen in nearly a million years. We also know that present temperatures are nearly as warm as any in the ice core record. Further warming in the coming decades is likely to exceed anything in the ice core records.

## What causes natural climatic swings?

Ice core records also show that there have been repeated climate changes over time. What causes these periodic (repeated) changes? Modest changes correspond to an 11-year cycle in the sun's intensity. About every 11 years there is a peak in incoming solar energy. More dramatic changes are associated with periodic shifts in the earth's orbit and tilt (fig. 9.9). These are known as the **Milankovitch cycles,** after the Serbian scientist Milutin Milankovitch, who first described them in the 1920s. There are three of these cycles: (1) the earth's elliptical orbit stretches and shortens in a 100,000-year cycle; (2) the earth's axis changes its angle of tilt in a 40,000-year cycle; (3) over a 26,000-year period, the axis wobbles like an out-of-balance spinning top. These variations seem to match banding patterns in sedimentary rocks.

**Figure 9.7** Dr. Mark Twickler, of the University of New Hampshire, holds a section of the 3,000 m Greenland ice sheet core, which records 250,000 years of climate history.

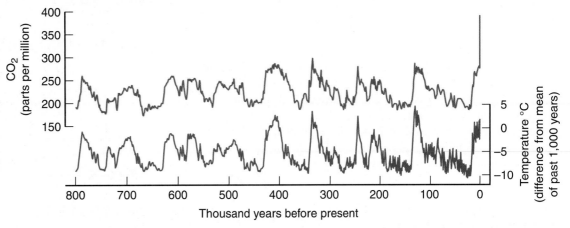

**Figure 9.8** Atmospheric $CO_2$ concentrations (*red line*) map very closely to temperatures (*blue, derived from oxygen isotopes*) in air bubbles from the Antarctic Vostok ice core. Temperatures lag behind the recent jump in $CO_2$, possibly because the ocean has been absorbing heat. In the 800,000-year EPICA ice core there is no evidence of temperatures or $CO_2$ higher than that anticipated within the coming century. *Sources:* UN Environment Programme; J. Jouzel et al. 2007. *EPICA Dome C Ice Core 800KYr Deuterium Data and Temperature Estimates.*

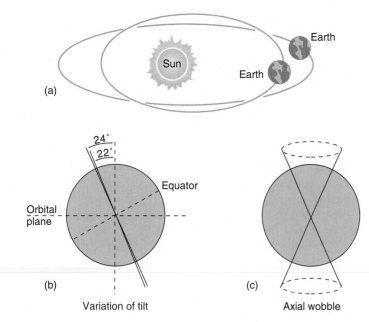

**Figure 9.9** Milankovitch cycles that may affect long-term climate conditions: (a) changes in the eccentricity of the earth's orbit, (b) shifting tilt of the axis, and (c) wobble of the earth.

The interplay of these cycles also seems to explain the glacial periods of the last 800,000 years, which you can see in the cold/warm cycles in figure 9.8. For example, when the wobble orients the north pole toward the sun in summer, then there is substantial summer warming and overall warming of the earth. When the wobble points toward the north pole away from the sun, then northern summers are cold, and there is global cooling. Similarly, when the axis tilts toward the sun, the poles warm, and when the axis is more parallel to the sun, the poles warm less.

Volcanic eruptions can cause sudden climate flips, but usually only for a few years. One exception was the explosion of Mount Toba in western Sumatra about 73,000 years ago. This was the largest volcanic cataclysm in the past 28 million years. The eruption ejected at least 2,800 km$^3$ of material, compared to only 1 km$^3$ emitted by Mount St. Helens in Washington State in 1980. Sulfuric acid and particulate material ejected into the atmosphere from Mount Toba are estimated to have dimmed incoming sunlight by 75 percent and to have cooled the whole planet by as much as 16°C for more than 160 years. In climate history, 160 years is a short time, however, and this was the largest eruption in 28 million years—so volcanoes are a notable but not dominant factor in climate trends.

## El Niño/Southern Oscillation has far-reaching effects

On the scale of years or decades, the climate also changes according to oscillations in the ocean and atmosphere. These coupled ocean-atmosphere oscillations occur in all the world's oceans, but the **El Niño/Southern Oscillation** (ENSO) is probably the most famous. ENSO affects weather throughout the Pacific and possibly farther, causing heavy monsoons or serious droughts.

The core of this system is a huge pool of warm surface water in the Pacific Ocean that sloshes slowly back and forth between Indonesia and South America like water in a giant bathtub. Most years, steady equatorial trade winds hold this pool in place in the western Pacific (fig. 9.10). From Southeast Asia to Australia, this concentration of warm equatorial water provides latent heat (water vapor) that drives strong upward convection (low pressure) in the atmosphere. Resulting heavy rains in Indonesia support dense tropical forests.

On the American side of the Pacific, cold upwelling water along the South American coast replaces westward-flowing surface waters. This upwelling deep water is rich in nutrients. It supports dense schools of anchovies and other fish. In the atmosphere, dry, sinking air in Mexico and California replaces the air moving steadily westward in the trade winds. Normally dry conditions in the southwestern United States are a result.

Every three to five years, for reasons that we don't fully understand, Indonesian convection (rising air currents) weaken, and westward wind and ocean currents fail. Warm surface water surges back east across the Pacific. Rains increase in the western United States and Mexico, and drought occurs in Indonesia. Upwelling currents that support South American fisheries also fail.

Fishermen in Peru were the first to notice irregular cycles of rising ocean temperatures because the fish disappeared when the water warmed. They named this event El Niño (Spanish for the Christ child) because they often occur around Christmas time. The counterpart to El Niño, when the eastern tropical Pacific cools, has come to be called La Niña (little girl).

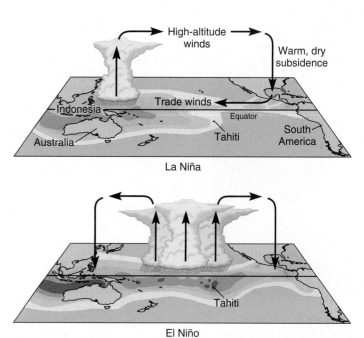

**Figure 9.10** The El Niño/La Niña/Southern Oscillation cycle. Every three to five years, surface trade winds that normally push warm water westward toward Indonesia weaken and allow this pool of water to flow eastward toward South America.

ENSO cycles have far-reaching effects. During an El Niño year, the northern jet stream—which is normally over Canada—splits and is drawn south over the United States. This pulls moist air from the Pacific and Gulf of Mexico inland, bringing intense storms and heavy rains from California across the Midwestern states. The intervening La Niña years bring hot, dry weather to the same areas. Oregon, Washington, and British Columbia, on the other hand, tend to have warm, sunny weather in El Niño years rather than their usual rain. Droughts in Australia and Indonesia during El Niño episodes cause disastrous crop failures and forest fires, including one in Borneo in 1983 that burned 3.3 million ha (8 million acres).

Some climatologists believe that El Niño conditions are becoming stronger or more frequent because of global climate change. There are signs that warm ocean-surface temperatures are spreading, which could contribute to El Niño strength or frequency. On the other hand, increased cloud cover over warmer oceans could reduce incoming solar energy intensity, and strong convection currents generated by these storms could pump heat into the stratosphere. This might have an overall cooling effect and act as a safety valve for global warming.

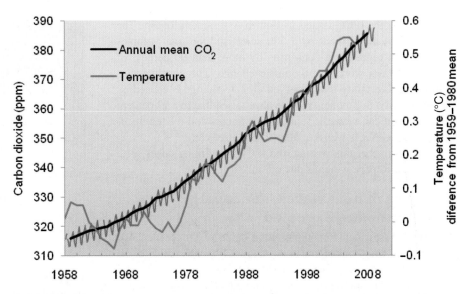

**Figure 9.11** Measurements of atmospheric $CO_2$ taken at the top of Mauna Loa, Hawaii, show an increase of 1.5–2.5 percent each year in recent years. For carbon dioxide, monthly mean (*red*) and annual mean (*black*) carbon dioxide are shown. Temperature represents 5-year mean anomalies. *Source: Data from NOAA Earth System Research Laboratory.*

## 9.3 How Do We Know the Climate Is Changing Faster than Usual?

Many scientists consider anthropogenic (human-caused) global climate change to be the most important environmental issue of our times. The possibility that humans might alter world climate is not a new idea. In 1859 John Tyndall measured the infrared absorption of various gases and described the greenhouse effect. In 1895, Svante Arrhenius, who subsequently received a Nobel Prize for his work in chemistry, predicted that $CO_2$ released by coal burning could cause global warming.

## Active Learning

### The IPCC's Fourth Assessment Report (AR4)

Open a web browser and find the IPCC's AR4 report at http://www.ipcc.ch. Because there are thousands of pages of PDF documents on this site, start with the Synthesis Report, which combines the findings of several working groups.

Find a figure in the synthesis report, and explain to your class what it tells you, using the ideas you have learned in this chapter and the explanations that accompany the figure. Be patient, and work with a colleague if that makes it easier. Present your explanation to the class, and see if they can understand your presentation.

The first evidence that human activities are increasing atmospheric $CO_2$ came from an observatory on top of the Mauna Loa volcano in Hawaii. The observatory was established in 1957 as part of an International Geophysical Year, and was intended to provide data on air chemistry in a remote, pristine environment. Surprisingly, measurements showed $CO_2$ levels increasing about 0.5 percent per year. Levels have risen from 315 ppm in 1958 to 388 ppm in 2009 (fig. 9.11). Note that this increase is shown in the graph as a jagged line. The line fluctuates because a majority of the world's land and vegetation are in the Northern Hemisphere. Every May a surge of plant growth extracts $CO_2$ from the atmosphere. Then, during the northern winter, levels rise again as respiration releases $CO_2$.

### Scientific consensus is clear

Because the climate is so complex, climate scientists worldwide have collaborated in collecting and sharing data, and in programming models to describe how the climate system works. Evidence shows regional variation in warming and cooling trends, and there are minor differences among models. But there is no disagreement about the direction of change among those who know the data and models. The evidence shows unequivocally, as in the Mauna Loa graph, that climate is changing, and the global average is warming because of increased retention of energy in the lower atmosphere.

The most comprehensive effort to describe the state of climate knowledge is that of the **Intergovernmental Panel on Climate Change (IPCC)**. As the name indicates, the IPCC is a collaboration among governments, with scientists and government representatives from 130 countries. The aim of the IPCC is to review scientific evidence on the causes and likely effects of human-caused climate change.

In 2007, the IPCC issued its Fourth Assessment Report. The result of 6 years of work by 2,500 scientists, the four volumes of the report represent a consensus by more than 90 percent of all the scientists working on climate change. The conclusion is a 90 percent certainty that observed climate change is caused by human activity. Subsequent reports have raised that to a 99 percent certainty. You can view the report, with figures and related documents, at the IPCC's website: http://www.ipcc.ch.

At the time of this writing, the IPCC is working on its Fifth Assessment Report, which is due out in 2013.

## Changes in heat waves, sea level, and storms are expected

The Fourth Assessment Report presents a variety of climate scenarios for predicted emissions of greenhouse gases. For each scenario, the IPCC modeled future emissions, starting in 2000. Scenarios differed in expected population growth, economic growth, energy conservation and efficiency, and adoption of greenhouse gas controls (or lack thereof). The different scenarios project a temperature increase by 2100 of 1–6°C (2–11°F) compared to temperatures at the end of the twentieth century (fig. 9.12, colored trend lines).

According to the IPCC, the "best estimate" for temperature rise is now about 2–4°C (about 3–8°F). A change of 4°C is just slightly less than the difference between now and the global temperature between now and the middle of the last glacial period, which was about 5°C cooler.

Observations since 2007 show that all the IPCC scenarios were too conservative. Greenhouse gas emissions, temperatures, sea level, and energy use have accelerated faster than projected by any of the IPCC projections (fig. 9.12, gray line). There is serious concern that increased heat stress and drought could cause increased deaths as well as crop failure and new waves of refugees from drought-stricken regions.

The IPCC projected in 2007 that sea levels should rise 17–57 cm (7–23 in.) by the end of this century. More recent estimates have raised this estimate to 1–2 m of sea-level rise by 2100. If recent rapid melting of polar ice sheets and Greenland glaciers continues, this change will be higher still. Complete melting of Greenland's ice sheet would raise sea level by more than 6 m (nearly 20 ft). This would flood most

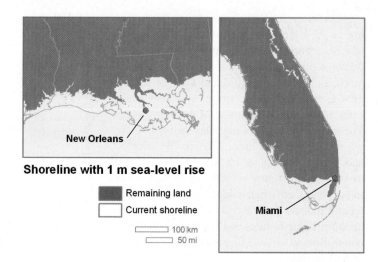

**Figure 9.13** Approximate change in land surface with the 1 m (3 ft) sea-level rise, which the IPCC says is possible by the year 2100. Some analysts expect a 2 m (6 ft) rise if no action is taken.

of Florida, a broad swath of the Gulf Coast, most of Manhattan Island, Shanghai, Hong Kong, Tokyo, Kolkata, Mumbai, and about two-thirds of the other largest cities in the world (fig. 9.13).

Tipping points are a concern for many climatologists. Projections indicate that if we don't control emissions in the next few decades we will pass points of no return in melting of permafrost, in the loss of Greenland's ice cap, and other factors.

The United States military is concerned about global warming. In 2007, the U.S. Military Advisory Board said, "Climate change, national security, and energy dependence are a related set of global challenges that will lead to tensions even in stable regions of the world." Some international aid agencies point to the civil war and accompanying humanitarian crisis in the Darfur region of Sudan. These problems are rooted in drought and food shortages caused by changing weather patterns that have led to years of below normal rainfall and desertification. Global climate change may bring more such conflicts along with the millions of refugees and tragic suffering that we see now in the African Sahel.

Policymakers have made little progress in finding solutions. Climate control is a classic free-rider problem, in which nobody wants to take action for fear that someone else might benefit from their sacrifices.

The question is whether the sacrifices need necessarily be as big as some policymakers suggest. Climate scientists point out that shifting our energy strategy from coal (our largest emitter of greenhouse gases and other pollutants) to wind, solar, and greater efficiency, could produce millions of new jobs and save billions in health care costs associated with coal burning.

## The main greenhouse gases are $CO_2$, $CH_4$, and $N_2O$

Since preindustrial times atmospheric concentrations of $CO_2$, methane ($CH_4$), and nitrous oxide ($N_2O$) have climbed by over 31 percent, 151 percent, and 17 percent, respectively (see fig. 9.1). Carbon dioxide is by far the most important of these because of its abundance and because it lasts for decades or centuries in the

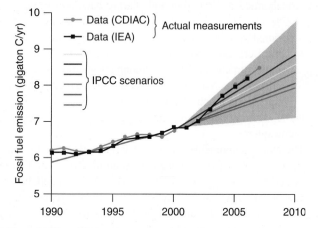

**Figure 9.12** Emissions scenarios and actual emissions observed after scenarios were modelled.

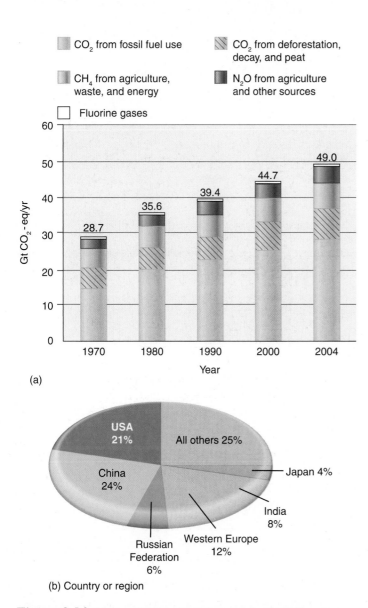

**Figure 9.14** (a) Contributions to global warming by different gases and activities and (b) by different countries. *Source:* Data from IPCC, 2007.

atmosphere (fig. 9.14a). Fossil fuel use is responsible for 80 percent of $CO_2$ emissions. Other sources include cement production and burning of forests and grasslands. Together these release more than 33 billion tons of $CO_2$ every year, on average (fig. 9.14a). About 3 billion tons of this excess carbon is taken up by terrestrial ecosystems, and around 2 billion tons are absorbed by the oceans, leaving an annual atmospheric increase of some 4 billion tons per year. If current trends continue, $CO_2$ concentrations could reach about 500 ppm (approaching twice the preindustrial level of 280 ppm) by the end of the twenty-first century.

Methane ($CH_4$) is much less abundant than $CO_2$, but it absorbs 23 times as much infrared energy per molecule and is accumulating in the atmosphere about twice as fast as $CO_2$. Methane can be produced anywhere organic matter decays without oxygen, especially under water. Natural gas, which is mainly $CH_4$, derives from ancient swamp material. Methane also is released by ruminant animals, wet-rice paddies, coal mines, landfills, wetlands, and pipeline leaks.

Reservoirs for hydroelectricity, usually promoted as a clean power source, are an important source of methane because they capture submerged, decaying vegetation. Philip Fearnside, an ecologist at Brazil's National Institute for Amazon Research, calculates that rotting vegetation in the reservoir behind the Cura-Una dam in Para Province emits so much carbon dioxide and methane every year that it causes three and a half times as much global warming as would generating the same amount of energy by burning fossil fuels. Tropical dams produce roughly 3 percent of global $CH_4$ emissions.

Nitrous oxide ($N_2O$) is produced mainly by chemical reactions between atmospheric N and O, which combine in the presence of heat from internal combustion engines. Other sources are burning of organic material and soil microbial activity.

Chlorofluorocarbons (CFCs) and other gases containing fluorine also store heat from infrared energy. CFC releases in developed countries have declined since many of their uses were banned, but increasing production in developing countries, such as China and India, remains a problem. Together, fluorine gases and $N_2O$ account for about 17 percent of human-caused global warming (fig. 9.14a).

The United States, with less than 5 percent of the world's population, releases one-quarter or more of the global $CO_2$ emissions. In 2007 China passed the United States in total $CO_2$ emissions (fig. 9.14b), but China's per capita emissions remain less than one-fifth those of the United States. India, with only one ton of $CO_2$ per person, has only one-twentieth as much as the United States. Oil-rich countries, such as the Middle Eastern oil emirates, have the highest per capita $CO_2$ output. Qatar, for example, produces more than three times as much $CO_2$ per person as Australia. But because these countries are small, their overall impact is relatively modest. To examine some of the larger per-capita emitters, see chapter 4, A Closer Look (p. 82).

Africa, in contrast, produces just over one ton of $CO_2$ per person per year. The lowest emissions in the world are in Chad, where per capita production is only one-thousandth that of the United States.

Some countries with high standards of living release relatively little $CO_2$. Sweden, for example, produces only 6.5 tons per person per year, or about one-third that of the United States. Remarkably, Sweden's adoption of renewable energy and conservation measures have reduced its carbon emissions by 40 percent over the past 30 years. At the same time, Sweden has seen dramatic increases in both personal income and quality of life measures.

Perhaps the biggest question in environmental science today is whether China and India, which now have the world's largest populations and also are among the fastest growing economies, will follow the development path of the United States and Canada or that of Sweden and Switzerland. Rising affluence in China has fueled a rapidly growing demand for energy, the vast majority of which comes from coal. China is now building at least one large coal-burning power plant per week. Another large source of $CO_2$ in China is cement production. Worldwide, cement manufacturing accounts for 4 percent of all $CO_2$ emissions. Chinese cement companies, stimulated by the world's largest building boom, now produce nearly half of the world's supply, and these plants are responsible for about 10 percent of all Chinese $CO_2$ emissions.

# Climate change in a nutshell: How does it work?

The greenhouse effect describes the heating of the earth's atmosphere. Roughly similar to a glass greenhouse, our atmosphere is transparent to light energy but is slow to release heat energy (or infrared radiation). In general, this "greenhouse effect" keeps average temperatures above freezing and supports life, but too much heating can be harmful in a greenhouse or in our atmosphere. Over the past 200 years, we have been emitting heat-absorbing gases ($CO_2$, $CH_4$, $N_2O$, CFCs) at a dramatically increased rate. As a consequence, more heat is retained in the atmosphere. Consequences include shorter winters, more heat waves, melting glaciers, declining polar ice, increased droughts in some areas, and increased storms in other areas.

## What are GHGs?

Greenhouses gases (GHGs) are molecules in the atmosphere that block long-wave energy from escaping to space. Water vapor is our most abundant GHG, but human activities have not caused as much change in atmospheric water vapor as other GHGs. We have dramatically increased $CO_2$, $CH_4$, $N_2O$, and other gases since industrialization began in about 1800.

These gases naturally keep our planet warm, but recent increases in GHGs are warming the planet enough to destabilize our economies and resource uses.

## Where do GHGs come from?

▼ Fossil fuel burning produces about 60% of GHG emissions, followed by deforestation (17%) and industrial and agricultural $N_2O$ (14%). Rice paddies, belching livestock, and tropical dams produce $CH_4$ (9% of emissions).

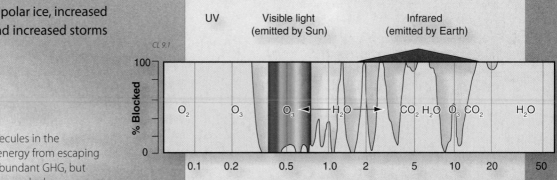

CL 9.1

UV | Visible light (emitted by Sun) | Infrared (emitted by Earth)

% Blocked — 100, 0

$O_2$   $O_3$   $O_3$ ← $H_2O$ → $CO_2$ $H_2O$ $O_3$ $CO_2$   $H_2O$

0.1   0.2   0.5   1.0   2   5   10   20   50

**Energy wavelengths (micrometers)**

Different molecules block different wavelengths. $CO_2$ and $H_2O$ especially prevent infrared energy from escaping the atmosphere.

| Gas | % of Climate Forcing* |
|---|---|
| Carbon dioxide ($CO_2$) | 60% |
| Methane ($CH_4$) | 20% |
| Nitrous oxide ($N_2O$) | 10% |
| Aerosols, other gases | 10% |

*Percentage of anthropogenic change: depends on (1) amount emitted, (2) energy- capture effectiveness, and (3) persistence in the atmosphere.

CL 9.3   CL 9.4   CL 9.5   CL 9.2   CL 9.10   CL 9.6   CL 9.9   CL 9.8   CL 9.7

$CO_2$

$N_2O$

$CH_4$

## Can You Explain:

1. What is a greenhouse gas? What are three main anthropogenic gases?

2. Explain the pink and blue bands in the maps at top right. What does the black line show?

3. Examine the New Orleans and Miami maps. Identify some strategies to protect these cities against rising sea levels and storm frequencies.

4. In this chapter, what are some strategies we have to reduce climate change?

## How do we know that recent climate changes are caused by human activity?

IPCC models show that observed temperature trends (black line ) do not fit mathematical models built *without* human-caused factors (blue shaded area shows range of model predictions). Observed trends do fit models built *with* factors such as fossil fuel use and forest clearing (pink shaded area). ▶

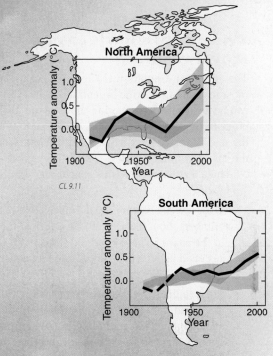

CL 9.11

### Hasn't the climate changed in geologic time?

Climate conditions have always changed, but never so dramatically since the beginning of civilization, and usually more slowly than now. Our current course is set for higher temperatures by 2100 than have occurred in at least 800,000 years. Current $CO_2$ concentrations are about 30 percent higher than at any time in the past 800,000 years, according to ice core data (▼). The rate of current climate change is also new: changes now occurring in 100 years took 800-5,000 years at the end of the ice ages.

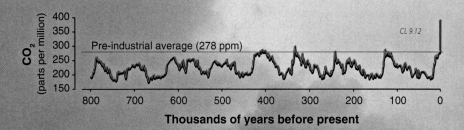

CL 9.12

## What effects are observed and expected?

**Disappearing ice:** Arctic ice, which helps stabilize climate, has declined by nearly half in summer. Mountain glaciers and snow, which provide water to about 75 percent of the western United States and over 1 billion people in Asia, are disappearing worldwide.

**Wildfire and pests:** Increased fire frequency and severity, aided by expanding parasites, is causing ecosystem change and even human mortality.

**Early spring:** Early onset of warm weather has led to early flowering, migrations, and hotter summers.

**Rising sea level:** We are committed to about 0.5 m rise. Without rapid $CO_2$ reductions, we may soon be committed to 2 m or more. ▶

**More storms:** More energetic atmospheric circulation is likely to bring more, heavier storms. Heavier rain and snow in the eastern U.S. may already be evident.

**Cumulative costs of climate change:** $5-90 trillion* by 2100, in damaged infrastructure, lost property values, health costs.

\* Pew Environment Group, 2010.

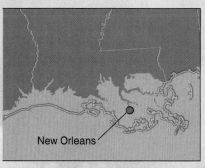

**Shoreline with 1 m sea-level rise**

- Remaining land
- Current shoreline

160 km (100 mi)

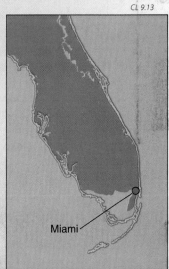

CL 9.13

### Observed changes are greater than models anticipated.

Observed GHG emissions (black lines) have accelerated faster than all the IPCC's projected scenarios (colored lines). Changes in temperature and sea level therefore may be greater than anticipated.

CL 9.14

## Are we committed to this path?

Not necessarily. If we adopt alternative plans, especially for energy production, transportation, and more efficient use of energy, we could constrain temperature change to only 2-4 degrees globally. We are committed to at least 20-40 cm of sea-level change, however, as the ocean continues to absorb excess heat from the atmosphere.

## Evidence of climate change is overwhelming

The American Geophysical Union, one of the nation's largest and most respected scientific organizations, has stated that, "As best as can be determined, the world is now warmer than it has been at any point in the last two millennia, and, if current trends continue, by the end of the century it will likely be hotter than at any point in the last two million years." The following points are some of the evidence that led them to this conclusion:

- Over the last century the average global temperature has climbed about 0.6°C (1°F). Nineteen of the 20 warmest years in the past 150 have occurred since 1980. Observed rises in sea level and declines in polar ice are consistent with this pattern (fig. 9.15a).

- Polar regions have warmed much faster than the rest of the world. In Alaska, western Canada, and eastern Russia, average temperatures have increased as much as 4°C (7°F) over the past 50 years. Permafrost is melting; houses, roads, pipelines, sewage systems, and transmission lines are collapsing as the ground sinks beneath them. Spruce beetle infestations in Alaska (made possible by warmer winters) have killed 250 million spruce trees on the Kenai Peninsula alone. Declining sea ice is leading to coastal erosion and relocation of coastal towns.

- Arctic sea ice is only half as thick now as it was 30 years ago, and the area covered by summer sea ice has decreased by about half in just three decades. By 2040, the Arctic Ocean could be totally ice-free in the summer. Populations of seals that have pups on arctic ice are collapsing. Polar bears, which must hunt seals on sea ice, were added to the Endangered Species List in 2008. An aerial survey in 2005 found bears swimming across as much as 260 km (160 mi) of open water to reach the pack ice. Loss of sea ice is also devastating for Inuit people whose traditional lifestyle depends on ice for travel and hunting.

- Ice shelves on the Antarctic Peninsula are breaking up and disappearing rapidly. A recent survey found that 90 percent of the glaciers on the peninsula are now retreating an average of 50 m per year. Emperor and Adélie penguin populations have declined by half over the past 50 years as the ice shelves melt (fig. 9.15b). Greenland's ice is melting at an accelerating rate. Greenland's massive ice cap holds enough water to raise sea level by about 6 m (about 20 ft) if it all melts.

- Nearly all alpine (mountain) glaciers are retreating rapidly. Mount Kilimanjaro has nearly lost its famous ice cap. Montana's Glacier National Park had 150 glaciers when it was created in 1910. Soon it will be Glacierless National Park (fig. 9.15c).

- So far, the oceans have been buffering the effects of our greenhouse emissions both by absorbing $CO_2$ directly and by storing heat. Deep-diving sensors show that the oceans are absorbing 0.85 watts per m$^2$ more than is radiated back to space. This absorption slows current warming, but also means that even if we reduce our greenhouse gas emissions today, it will take centuries to dissipate that stored heat. The higher levels of $CO_2$ being absorbed are acidifying the oceans, and could have adverse effects on sea life. Mollusks and corals, for example, have a more difficult time making calcium carbonate shells and skeletons in acidic water.

- Sea level has risen worldwide approximately 15–20 cm (6–8 in.) in the past century. About one-quarter of this increase is ascribed to melting glaciers; roughly half is due to thermal expansion of seawater. If all of Antarctica were to melt, the resulting rise in sea level could be several hundred meters.

- Satellite images and surface measurements show that growing seasons are now as much as three weeks longer in a band across northern Eurasia and North America than they were 30 years ago. Southern plants and animals, are now extending their territories into arctic regions, while native species, such as musk ox, caribou, walrus, and seal are declining.

- Droughts are becoming more frequent and widespread. In Africa, for example, droughts have increased about 30 percent since 1970. Marginal farmlands are drying further as warmer temperatures evaporate available moisture.

- Biologists report that plants and animals are breeding earlier or extending their range into new territory. In Europe and North America, 57 butterfly species have disappeared from the southern end of their range or extended the northern limits. Many plants may be unable to migrate as rapidly as conditions are changing: we now are forcing them to move much faster than they did at the end of the last ice age (fig. 9.15d).

- Coral reefs worldwide are "bleaching" (losing the colorful algae they rely on for survival) as water temperatures rise above 30°C (85°F). With reefs nearly everywhere threatened by pollution, overfishing, and other stressors, scientists worry that rapid climate change could be the final blow for many species in these complex, biologically rich ecosystems.

- Storms are becoming stronger and more damaging. Extreme rainfall, snowfall, hurricane frequency, and other events suggest that ocean warming and more vigorous atmospheric circulation are having an effect on weather. Insurance companies are dropping storm coverage and raising premium rates. This action suggests that even financial corporations understand that something novel is happening with the climate (see Exploring Science, p. 220).

## Controlling emissions is cheap compared to climate change

A 2010 study by the Pew Trust evaluated estimates of the cost of lost ecological services by 2100. Costs included factors such as lost agricultural productivity from drought, damage to infrastructure from flooding and storms, lost biological productivity, health costs from heat stress, and lost water supplies to the billion or so people who depend on snowmelt for drinking and irrigation.

**Figure 9.15** These examples are evidence of climate change. (a) Observed temperatures have increased in recent decades. Blue lines show uncertainty (range of possible values) for global averages (red lines). (b) Ice-dependent penguin populations are already declining sharply. (c) Alpine glaciers everywhere are retreating rapidly. These images show the Grinnell Glacier in Glacier National Park in 1911 and 1998. By 2030, there may be no glaciers in Glacier National Park. (d) Climatic conditions for wheat could be in central Canada, rather than the central U.S., by 2050. (e) Surface temperature projections from IPCC scenario B1, which assumes rapid adoption of new technology and a declining population after 2050. *Source:* IPCC, 2007.

# How Do We Know That Climate Change Is Human-caused?

O ur climate system is one vast manipulative experiment: we are injecting greenhouse gases into the atmosphere and observing the changes that result.

In most manipulative experiments, though, we have controls, which we can compare to treatments to be certain of the effects. Since we have only one earth, we have no controls

in this experiment. So how do we test a hypothesis in an uncontrolled experiment?

One approach is to use models. You build a computer model, a complex set of equations,

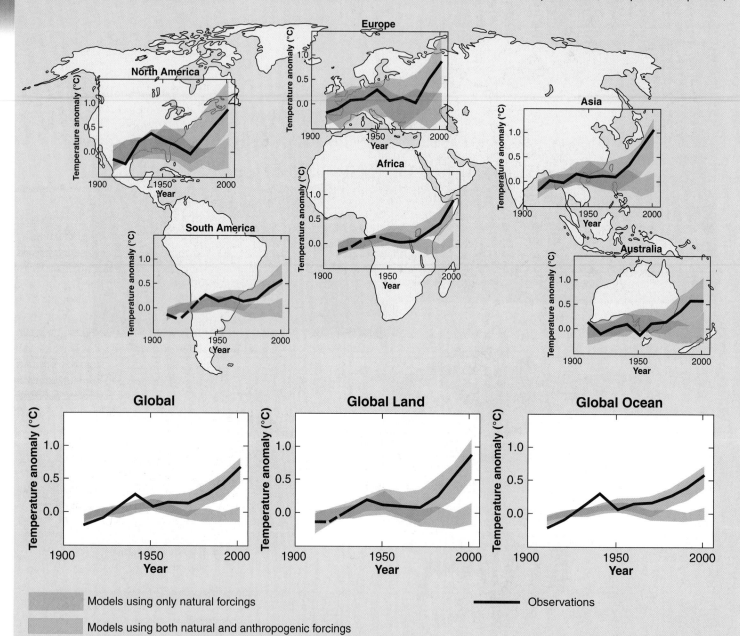

**Figure 1** Comparison of observed continental and global changes in surface temperature with results simulated by climate models using either natural or both natural and anthropogenic forcing. Decadal averages of observations are shown to the period 1906–2006 black linel plotted against the center of the decade and relative to the corresponding average or the period 1901–1960. Lines are dashed where spatial coverage is less than 50 percent. Blue shaped bands show the 6 to 95 percent range to 19 simultations from the climate models using only the nature forcings due to solar activity and vocances. Pink shaded bands show the 5 to 95 percent range for 58 simulations for 14 climate models using both natural and anthrogenic forcings. *Source:* POC 2008.

that include all the known natural causes of climate fluctuation, such as Milankovitch cycles and solar variation. You also include the known human-caused inputs (fossil fuel emissions, methane, aerosols, soot, and so on). Then you run the model and see if it can reproduce observed past changes in temperatures.

If you can accurately "predict" past changes, then your model is a good description of how the system works. You've done a good job of representing how the atmosphere responds to $CO_2$ inputs, how oceans absorb heat, how changes in snow cover accelerate energy absorption, and so on.

If you can create a model that represents the system quite well, then you can re-run the model, but this time you leave out all the anthropogenic inputs. If the model *without* human inputs is *inconsistent* with observed changes in temperature, and if the model *with* human inputs is *consistent* with observations, then you can be extremely confident, beyond the shadow of a reasonable doubt, that human inputs had made the difference and caused temperature changes.

This modeling approach is precisely what climate scientists have done. As you can see in the IPCC's summary of model results (fig. 1), observed trends do not fit the models run with only natural changes (in blue). Observed trends do fit models that include human inputs, however.

The Pew report found that climate change is likely to cost between $5 trillion and $90 trillion by 2100, depending on how economic discount rates and other factors are calculated. In a study issued on behalf of the British government, Sir Nicholas Stern, former chief economist of the World Bank, estimated the immediate costs of climate change would be at least 5 percent of the global GDP each year. Including less immediate costs, such as declining biological productivity, the damage could equal 20 percent of the annual global economy.

In contrast, the Stern report estimated it would cost only about 1 percent of global GDP to reduce greenhouse gas emissions now to avoid the worst impacts of climate change. The IPCC says it would cost even less, only 0.12 percent of annual global GDP to reduce carbon emissions the 2 percent per year necessary to stabilize world climate.

For many people, global climate change is a moral and ethical issue as well as a practical one. Religious leaders are joining with scientists and business leaders to campaign for measures to reduce greenhouse gas emissions. Ultimately, the people likely to suffer most from global warming are the poorest in Africa, Asia, and Latin America who have contributed least to the problem. There is also a question of intergenerational equity. The actions we take—or fail to take—in the next 10 to 20 years will have a profound effect on those living in the second half of this century and in the next. What kind of world are we leaving to our children and grandchildren? What price will they pay if we fail to act?

## Why are there disputes over climate evidence?

Scientific studies have long been unanimous about the direction of climate trends, but commentators on television, newspapers, and radio continue to fiercely dispute the evidence. Why is this? Part of the reason may be that change is threatening, and many of us would rather ignore it or dispute it than acknowledge it. Part of the reason may be a lack of information. Another reason is that while scientists tend to look at trends in data, the public might be more impressed by one or two recent events, such as an especially snowy winter in their local area. And on talk radio and TV, colorful opinions sell better than evidence. Climate scientists offer the following responses to some of the claims in the popular media:

*Reducing climate change requires abandoning our current way of life.* Reducing climate change doesn't necessarily require using *less* energy, it requires that we use *different* energy. If we replace coal-powered electricity with wind, solar, natural gas, and improved efficiency, we can drastically cut our emissions but keep our computers, TVs, cars, and other conveniences. Reducing coal dependence will also reduce air pollution, health expenditures, and destruction of vegetation and buildings (see discussion later in this chapter).

*There is no alternative to current energy systems.* Without investments in alternative energy sources, this would be true, but Chinese and European energy companies are demonstrating that this claim is false. European and Chinese businesses are showing that alternative energy and improved efficiency can already provide what we need and that there's a great deal of money to be made in new technology. In the coming years there is likely to be more profit in new technologies than in the traditional energy and transportation technologies of the 1940s.

*A comfortable lifestyle requires high $CO_2$ output.* The data show this claim is incorrect. Most northern European countries have higher standards of living (in terms of education, health care, life span, vacation time, financial security) than residents of the United States and Canada, yet their $CO_2$ emissions are as low as half those of North Americans. Residents of San Francisco consume about 1/6 as much energy as residents of Kansas City, yet quality of life is not necessarily six times greater in Kansas City than in San Francisco.

*Natural changes such as solar variation can explain observed warming.* Solar input fluctuates, but changes are slight and do not coincide with the direction of changes in temperatures (fig. 9.16). Milankovitch cycles also cannot explain the rapid changes in the past few decades. Increased GHG emissions, however, do correspond closely with observed temperature and sea-level changes (see fig. 9.13).

*The climate has changed before, so this is nothing new.* Today's $CO_2$ level of roughly 390 ppm exceeds by at least 30 percent anything the earth has seen for nearly a million years, and perhaps as long as 15 million years. Recent change is also far more dramatic than natural fluctuations. Antarctic ice cores indicate that $CO_2$ concentrations for the past 800,000 years have varied from 180 to 300 ppm (see fig. 9.8). This natural variation

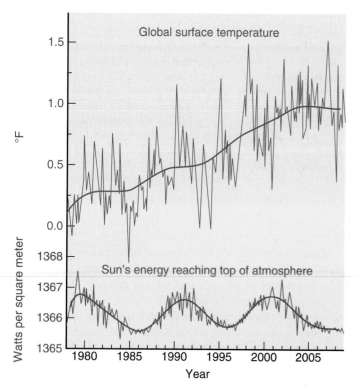

**Figure 9.16** The sun's energy received at the top of the earth's atmosphere has been measured by satellites since 1978. It has followed its natural 11-year cycle of small ups and downs, but with no net increase (*bottom*). Over the same period, global temperature has risen markedly (*top*). *Source:* Climate Change Compendium, 2009.

in $CO_2$ appears to be a feedback in glacial cycles, resulting from changes in biotic activity in warm periods. Because temperature has closely tracked $CO_2$ over time, it is likely that temperatures by 2100 will exceed anything in the past million years. The rate of change is probably also unprecedented. Changes that took 1,000-5,000 years at the end of ice ages are now occurring on the scale of a human lifetime.

*Temperature changes are leveling off.* On short time frames, this leveling off happens from time to time, (fig. 9.16), but over decades the trends in surface air temperatures and in sea level continue to rise. Climatologists don't fully understand the slight slowing of temperature changes, but some evidence suggests that heat absorption in deeper ocean layers may account for the slowing rate of increase in several recent years.

*We had cool temperatures and snowstorms last year, not heat and drought.* Regional differences in temperature and precipitation trends, including increased storm activity, are predicted by climate models. Some of the increasing rain and snow have occurred in heavily populated areas such as the eastern United States (fig. 9.17). Global average conditions, however, continue to trend toward warmer climate and widespread drought.

*Climate scientists don't know everything, and they have made errors and misstatements.* The gaps and uncertainties in climate data are minute compared to the evident trends. There are many unknowns, such as details of precipitation change or interaction of long-term cycles such as El Niño, but the trends are unequivocal. Climatologist James Hansen has noted that while most people make occasional honest mistakes, fraud in data collection is almost unheard of. The scientific process ensures transparency and eventual exposure of errors. Despite this effort, Hansen notes, prominent climate scientists are regularly subjected to personal attacks from climate change deniers who, lacking evidence for their arguments, resort to harassment to suppress discussion.

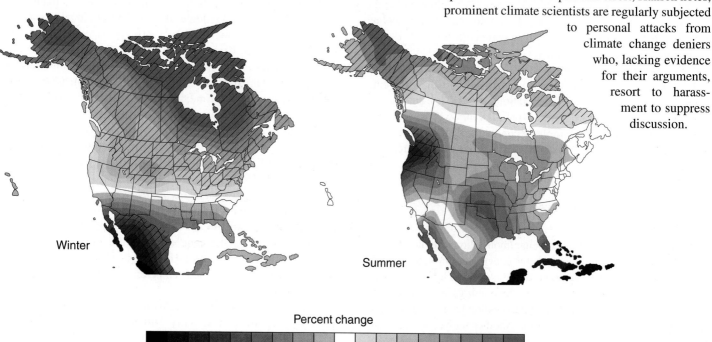

**Figure 9.17** Projected change in precipitation from recent averages to 2100. Values are averages of 15 climate models. Changes are likely to vary regionally and seasonally. *Source:* Climate Change Compendium, 2009.

http://www.mhhe.com/cunningham6e

## 9.4 Envisioning Solutions

Former president Bill Clinton has argued that combating climate change doesn't have to mean economic hardship. It could be the biggest development stimulus since World War II, creating millions of jobs and saving trillions of dollars in foreign fuel imports. What are some of the strategies we have available?

There are many possible approaches. We can reduce dependence on coal, which produces more $CO_2$ per unit energy than any other fuel. We can work to internalize the many hidden costs (such as health costs, biodiversity and recreation costs, military expenditures to protect oil fields) that keep fossil fuels cheaper than alternatives. We could institute fees for selling fossil fuels—these would help fossil fuel prices represent their many hidden costs. We can invest in new technologies, which have improved greatly in recent years despite minute levels of investments in most countries. We can share alternative technologies with developing countries, to ensure that they have low-carbon futures. We can invest in efficiency, so that our personal energy costs can decline. We can reduce emissions through deforestation, our largest non-fuel cause of $CO_2$ emissions (see chapter 6).

Our favored plan thus far has been to institute emissions trading. By instituting a legal cap on emissions, then allowing companies to buy and sell shares of that total cap, many strategists think we can keep emissions down and make money all at once. A vigorous market for emissions trading already exists. In 2006, about 700 million tons of carbon equivalent credits were exchanged for some (U.S.) $3.5 billion. In 2008, trade was the equivalent of 4.8 billion tons of carbon reduction. Other strategists are not so sure this is a real solution. Climate scientists James Hansen argues that European carbon markets have made traders rich but have failed to address carbon emissions.

### International protocols have tried to establish common rules

One of the centerpieces of the 1992 United Nations Earth Summit meeting in Rio de Janeiro was the Framework Convention on Climate Change, which set an objective of stabilizing greenhouse gas emissions to reduce the threats of global warming. At a follow-up conference in Kyoto, Japan, in 1997, 160 nations agreed to roll back $CO_2$, methane, and nitrous oxide emissions about 5 percent below 1990 levels by 2012. Three other greenhouse gases, hydrofluorocarbons, perfluorocarbons, and sulfur hexafluoride, would also be reduced, although from what level was not decided. Known as the **Kyoto Protocol**, this treaty set different limits for individual nations, depending on their output before 1990. Poorer nations, such as China and India, were exempted from emission limits to allow development to increase their standard of living. Wealthy countries created the problem, the poorer nations argue, and the wealthy should solve it.

Although the United States took a lead role in negotiating a compromise at Kyoto that other countries could accept, President George W. Bush refused to honor U.S. commitments. Claiming that reducing carbon emissions would be too costly for the U.S. economy, he said, "We're going to put the interests of our own country first and foremost." The United States, which depends solely on voluntary efforts to limit greenhouse gas emissions, had a 2 percent rise in those releases in 2007. At this rate, the U.S. will be 25 percent above 1990 emissions by 2012.

Many of the largest business conglomerates in America have joined environmental groups to call for strong national legislation to achieve significant reductions of greenhouse gas emissions. Those companies would prefer a single national standard rather than a jumble of conflicting local and state rules. Knowing that climate controls are inevitable, they'd rather know now how they'll have to adapt rather than wait until a crisis causes us to demand sudden, radical changes.

The 2009 Copenhagen climate conference had little more immediate success than did Kyoto. Arguments were similar, but this time countries made at least verbal pledges to control emissions and to invest in alternative futures for developing nations. Where these promises will go remains to be seen.

### A wedge approach could fix the problem

As you know from the opening case study, a combination of relatively simple policy changes could stabilize our climate. Steven Pacala and Robert Socolow's work shows that we already have the scientific, technical, and industrial know-how to stabilize our $CO_2$ emissions over the next half century, while still meeting the world's energy needs. In several recent publications, this group examines a portfolio of 14 policy options for reducing our $CO_2$ output. None of the options is going to please everybody, and some will be more popular than others, but the potential benefits of the entire portfolio are large enough that not every option must be used.

To avoid a doubling of atmospheric $CO_2$ we need to reduce our annual carbon emissions by about 7 billion tons (gigatons or GT) by 2058. To make this easier to understand, the Princeton scientists divide the "stabilization triangle" between our current path and the flat emissions that we need in order to avoid doubling $CO_2$ levels into 14 "wedges" (table 9.2). Each wedge represents 1 GT (1 billion tons) of carbon emissions avoided in 2058, compared to a "business as usual" scenario. Accomplishing just half of these wedges could level off our emissions. Accomplishing all of them could return to levels well below those envisioned in the Kyoto Protocol.

Because most of our $CO_2$ emissions come from fossil fuel combustion, energy conservation and a switch to renewable fuels probably are the first places we should look. Two wedges (2 GT reduction in carbon emissions, or about one-quarter of what is needed to stabilize emissions) could be accomplished by doubling our average fuel economy from the expected 30 miles per gallon in 2058 to 60 mpg, and by halving the number of miles driven each year by switching to walking, biking, or using mass transit.

We could save another 2 GT, simply by installing the most efficient lighting and appliances available, along with improved insulation in buildings. Improving power plant efficiency, and reducing the energy consumption of industrial processes could reduce carbon output one wedge (1 GT). Capturing and storing $CO_2$ released by power plants, methane wells, and other large sources could save another billion tons of carbon. Much of this $CO_2$ could be injected into oil wells to improve crude oil production.

Altogether these policy changes add up to considerably more than the 7 GT per year reduction we need to make by 2058 to

**Table 9.2 | Actions to Reduce Global $CO_2$ Emissions by 1 Billion Tons over 50 Years**

1. Double the fuel economy for 2 billion cars from 30 to 60 mpg.
2. Cut average annual travel per car from 10,000 to 5,000 miles.
3. Improve efficiency in heating, cooling, lighting, and appliances by 25 percent.
4. Update all building insulation, windows, and weather stripping to modern standards.
5. Boost efficiency of all coal-fired power plants from 32 percent today to 60 percent (through co-generation of steam and electricity).
6. Replace 800 large coal-fired power plants with an equal amount of gas-fired power (four times current capacity).
7. Capture $CO_2$ from 800 large coal-fired, or 1,600 gas-fired, power plants and store it securely.
8. Replace 800 large coal-fired power plants with an equal amount of nuclear power (twice the current level).
9. Add 2 million 1 MW windmills (50 times current capacity).
10. Generate enough hydrogen from wind to fuel a billion cars (4 million 1 MW windmills).
11. Install 2,000 GW of photovoltaic energy (700 times current capacity).
12. Expand ethanol production to 2 trillion liters per year (50 times current levels).
13. Stop all tropical deforestation and replant 300 million ha of forest.
14. Apply conservation tillage to all cropland (10 times current levels).

Source: Data from Pacala and Socolow, 2004.

avoid doubling atmospheric $CO_2$ concentrations. If we used all 14 available options, we could reverse the present trajectory and move toward zero greenhouse emissions.

Individuals can make many contributions to this effort (see What Can You Do? p. 225). There are also increasing numbers of businesses and organizations willing to help you out by selling carbon credits. There are many organizations you can pay to plant trees, or do other carbon storage activities to compensate for your carbon emissions. British Petroleum, for example, will compensate for the $CO_2$ emitted by a year's driving of the average car for about $40. You could make a guilt-free round-trip airplane flight from New York to Los Angeles for about $6.25. Or Carbonfund.org will offset for all the greenhouse gas emissions (both direct and indirect) for the average American for $99 per year.

Of course you should be thoughtful about your investment. In some places, planting trees is inappropriate; in other places different actions might be best. Fast-growing trees, such as the eucalyptus or pines often used in reforestation programs, can dry streams and springs and deplete soil nutrients, and sometimes newly planted forests are harvested quickly. What do you think of this strategy? How might it fit into a collection of approaches, including those on p. 225?

## Local initiatives are everywhere

Many countries are working to reduce greenhouse emissions. The United Kingdom, for example, had already rolled $CO_2$ emissions back to 1990 levels by 2000 and vowed to reduce them 60 percent by 2050. Britain already has started to substitute natural gas for coal, promote energy efficiency in homes and industry, and raise its already high gasoline tax. Plans are to "decarbonize" British society and to decouple GNP growth from $CO_2$ emissions. New carbon taxes are expected to lower $CO_2$ releases and trigger a transition to renewable energy over the next five decades. New Zealand Prime Minister Helen Clark pledged that her country will be the first to be **"carbon neutral,"** that is, to reduce net greenhouse gas emissions to zero, although she didn't say when this will occur.

Germany, also, has reduced its $CO_2$ emissions at least 10 percent by switching from coal to gas and by encouraging energy efficiency throughout society. Atmospheric scientist Steve Schneider calls this a "no regrets" policy; even if we didn't need to stabilize our climate, many of these steps save money, conserve resources, and have other environmental benefits. Nuclear power also is being promoted as an alternative to fossil fuels. It's true that nuclear reactions don't produce greenhouse gases, but security worries and unresolved problems of how to store wastes safely make this option unacceptable to many people.

Many people believe renewable energy sources offer the best solution to climate problems. Chapter 12 discusses options for conserving energy and switching to renewable sources, such as solar, wind, geothermal, biomass, and fuel cells. Denmark, the world's leader in wind power, now gets 20 percent of its electricity from windmills. Plans are to generate half of the nation's electricity from offshore wind farms by 2030. Even China has promised to cut 10 percent of its $CO_2$ emissions per unit of economic output by shifting to renewable energy and conservation.

In the United States, more than 700 cities and 39 states have announced their own plans to combat global warming. And 450 college campuses have pledged to reduce greenhouse emissions. Some have promised to be carbon neutral by 2020. Some corporations are following suit. British Petroleum has set a goal of cutting $CO_2$ releases from all its facilities by 10 percent before 2010. Each of us can make a contribution in this effort. As Pacala and Socolow point out, simply driving less and buying high-mileage vehicles could save about 2 billion tons of carbon emissions over the next 50 years.

In the midst of all the debate about how serious the consequences of global climate change may or may not be, we need to remember that many of the proposed solutions are advantageous in their own right. Moving from fossil fuels to renewable energy sources such as solar or wind power, for example, would free us from dependence on foreign oil and would improve air quality. Planting trees makes the world a more pleasant place to live and provides habitat for wildlife. Making buildings more energy efficient and buying high-mileage vehicles saves money in the long run. Walking, biking, and climbing stairs are good for your health as well as reducing traffic congestion and energy consumption. Reducing waste, recycling, and other forms of sustainable living improve our environment in many ways in addition to helping fight climate change. It's important to focus on these positive effects rather than to look only at the gloom-and-doom scenarios for global climate catastrophes. As the Irish statesman and philosopher Edmund Burke said, "Nobody made a greater mistake than he who did nothing because he could do only a little."

## Reducing Individual CO₂ Emissions

Each of us can take steps to reduce global warming. While individually each change may have only a small impact, collectively they add up. Furthermore, most will save money in the long run and have other environmental and health benefits by reducing air pollution and resource consumption. The savings vary depending on where and how you live, but the following are averages for the United States.

| | CO$_2$ Reduction (Pounds per Year) | Approximate Yearly Savings (U.S. $) |
|---|---|---|
| 1. Keep your car tires at full pressure, avoid quick starts and stops, and drive within the speed limit. | 1,100 | $130 |
| 2. Carpool, walk, or take the bus once per week. | 800 | $100 |
| 3. Turn off the lights when you leave a room. | 300 | $10 |
| 4. Replace 10 incandescent light bulbs with compact fluorescent bulbs (100 pounds/bulb). | 1,000 | $50 |
| 5. Raise your air conditioning 2°. | 400 | $20 |
| 6. Lower your furnace thermostat 2°. | 550 | $50 |
| 7. When heating or cooling, close doors and windows. | 500 | $20 |
| 8. When heating or cooling aren't needed, open doors and windows. | 500 | $20 |
| 9. Unplug TVs, DVD players, computers, and other instant-on electronics. | 250 | $20 |
| 10. Eat local, seasonal food (average savings; values vary enormously). | 250 | $25 |
| 11. Take only five-minute showers. | 250 | $25 |
| 12. Take the train instead of flying 500 miles. | 300 | $100 |
| 13. Air dry your clothes. | 700 | $100 |
| 14. Replace your old car, truck, or SUV with one that gets at least 50 mpg. | 6,000 | $750 |
| 15. Defrost your refrigerator and keep coils and door seals clean. | 700 | $100 |

*Source:* Interfaith Power and Light, 2007.

## Are there other ways to control carbon?

It is possible, though expensive, to store $CO_2$ by injecting it deep into geologic formations. Since 1996, Norway's Statoil has been pumping more than 1 million metric tons of $CO_2$ per year into an aquifer 1,000 m below the seafloor in the North Sea. The pressurized $CO_2$ enhances oil recovery. It also saves money because otherwise the company would have to pay a $50 per ton carbon tax on its emissions. Around the world, deep, briny aquifers could store a century worth of $CO_2$ output at current fossil fuel consumption rates. A number of companies have started, or are now planning, similar schemes (fig. 9.18).

Proponents of **carbon management**, as these various projects are called, argue that it may be cheaper to clean up fossil fuel effluents than to switch to renewable energy sources. By far, the easiest way to remove $CO_2$ from a coal-fired power plant is the integrated gasification combined cycle (IGCC) technology described in chapter 12. Utilities, eager to continue business as usual, are touting "clean-coal" techniques and carbon sequestration as the answer to global warming. These approaches are feasible. Geological formations around the world could hold hundreds of years' worth of $CO_2$ at current production levels. These formations, however, aren't necessarily near the sites where we now produce $CO_2$. Shipping billions of tons of $CO_2$ long distances could become a serious bottleneck. It may be far more efficient—and more environmentally benign—to switch to local alternative energy sources or to ship energy (electricity) or carbon-neutral fuels (ethanol or hydrogen) to places where they're needed.

Most attention is focused on $CO_2$ because it lasts in the atmosphere for about 120 years, on average. Methane and other greenhouse gases dissipate faster, but they are much more powerful infrared absorbers. Focusing on methane could make a key difference. Reducing gas pipeline leaks would conserve this valuable resource as well as help the environment. Capturing or burning methane from landfills, oil wells, and coal mines would make an important contribution to both fuel and climate problems. Rice paddies are important methane sources: changing flooding schedules and fertilization techniques can reduce the amount of submerged, rotting vegetation. Ruminant animals (such as cows, camels, and buffalo) create large amounts of methane from digestive systems. Feeding them more grass and less corn can reduce these emissions. Some analysts have suggested that eating less beef—skipping just one day per week—could reduce our individual contributions to climate change more than driving a hybrid Toyota Prius would.

Soot, while not mentioned in the Kyoto Protocol, is also important in global warming. Dark, airborne particles absorb both ultraviolet and visible light, converting them to heat energy. According to some calculations, reducing soot from diesel engines, coal-fired generators, forest fires, and wood stoves might reduce net global warming by 40 percent within three to five years. Curbing soot emissions would also have beneficial health effects.

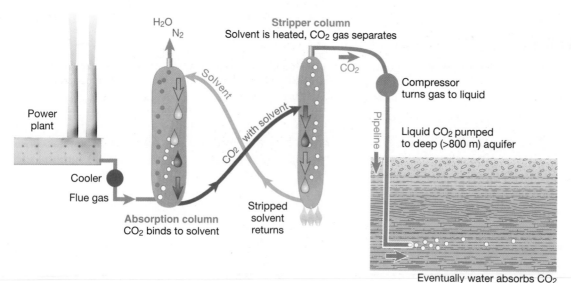

**Figure 9.18** One method of carbon capture and storage uses a liquid solvent, such as ammonia, to capture $CO_2$. Steam and nitrogen and released, and the $CO_2$ is compressed and pumped to deep aquifers for permanent storage.

# Active Learning

## Calculate Your Carbon Reductions

How much global warming can you avoid through personal efforts? It's difficult to compare actions as different as walking to work and planting a tree, but most of our $CO_2$ emissions result from burning fossil fuels. The exact amount of $CO_2$ you save depends on the source of your energy and how you use it. Coal, for instance, produces about twice as much $CO_2$ per unit of energy delivered as natural gas. Wind, solar, and hydropower, on the other hand, don't emit any $CO_2$ at all. It's often easier to find energy consumption data for appliances.

The Tufts University Climate Initiative provides the following information:

The average desktop computer uses about 120 watts (the monitor uses 75 watts, and the CPU uses 45 watts). Laptops use considerably less, around 30 watts total.

1. Suppose you keep your computer on 24 hours a day. How much energy does it use every year?

2. If electricity costs 11 cents per kWh, how much does it cost per year to keep your computer running all the time?

3. If your electricity source produces 1.45 lbs of $CO_2$ per kWh delivered to your home (the average for coal-fired power), how much $CO_2$ is released every year to keep your computer always on?

4. Suppose you turn your computer off for 12 hours per day when you're not using it. How much energy would you save over a year?

5. How much $CO_2$ would that save per year?

6. How much money would you save per year?

---

*Answers:* 1. 120 watts/hour = 0.12 kWh × 24 hrs/day × 365 days/yr = 1,051 kWh/yr. 2. 1,051 kWh × $0.11 = $115.63/yr. 3. 1,051 kWh/yr × 1.45 lbs/kWh = 1,524 lbs/yr. 4. 0.12 kWh × 12 hrs/day × 365 days/yr = 525.6 kWh/yr. 5. 525.6 kWh/yr × 1.45 lbs/kWh = 762 lbs/yr. 6. 525.6 kWh × $0.11 = $57.81/yr.

## 9.5 Air Pollution

Evidence for climate change shows that human activities can influence global climate processes. Climate change is probably the air quality issue with the broadest and most permanent effects on the lives of future generations. But other issues are important to understand for environmental quality today. In this section, we discuss more direct and immediate health an environmental effects of air quality.

According to the Environmental Protection Agency (EPA), Americans release about 150 million metric tons of air pollution (not counting carbon dioxide or wind-blown soil) each year. Worldwide emissions of these pollutants are around 2 billion metric tons per year. Even remote, pristine wilderness areas are now affected. Over the past 20 years, however, air quality has improved in most cities in Western Europe, North America, and Japan. Many young people might be surprised to learn that, a generation ago, most American cities were much dirtier than they are today. The EPA estimates that, since 1990, when regulation of the most hazardous materials began, air toxics emissions have been reduced more than 1 million tons per year. This is almost ten times the reductions achieved in the previous 20 years. Since the 1970s, the levels of major pollutants monitored by the EPA have decreased in the United States, despite population growth of more than 30 percent. Pollution reductions have resulted mainly from greater efficiency and pollution-control technologies in factories, power plants, and automobiles. Our success in controlling some of the most serious air pollutants gives us hope for similar progress in other environmental problems.

While developed countries have been making progress, however, air quality in the developing world has been getting much worse. Especially in the burgeoning megacities of rapidly industrializing countries (chapter 14), air pollution often exceeds World Health Organization standards by large margins. In Lahore, Pakistan, and Xi'an, China, for instance, airborne dust,

http://www.mhhe.com/cunningham6e

**Figure 9.19** While air quality is improving in many industrialized countries, newly developing countries have growing pollution problems. Xi'an, China, often has particulate levels above 300 µg/m³.

smoke, and dirt often are ten times higher than levels considered safe for human health (fig. 9.19).

Studies of air pollutants over southern Asia reveal that a 3 km (2 mi) thick toxic cloud of ash, acids, aerosols, dust, and photochemical reactants covers the entire Indian subcontinent for much of the year. Nobel laureate Paul Crutzen estimates that up to 2 million people in India alone die each year from atmospheric pollution. Produced by forest fires, the burning of agricultural wastes, and dramatic increases in the use of fossil fuels, the Asian smog layer cuts the amount of solar energy reaching the earth's surface beneath it by up to 15 percent. Meteorologists suggest that the cloud—80 percent of which is human-made—could disrupt monsoon weather patterns and cut rainfall over

northern Pakistan, Afghanistan, western China, and central Asia by up to 40 percent.

When this "Asian Brown Cloud" drifts out over the Indian Ocean at the end of the monsoon season, it cools sea temperatures and may be changing El Niño/Southern Oscillation patterns in the Pacific Ocean as well. As UN Environment Programme Executive Director Klaus Töpfer said, "There are global implications because a pollution parcel like this, which stretches 3 km high, can travel half way round the globe in a week."

## We describe pollutants according to sources

In the United States, principal pollutants are identified and regulated by the Clean Air Act of 1970. A **point source** is a smokestack or some other concentrated pollution origin. **Primary pollutants** are released in a harmful form. Secondary pollutants, by contrast, become hazardous after reactions in the air. **Photochemical oxidants** (compounds created by reactions driven by solar energy) and atmospheric acids are probably the most important secondary pollutants. **Fugitive**, or **nonpoint-source**, **emissions** are those that do not go through a smokestack. By far the most massive example of this category is dust from soil erosion, strip mining, rock crushing, and building construction (and destruction). Leaking valves and pipe joints contribute as much as 90 percent of the hydrocarbons and volatile organic chemicals emitted from oil refineries and chemical plants.

**Conventional**, or **criteria, pollutants** are a group of seven major pollutants (sulfur dioxide, carbon monoxide, particulates, volatile organic compounds, nitrogen oxides, ozone, and lead) that contribute the largest volume of air-quality degradation and are considered the most serious threat of all air pollutants to human health and welfare. Transportation and power plants are the dominant sources of most criteria pollutants (fig. 9.20). Since 1970 the Clean Air Act has mandated that the EPA set allowable limits for

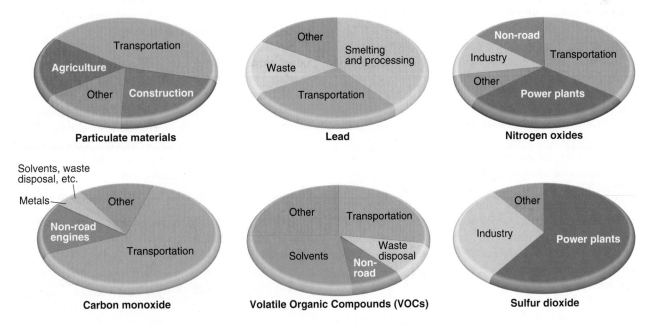

**Figure 9.20** Anthropogenic sources of six of the primary "criteria" air pollutants in the United States. *Source: UNEP, 1999.*

concentrations of these pollutants in **ambient air** (the air around us), especially in cities.

The EPA also monitors **unconventional pollutants**, compounds that are produced in less volume than conventional pollutants but that are especially toxic or hazardous. Among these are asbestos, benzene, beryllium, mercury, polychlorinated biphenyls (PCBs), and vinyl chloride. Most of these materials have no natural source in the environment (to any great extent) and are, therefore, only anthropogenic in origin.

In 2009, in following a directive from the Supreme Court, the EPA announced that it would add $CO_2$ and other greenhouse gases to its list of regulated pollutants. This proposal has been controversial: On the one hand, greenhouse gases have tremendous effects on human health and the environment, causing heat stress, drought, and other problems. On the other hand, $CO_2$ doesn't directly harm health in the way that sulfur dioxide or carbon monoxide do. The EPA plan brings the United States a step closer to regulations already in place in Europe, Japan, and elsewhere. This decision remains controversial, however, with coal-producing states opposed and many others in favor. Details of how to regulate greenhouse gases have yet to be worked out.

## Conventional pollutants are common and serious

Most conventional pollutants are produced primarily from burning fossil fuels, especially in coal-powered electric plants and in cars and trucks, as well as in processing natural gas and oil. Others, especially sulfur and metals, are by-products of mining and manufacturing processes. Of the 188 air toxics listed in the Clean Air Act, about two-thirds are volatile organic compounds (VOCs), and most of the rest are metal compounds. In this section we will discuss the characteristics and origin of the major pollutants.

**Sulfur dioxide** ($SO_2$) is a colorless, corrosive gas that damages both plants and animals. Once in the atmosphere, it can be further oxidized to sulfur trioxide ($SO_3$), which reacts with water vapor or dissolves in water droplets to form sulfuric acid ($H_2SO_4$), a major component of acid rain. Sulfur dioxide and sulfate ions are probably second only to smoking as causes of air-pollution–related health damage. Sulfate particles and droplets also reduce visibility in the United States by as much as 80 percent.

**Nitrogen oxides** ($NO_x$) are highly reactive gases formed when combustion initiates reactions between atmospheric nitrogen and oxygen. The initial product, nitric oxide (NO), oxidizes further in the atmosphere to nitrogen dioxide ($NO_2$), a reddish-brown gas that gives photochemical smog its distinctive color. Because these gases convert readily from one form to the other, the general term $NO_x$ is used to describe these gases. Nitrogen oxides combine with water to form nitric acid ($HNO_3$), which is also a major component of acid precipitation. Excess nitrogen in water is causing eutrophication of inland waters and coastal seas. It may also encourage the growth of weedy species that crowd out native plants.

**Carbon monoxide** (CO) is less common but more dangerous than the principal form of atmospheric carbon, carbon dioxide ($CO_2$). CO is a colorless, odorless, but highly toxic gas produced mainly by incomplete combustion of fuel (coal, oil, charcoal, wood, or gas). CO inhibits respiration in animals by binding irreversibly to hemoglobin in blood. In the United States, two-thirds of the CO emissions are created by internal combustion engines in transportation. Land-clearing fires and cooking fires also are major sources. About 90 percent of the CO in the air is consumed in photochemical reactions that produce ozone.

**Particulate material** includes dust, ash, soot, lint, smoke, pollen, spores, algal cells, and many other suspended materials. Aerosols, or extremely minute particles or liquid droplets suspended in the air, are included in this class. Particulates often are the most apparent form of air pollution, since they reduce visibility and leave dirty deposits on windows, painted surfaces, and textiles. Breathable particles smaller than 2.5 μm are among the most dangerous of this group because they can damage lung tissues. Asbestos fibers and cigarette smoke are among the most dangerous respirable particles in urban and indoor air because they are carcinogenic.

**Volatile organic compounds** (VOCs) are organic (carbon containing) gases. Plants, bogs, and termites are the largest sources of VOCs, especially isoprenes ($C_5H_8$), terpenes ($C_{10}H_{15}$), and methane ($CH_4$). These volatile hydrocarbons are generally oxidized to CO and $CO_2$ in the atmosphere.

More dangerous synthetic organic chemicals, such as benzene, toluene, formaldehyde, vinyl chloride, phenols, chloroform, and trichloroethylene, are released by human activities. Principal sources are incompletely burned fuels from vehicles, power plants, chemical plants, and petroleum refineries. These chemicals play an important role in the formation of photochemical oxidants.

Photochemical oxidants are products of secondary atmospheric reactions driven by solar energy (table 9.3). One of the most important of these reactions involves formation of singlet (atomic) oxygen by splitting nitrogen dioxide ($NO_2$). This atomic oxygen then reacts with another molecule of $O_2$ to make ozone ($O_3$). Although ozone is important in the stratosphere, in ambient air it is highly reactive and damages vegetation, animal tissues, and building materials. Ozone's acrid, biting odor is a distinctive characteristic of photochemical smog.

**Lead and Other Toxic Elements**   Toxic metals and halogens are chemical elements that are toxic when concentrated and released in the environment. Principal metals of concern are lead, mercury, arsenic, nickel, beryllium, cadmium, thallium, uranium, cesium, and plutonium. Halogens (fluorine, chlorine, bromine, and iodine) are highly reactive toxic elements. Most of these materials are mined and used in manufacturing. Metals commonly occur as trace elements in fuels, especially coal.

| Table 9.3 | Photochemical Oxidant Production | |
|---|---|
| **Steps** | **Photochemical Products** |
| 1. NO + VOC → | $NO_2$ (nitrogen dioxide) |
| 2. $NO_2$ + UV sunlight → | NO + O (nitric oxide + atomic oxygen) |
| 3. O + $O_2$ → | $O_3$ (ozone) |
| 4. $NO_2$ + VOC → | PAN (peroxyacetyl nitrate) |

Lead and mercury are widespread neurotoxins that damage the nervous system. By some estimates, 20 percent of all inner-city children suffer some degree of developmental retardation from high environmental lead levels. Long-range transport of lead and mercury through the air is causing bioaccumulation in remote aquatic ecosystems, such as arctic lakes and seas. Chlorine is a toxic halogen widely used in bleach, plastics, and other products. Methyl bromide (a powerful fungicide used in agriculture) and **chlorofluorocarbons** (propellants and refrigerants) are also implicated in ozone depletion.

## Indoor air can be more dangerous than outdoor air

We have spent a considerable amount of effort and money to control the major outdoor air pollutants, but we have only recently become aware of the dangers of indoor air pollutants. The U.S. EPA has found that indoor concentrations of toxic air pollutants are often higher than outdoors. Furthermore, people generally spend more time inside than out and therefore are exposed to higher doses of these pollutants. In some cases, indoor air in homes has chemical concentrations that would be illegal outside or in the workplace. Under some circumstances, compounds such as chloroform, benzene, carbon tetrachloride, formaldehyde, and styrene can be 70 times higher in indoor air than in outdoor air.

**Figure 9.21** Some 2.5 billion people, mainly women and children, spend hours each day in poorly ventilated kitchens and living spaces where carbon monoxide, particulates, and cancer-causing hydrocarbons often reach dangerous levels.

Molds, pathogens, and other biohazards also represent serious indoor pollutants.

Cigarette smoke is without doubt the most important air contaminant in developed countries in terms of human health. The U.S. surgeon general has estimated that 400,000 people die each year in the United States from emphysema, heart attacks, strokes, lung cancer, or other diseases caused by smoking. These diseases are responsible for 20 percent of all mortality in the United States, or four times as much as infectious agents. Total costs for early deaths and smoking-related illnesses are estimated to be $100 billion per year. Eliminating smoking probably would save more lives than any other pollution-control measure.

In the less-developed countries of Africa, Asia, and Latin America, where such organic fuels as firewood, charcoal, dried dung, and agricultural wastes make up the majority of household energy, smoky, poorly ventilated heating and cooking fires represent the greatest source of indoor air pollution (fig. 9.21). The World Health Organization (WHO) estimates that 2.5 billion people—more than one-third of the world's population—are adversely affected by pollution from this source. In particular, women and small children spend long hours each day around open fires or unventilated stoves in enclosed spaces.

## 9.6 Interactions Between Climate and Air Pollution

Physical processes in the atmosphere transport, concentrate, and disperse air pollutants. To comprehend the global effects of air pollution, it is necessary to understand how climate processes interact with pollutants. Global warming in which pollutants are altering the earth's energy budget, is the best-known case of interaction between anthropogenic pollutants and the atmosphere. In this section we will survey other important climate-pollution interactions.

### Air pollutants can travel far

Dust and fine aerosols can be carried great distances by the wind. Pollution from the industrial belt between the Great Lakes and the Ohio River Valley regularly contaminates the Canadian Maritime Provinces and sometimes can be traced as far as Ireland. Similarly, dust storms from China's Gobi and Takla Makan Deserts routinely close schools, factories, and airports in Japan and Korea, and often reach western North America. In one particularly severe dust storm in 1998, chemical analysis showed that 75 percent of the particulate pollution in Seattle, Washington, air came from China. Similarly, dust from North Africa regularly crosses the Atlantic and contaminates the air in Florida and the Caribbean Islands (fig. 9.22). This dust can carry pathogens and is thought to be the source of diseases attacking Caribbean corals. Soil scientists estimate that 3 billion tons of sand and dust are blown around the world every year.

Increasingly sensitive monitoring equipment has begun to reveal industrial contaminants in places usually considered among the cleanest in the world. Samoa, Greenland, and even Antarctica and the North Pole all have heavy metals, pesticides, and radioactive elements in their air. Since the 1950s, pilots flying in the high

**Figure 9.22** A massive dust storm extends more than 1,600 km (1,000 mi) from the coast of western Sahara and Morocco. Storms such as this can easily reach the Americas, and they have been linked both to the decline of coral reefs in the Caribbean and to the frequency and intensity of hurricanes formed in the eastern Atlantic Ocean.

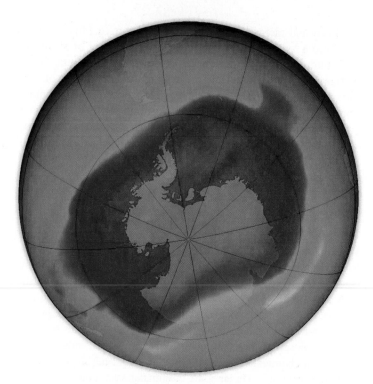

**Figure 9.23** In 2006, stratospheric ozone was depleted over an area (*dark, irregular circle*) that covered 29.5 million km², or more than the entire Antarctic continent. Although CFC production is declining, this was the largest area ever recorded.

Arctic have reported dense layers of reddish-brown haze clouding the arctic atmosphere. Aerosols of sulfates, soot, dust, and toxic heavy metals, such as vanadium, manganese, and lead, travel to the pole from the industrialized parts of Europe and Russia.

Circulation of the atmosphere tends to transport contaminants toward the poles. Volatile compounds evaporate from warm areas, travel through the atmosphere, then condense and precipitate in cooler regions. Over several years, contaminants migrate to the coldest places, generally at high latitudes, where they bioaccumulate in food chains. Whales, polar bears, sharks, and other top carnivores in polar regions have been shown to have dangerously high levels of pesticides, metals, and other hazardous air pollutants in their bodies. The Inuit people of Broughton Island, well above the Arctic Circle, have higher levels of polychlorinated biphenyls (PCBs) in their blood than any other known population, except victims of industrial accidents. Far from any source of this industrial by-product, these people accumulate PCBs from the flesh of fish, caribou, and other animals they eat.

## Ozone in the stratosphere is harmed by CFCs

Long-range pollution transport and the chemical reactions of atmospheric gases and pollution produce the phenomenon known as the ozone hole (fig. 9.23). The ozone "hole," really a thinning of ozone concentrations in the stratosphere, was discovered in 1985 but has probably been developing since at least the 1960s.

Chlorine-based aerosols, such as chlorofluorocarbons (CFCs), are the principal agents of ozone depletion. Nontoxic, nonflammable, chemically inert, and cheaply produced, CFCs were extremely useful as industrial gases and in refrigerators, air conditioners, styrofoam insulation, and aerosol spray cans for many years. From the 1930s until the 1980s, CFCs were used all over the world and widely dispersed through the atmosphere.

Ozone ($O_3$) is a pollutant near the ground because it irritates skin and plant tissues; but in the stratosphere ozone is valuable. The $O_3$ molecule is especially effective at absorbing ultraviolet (UV) radiation as it enters the atmosphere from space. UV radiation damages plant and animal cells, potentially causing mutations that produce cancer. A 1 percent loss of ozone could result in about a million extra human skin cancers per year worldwide. Excessive UV exposure could reduce agricultural production and disrupt ecosystems. Scientists worry, for example, that high UV levels in Antarctica could reduce populations of plankton, the tiny floating organisms that form the base of a food chain that includes fish, seals, penguins, and whales in Antarctic seas.

Antarctica's exceptionally cold winter temperatures (−85° to −90°C) help break down ozone. During the long, dark, winter months, strong winds known as the circumpolar vortex circle the pole. These winds isolate antarctic air and allow stratospheric temperatures to drop low enough to create ice crystals at high altitudes—something that rarely happens elsewhere in the world. Ozone and chlorine-containing molecules are absorbed on the surfaces of these ice particles. When the sun returns in the spring, it provides energy to liberate

## Table 9.4 | Stratospheric Ozone Destruction by Chlorine Atoms and UV Radiation

| Steps | Products |
|---|---|
| 1. $CFCl_3$ (chlorofluorocarbon) + UV energy | $CFCl_2$ + Cl |
| 2. Cl + $O_3$ | $ClO$ + $O_2$ |
| 3. $O_2$ + UV energy | 2O |
| 4. ClO + 2O | $O_2$ + Cl |
| 5. Return to step 2 | |

chlorine ions, which readily bond with ozone, breaking it down to molecular oxygen (table 9.4). It is only during the antarctic spring (September through December) that conditions are ideal for rapid ozone destruction. During that season, temperatures are still cold enough for high-altitude ice crystals, but the sun gradually becomes strong enough to drive photochemical reactions.

As the antarctic summer arrives, temperatures warm slightly, the circumpolar vortex weakens, and air from warmer latitudes mixes with antarctic air, replenishing ozone concentrations in the ozone hole. Slight decreases worldwide result from this mixing, however. Ozone re-forms naturally, but not nearly as fast as it is destroyed. Since the chlorine atoms are not themselves consumed in reactions with ozone, they continue to destroy ozone for years, until they finally precipitate or are washed out of the air. In 2000 the region of ozone depletion covered 29.8 million $km^2$ (about the size of North America).

## CFC control has shown remarkable success

The discovery of stratospheric ozone losses brought about a remarkably quick international response. In 1987 an international meeting in Montreal, Canada, produced the Montreal Protocol, the first of several major international agreements on phasing out most use of CFCs by 2000. As evidence accumulated, showing that losses were larger and more widespread than previously thought, the deadline for the elimination of all CFCs (halons, carbon tetrachloride, and methyl chloroform) was moved up to 1996, and a $500 million

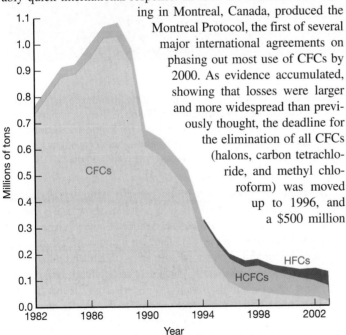

**Figure 9.24** The Montreal Protocol has been remarkably successful in eliminating CFC production. The remaining HFC and HCFC use is primarily in developing countries, such as China and India.

fund was established to assist poorer countries in switching to non-CFC technologies. Fortunately, alternatives to CFCs for most uses already exist. The first substitutes are hydrochlorofluorocarbons (HCFCs), which release much less chlorine per molecule. Eventually, scientists hope to develop halogen-free molecules that work as well and are no more expensive than CFCs.

There is evidence that the CFC ban is already having an effect. CFC production in most industrialized countries has fallen sharply since 1988 (fig. 9.24), and CFCs are now being removed from the atmosphere more rapidly than they are being added. In 50 years or so, stratospheric ozone levels are expected to be back to normal.

## Urban dust domes, smog, and heat islands

**Temperature inversions** can concentrate dangerous levels of pollutants within cities. Normally, air cools with elevation above the earth's surface. An inversion reverses this situation, with cool, dense air lying below a warmer, lighter layer. This condition is very stable: the cool air tends to remain in place, and pollutants accumulate near the ground, where they irritate our lungs and eyes. Stable inversion conditions are usually created by rapid nighttime cooling in a valley, where air movement is restricted.

Los Angeles has ideal conditions for inversions. Mountains surround the city on three sides, reducing wind movement; heavy traffic and industry create a supply of pollutants; skies are generally clear at night, allowing rapid radiant heat loss, and the ground cools quickly. Surface air layers are cooled by contact with the cool ground surface, while upper layers remain relatively warm, and an inversion results. As long as the atmosphere is still and stable, pollutants accumulate near the ground where they are produced and where we breathe them.

Abundant sunlight in Los Angeles initiates photochemical oxidation in the concentrated aerosols and gaseous chemicals in the inversion layer. A brown haze of ozone and nitrogen dioxide, quickly develops. Although recent air quality regulations have helped tremendously, on summer days, ozone concentrations in the Los Angeles basin still can reach unhealthy levels.

**Heat islands** and **dust domes** occur in cities even without inversion conditions. With their low albedo, concrete and brick surfaces in cities absorb large amounts of solar energy. A lack of vegetation or water results in very slight evaporation (latent heat production); instead, available solar energy is turned into heat. As a result, temperatures in cities are frequently 3° to 5°C (5° to 9°F) warmer than in the surrounding countryside, a condition known as an urban heat island. Tall buildings create convective updrafts that sweep pollutants into the air. Stable air masses created by this heat island over the city concentrate pollutants in a dust dome.

## 9.7 Effects of Air Pollution

Air pollution is equally serious for ecosystem health and for human health. In this section we review primary effects of air pollution.

### Polluted air damages lungs and tissues

Consequences of breathing dirty air include increased probability of heart attacks, respiratory diseases, and lung cancer. This can mean as much as a five to ten-year decrease in life expectancy if you live in the worst parts of Los Angeles or Baltimore, for example. Of course, the intensity and duration of your exposure, as well as your age and general health, are extremely important: you are much more likely to be at risk if you are very young, very old, or already suffering from some respiratory or cardiovascular disease. Bronchitis and emphysema are common chronic conditions resulting from air pollution. The U.S. Office of Technology Assessment estimates that 250,000 people suffer from pollution-related bronchitis and emphysema in the United States, and some 50,000 excess deaths each year are attributable to complications of these diseases, which are probably second only to heart attack as a cause of death.

Conditions are often much worse in developing countries. The United Nations estimates that at least 1.3 billion people around the world live in areas where the air is dangerously polluted. In many parts of the former Soviet Union, for example, respiratory ailments, cardiovascular diseases, lung cancer, infant mortality, and miscarriages are as much as 50 percent higher than in countries with cleaner air. And in China, city dwellers are four to six times more likely than country folk to die of lung cancer. The World Health Organization estimates that 4 million people die each year from diseases exacerbated by air pollution.

How does air pollution cause these health effects? Because they are strong oxidizing agents, sulfates, $SO_2$, $NO_x$, and $O_3$ irritate and damage delicate tissues in the eyes and lungs. Fine, suspended particulate materials penetrate deep into the lungs, causing irritation, scarring, and even tumor growth. Heart stress results from impaired lung functions. Carbon monoxide binds to hemoglobin, reducing oxygen flow to the brain. Headaches, dizziness, and heart stress result. Lead also binds to hemoglobin, damaging critical neurons in the brain and resulting in mental and physical impairment and developmental retardation.

## Plants are sensitive to pollutants

In the early days of industrialization, fumes from furnaces, smelters, refineries, and chemical plants often destroyed vegetation and created desolate, barren landscapes around mining and manufacturing centers. The copper-nickel smelter at Sudbury, Ontario, is a spectacular example. Starting in 1886, open-bed roasting was used to purify sulfide ores of nickel and copper. The resulting sulfur dioxide and sulfuric acid destroyed almost all plant life within about 30 km (18.6 mi) of the smelter. Rains washed away the exposed soil, leaving a barren moonscape of blackened bedrock (fig. 9.25). Recently, emission controls have been introduced, and the environment is beginning to recover, although exposed rock is still black, and the forest cover is mostly small and rather spindly.

Certain combinations of environmental factors have **synergistic effects** in which the injury caused by exposure to two factors together is more than the sum of exposure to each factor individually. For instance, white pine seedlings exposed to subthreshold concentrations of ozone and sulfur dioxide individually do not suffer any visible injury. If the same concentrations of pollutants are given together, however, visible damage occurs.

(a)

(b)

**Figure 9.25** (a) In 1975, acid precipitation from the copper-nickel smelters (tall stacks in background) had killed all the vegetation and charred the pink granite bedrock black for a large area around Sudbury, Ontario. (b) By 2005, a scrubby forest was growing again around Sudbury, but the rock surfaces remain stained black.

Pollutant levels too low to produce visible symptoms of damage may still have important effects. Field studies show that yields in some crops, such as soybeans, may be reduced as much as 50 percent by currently existing levels of oxidants in ambient air. Some plant pathologists suggest that ozone and photochemical oxidants are responsible for as much as 90 percent of agricultural, ornamental, and forest losses from air pollution. The total costs of this damage may be as much as $10 billion per year in North America alone.

## Smog and haze reduce visibility

We have only recently realized that pollution affects rural areas as well as cities. Even supposedly pristine places such as our national parks are suffering from air pollution. Grand Canyon National Park, where maximum visibility used to be 300 km (185 mi), is now so smoggy on some winter days that visitors can't see the opposite rim only 20 km (12.5 mi) across the canyon. Mining operations, smelters, and power plants (some of which were moved to the desert to improve air quality in cities such as Los Angeles) are the main culprits. Huge regions are affected by pollution. A gigantic "haze blob" as much as 3,000 km (about 2,000 mi) across covers much of the eastern United States in the summer, cutting visibility as much as 80 percent. People become accustomed to these conditions and don't realize that the air once was clear. Studies indicate, however, that, if all human-made sources of air pollution were shut down, the air would clear up in a few days, and there would be about 150-km (90-mi) visibility nearly everywhere, rather than the 15 km to which we have become accustomed.

## SO$_4$ and NO$_x$ produce acid deposition

**Acid precipitation**, the deposition of wet, acidic solutions or dry, acidic particles from the air, became widely recognized as a pollution problem only in the last 20 years. But the concept has been recognized since the 1850s. We describe acidity in terms of pH, with substances below pH 7 being acidic (chapter 2). Normal, unpolluted rain generally has a pH of about 5.6 due to carbonic acid created when rainwater reacts with $CO_2$ in the air. Downwind of industrial areas, rainfall acidity can reach levels below pH 4.3, more than ten times as acidic as normal rain. Acid fog, snow, mist, and dew can deposit damaging acids on plants, in water systems, and on buildings. Furthermore, fallout of dry sulfate and nitrate particles can account for as much as half of the acidic deposition in some areas.

A vigorous program of pollution control has been undertaken by Canada, the United States, and several European countries since the widespread recognition of acid rain. SO$_2$ and NO$_x$ emissions from power plants have decreased dramatically over the past three decades over much of Europe and eastern North America as a result of pollution-control measures. However, rain falling in these areas remains acidic

**Figure 9.27** A Fraser fir forest on Mount Mitchell, North Carolina, killed by acid rain, insect pests, and other stressors.

(fig. 9.26). Apparently, alkaline dust that would once have neutralized acids in air has been depleted by years of acid rain and is now no longer effective.

**Acid Deposition Damages Ecosystems** Aquatic ecosystems in Scandinavia were among the first discovered to be damaged by acid precipitation. Prevailing winds from Germany, Poland, and other parts of Europe deliver acids generated by industrial and automobile emissions—principally $H_2SO_4$ and $HNO_3$. The thin, acidic soils and nutrient-poor lakes and streams in the mountains of southern Norway and Sweden have been severely affected by this acid deposition. Most noticeable is the reduction of trout, salmon, and other game fish, whose eggs and fry die below pH 5. Aquatic plants, insects, and invertebrates also suffer. Many lakes in Sweden are now so acidic that they will no longer support game fish or other sensitive aquatic organisms. Large parts of Europe and eastern North America have also been damaged by acid precipitation.

Acidic rainfall, clouds, and snow have devastated forests in some regions. A detailed 1980 ecosystem inventory on Camel's Hump Mountain in Vermont found that seedling production, tree density, and viability of spruce-fir forests at high elevations had declined about 50 percent in 15 years. On Mount Mitchell in North Carolina, nearly all the trees above 2,000 m (6,000 ft) have lost needles, and about half are dead (fig. 9.27). Damage has been reported throughout Europe, from the Netherlands to Switzerland, as well as in China and the states of the former Soviet Union. In 1985 West German foresters estimated that about half the total forest area in West Germany (more than 4 million ha) was declining. The loss to the forest industry is estimated to be about 1 billion euros per year.

High-elevation forests are most severely affected. Mountain tops often have thin, acidic soils under normal conditions, with little ability to buffer,

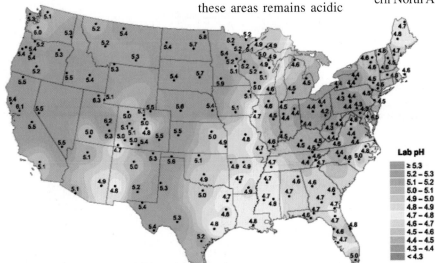

**Figure 9.26** Acid precipitation over the United States, 2000. *Source:* Data from National Acid Deposition Program, 2001.

Lab pH

≥ 5.3
5.2 – 5.3
5.1 – 5.2
5.0 – 5.1
4.9 – 5.0
4.8 – 4.9
4.7 – 4.8
4.6 – 4.7
4.5 – 4.6
4.4 – 4.5
4.3 – 4.4
< 4.3

**Figure 9.28** Atmospheric acids, especially sulfuric and nitric acids, have almost completely eaten away the face of this medieval statue. Each year, the total losses from air pollution damage to buildings and materials amount to billions of dollars.

or neutralize, acid precipitation. Acidic fog and mist frequently rest on mountaintops, lengthening plants' exposure to acidity. Mountaintops also catch more rain, snow, and fog than lowlands, so they are more exposed to acidic deposition.

The most visible mechanism of forest decline is direct damage to plant tissues and seedlings. Nutrient availability in forest soils is also depleted, however. Acids can also dissolve and mobilize toxic concentrations of metals, such as aluminum, and weakened trees become susceptible to diseases and insect pests.

**Buildings and Monuments Show Clear Damage**    In cities throughout the world, air pollution is destroying some of the oldest and most glorious buildings and works of art. Smoke and soot coat buildings, paintings, and textiles. Acids dissolve limestone and marble, destroying features and structures of historic buildings (fig. 9.28). The Parthenon in Athens, the Taj Mahal in Agra, the Coliseum in Rome, medieval cathedrals in Europe, and the Washington Monument in Washington, D.C., are slowly dissolving and flaking away because of acidic fumes in the air. On a more mundane level, air pollution and acid precipitation corrode steel in reinforced concrete, weakening buildings, roads, and bridges. Limestone, marble, and some kinds of sandstone flake and crumble. The Council on Environmental Quality estimates that U.S. economic losses from architectural damage caused by air pollution amount to about $4.8 billion in direct costs and $5.2 billion in property-value losses each year.

## 9.8  Air Pollution Control

"Dilution is the solution to pollution." This idea has long been our main approach to air pollution control. Tall smokestacks were built to send emissions far from the source, where they became difficult to detect or trace. As emissions have increased with global industrialization, though, dilution is no longer an effective strategy. There is no "away" to which we can throw our waste products. We need different strategies for pollution control.

## The best strategy is reducing production

Since most air pollution in the developed world is associated with transportation and energy production, the most effective strategy would be conservation: reducing electricity consumption, insulating homes and offices, and developing better public transportation could all greatly reduce air pollution in the United States, Canada, and Europe. Alternative energy sources, such as wind and solar power, produce energy with little or no pollution, and these and other technologies are becoming economically competitive (chapter 12). In addition to conservation, pollution can be controlled by technological innovation.

*Particulate removal* involves filtering air emissions. Filters trap particulates in a mesh of cotton cloth, spun glass fibers, or asbestos-cellulose. Industrial air filters are generally giant bags 10 to 15 m long and 2 to 3 m wide. Effluent gas is blown through the bag, much like the bag on a vacuum cleaner. Every few days or weeks, the bags are opened to remove the dust cake. Electrostatic precipitators are the most common particulate controls in power plants. Ash particles pick up an electrostatic surface charge as they pass between large electrodes (fig. 9.29). The electrically charged particles then precipitate (collect) on an oppositely charged collecting plate. These precipitators consume a large amount of electricity, but maintenance is relatively simple, and collection efficiency can be as high as 99 percent. The ash collected by both of these techniques is a solid waste (often hazardous due to the heavy metals and other trace components of coal or other ash source) and must be buried in landfills or other solid waste disposal sites.

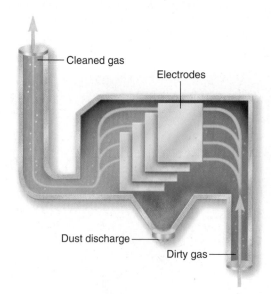

**Figure 9.29** An electrostatic precipitator traps particulate material. Particles are given an electrical charge, which makes them attracted to electrically charged plates. Effluent passes between these plates, leaving particles behind, on its way to the smoke stack.

*Sulfur removal* is important because sulfur oxides are among the most damaging of all air pollutants in terms of human health and ecosystem viability. Switching from soft coal with a high sulfur content to low-sulfur coal is the surest way to reduce sulfur emissions. High-sulfur coal is frequently politically or economically expedient, however. In the United States, Appalachia, a region of chronic economic depression, produces mostly high-sulfur coal. In China, much domestic coal is rich in sulfur. Switching to cleaner oil or gas would eliminate metal effluents as well as sulfur. Cleaning fuels is an alternative to switching. Coal can be crushed, washed, and gasified to remove sulfur and metals before combustion. This improves heat content and firing properties but may replace air pollution with solid waste and water pollution problems; furthermore, these steps are expensive.

Sulfur can also be removed to yield a usable product instead of simply a waste disposal problem. Elemental sulfur, sulfuric acid, and ammonium sulfate can all be produced using catalytic converters to oxidize or reduce sulfur. Markets have to be reasonably close and fly ash contamination must be reduced as much as possible for this procedure to be economically feasible.

*Nitrogen oxides* ($NO_x$) can be reduced in both internal combustion engines and industrial boilers by as much as 50 percent by carefully controlling the flow of air and fuel. Staged burners, for example, control burning temperatures and oxygen flow to prevent formation of $NO_x$. The catalytic converter on your car uses platinum-palladium and rhodium catalysts to remove up to 90 percent of $NO_x$, hydrocarbons, and carbon monoxide at the same time.

*Hydrocarbon controls* mainly involve complete combustion or the control of evaporation. Hydrocarbons and volatile organic compounds are produced by incomplete combustion of fuels or by solvent evaporation from chemical factories, paints, dry cleaning, plastic manufacturing, printing, and other industrial processes. Closed systems that prevent escape of fugitive gases can reduce many of these emissions. In automobiles, for instance, positive crankcase ventilation (PCV) systems collect oil that escapes from around the pistons and unburned fuel and channels them back to the engine for combustion. Controlling leaks from industrial valves, pipes, and storage tanks can have a significant impact on air quality. Afterburners are often the best method for destroying volatile organic chemicals in industrial exhaust stacks.

## Clean air legislation is controversial

Through most of human history, the costs of pollution have been borne by the public, which breathes or grows crops in polluted air, rather than by polluters themselves. Rules to control pollution have often sought to make polluters pay for pollution control, in order to reduce public expenses for health care and other costs associated with pollution. Naturally, emitters of pollutants have objected to these rules. It is easier and more profitable to externalize the costs of pollution, and let the public absorb the expenses. Health advocates, on the other hand, argue that industries should pay for pollution prevention. Because of these contrasting interests, clean air laws have always been controversial.

Over time countless ordinances have prohibited emission of objectionable smoke and odors. The city of London tried to ban coal burning as early as the sixteenth century, a ban that had little effect.

The Clean Air Act of 1963 was the first national legislation in the United States aimed at air pollution control. The act provided federal grants to states to combat pollution but was careful to preserve states' rights to set and enforce air quality regulations. It soon became obvious that some pollution problems cannot be solved on a local basis.

In 1970, an extensive set of amendments essentially rewrote the Clean Air Act. These amendments identified the "criteria" pollutants discussed earlier in this chapter, and established primary and secondary standards for ambient air quality. Primary standards are intended to protect human health. Secondary standards are set to protect materials, crops, climate, visibility, and personal comfort.

Since 1970 the Clean Air Act has been modified, updated, and amended many times. The most significant amendments were in the 1990 update. Amendments have involved acrimonious debate, with bills sometimes languishing in Congress from one session to the next because of disputes over burdens of responsibility and cost and definitions of risk. A 2002 report concluded that simply by enforcing existing clean air legislation, the United States could save at least 6,000 lives per year and prevent 140,000 asthma attacks.

Throughout its history the Clean Air Act has been controversial. Victims of air pollution demand more protection; industry and special interest groups complain that controls are too expensive. One of the most contested aspects of the act is the "**new source review**," which was established in 1977. This provision was originally adopted because industry argued that it would be intolerably expensive to install new pollution-control equipment on old power plants and factories that were about to close down anyway. Congress agreed to "grandfather" or exempt existing equipment from new pollution limits with the stipulation that when they were upgraded or replaced, more stringent rules would apply. The result was that owners kept old facilities operating precisely because they were exempted from pollution control. In fact, corporations poured millions into aging power plants and factories, expanding their capacity rather than build new ones. Thirty years later, most of those grandfathered plants are still going strong, and continue to be among the biggest contributors to smog and acid rain.

The Clinton administration attempted to force utilities to install modern pollution control on old power plants when they replaced or repaired equipment. President Bush, however, said that determining which facilities are new, and which are not, represented a cumbersome and unreasonable imposition on industries. The EPA subsequently announced it would abandon new source reviews, depending instead on voluntary emissions controls and a trading program for air pollution allowances.

A compromise approach for handling pollutants has been **cap-and-trade** agreements. A cap-and-trade approach sets maximum emission levels for pollutants. Facilities can then buy and sell emission "credits," or permitted allotments of pollutants. Companies can decide if it's cheaper to install pollution control equipment or to simply buy someone else's credits.

Cap-and-trade has worked well for sulfur dioxide. When trading began in 1990, economists estimated that eliminating 10 million tons of sulfur dioxide would cost $15 billion per year. Left to find the most economical ways to reduce emissions, however, utilities have been able to reach clean air goals for one-tenth that price. A serious shortcoming of this approach is that while trading has resulted in overall pollution reduction, some local "hot spots" remain where owners have found it cheaper to pay someone else to reduce pollution than to do it themselves.

## 9.9 Current Conditions and Future Prospects

Although the United States has not yet achieved the Clean Air Act goals in many parts of the country, air quality has improved dramatically in the last decade in terms of the major large-volume pollutants. For 23 of the largest U.S. cities, the number of days each year in which air quality reached the hazardous level is down 93 percent from a decade ago. Of 97 metropolitan areas that failed to meet clean air standards in the 1980s, 41 are now in compliance. For many cities, this is the first time they met air quality goals in 20 years.

There have been some notable successes and some failures. The EPA estimates that between 1970 and 1998, lead fell 98 percent, $SO_2$ declined 35 percent, and CO shrank 32 percent. Filters, scrubbers, and precipitators on power plants and other large stationary sources are responsible for most of the particulate and $SO_2$ reductions. Catalytic converters on automobiles are responsible for most of the CO and $O_3$ reductions.

The only conventional "criteria" pollutants that have not dropped significantly are particulates and $NO_x$. Because automobiles are the main source of $NO_x$, cities, such as Nashville, Tennessee, and Atlanta, Georgia, where pollution comes largely from traffic, still have serious air quality problems. Rigorous pollution controls are having a positive effect on Southern California air quality. Los Angeles, which had the dirtiest air in the nation for decades, wasn't even in the top 20 polluted cities in 2007.

Particulate matter (mostly dust and soot) is produced by agriculture, fuel combustion, metal smelting, concrete manufacturing, and other activities. Industrial cities, such as Baltimore, Maryland, and Baton Rouge, Louisiana, also have continuing problems. Eighty-five other urban areas are still considered nonattainment regions. In spite of these local failures, however, 80 percent of the United States now meets the National Ambient Air Quality Standards. This improvement in air quality is perhaps the greatest environmental success story in our history.

### Air pollution remains a problem, especially in developing regions

The outlook is not so encouraging in other parts of the world. The major metropolitan areas of many developing countries are growing at explosive rates to incredible sizes (chapter 14), and environmental quality is abysmal in many of them. Mexico City remains notorious for bad air. Pollution levels exceed WHO health standards 350 days per year, and more than half of all city children have lead levels in their blood high enough to lower intelligence and retard development. Mexico City's 131,000 industries and 2.5 million vehicles spew out more than 5,500 tons of air pollutants daily. Santiago, Chile, averages 299 days per year on which suspended particulates exceed WHO standards of 90 mg/m³.

While China is making efforts to control air and water pollution (chapter 1), many of China's 400,000 factories have no air pollution controls. Experts estimate that home coal burners and factories emit 10 million tons of soot and 15 million tons of sulfur dioxide annually and that emissions have increased rapidly over the past 20 years. Seven of the ten cities in the world with the worst air quality are in China. Sheyang, an industrial city in northern China, is thought to have the world's worst continuing particulate problem, with peak winter concentrations over 700 mg/m³ (nine times U.S. maximum standards). Airborne particulates in Sheyang exceed WHO standards on 347 days per year. It's estimated that air pollution is responsible for 400,000 premature deaths every year in China. Beijing, Xi'an, and Guangzhou also have severe air pollution problems. The high incidence of cancer in Shanghai is thought to be linked to air pollution.

### Many places have improved greatly

Not all is pessimistic, however. There have been some spectacular successes in air pollution control. Sweden and West Germany (countries affected by forest losses due to acid precipitation) cut their sulfur emissions by two-thirds between 1970 and 1985. Austria and Switzerland have gone even further, regulating even motorcycle emissions. The Global Environmental Monitoring System (GEMS) reports declines in particulate levels in 26 of 37 cities worldwide. Sulfur dioxide and sulfate particles, which cause acid rain and respiratory disease, have declined in 20 of these cities.

Even poor countries can control air pollution. Delhi, India, for example was once considered one of the world's ten most polluted cities. Visibility often was less than 1 km on smoggy days. Health experts warned that breathing Delhi's air was equivalent to smoking two packs of cigarettes per day. Pollution levels exceeded World Health Organization standards by nearly five times. Respiratory diseases were widespread, and the cancer rate was significantly higher than surrounding rural areas. The biggest problem was vehicle emissions, which contributed about 70 percent of air pollutants (industrial emissions made up 20 percent, while burning of garbage and firewood made up most of the rest).

In the 1990s, catalytic converters were required for automobiles, and unleaded gasoline and low-sulfur diesel fuel were introduced. In 2000, more than private automobiles were required to meet European standards, and in 2002, more than 80,000 buses, auto-rickshaws, and taxis were required to switch from liquid fuels to compressed natural gas (fig. 9.30). Sulfur dioxide and carbon monoxide levels have dropped 80 percent and 70 percent, respectively, since 1997. Particulate emissions dropped by about 50 percent. Residents report that the air is dramatically clearer and more healthy. Unfortunately, rising

**Figure 9.30** Air quality in Delhi, India, has improved dramatically since buses, auto-rickshaws, and taxis were required to switch from liquid fuels to compressed natural gas. This is one of the most encouraging success stories in controlling pollution in the developing world.

prosperity, driven by globalization of information management, has doubled the number of vehicles on the roads, threatening this progress. Still, the gains made in New Delhi are encouraging for people everywhere.

Twenty years ago, Cubatao, Brazil, was described as the "Valley of Death," one of the most dangerously polluted places in the world. A steel plant, a huge oil refinery, and fertilizer and chemical factories churned out thousands of tons of air pollutants every year that were trapped between onshore winds and the uplifted plateau on which São Paulo sits. Trees died on the surrounding hills. Birth defects and respiratory diseases were alarmingly high. Since then, however, the citizens of Cubatao have made remarkable progress in cleaning up their environment. The end of military rule and restoration of democracy allowed residents to publicize their complaints. The environment became an important political issue. The state of São Paulo invested about $100 million and the private sector spent twice as much to clean up most pollution sources in the valley. Particulate pollution was

reduced 75 percent, ammonia emissions were reduced 97 percent, hydrocarbons that cause ozone and smog were cut 86 percent, and sulfur dioxide production fell 84 percent. Fish are returning to the rivers, and forests are regrowing on the mountains. Progress is possible! We hope that similar success stories will be obtainable elsewhere.

## Conclusion

We appear to be at a tipping point in our attitudes toward climate change. Where, a few years ago, most people in America thought that this was just a wild theory of a small group of crazy scientists, we've gone to a widespread acceptance that the science of global warming is indisputable. The surprising success of former Vice President Al Gore's documentary, *An Inconvenient Truth*, has been a powerful force in this social transformation. Perhaps more important is that many people can actually see tangible proof in their own lives that something strange is happening to our climate.

But is it too late to do anything? Most scientists believe there is time, if we act quickly and effectively, to avoid the worst consequences of global climate change. It's encouraging to know that we don't need a technological miracle to save us from this impending catastrophe. We have the ability to dramatically reduce our greenhouse gas emissions right now. And it will probably save money and create jobs to do so.

The success of the Montreal Protocol in eliminating CFCs is a landmark in international cooperation on an environmental program. While the stratospheric ozone hole continues to grow because of global warming effects and the residual chlorine in the air released decades ago, we expect the ozone depletion to end in about 50 years. This is one of the few global environmental threats that has had such a rapid and successful resolution. Let's hope that others will follow.

Progress in reducing local pollution in developing countries, such as Brazil and India, also is encouraging. Problems that once seemed overwhelming can be overcome. In some cases, it requires lifestyle changes or different ways of doing things to bring about progress, but as the Chinese philosopher Lao Tsu wrote, "A journey of a thousand miles must begin with a single step."

## Practice Quiz

1. What are the "stabilization wedges" suggested by Pacala and Socolow at Princeton University (see table 9.2)? How many wedges do we need to accomplish to flatten our $CO_2$ emissions?
2. What is the *greenhouse effect*, and how does it work?
3. Why are we worried about greenhouse gases?
4. What is the *thermohaline ocean conveyor* and what is happening to it?
5. Describe the El Niño/Southern Oscillation.
6. What gas, action, and country make the largest contribution to global warming?
7. What has been the greatest air pollution control success in the United States since 1970?
8. Define *primary air pollutant, secondary air pollutant, photochemical oxidant, point source*, and *fugitive emissions*.
9. What is destroying stratospheric ozone, and where does this happen?
10. What is the "new source review"?

# Critical Thinking and Discussion Questions

Apply the principles you have learned in this chapter to discuss these questions with other students.

1. El Niño is a natural climate process, but some scientists suspect it is changing because of global warming. What sort of evidence would you look for to decide if El Niño has gotten stronger recently?

2. One of the problems with the Kyoto Protocol and with the Clean Air Act is that economists and scientists define problems differently and have contrasting priorities. How would an economist and an ecologist explain disputes over the Kyoto Protocol differently?

3. Economists and scientists often have difficulty reaching common terms for defining and solving issues such as the Clean Air Act renewal. How might their conflicting definitions be reshaped to make the discussion more successful?

4. Why do you think controlling greenhouse gases is such a difficult problem? List some of the technological, economic, political, emotional, and other factors involved. Whose responsibility is it to reduce our impacts on climate?

5. Air pollution often originates in one state or country but causes health and crop damage in other areas. For example, mercury from Midwestern power plants is harming plants, water, and health in eastern states. How should states, or countries, negotiate the costs of controlling these pollutants?

---

# Data Analysis | Examining the IPCC Fourth Assessment Report (AR4)

The Intergovernmental Panel on Climate Change (IPCC) has a rich repository of figures and data, and because these data are likely to influence some policy actions in your future, it's worthwhile taking a few minutes to look at the IPCC reports.

The most brief and to the point is the Summary for Policy Makers (SPM) that accompanies the Fourth Assessment Report.

You can find the summary here: http://www.ipcc.ch/ipccreports/ar4-syr.htm. The full report is also available here.

Open the SPM and look at the first page of text; then look at the first figure, SPM1 (reproduced here). Look at this figure carefully and answer the following questions:

1. What is the subject of each graph? Why are all three shown together?

2. Carefully read the caption. What are the blue shaded areas? Why are they there?

3. The left axis for all three graphs shows the difference between each year's observations and an average value. What values are averaged?

4. What does the central trend line in each graph represent? In the third graph, what is the value of that line, in million $km^2$, for the most recent year shown? Approximately what year had the lowest value shown? What does a decline in this graph represent on the ground?

5. Why is the trend in the snow cover graph less steep than the trends in the other two graphs?

6. Nearly every page of the IPCC report has graphs that show quite interesting details when you take the time to look at them. Choose two other graphs in the SPM document and explain the main messages they give.

See if you can explain them clearly enough to communicate the main idea to a friend or family member. Have different students select different graphs and explain them to the class.

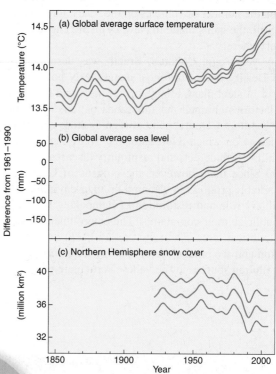

Changes in temperature, sea level, and Northern Hemisphere snow cover

(a) Global average surface temperature

(b) Global average sea level

(c) Northern Hemisphere snow cover

See the evidence: view the IPCC report at http://www.ipcc.ch/graphics/graphics/syr/spm1.jpg.

For Additional Help in Studying This Chapter, please visit our website at www.mhhe.com/cunningham6e. You will find practice quizzes, key terms, answers to end of chapter questions, additional case studies, an extensive reading list, and Google Earth™ mapping quizzes.

ENVIRONMENTAL SCIENCE

# 10 Water: Resources and Pollution

Between 2000 and 2010, the surface level of Lake Mead, the largest reservoir on the Colorado River, fell more than 100 ft (30.5 m) during the worst drought in recorded history. If water levels fall another 100 ft, the reservoir will reach "dead pool" levels at which it can provide neither the water nor the electrical power on which millions of people depend.

## Learning Outcomes

*After studying this chapter, you should be able to answer the following questions:*

- Where does our water come from? How do we use it?
- Where and why do water shortages occur?
- How can we increase water supplies? What are some costs of these methods?
- How can *you* conserve water?
- What is *water pollution*? What are its sources and effects?
- Why are sewage treatment and clean water important in developing countries?
- How can we control water pollution?

*I tell you gentlemen; you are piling up a heritage of conflict and litigation of water rights, for there is not sufficient water to supply the land.*

— JOHN WESLEY POWELL

# CASE STUDY

## When Will Lake Mead Go Dry?

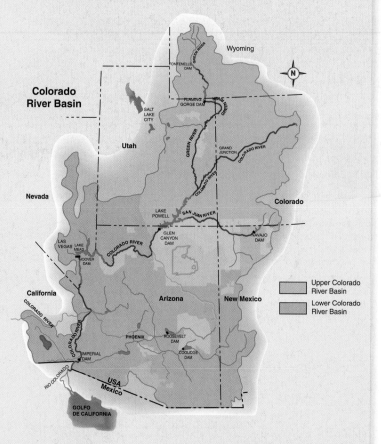

The Colorado River is the lifeblood of the American Southwest. More than 30 million people and a $1.2 trillion regional economy in cities, such as Los Angeles, Phoenix, Las Vegas, and Denver, depend on its water. But the sustainability of this essential resource is in doubt. Drought, climate change, and rapid urban growth are creating worries about the future of the entire watershed.

In 2008, Tim Barnett and David Pierce from the Scripps Institute in California published a provocative article suggesting that both Lake Mead and Lake Powell could reach levels within a decade or so at which neither would be able to either produce power or provide water for urban or agricultural use if no changes are made in current water allocations. Representing more than 85 percent of the water storage for the entire Colorado system, reaching "dead pool" levels in these huge lakes would be a catastrophe for the whole region. This warning is based on both historical records and climate models that suggest a 10 to 30 percent run off reduction in the area over the next 50 years.

The roots of this problem can be traced to the Colorado Compact of 1922, which allocated water rights for the seven states that adjoin the river. The previous decade had been the wettest in more than a thousand years. The estimated annual river flow of 18 million acre-feet (22 billion m³) negotiators thought they could allocate was about 20 percent higher than the twentieth-century average. The error didn't matter much at the time, because none of the states were able to withdraw their full share of water.

As cities have grown, however, and agriculture has expanded over the past century, competing claims for water have repeatedly caused tensions and disputes. Cumulatively, massive water diversion projects, such as the Colorado River Aqueduct, which provides water for Los Angeles, the All-American Canal, which irrigates California's Imperial Valley, or the Central Arizona Project, which transports water over the mountains and across the desert to Phoenix and Tucson, are capable of diverting the entire river flow. In 1944, the United States agreed to provide 1.5 million acre-feet to Mexico so there would be at least a little water (although of dubious quality) in the river when it crossed the border.

To make matters worse, climate change is expected to decrease river flows by 10 to 30 percent over the next 50 years. There may be only half as much water in the river in a few decades than negotiators once thought they had to distribute between the states. The Southwest is currently in its eighth year of drought, which may be the first hint of that change. The maximum water level in Lake Mead (an elevation of 1,220 feet, or 372 m) was last reached in 2000. Since then, the lake level has been dropping about 12 feet (3.6 m) per year, reaching 1,097 feet in 2010. The minimum power level (the height at which electricity can be produced) is 1,050 feet (320 m). The minimum level at which water can be drawn off by gravity is 900 feet (274 m). Barnett and Pierce estimate that without changes in current management plans, there's a 50 percent chance minimum power pool levels in both Lakes Mead and Powell will be reached by 2017 and that there's an equal chance that live storage in both lakes will be gone by about 2021.

Already, we're at or beyond the sustainable limits of the river. Currently, Lake Powell is only 58 percent full, and Lake Mead holds only 43 percent of its maximum volume (fig 10.1). The shores of both lakes now display a wide "bath-tub ring" of deposited minerals left by the receding water. One suggestion has been to drain Lake Powell in order to ensure a water supply for Lake Mead. This solution is strenuously opposed by many of the 3 million people per year who recreate in its red rock canyons and sparkling blue water. On the other hand, think of the cost and disruption if Los Angeles, Phoenix, Las Vegas, and other major metropolitan areas of the region were to run out of water and power.

The American Southwest isn't alone in facing this problem. The United Nations warns that water supplies are likely to become one of the most pressing environmental issues of the twenty-first century. By 2025, two-thirds of all humans could be living in places where water resources are inadequate. In this chapter, we'll look at the sources of our fresh water, what we do with it, and how we might protect its quality and extend its usefulness. For further reading, see:

Barnett, T. P., and D. W. Pierce. 2008. When will Lake Mead go dry? *Journal of Water Resources Research.* Vol. 44, W03201.

Powell, James L. 2009. *Dead Pool: Lake Powell, Global Warming, and the Future of Water in the West.* University of California Press.

**Figure 10.1** The Colorado River flows 2,330 km (1,450 mi) through seven western states. Its water supports 30 million people and a $1.2 trillion regional economy, but drought, climate change, and rapid urban growth threaten the sustainability of this resource.

# 10.1 Water Resources

Water is a marvelous substance—flowing, swirling, seeping, constantly moving from sea to land and back again. It shapes the earth's surface and moderates our climate. Water is essential for life. It is the medium in which all living processes occur (chapter 2). Water dissolves nutrients and distributes them to cells, regulates body temperature, supports structures, and removes waste products. About 60 percent of your body is water. You could survive for weeks without food, but only a few days without water. Water also is needed for agriculture, industry, transportation, and a host of other human uses. In short, clean freshwater is one of our most vital natural resources.

## The hydrologic cycle constantly redistributes water

The water we use cycles endlessly through the environment. The total amount of water on our planet is immense—more than 1,404 million km³ (370 billion billion gal) (table 10.1). This water evaporates from moist surfaces, falls as rain or snow, passes through living organisms, and returns to the ocean in a process known as the **hydrologic cycle** (see fig. 2.18). Every year, about 500,000 km³, or a layer 1.4 m thick, evaporates from the oceans. More than 90 percent of that moisture falls back on the ocean. The 47,000 km³ carried onshore joins some 72,000 km³ evaporated from lakes, rivers, soil, and plants to become our annual, renewable freshwater supply. Plants play a major role in the hydrologic cycle, absorbing groundwater and pumping it into the atmosphere by transpiration (transport plus evaporation). In tropical forests, as much as 75 percent of annual precipitation is returned to the atmosphere by plants.

| Table 10.1 | Units of Water Measurement |
| --- |
| One cubic kilometer (km³) equals 1 billion cubic meters (m³), 1 trillion liters, or 264 billion gal. |
| One acre-foot is the amount of water required to cover an acre of ground 1 ft deep. This is equivalent to 325,851 gal, or 1.2 million liters, or 1,234 m³, approximately the amount consumed annually by a family of four in the United States. |
| One cubic foot per second of river flow equals 28.3 liters per second, or 449 gal per minute. |

Solar energy drives the hydrologic cycle by evaporating surface water, which becomes rain and snow. Because water and sunlight are unevenly distributed around the globe, water resources are very uneven. At Iquique in the Chilean desert, for instance, no rain has fallen in recorded history. At the other end of the scale, 26.5 m (86.8 ft) of rain was recorded in 1860 in Cherrapunji in India. Figure 10.2 shows current patterns of precipitation around the world, but climate change is altering that map. Cherrapunji, for example, only receives about one-third as much rain today as it did a century ago.

Most of the world's rainiest regions are tropical, where heavy rainy seasons occur, or in coastal mountain regions. Deserts occur on every continent just outside the tropics (the Sahara, the Namib, the Gobi, the Sonoran, and many others). Rainfall is also slight at very high latitudes, another high-pressure region.

Mountains also influence moisture distribution. The windward sides of mountain ranges, including the Pacific Northwest and the flanks of the Himalayas, are typically wet and have large rivers;

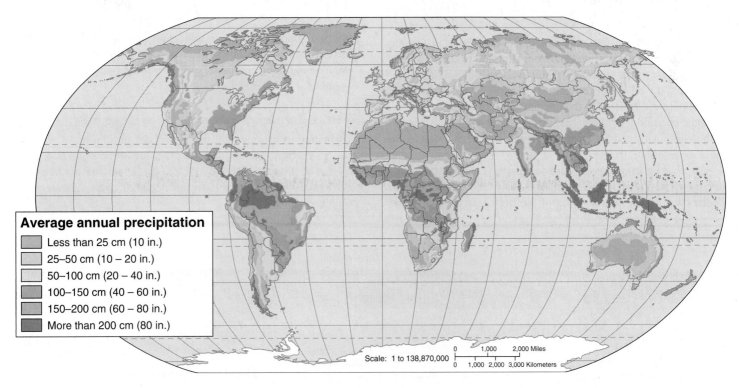

**Average annual precipitation**
- Less than 25 cm (10 in.)
- 25–50 cm (10 – 20 in.)
- 50–100 cm (20 – 40 in.)
- 100–150 cm (40 – 60 in.)
- 150–200 cm (60 – 80 in.)
- More than 200 cm (80 in.)

Scale: 1 to 138,870,000

**Figure 10.2** Average annual precipitation. Note wet areas that support tropical rainforests occur along the equator, while the major world deserts occur in zones of dry, descending air between 20° and 40° north and south.

on the leeward sides of mountains, in areas known as the rain shadow, dry conditions dominate, and water can be very scarce. The windward side of Mount Waialeale on the island of Kauai, for example, is extremely wet, with an annual rainfall around 1,200 cm (460 in.). The leeward side, only a few kilometers away, has an average yearly rainfall of only 46 cm (18 in.).

An important consideration in water availability is whether there is rainfall year-round, especially in the growing season. Another question is whether hot, dry weather evaporates available moisture. These factors help determine the amount and variety of biological activity in a place (chapter 5).

## 10.2 Major Water Compartments

The distribution of water often is described in terms of interacting compartments in which water resides, sometimes briefly and sometimes for eons (table 10.2). The length of time water typically stays in a compartment is its **residence time**. On average, a water molecule stays in the ocean for about 3,000 years, for example, before it evaporates and starts through the hydrologic cycle again. Nearly all the world's water is in the oceans (fig. 10.3). Oceans play a crucial role in moderating the earth's temperature, and over 90 percent of the world's living biomass is contained in the oceans. What we mainly need, though, is fresh water. Amazingly, only about .02 percent of the world's water is in a form accessible to us and to other organisms that rely on fresh water.

### Glaciers, ice, and snow contain most surface, fresh water

Of the 2.4 percent of all water that is fresh, nearly 90 percent is tied up in glaciers, ice caps, and snowfields. Although most of this ice is located in Antarctica, Greenland, and the floating ice cap in the Arctic, alpine glaciers and snowfields supply water to billions of people. The winter snowpack on the western slope of the Rocky Mountains, for example, provides 75 percent of the flow in the Colorado River described in the opening case study of this chapter. Drought conditions already have reduced snowfall (and runoff) in the western United States, and global warming is projected to cause even further declines.

As chapter 15 discusses, climate change is shrinking glaciers and snowfields nearly everywhere (fig. 10.4). In Asia, the Tibetan glaciers that are the source of six of the world's largest rivers and

**Table 10.2 | Earth's Water Compartments**

| Compartment | Volume (1,000 km³) | Percent of Total Water | Average Residence Time |
|---|---|---|---|
| Total | 1,386,000 | 100 | 2,800 years |
| Oceans | 1,338,000 | 96.5 | 3,000 to 30,000 years* |
| Ice and snow | 24,364 | 1.76 | 1 to 100,000 years* |
| Saline groundwater | 12,870 | 0.93 | Days to thousands of years* |
| Fresh groundwater | 10,530 | 0.76 | Days to thousands of years* |
| Fresh lakes | 91 | 0.007 | 1 to 500 years* |
| Saline lakes | 85 | 0.006 | 1 to 1,000 years* |
| Soil moisture | 16.5 | 0.001 | 2 weeks to 1 year* |
| Atmosphere | 12.9 | 0.001 | 1 week |
| Marshes, wetlands | 11.5 | 0.001 | Months to years |
| Rivers, streams | 2.12 | 0.0002 | 1 week to 1 month |
| Living organisms | 1.12 | 0.0001 | 1 week |

*Depends on depth and other factors.
*Source:* Data from UNEP, 2002.

supply drinking water for 3 billion people are shrinking rapidly. There are warnings that these glaciers could vanish in a few decades, which would bring enormous suffering and economic losses to the continent.

### Groundwater stores large resources

Originating as precipitation that percolates into layers of soil and rock, groundwater makes up the largest compartment of liquid, fresh water. The groundwater within 1 km of the surface is more than 100 times the volume of all the freshwater lakes, rivers, and reservoirs combined.

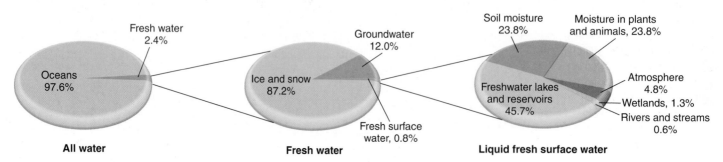

**Figure 10.3** Less than 1 percent of fresh water, and less than 0.02 percent of all water, is fresh, liquid surface water on which terrestrial life depends.
*Source:* U.S. Geological Survey.

http://www.mhhe.com/cunningham6e

**Figure 10.4** Glaciers and snowfields provide much of the water on which billions of people rely. The snowpack in the western Rocky Mountains, for examples, supplies about 75 percent of the annual flow of the Colorado River. Global climate change is shrinking glaciers and causing snowmelt to come earlier in the year, disrupting this vital water source.

Plants get moisture from a relatively shallow layer of soil containing both air and water, known as the **zone of aeration** (fig. 10.5). Depending on rainfall amount, soil type, and surface topography, the zone of aeration may be a few centimeters or many meters deep. Lower soil layers, where all soil pores are filled with water, make up the **zone of saturation**, the source of water in most wells; the top of this zone is the **water table**.

Geologic layers that contain water are known as **aquifers**. Aquifers may consist of porous layers of sand or gravel or of cracked or porous rock. Below an aquifer, relatively impermeable layers of rock or clay keep water from seeping out at the bottom. Instead, water seeps more or less horizontally through the porous layer. Depending on geology, it can take from a few hours to several years for water to move a few hundred meters through an aquifer. If impermeable layers lie above an aquifer, pressure can develop within the water-bearing layer. Pressure in the aquifer can make a

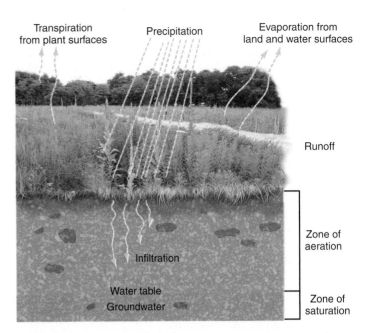

**Figure 10.5** Precipitation that does not evaporate or run off over the surface percolates through the soil in a process called infiltration. The upper layers of soil hold droplets of moisture between air-filled spaces. Lower layers, where all spaces are filled with water, make up the zone of saturation, or groundwater.

well flow freely at the surface. These free-flowing wells and springs are known as *artesian* wells or springs.

Areas where surface water filters into an aquifer are **recharge zones** (fig. 10.6). Most aquifers recharge extremely slowly, and road and house construction or water use at the surface can further slow recharge rates. Contaminants can also enter aquifers through recharge zones. Urban or agricultural runoff in recharge zones is often a serious problem. The people who don't have access to clean surface water generally depend on groundwater for drinking and other uses. Every year 700 km$^3$ are withdrawn by humans, mostly from shallow, easily polluted aquifers.

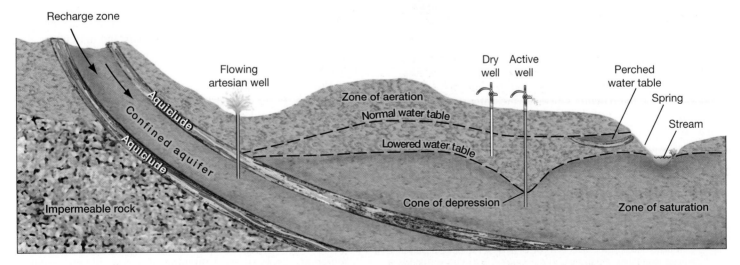

**Figure 10.6** An aquifer is a porous or cracked layer of rock. Impervious rock layers (aquicludes) keep water within a confined aquifer. Pressure from uphill makes an artesian well flow freely. Pumping can create a cone of depression, which leaves shallower wells dry.

## Rivers, lakes, and wetlands cycle quickly

Fresh, flowing surface water is one of our most precious resources. Rivers contain a relatively small amount of water at any one time. Most rivers would begin to dry up in weeks or days if they were not constantly replenished by precipitation, snowmelt, or groundwater seepage.

We compare the size of rivers in terms of **discharge**, or the amount of water that passes a fixed point in a given amount of time. This is usually expressed as liters or cubic feet of water per second. The 16 largest rivers in the world carry nearly half of all surface runoff on the earth, and a large fraction of that occurs in a single river, the Amazon, which carries nearly as much water as the the next seven biggest rivers together.

Lakes contain nearly 100 times as much water as all rivers and streams combined, but much of this water is in a few of the world's largest lakes. Lake Baikal in Siberia, the Great Lakes of North America, the Great Rift Lakes of Africa, and a few other lakes contain vast amounts of water, not all of it fresh. Worldwide, lakes are almost as important as rivers in terms of water supplies, food, transportation, and settlement.

Wetlands—bogs, swamps, wet meadows, and marshes—play a vital and often unappreciated role in the hydrologic cycle. Their lush plant growth stabilizes soil and holds back surface runoff, allowing time for infiltration into aquifers and producing even, year-long stream flow. When wetlands are disturbed, their natural water-absorbing capacity is reduced, and surface waters run off quickly, resulting in floods and erosion during the rainy season and low stream flow the rest of the year.

## The atmosphere is one of the smallest compartments

The atmosphere contains only 0.001 percent of the total water supply, but it is the most important mechanism for redistributing water around the world. An individual water molecule resides in the atmosphere for about ten days, on average. Some water evaporates and falls within hours. Water can also travel halfway around the world before it falls, replenishing streams and aquifers on land.

# 10.3 Water Availability and Use

Clean, fresh water is essential for nearly every human endeavor. Collectively, we now appropriate more than half of all the freshwater in the world. Perhaps more than any other environmental factor, the availability of water determines the location and activities of humans on the earth. **Renewable water supplies** are resources that are replenished regularly—mainly surface water and shallow groundwater. Renewable water is most plentiful in the tropics, where rainfall is heavy, followed by midlatitudes, where rainfall is regular.

## Many countries experience water scarcity and stress

As you can see in figure 10.2, South America, West Central Africa, and South and Southeast Asia all have areas of very high rainfall. Brazil and the Democratic Republic of Congo, because they have both high precipitation and large land areas, are among the most water-rich countries on earth. Canada and Russia, which both have large areas with high rain and snowfall, also have large annual water supplies.

The highest per capita water supplies generally occur in countries with wet climates and low population densities. Iceland, for example, has about 160 million gallons (605,000 m$^3$) per person per year. In contrast, Bahrain, where temperatures are extremely high and rain almost never falls, has essentially no natural fresh water. Almost all of Bahrain's water comes from imports and desalinized seawater. Egypt, in spite of the fact that the Nile River flows through it, has only about 11,000 gallons of water annually per capita, or about 15,000 times less than Iceland.

Periodic droughts create severe regional water shortages. Droughts are most common and often most severe in semiarid zones where moisture availability is the critical factor in determining plant and animal distribution. Undisturbed ecosystems often survive extended droughts with little damage, but introduction of domestic animals and agriculture disrupts native vegetation and undermines natural adaptations to low moisture levels.

Droughts are often cyclic, and land-use practices exacerbate their effects. In the United States, the worst drought—so far—in economic and social terms was in the 1930s. Poor soil conservation practices and a series of dry years in the Great Plains combined to create the "dust bowl." Wind stripped topsoil from millions of hectares of land, and billowing dust clouds turned day into night. Thousands of families were forced to leave farms and migrate to other areas.

As the opening case study shows, much of the western United States has been exceptionally dry over the past decade. Many places are experiencing water crises (fig 10.7). Is this just a temporary cycle or the beginning of a new climatic regime? The United States government projects that 36 states will have water deficits by 2012. Increased temperatures, disturbed weather

## Active Learning

### Mapping the Water-Rich and Water-Poor Countries

The top ten water-rich countries, in terms of water availability per capita, and the ten most water-poor countries are listed below. Locate these countries on the political map at the end of your book. Describe the patterns. Where are the water-rich countries concentrated? (Hint: does latitude matter?) Where are the water-poor countries most concentrated?

**Water-rich countries:** Iceland, Surinam, Guyana, Papua New Guinea, Gabon, Solomon Islands, Canada, Norway, Panama, Brazil

**Water-poor countries:** Kuwait, Egypt, United Arab Emirates, Malta, Jordan, Saudi Arabia, Singapore, Moldavia, Israel, Oman

*Answer:* Water-rich countries (per capita) are either in the far north, where populations and evaporation are low, or in the tropics. Water-poor countries are in the desert belt at about 15° to 25° latitude or are densely populated island nations (e.g., Malta, Singapore).

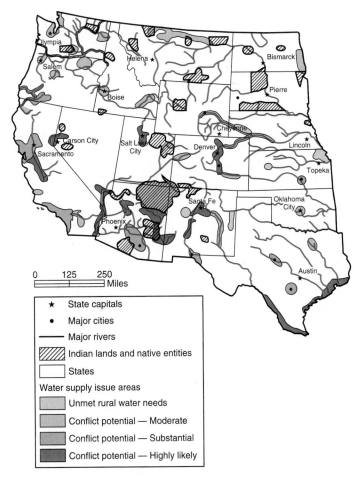

**Figure 10.7** Rapidly growing populations in arid regions are straining available water supplies. By 2025, the Department of the Interior warns that shortage could cause conflicts in many areas. *Source:* Data from U. S. Department of Interior.

Powell recommended that the political organization of the West be based on watersheds so that everyone in a given jurisdiction would be bound together by the available water. He thought that farms should be limited to local surface-water supplies, and that cities should be small, oasis settlements. Instead, we've built huge metropolitan areas, such as Los Angeles, Phoenix, Las Vegas, and Denver in places where there is little or no natural water supply. Will they survive impending shortages?

## Agriculture is our greatest water user

In contrast to energy resources, which usually are consumed when used, water can be used over and over if it is not too badly contaminated. Water **withdrawal** is the total amount of water taken from a water body. Much of this water could be returned to circulation in a reusable form. Water **consumption**, on the other hand, is loss of water due to evaporation, absorption, or contamination.

The natural cleansing and renewing functions of the hydrologic cycle replace the water we need if natural systems are not overloaded or damaged. Water is a renewable resource, but renewal takes time. The rate at which many of us now use water may make it necessary to conscientiously protect, conserve, and replenish our water supply.

Water use has been increasing about twice as fast as population growth over the past century. Water withdrawals are expected to continue to grow as more land is irrigated to feed an expanding population (fig. 10.8). Conflicts increase as different countries, economic sectors, and other stakeholders compete for the same, limited water supply. Water wars may well be the major source of hostilities in the twenty-first century.

Worldwide, agriculture claims about 70 percent of total water withdrawal, ranging from 93 percent of all water used in India to only 4 percent in Kuwait, which cannot afford to spend its limited water on crops. In many developing countries and in parts of the United States, the most common type of irrigation is to simply flood the whole field or run water in rows between crops. As much as half the water can be lost through evaporation or seepage from unlined

patterns, population growth, urban sprawl, waste, and wasteful uses all will contribute to these shortages. The effects on water supplies may well be the most serious consequences of global climate change.

If the government had listened to Major John Wesley Powell, the settlement patterns in the western United States would be very different than they are today. Powell, who lead the first expedition down the Colorado River, went on to be the first head of the U.S. Geological Survey. In that capacity, he did a survey of the agricultural and settlement potential of the western desert. His conclusion, quoted at the beginning of this chapter, was that there isn't enough water to support a large human population.

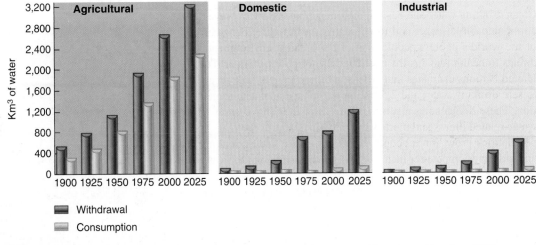

**Figure 10.8** Growth of water withdrawal and consumption, by sector, with projected levels to 2025. *Source:* UNEP, 2002.

irrigation canals bringing water to fields. Sprinklers are more efficient in distributing water, but they are more costly and energy intensive. Water-efficient drip irrigation can save significant amounts of water but currently is used on only about 1 percent of the world's croplands.

Because of worries about decreasing flow in the Colorado River, Los Angeles has signed a "dry year option" with the Palo Verde Irrigation District south of Las Vegas. The city will pay 7,000 farmers to leave land fallow during droughts and ship their water to the city. By changing crops and rotating fallow fields, farmers hope to stay in business during bad times while avoiding battles over a dwindling supply. According to the Pacific Institute, farming uses 85 percent of California's water to produce 2 percent of its economic output. Reducing farm consumption by 20 percent per year could double the urban water supply, but those who depend on agricultural income think this is a terrible idea.

Industry uses about one-fourth of water withdrawals worldwide. Some European countries use 70 percent of water for industry; less-industrialized countries use as little as 5 percent. Cooling water for power plants is by far the largest single industrial use of water, typically accounting for 50 to 75 percent of industrial withdrawal. A rapidly growing demand for water is for biofuel production. It currently takes 4 to 5 liters of water to produce 1 liter of ethanol. Water shortages may limit a switch to biofuels.

Domestic, or household, water use accounts for only about 6 percent of world water use. This includes water for drinking, cooking, and washing. The amount of water used per household varies enormously, however, depending on a country's wealth. The United Nations reports that people in developed countries consume on average, about ten times more water daily than those in developing nations. Poorer countries can't afford the infrastructure to obtain and deliver water to citizens. Inadequate water supplies, on the other hand, prevent agriculture, industry, sanitation, and other developments that reduce poverty.

## 10.4 Freshwater Shortages

Clean drinking water and basic sanitation are necessary to prevent communicable diseases and to maintain a healthy life. For many of the world's poorest people, one of the greatest environmental threats to health remains the continued use of polluted water. The United Nations estimates that at least a billion people lack access to safe drinking water and 2.5 billion don't have adequate sanitation. These deficiencies result in hundreds of millions of cases of water-related illness and more than 5 million deaths every year. As populations grow, more people move into cities, and agriculture and industry compete for increasingly scarce water supplies, water shortages are expected to become even worse.

By 2025 two-thirds of the world's people may be living in water-stressed countries—defined by the United Nations as consumption of more than 10 percent of renewable freshwater resources. One of the United Nations Millennium goals is to reduce by one-half the proportion of people without reliable access to clean water and improved sanitation.

There have been many attempts to enhance local supplies and redistribute water. Towing icebergs from Antarctica has been proposed, and creating rain in dry regions has been accomplished, with mixed success, by cloud seeding—distributing condensation nuclei in humid air to help form raindrops. Desalination is locally important: in the arid Middle East, where energy and money are available but water is scarce, desalination is sometimes the principal source of water. Some American cities, such as Tampa, Florida, and San Diego, California, also depend partly on energy-intensive desalination.

## Many people lack access to clean water

The World Health Organization considers an average of 1,000 m$^3$ (264,000 gal) per person per year to be a necessary amount of water for modern domestic, industrial, and agricultural uses. Some 45 countries, most of them in Africa or the Middle East, cannot meet the minimum essential water needs of all their citizens. In some countries, the problem is access to *clean* water. In Mali, for example, 88 percent of the population lacks clean water; in Ethiopia, it is 94 percent. Rural people often have less access to clean water than do city dwellers. Causes of water shortages include natural deficits, overconsumption by agriculture or industry, and inadequate funds for purifying and delivering good water.

More than two-thirds of the world's households have to fetch water from outside the home (fig. 10.9). This is heavy work, done mainly by women and children and sometimes taking several hours a day. Improved public systems bring many benefits to these poor families.

Availability doesn't always mean affordability. A typical poor family in Lima, Peru, for instance, uses one-sixth as much water as a middle-class American family but pays three times as much for it. If they followed government recommendations to boil all water to prevent cholera, up to one-third of the poor family's income could be used just in acquiring and purifying water.

**Figure 10.9** Village water supplies in Ghana.

Investments in rural development have brought significant improvements in recent years. Since 1990, nearly 800 million people—about 13 percent of the world's population—have gained access to clean water. The percentage of rural families with safe drinking water has risen from less than 10 percent to nearly 75 percent.

## Groundwater supplies are being depleted

Groundwater provides nearly 40 percent of the fresh water for agricultural and domestic use in the United States. Nearly half of all Americans and about 95 percent of the rural population depend on groundwater for drinking and other domestic purposes. Overuse of these supplies dries up wells, natural springs, and even groundwater-fed wetlands, rivers, and lakes. Pollution of aquifers through dumping of contaminants on recharge zones, leaks through abandoned wells, or deliberate injection of toxic wastes can make this valuable resource unfit for use.

In many areas of the United States, groundwater is being withdrawn from aquifers faster than natural recharge can replace it. On a local level, this causes a cone of depression in the water table. On a broader scale, heavy pumping can deplete a whole aquifer. The Ogallala Aquifer underlies eight Great Plains states from Texas to North Dakota. This porous bed of sand, gravel, and sandstone once held more water than all the freshwater lakes, streams, and rivers on the earth. Excessive pumping for irrigation has removed so much water that wells have dried up in many places, and farms, ranches, even whole towns are being abandoned. Recharging many such aquifers will take thousands of years. Using "fossil" water like this is essentially water mining. For all practical purposes, these aquifers are nonrenewable resources.

Water withdrawal also allows aquifers to collapse. Subsidence, or sinking of the ground surface, follows. The San Joaquin Valley in California has sunk more than 10 m (33 ft) in the past 50 years because of excessive groundwater pumping. Where aquifers become compressed, recharge becomes impossible.

Another consequence of aquifer depletion is saltwater intrusion. Along coastlines and in areas where saltwater deposits are left from ancient oceans, overuse of freshwater reservoirs often allows saltwater to intrude into aquifers used for domestic and agricultural purposes.

## Diversion projects redistribute water

Dams and canals are a foundation of civilization because they store and redistribute water for farms and cities. Many great civilizations have been organized around large-scale canal systems, including ancient empires of Sumeria, Egypt, and India. As modern dams and water diversion projects have grown in scale and number, though, their environmental costs have raised serious questions about efficiency, costs, and the loss of river ecosystems.

More than half of the world's 227 largest rivers have been dammed or diverted. Of the 50,000 large dams in the world, 90 percent were built in the twentieth century. Half of those are in China, and China continues to build and plan dams on its remaining rivers. Dams are justified in terms of flood control, water storage, and electricity production. However, the costs of relocating villages, as well as lost fishing, farming, and water losses to evaporation, are enormous. Economically speaking, at least one-third of the world's large dams should never have been built.

The largest water diversion project in the world is now being built in China. It's projected to move more than twice the flow of the Colorado River described in the opening case study for this chaper. The initial cost estimate of this scheme is estimated to be (U.S.) $62 billion, but it could easily be twice that much. But without more water, Beijing, the national capital and home to about 20 million people, might have to be moved (see What Do You Think? p. 248).

Las Vegas, Nevada, facing a similar situation with the drying of Lake Mead—which supplies 40 percent of its water—has started a $3.5 billion, 525 km (326 m) pipeline to tap aquifers in the northeastern part of the state. Local ranchers fear that groundwater pumping will decimate the range, destroy native vegetation, and cause massive dust storms. They point to the Owens Valley in California, where a similar water grab by Los Angeles in 1913 dried up the river and destroyed both ranching and economic development. Las Vegas also has suggested that if local water supplies fail, they may ask states east of the Mississippi to share some of their water. If you live in a moist area, how would you feel about sharing your resources?

Las Vegas is also digging a $3.5 billion tunnel that will burrow into Lake Mead, 100 m (300 ft) below the normal outlet (fig. 10.10). Even if the lake reaches the "dead pool" level as warned in the beginning of this chapter, the city will still be able to draw off water. Of course this might prevent refilling the reservoir to provide water and power to downstream users. If you lived downstream, how would you feel about this outcome?

One of the most disastrous diversions in world history is that of the Aral Sea. Situated in arid Central Asia, on the border of Kazakhstan and Uzbekistan, the Aral Sea is a shallow inland sea fed by rivers from distant mountains. Starting in the 1950s, the

**Figure 10.10** Hoover Dam powers Las Vegas, Nevada. Lake Mead, behind the dam, loses about 1.3 billion m³ per year to evaporation. Reduced inflows now threaten the viability of this system.

# What Do YOU Think?

## China's South-to-North Water Diversion

Water is inequitably distributed in China. In the south, torrential monsoon rains cause terrible floods. A 1931 flood on the Yangtze displaced 56 million people and killed 3.7 million (the worst natural disaster in recorded history). Northern and western China, on the other hand, are too dry, and getting drier. At least 200 million Chinese live in areas without sufficient fresh water. The government has warned that unless new water sources are found soon, many of those people (including the capital Beijing, with roughly 20 million residents) will have to be moved. But where could they go? Southern China has water, but doesn't need more people.

The solution, according to the government, is to transfer some of the extra water from south to north. A gargantuan project is now underway to do just that. Work has begun to build three major canals to carry water from the Yangtze River to northern China. Ultimately, it's planned to move 45 billion m³ per year (more than twice the flow of the Colorado River through the U.S. Grand Canyon) 1,600 km (1,000 mi) north. The initial cost estimate of this scheme is about 400 billion yuan (roughly U.S. $62 billion), but it could easily be twice that much.

The eastern route uses the Grand Canal, built by Zhou and Sui emperors 1,500 years ago across the coastal plain between Shanghai and Beijing. This project is already operational. It's relatively easy to pump water through the existing waterways, but they're so polluted by sewage and industrial waste that northern cities—even though they're desperately dry—are reluctant to accept this water.

The central route will draw water from the reservoir behind the recently completed Three Gorges Dam on the Yangtze. Part of the motivation for building this controversial dam and flooding the historic Three Gorges (see related story "Three Gorges Dam" at www.mhhe.com/ cunningham6e) was to provide energy and raise the river level for the South-to-North project. This middle canal will cross several major mountain ranges and dozens of rivers, including the Han and the Yellow Rivers. Currently, work is in progress on raising the Danjiangkou Dam and enlarging its reservoir as part of this route. In 2010, relocation started for 300,000 people who are being displaced by this reservoir, but planners say it's justified by the benefit to a hundred times as many in North China. It's hoped this segment will be finished by 2020.

The western route is the most difficult and expensive. It would tunnel through rugged mountains, across aqueducts, and over deep canyons for more than 250 km (160 mi), from the upper Yangtze to the Yellow River, where they both spill off the Tibetan Plateau. This phase won't be finished until at least 2050. If global warming melts all Tibet's glaciers, however, it may not be feasible anyway.

Planners have waited a lifetime to see this project move forward. Revolutionary leader Mao Zedong proposed it 50 years ago. Environmental scientists worry, however, that drawing down the Yangtze will worsen pollution problems (already exacerbated by the Three Gorges Dam), dry up downstream wetlands, and possibly even alter ocean circulation and climate along China's eastern coast. Although southern China has too much water during the rainy season, even there cities face water shortages because of rapidly growing populations and severe pollution problems. At least half of all major Chinese rivers are too polluted for human consumption. Drawing water away from the rivers on which millions rely only makes pollution problems worse.

What do you think? Are there other ways that China could adapt to uneven water distribution? If you were advising the Chinese government, what safeguards would you recommend to avoid unexpected consequences from the gargantuan project?

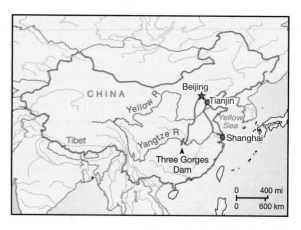

With the Yellow River nearly depleted by overuse, northern China now plans canals (red) to deliver Yangtze water to Beijing.

Soviet Union began diverting these rivers to water cotton fields and rice fields. Gradually, the Aral Sea has evaporated, leaving vast, toxic salt flats (fig. 10.11). The economic value of the cotton and rice has probably never met the cost of lost fisheries, villages, and health.

Recently some river flow has been restored to the "Small Aral" or northern lobe of the once-great sea. Water levels have risen 8 m and native fish are being reintroduced. It's hoped that one day commercial fishing may be resumed. The fate of the larger, southern remnant is more uncertain. There may never be enough water to refill it, and if there were, the toxins left in the lake bed could make it unusable anyway.

## Questions of justice often surround dam projects

While dams provide hydroelectric power and water to distant cities, local residents often suffer economic and cultural losses. In some cases, dam builders have been charged with using public money to increase the value of privately held farmlands, as well as encouraging inappropriate farming and urban growth in arid lands.

On India's Narmada River, a proposed series of 30 dams has incited bitter protest. Many of the 1 million villagers and tribal people being displaced by this project have engaged in civil disobedience and mass protests, which have gone on for the past 20 years

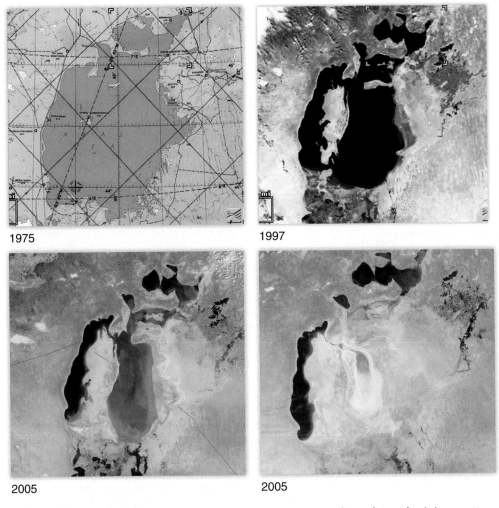

1975

1997

2005

2005

**Figure 10.11** For 30 years, rivers feeding the Aral Sea have been diverted to irrigate cotton and rice fields. The main body of the sea has lost more than 90 percent of its volume. Dust storms from remaining salt flats now contaminate the region.

But it pales in comparison to the potential catastrophe if the Three Gorges Dam on the Yangtze were to collapse. As one engineer says, "It would be a flood of Biblical proportions for the 100 million people who live downstream."

## Would you fight for water?

Many environmental scientists have warned that water shortages could lead to wars between nations. *Fortune* magazine wrote, "Water will be to the 21st century what oil was to the 20th." With one-third of all humans living in areas with water stress now, the situation could become much worse as the population grows and climate change dries up some areas and brings more severe storms to others. Already we've seen skirmishes—if not outright warfare—over insufficient water. In Kenya, for instance, nomadic tribes have fought over dwindling water and grazing. An underlying cause of the genocide now occurring in the Darfur region of Sudan is water scarcity. When rain was plentiful, Arab pastoralists and African farmers coexisted peacefully. Drought—perhaps caused by global warming—has upset that truce. The hundreds of thousands who have fled to Chad could be considered climate refugees as well as war victims.

Although they haven't usually risen to the level of war, there have been at least 37 military confrontations in the past 50 years in which water has been at least one of the motivating factors. Thirty of those conflicts have been between Israel and its neighbors. India, Pakistan, and Bangladesh also have confronted each other over water rights, and Turkey and Iraq threatened to send their armies to protect access to the water in the Tigris and Euphrates Rivers. Water can even be used as a weapon. Saddam Hussein cut off water flow into the massive Iraq marshes as a way of punishing his enemies among the Marsh Arabs. Drying of the marshes drove 140,000 people from their homes and destroyed a unique way of life. It also caused severe ecological damage to what is regarded by many as the original Garden of Eden.

Public anger over privatization of the public water supply in Bolivia sparked a revolution that overthrew the government in 2000. Water sales are already a $400-billion-a-year business. Multinational corporations are moving to take control of water systems in many countries. Who owns water and how much they are able to charge for it could become the question of the century. Investors are now betting on scarce water resources by buying future water rights. One Canadian water company, Global Water Corporation, puts it best: "Water has moved from being an endless commodity that may be taken for granted to a rationed necessity that may be taken by force."

or more. In neighboring Nepal, there are fears that earthquakes will cause dams to collapse, leading to catastrophic flooding.

International Rivers, an environmental and human rights organization reports that dam projects have forced more than 23 million people from their homes and land, and many are still suffering the impacts of dislocation years after it occurred. Often the people being displaced are ethnic minorities. Currently, at least 144 dams on eight rivers in Southeast Asia have been proposed or are under construction. This includes the Lancang (Upper Mekong), the Nu (Upper Salween), and the Jinsha (Upper Yangtze). Several of these projects are in or adjacent to the Three Rivers World Heritage Site, threatening the ecological and cultural integrity of one of the most spectacular and biologically rich areas in the world.

There's increasing concern that big dams in seismically active areas can trigger earthquakes. In more than 70 cases worldwide, large dams have been linked with increased seismic activity. Geologists suggest that filling the reservoir behind the nearby Zipingpu Dam on the Min River caused the devastating 7.9-magnitude Sichuan earthquake that killed an estimated 90,000 people in 2008. If true, it would be the world's deadliest dam-induced earthquake ever.

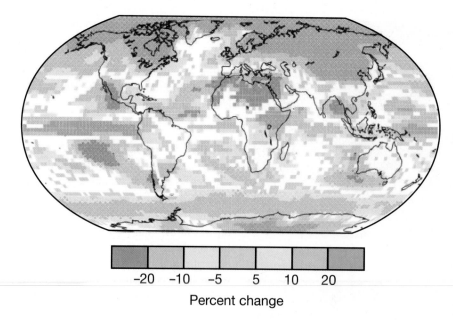

-20  -10  -5  5  10  20

Percent change

**Figure 10.12** Relative changes in precipitation (in percentage) for the period 2090–2099 compared to 1980–1989, predicted by the Intergovernmental Panel on Climate Change. *Source:* IPCC, 2007.

Freshwater shortages may become much worse in the future because of global climate change. Figure 10.12 shows the best estimate from the Intergovernmental Panel on Climate Change (IPCC) on likely changes in global precipitation for the period 2090–2099 compared to 1980–1989. White areas are where models are inconclusive. How does this map compare to figure 10.2? Which areas are most likely to suffer from water shortages by the end of this century? How do these projections impact the case study on Lake Mead?

# 10.5 Water Management and Conservation

Watershed management and conservation are often more economical and environmentally sound ways to prevent flood damage and store water for future use than building huge dams and reservoirs. A **watershed**, or catchment, is all the land drained by a stream or river. It has long been recognized that retaining vegetation and groundcover in a watershed helps hold back rainwater and lessens downstream floods. In 1998 Chinese officials acknowledged that unregulated timber cutting upstream on the Yangtze contributed to massive floods that killed 30,000 people. Similarly, after disastrous floods in the upper Mississippi Valley in 1993, it was suggested that, rather than allowing residential, commercial, or industrial development on floodplains, these areas should be reserved for water storage, aquifer recharge, wildlife habitat, and agriculture. Unfortunately, this advice has been ignored in most places. Further discussion of flooding hazards can be found in chapter 11.

Sound farming and forestry practices can reduce runoff. Retaining crop residue on fields reduces flooding, and minimizing plowing and forest cutting on steep slopes protects watersheds.

Effects of deforestation on weather and water supplies are discussed in chapter 6. Wetlands conservation preserves natural water storage capacity and aquifer recharge zones. A river fed by marshes and wet meadows tends to run consistently clear and steady, rather than in violent floods.

A series of small dams on tributary streams can hold back water before it becomes a great flood. Ponds formed by these dams provide useful wildlife habitat and stock-watering facilities. They also catch soil where it could be returned to the fields. Small dams can be built with simple equipment and local labor, eliminating the need for massive construction projects and huge dams.

In 1998 U.S. Forest Service chief Mike Dombeck announced a major shift in his agency's priorities. "Water," he said, "is the most valuable and least appreciated resource the national forests provide. More than 60 million people in 33 states obtain their drinking water from national forest lands. Protecting watersheds is far more economically important than logging or mining, and will be given the highest priority in forest planning."

## Everyone can help conserve water

We could probably save as much as half of the water we now use for domestic purposes without great sacrifice or serious changes in our lifestyles. Simple steps, such as taking shorter showers, fixing leaks, and washing cars, dishes, and clothes as efficiently as possible, can go a long way toward forestalling the water shortages that many authorities predict. Isn't it better to adapt to more conservative uses now when we have a choice than to be forced to do it by scarcity in the future?

Conserving appliances, such as low-volume shower heads and efficient dishwashers, can reduce water consumption greatly (see What Can You Do? p. 251). If you live in an arid part of the country, you might consider whether you really need a lush, green lawn that requires constant watering, feeding, and care. Planting native vegetation can be both ecologically sound and aesthetically pleasing (fig. 10.13). As part of its water conservation efforts, Las Vegas is paying residents to replace turf with natural vegetation, has asked golf courses to rip up fairways, is encouraging hotels to use recycled water in fountains, and water cops patrol the streets to identify illegal watering or car washing.

Toilets are our greatest domestic water user (fig. 10.14). Usually each flush uses several gallons of water to dispose of a few ounces of waste. On average, each person in the United States uses about 50,000 L (13,000 gal) of drinking-quality water annually to flush toilets. Low-flush toilets can drastically reduce this water use. Gray water (recycled from other uses) could be used for flushing, but installing separated plumbing systems is expensive.

California already uses more than 555 million m$^3$ (450,000 acre-feet) of recycled water annually—mostly for irrigation. That's equivalent to about two-thirds of the water consumed by Los Angeles every year.

## What Can **YOU** Do?

## Saving Water and Preventing Pollution

Each of us can conserve much of the water we use and avoid water pollution in many simple ways.

- Don't flush every time you use the toilet. Take shorter showers, and shower instead of taking baths.

- Don't let the faucet run while brushing your teeth or washing dishes. Draw a basin of water for washing and another for rinsing dishes. Don't run the dishwasher when it's half full.

- Use water-conserving appliances: low-flow showers, low-flush toilets, and aerated faucets.

- Fix leaking faucets, tubs, and toilets. A leaky toilet can waste 50 gal per day. To check your toilet, add a few drops of dark food coloring to the tank and wait 15 minutes. If the tank is leaking, the water in the bowl will change color.

- Put a brick or full water bottle in your toilet tank to reduce the volume of water in each flush.

- Dispose of used motor oil, household hazardous waste, batteries, and so on responsibly. Don't dump anything down a storm sewer that you wouldn't want to drink.

- Avoid using toxic or hazardous chemicals for simple cleaning or plumbing jobs. A plunger or plumber's snake will often unclog a drain just as well as caustic acids or lye. Hot water and soap can accomplish most cleaning tasks.

- If you have a lawn, use water, fertilizer, and pesticides sparingly. Plant native, low-maintenance plants that have low water needs.

- If possible, use recycled (gray) water for lawns, house plants, and car washing.

is now saving some 144 million l (38 million gal) per day—a tenth the volume of Lake Erie—compared with per capita consumption rates of 20 years ago. With 37 million more people in the United States now than in 1980, we get by with 10 percent less water. New requirements for water-efficient fixtures in many cities help conserve water on the home front. More efficient irrigation methods on farms also are a major reason for the downward trend. New sprinkler systems have small spray heads just a foot or so above the plant tops and apply water much more directly. Even better is drip irrigation, which applies water directly to plant roots. California and Florida farmers currently water about 500,000 ha with this technique.

Pricing has an effect on our water useage. Ironically, water from Lake Mead, which is facing a supply crisis currently costs Las Vegas residents 33 cents per m³. By comparison, the same amount costs $3 in Atlanta and $7 in Copenhagen, where water is abundant. What do you think those prices do to motivate conservation?

Charging a higher proportion of real costs to users of public water projects can rationalize use patterns as will water marketing policies that allow prospective users to bid on water rights. Some countries already have effective water pricing and allocation policies that encourage the most socially beneficial uses and discourage wasteful water uses. It will be important, as water markets develop, to be sure that environmental, recreational, and wildlife values are not sacrificed to the lure of high-bidding industrial and domestic users.

Several countries with desperate water shortages, including Singapore, Australia, and parts of the United States, are using recycled water for drinking. Former Australian Environment Minister Malcolm Turnbull said, "It may sound yucky, but we're not getting rain; we've got no choice."

**Figure 10.13** By using native plants in a natural setting, residents of Phoenix save water and fit into the surrounding landscape.

## Efficiency is reducing water use in many areas

Growing recognition that water is a precious and finite resource has changed policies and encouraged conservation across the United States. Despite a growing population, the United States

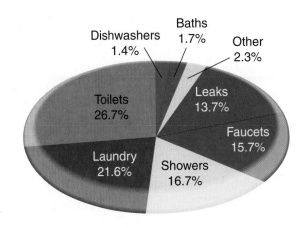

**Figure 10.14** Typical household water use in the United States.
*Source:* Data from the American Water Works Association, 2010.

**Figure 10.15** Sewer outfalls, industrial effluent pipes, acid draining out of abandoned mines, and other point sources of pollution are generally easy to recognize. Pollution-control laws have made this sight less common today than it once was.

## 10.6 Water Pollution

Any physical, biological, or chemical change in water quality that adversely affects living organisms or makes water unsuitable for desired uses can be considered pollution. There are natural sources of water contamination, such as poison springs, oil seeps, and sedimentation from erosion, but here we'll focus primarily on human-caused changes that affect water quality or usability.

### Pollution includes point sources and nonpoint sources

Pollution-control standards and regulations usually distinguish between point and nonpoint pollution sources. Factories, power plants, sewage treatment plants, underground coal mines, and oil wells are classified as **point sources** because they discharge pollution from specific locations, such as drain pipes, ditches, or sewer outfalls (fig. 10.15). These sources are discrete and identifiable, so they are relatively easy to monitor and regulate. It is generally possible to divert effluent from the waste streams of these sources and treat it before it enters the environment.

In contrast, **nonpoint sources** of water pollution are diffuse, having no specific location where they discharge into a particular body of water. They are much harder to monitor and regulate than point sources because their origins are hard to identify. Nonpoint sources include runoff from farm fields and feedlots, golf courses, lawns and gardens, construction sites, logging areas, roads, streets, and parking lots. While point sources may be fairly uniform and predictable throughout the year, nonpoint sources are often highly episodic. The first heavy rainfall after a dry period may flush high concentrations of gasoline, lead, oil, and rubber residues off city streets, for instance, while subsequent runoff may be much cleaner.

Perhaps the ultimate in diffuse, nonpoint pollution is atmospheric deposition of contaminants carried by air currents and precipitated into watersheds or directly onto surface waters as rain, snow, or dry particles. The Great Lakes, for example, have been found to be accumulating industrial chemicals, such as PCBs (polychlorinated biphenyls) and dioxins, as well as agricultural toxins, such as the insecticide toxaphene, that cannot be accounted for by local sources alone. The nearest sources for many of these chemicals are sometimes thousands of kilometers away.

### Biological pollution includes pathogens and waste

Although the types, sources, and effects of water pollutants are often interrelated, it is convenient to divide them into major categories for discussion (table 10.3). Here, we look at some of the important sources and effects of different pollutants.

**Pathogens** The most serious water pollutants in terms of human health worldwide are pathogenic (disease-causing) organisms (chapter 8). Among the most important waterborne diseases are typhoid, cholera, bacterial and amoebic dysentery, enteritis, polio, infectious hepatitis, and schistosomiasis. Malaria, yellow fever,

### Table 10.3 | Major Categories of Water Pollutants

| Category | Examples | Sources |
|---|---|---|
| **Cause of Ecosystem Disruption** | | |
| 1. Oxygen-demanding wastes | Animal manure, plant residues | Sewage, agricultural runoff, paper mills, food processing |
| 2. Plant nutrients | Nitrates, phosphates, ammonium | Agricultural and urban fertilizers, sewage, manure |
| 3. Sediment | Soil, silt | Land erosion |
| 4. Thermal changes | Heat | Power plants, industrial cooling |
| **Cause of Health Problems** | | |
| 1. Pathogens | Bacteria, viruses, parasites | Human and animal excreta |
| 2. Inorganic chemicals | Salts, acids, caustics, metals | Industrial effluents, household cleansers, surface runoff |
| 3. Organic chemicals | Pesticides, plastics, detergents, oil, gasoline | Industrial, household, and farm use |
| 4. Radioactive materials | Uranium, thorium, cesium, iodine, radon | Mining and processing of ores, power plants, weapons production, natural sources |

and filariasis are transmitted by insects that have aquatic larvae. Altogether, at least 25 million deaths each year are blamed on water-related diseases. Nearly two-thirds of the mortalities of children under 5 years old in poorer countries are linked to these diseases.

The main source of these pathogens is untreated or improperly treated human wastes. Animal wastes from feedlots or fields near waterways and food processing factories with inadequate waste treatment facilities also are sources of disease-causing organisms.

In developed countries, sewage treatment plants and other pollution-control techniques have reduced or eliminated most of the worst sources of pathogens in inland surface waters. Furthermore, drinking water is generally disinfected by chlorination, so epidemics of waterborne diseases are rare in these countries. The United Nations estimates that 90 percent of the people in developed countries have adequate (safe) sewage disposal, and 95 percent have clean drinking water.

The situation is quite different in less-developed countries, where billions of people lack adequate sanitation and access to clean drinking water. Conditions are especially bad in remote, rural areas, where sewage treatment is usually primitive or nonexistent and purified water is either unavailable or too expensive to obtain. The World Health Organization estimates that 80 percent of all sickness and disease in less-developed countries can be attributed to waterborne infectious agents and inadequate sanitation.

Detecting specific pathogens in water is difficult, time-consuming, and costly, so water quality is usually described in terms of concentrations of **coliform bacteria**—any of the many types that commonly live in the colon, or intestines, of humans and other animals. The most common of these is *Escherichia coli* (or *E. coli*). Other bacteria such as *Shigella*, *Salmonella*, or *Listeria*, can also cause serious, even fatal, illness. If any coliform bacteria

are present in a water sample, infectious pathogens are assumed to be present as well, and the Environmental Protection Agency (EPA) considers the water unsafe for drinking.

**Biological Oxygen Demand** The amount of oxygen dissolved in water is a good indicator of water quality and of the kinds of life it will support. An oxygen content above 6 parts per million (ppm) will support game fish and other desirable forms of aquatic life. At oxygen levels below 2 ppm, water will support mainly worms, bacteria, fungi, and other detritus feeders and decomposers. Oxygen is added to water by diffusion from the air, especially when turbulence and mixing rates are high, and by photosynthesis of green plants, algae, and cyanobacteria. Turbulent, rapidly flowing water is constantly aerated, so it often recovers quickly from oxygen-depleting processes. Oxygen is removed from water by respiration and chemical processes that consume oxygen. Because oxygen is so important in water, **dissolved oxygen (DO)** levels are often measured to compare water quality in different places.

Adding organic materials, such as sewage or paper pulp, to water stimulates activity and oxygen consumption by decomposers. Consequently, **biochemical oxygen demand (BOD)**, or the amount of dissolved oxygen consumed by aquatic microorganisms, is another standard measure of water contamination. Alternatively, chemical oxygen demand (COD) is a measure of all organic matter in water.

Downstream from a point source, such as a municipal sewage plant discharge, a characteristic decline and restoration of water quality can be detected either by measuring DO content or by observing the types of flora and fauna that live in successive sections of the river. The oxygen decline downstream is called the **oxygen sag** (fig. 10.16). Upstream from the pollution source,

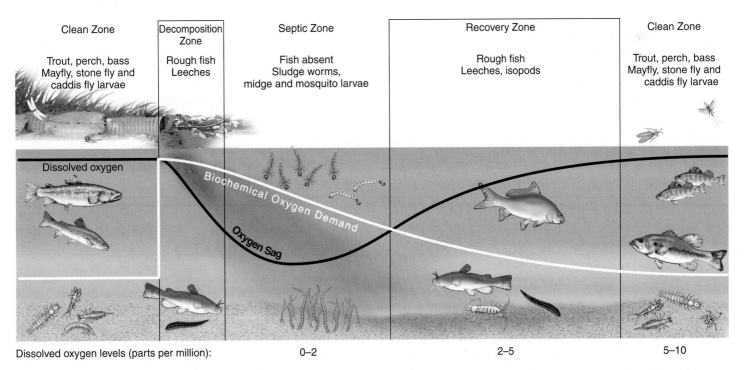

**Figure 10.16** Oxygen sag downstream of an organic source. A great deal of time and distance may be required for the stream and its inhabitants to recover.

oxygen levels support normal populations of clean-water organisms. Immediately below the source of pollution, oxygen levels begin to fall as decomposers metabolize waste materials. Rough fish, such as carp, bullheads, and gar, are able to survive in this oxygen-poor environment, where they eat both decomposer organisms and the waste itself.

Farther downstream, the water may become so oxygen depleted that only the most resistant microorganisms and invertebrates can survive. Eventually, most of the nutrients are used up, decomposer populations are smaller, and the water becomes oxygenated once again. Depending on the volumes and flow rates of the effluent plume and the river receiving it, normal communities may not appear for several miles downstream.

**Plant Nutrients and Cultural Eutrophication**  Water clarity (transparency) is affected by sediments, chemicals, and the abundance of plankton organisms; clarity is a useful measure of water quality and water pollution. Rivers and lakes that have clear water and low biological productivity are said to be **oligotrophic** (*oligo* = little + *trophic* = nutrition). By contrast, **eutrophic** (*eu* + *trophic* = well-nourished) waters are rich in organisms and organic materials. Eutrophication, an increase in nutrient levels and biological productivity, often accompanies successional changes (chapter 5) in lakes. Tributary streams bring in sediments and nutrients that stimulate plant growth. Over time, ponds and lakes often fill in, becoming marshes or even terrestrial biomes. The rate of eutrophication depends on water chemistry and depth, volume of inflow, mineral content of the surrounding watershed, and biota of the lake itself.

Human activities can greatly accelerate eutrophication, an effect called **cultural eutrophication**. Cultural eutrophication is mainly caused by increased nutrient input into a water body. Increased productivity in an aquatic system sometimes can be beneficial. Fish and other desirable species may grow faster, providing a welcome food source. Often, however, eutrophication produces "blooms" of algae or thick growths of aquatic plants stimulated by elevated phosphorus or nitrogen levels (fig. 10.17). Bacterial populations then increase, fed by larger amounts of organic matter. The water often becomes cloudy, or turbid, and has unpleasant tastes and odors. Cultural eutrophication can accelerate the "aging" of a water body enormously over natural rates. Lakes and reservoirs that normally might exist for hundreds or thousands of years can be filled in a matter of decades.

Eutrophication also occurs in marine ecosystems, especially in nearshore waters and partially enclosed bays or estuaries. Partially enclosed seas, such as the Black, Baltic, and Mediterranean Seas, tend to be in especially critical condition. During the tourist season, the coastal population of the Mediterranean, for example, swells to 200 million people. Eighty-five percent of the effluents from large cities go untreated into the sea. Beach pollution, fish kills, and contaminated shellfish result. Extensive "dead zones" often form where rivers dump nutrients into estuaries and shallow seas (see Exploring Science, p. 255). A federal study of the condition of U.S. coastal waters found that 28 percent of estuaries are impaired for aquatic life, and 80 percent of all coastal water is in fair to poor condition.

**Figure 10.17** Eutrophic lake. Nutrients from agriculture and domestic sources have stimulated growth of algae and aquatic plants. This reduces water quality, alters species composition, and lowers the lake's recreational and aesthetic values.

Marine animals in hypoxic zones die not only because of depleted oxygen, but also because of high concentrations of harmful organisms, including toxic algae, pathogenic fungi, and parasitic protists. Excessive nutrients support blooms of these deadly aquatic microorganisms in polluted nearshore waters. Red tides—and other colors, depending on the species involved—have become increasingly common where nutrients and wastes wash down rivers. (See related story "A Flood of Pigs" at **www.mhhe.com/cunningham6e**.)

## Inorganic pollutants include metals, salts, and acids

Some toxic inorganic chemicals are naturally released into water from rocks by weathering processes (chapter 11). Humans accelerate the transfer rates in these cycles thousands of times above natural background levels by mining, processing, using, and discarding minerals.

Among the chemicals of greatest concern are heavy metals, such as mercury, lead, tin, and cadmium. Supertoxic elements, such as selenium and arsenic, also have reached hazardous levels in some waters. Other inorganic materials, such as acids, salts, nitrates, and chlorine, that are nontoxic at low concentrations may become concentrated enough to lower water quality and adversely affect biological communities.

**Metals**  Many metals, such as mercury, lead, cadmium, and nickel, are highly toxic in minute concentrations. Because metals are highly persistent, they accumulate in food chains and have a cumulative effect in humans.

Currently the most widespread toxic metal contamination in North America is mercury released from incinerators and coal-burning power plants. Transported through the air, mercury precipitates in water supplies, where it bioconcentrates in food webs

In the 1980s shrimp boat crews noticed that certain locations off the Gulf Coast of Louisiana were emptied of all aquatic life. Since the region supports shrimp, fish, and oyster fisheries worth $250 to $450 million per year, these "dead zones" were important to the economy as well as to the Gulf's ecological systems. In 1985, Nancy Rabelais, a scientist working with Louisiana Universities Marine Consortium, began mapping areas of low oxygen concentrations in the Gulf waters. Her results, published in 1991, showed that vast areas, just above the floor of the Gulf, had oxygen concentration less than 2 parts per million (ppm), a level that eliminated all animal life except primitive worms. Healthy aquatic systems usually have about 10 ppm dissolved oxygen. What caused this hypoxic (oxygen-starved) area to develop?

Rabelais and her team tracked the phenomenon for several years, and it became clear that the dead zone was growing larger over time, that poor shrimp harvests coincided with years when the zone was large, and that the size of the dead zone, which ranges from 5,000 to 20,000 km² (about the size of New Jersey), depended on rainfall and runoff rates from the Mississippi River. Excessive nutrients, mainly nitrogen, from farms and cities far upstream on the Mississippi River, were the suspected culprit.

How did Rabelais and her team know that nutrients were the problem? They noticed that each year, 7–10 days after large spring rains in the agricultural parts of the upper Mississippi watershed, oxygen concentrations in the Gulf drop from 5 ppm to below 2 ppm. These rains are known to wash soil, organic debris, and last year's nitrogen-rich fertilizers from farm fields. The scientists also knew that saltwater ecosystems normally have little available nitrogen, a key nutrient for algae and plant growth. Pulses of agricultural runoff were followed by a profuse growth of algae and phytoplankton (tiny floating plants). Such a burst of biological activity produces an excess of dead plant cells and fecal matter that drifts to the seafloor. Shrimp, clams, oysters, and other filter feeders normally consume this debris, but they can't keep up with the sudden flood of material. Instead, decomposing bacteria in the sediment break down the debris, and they consume most of the available dissolved oxygen as well. Putrefying sediments also produce hydrogen sulfide, which further poisons the water near the seafloor.

In well-mixed water bodies, as in the open ocean, oxygen from upper layers of water is frequently mixed into lower water layers. Warm, protected water bodies are often stratified, however, as abundant sunlight keeps the upper layers warmer, and less dense, than lower layers. Denser lower layers cannot mix with upper layers unless strong currents or winds stir the water.

Many enclosed coastal waters, including Chesapeake Bay, Long Island Sound, the Mediterranean Sea, and the Black Sea, tend to be stratified and suffer hypoxic conditions that destroy bottom and near-bottom communities. There are about 200 dead zones around the world, and the number has doubled each decade since dead zones were first observed in the 1970s. The Gulf of Mexico is second in size behind a 100,000 km² dead zone in the Baltic Sea.

Can dead zones recover? Yes. Water is a forgiving medium, and organisms use nitrogen quickly. In 1996 in the Black Sea region, farmers in collapsing communist economies cut their nitrogen applications by half out of economic necessity; the Black Sea dead zone disappeared, while farmers saw no drop in their crop yields. In the Mississippi watershed, farmers can afford abundant fertilizer, and they fear they can't afford to risk underfertilizing. Because of the great geographic distance between the farm states and the Gulf, Midwestern states have been slow to develop an interest in the dead zone. At the same time, concentrated feedlot production of beef and pork is rapidly increasing, and feedlot runoff is the fastest growing, and least regulated, source of nutrient enrichment in rivers.

In 2001, federal, state, and tribal governments forged an agreement to cut nitrogen inputs by 30 percent and reduce the size of the dead zone to 5,000 km². This agreement represented astonishingly quick research and political response to scientific results, but it doesn't appear to be enough. Computer models suggest that it would take a 40–45 percent reduction in nitrogen to achieve the 5,000 km² goal.

Human activities have increased the flow of nitrogen reaching U.S. coastal waters by four to eight times since the 1950s. Phosphorus, another key nutrient, has tripled. Clearly, water pollution can connect far-distant places and people, such as Midwestern farmers and Louisiana shrimpers.

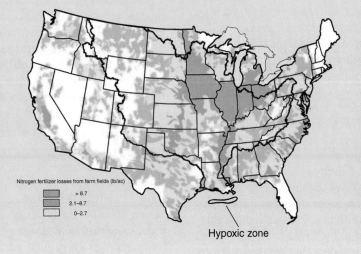

Nitrogen fertilizer losses from farm fields (lb/ac)

- > 8.7
- 2.1–8.7
- 0–2.7

Hypoxic zone

to reach dangerous levels in top predators. As a general rule, Americans are warned not to eat more than one meal of fish per week (fig. 10.18). Top marine predators, such as shark, swordfish, bluefin tuna, and king mackerel, tend to have especially high mercury content. Pregnant women and small children should avoid these species entirely. Public health officials estimate that 600,000 American children now have mercury levels in their bodies high enough to cause mental and developmental problems, while one

**Figure 10.18** Mercury contamination is the most common cause of impairment of U.S. rivers and lakes. Forty-five states have issued warnings about eating locally caught freshwater fish. Long-lived, top predators are especially likely to bioaccumulate toxic concentrations of mercury.

woman in six in the United States has blood-mercury concentrations that would endanger a fetus.

Mine drainage and leaching of mining wastes are serious sources of metal pollution in water. A survey of water quality in eastern Tennessee found that 43 percent of all surface streams and lakes and more than half of all groundwater used for drinking supplies were contaminated by acids and metals from mine drainage. In some cases, metal levels were 200 times higher than what is considered safe for drinking water.

**Nonmetallic Salts**   Some soils contain high concentrations of soluble salts, including toxic selenium and arsenic (see related story "Arsenic in Drinking Water" at www.mhhe.com/cunningham6e). Tens of millions of people are at risk in India and Bangladesh where groundwater is polluted with arsenic. Irrigation and drainage of desert soils can mobilize toxic salts and result in serious pollution problems, as in Kesterson Marsh in California, where selenium poisoning killed thousands of migratory birds in the 1980s.

Ordinarily nontoxic salts, such as sodium chloride (table salt), that are harmless at low concentrations also can be mobilized by irrigation and concentrated by evaporation, reaching levels that are dangerous for plants and animals. Salinity levels in the Colorado River and surrounding farm fields have become so high in recent years that millions of hectares of valuable croplands have had to be abandoned. In northern states, millions of tons of sodium chloride and calcium chloride are used to melt road ice in the winter. Leaching of road salts into surface waters has deleterious effects on some aquatic ecosystems.

**Acids and Bases**   Acids are released as by-products of industrial processes, such as leather tanning, metal smelting and plating, petroleum distillation, and organic chemical synthesis. Coal mining is an especially important source of acid water pollution.

Sulfur compounds in coal react with oxygen and water to make sulfuric acid. Thousands of kilometers of streams in the United States have been acidified by acid mine drainage, some so severely that they are essentially lifeless.

Acid precipitation (chapter 9) also acidifies surface-water systems. In addition to damaging living organisms directly, these acids leach aluminum and other elements from soil and rock, further destabilizing ecosystems.

## Organic chemicals include pesticides and industrial substances

Thousands of different natural and synthetic organic chemicals are used in the chemical industry to make pesticides, plastics, pharmaceuticals, pigments, and other products that we use in everyday life. Many of these chemicals are highly toxic (chapter 8). Exposure to very low concentrations (perhaps even parts per quadrillion, in the case of dioxins) can cause birth defects, genetic disorders, and cancer. Some can persist in the environment because they are resistant to degradation and toxic to organisms that ingest them.

The two principal sources of toxic organic chemicals in water are (1) improper disposal of industrial and household wastes and (2) pesticide runoff from farm fields, forests, roadsides, golf courses, and private lawns. The EPA estimates that about 500,000 metric tons of pesticides are used in the United States each year. Much of this washes into the nearest waterway, where it passes through ecosystems and may accumulate in high levels in non-target organisms. The bioaccumulation of DDT in aquatic ecosystems was one of the first of these pathways to be understood (chapter 8). Dioxins and other chlorinated hydrocarbons (hydrocarbon molecules that contain chlorine atoms) have been shown to accumulate to dangerous levels in the fat of salmon, fish-eating birds, and humans and to cause health problems similar to those resulting from toxic metal compounds.

Hundreds of millions of tons of hazardous organic wastes are thought to be stored in dumps, landfills, lagoons, and underground tanks in the United States (chapter 13). Many, perhaps most, of these sites have leaked toxic chemicals into surface waters, groundwater, or both. The EPA estimates that about 26,000 hazardous waste sites will require cleanup because they pose an imminent threat to public health, mostly through water pollution.

## Is bottled water safer?

It has become trendy to drink bottled water. Every year, Americans buy about 28 billion bottles of water at a cost of about $15 billion with the mistaken belief that it's safer than tap water. Worldwide, some 160 billion liters (42 billion gallons) of bottled water are consumed annually. Public health experts say that municipal water is often safer than bottled water because most large cities test their water supplies every hour for up to 25 different chemicals and pathogens, while the requirements for bottled water are much less rigorous. About one-quarter of all bottled water in the United States is simply reprocessed municipal water, and much of the rest is drawn from groundwater aquifers, which may or may not be safe. A recent survey of bottled water in China found that two-thirds of the samples tested had dangerous levels of pathogens and toxins.

Though the plastics used for bottling water are easily recycled, 80 percent of the bottles purchased in the United States end up in a landfill (the recycling rate is even poorer in most other countries). Overall, the average energy cost to make the plastic, fill the bottle, transport it to market, and then deal with the waste would be "like filling up a quarter of every bottle with oil," says water-expert Peter Gleick. Furthermore, it takes 3 to 5 times as much water to make the bottles as they hold. In blind tasting tests, most adults either can't tell the difference between municipal and bottled water, or they actually prefer municipal water. Furthermore, water that's been sitting in plastic bottles for weeks or months can leach out plasticizers and other toxic chemicals.

In most cases, bottled water is expensive, wasteful, and often less safe than most municipal water. Drink tap water and do a favor for your environment, your budget, and, possibly, your health.

## Sediment and heat also degrade water

Sediment is a natural and necessary part of river systems. Sediment fertilizes floodplains and creates fertile deltas. But human activities, chiefly farming and urbanization, greatly accelerate erosion and increase sediment loads in rivers. Silt and sediment are considered the largest source of water pollution in the United States, being responsible for 40 percent of the impaired river miles in EPA water quality surveys. Cropland erosion contributes about 25 billion metric tons of soil, sediment, and suspended solids to world surface waters each year. Forest disturbance, road building, urban construction sites, and other sources add at least 50 billion additional tons.

This sediment fills lakes and reservoirs, obstructs shipping channels, clogs hydroelectric turbines, and makes purification of drinking water more costly. Sediments smother gravel beds in which insects take refuge and fish lay their eggs. Sunlight is blocked, so that plants cannot carry out photosynthesis, and oxygen levels decline. Murky, cloudy water also is less attractive for swimming, boating, fishing, and other recreational uses (fig. 10.19). Sediment washed into the ocean clogs estuaries and coral reefs.

**Thermal pollution**, usually effluent from cooling systems of power plants or other industries, alters water temperature. Raising or lowering water temperatures from normal levels can adversely affect water quality and aquatic life. Water temperatures are usually much more stable than air temperatures, so aquatic organisms tend to be poorly adapted to rapid temperature changes. Lowering the temperature of tropical oceans by even 1° can be lethal to some corals and other reef species. Raising water temperatures can have similar devastating effects on sensitive organisms. Oxygen solubility in water decreases as temperatures increase, so species requiring high oxygen levels are adversely affected by warming water.

Humans also cause thermal pollution by altering vegetation cover and runoff patterns. Reducing water flow, clearing streamside trees, and adding sediment all make water warmer and alter the ecosystems in a lake or stream.

Warm-water plumes from power plants often attract fish and birds, which find food and refuge there, especially in cold weather. This artificial environment can be a fatal trap, however. Florida's manatees, an endangered mammal, are attracted to the abundant food supply and warm water in power plant thermal plumes. Often they are enticed into spending the winter much farther north than they normally would. On several occasions, a midwinter power plant breakdown has exposed a dozen or more of these rare animals to a sudden, deadly thermal shock.

## 10.7 Water Quality Today

Surface-water pollution is often both highly visible and one of the most common threats to environmental quality. In more-developed countries, reducing water pollution has been a high priority over the past few decades. Billions of dollars have been spent on control programs, and considerable progress has been made. Still, much remains to be done.

### The 1972 Clean Water Act protects our water

Like most developed countries, the United States and Canada have made encouraging progress in protecting and restoring water quality in rivers and lakes over the past 40 years. In 1948 only about one-third of Americans were served by municipal sewage systems, and most of those systems discharged sewage without any treatment or with only primary treatment (the bigger lumps of waste are removed). Most people depended on cesspools and septic systems to dispose of domestic wastes.

**Areas of Progress** The 1972 Clean Water Act established a National Pollution Discharge Elimination System (NPDES), which requires an easily revoked permit for any industry, municipality, or other entity dumping wastes in surface waters. The permit requires disclosure of what is being dumped and gives regulators valuable data and evidence for litigation. As a consequence, only about 10 percent of our water pollution now comes from industrial and municipal point sources. One of the biggest improvements has been in sewage treatment.

Since the Clean Water Act was passed in 1972, the United States has spent more than $180 billion in public funds and perhaps ten times as much in private investments on water pollution control. Most of that effort has been aimed at point sources, especially to

**Figure 10.19** Sediment and industrial waste flow from this drainage canal into Lake Erie.

build or upgrade thousands of municipal sewage treatment plants. As a result, nearly everyone in urban areas is now served by municipal sewage systems, and no major city discharges raw sewage into a river or lake except as overflow during heavy rainstorms.

This campaign has led to significant improvements in surface-water quality in many places. Fish and aquatic insects have returned to waters that formerly were depleted of life-giving oxygen. Swimming and other water-contact sports are again permitted in rivers, in lakes, and at ocean beaches that once were closed by health officials.

The Clean Water Act goal of making all U.S. surface waters "fishable and swimmable" has not been fully met, but currently the EPA reports that 91 percent of all monitored river miles and 88 percent of all assessed lake acres are suitable for their designated uses. This sounds good, but you have to remember that not all water bodies are monitored. Furthermore, the designated goal for some rivers and lakes is merely to be "boatable." Water quality doesn't have to be very high to allow boating. Even in "fishable" rivers and lakes, there isn't a guarantee that you can catch anything other than rough fish, such as carp or bullheads, nor can you be sure that what you catch is safe to eat. Even with billions of dollars of investment in sewage treatment plants, elimination of much of the industrial dumping and other gross sources of pollutants, and a general improvement in water quality, the EPA reports that 21,000 water bodies still do not meet their designated uses (fig. 10.20). According to the EPA, an overwhelming majority of the American people—almost 218 million—live within 16 km (10 mi) of an impaired water body.

In 1998 a new regulatory approach to water quality assurance was instituted by the EPA. Rather than issue standards on a river-by-river approach or factory-by-factory permit discharge, the focus was changed to watershed-level monitoring and protection.

Some 4,000 watersheds are now monitored for water quality. You can find information about your watershed at www.epa.gov/owow/tmdl/. The intention of this program is to give the public more and better information about the health of their watersheds. In addition, states can have greater flexibility as they identify impaired water bodies and set priorities, and new tools can be used to achieve goals. States are required to identify waters not meeting water quality goals and to develop **total maximum daily loads (TMDL)** for each pollutant and each listed water body. A TMDL is the amount of a particular pollutant that a water body can receive from both point and nonpoint sources. It considers seasonal variation and includes a margin of safety.

Currently, all 56 U.S. states and territories have submitted TMDL lists, and the EPA has approved most of them. Of the 5.6 million km of rivers monitored, only 480,000 km fail to meet their clean water goals. Similarly, of 40 million lake hectares, only 12.5 percent (in about 20,000 lakes) fail to meet their goal. To give states more flexibility in planning, the EPA has proposed new rules that include allowances for reasonably foreseeable increases in pollutant loadings to encourage "Smart Growth." In the future, TMDLs also will include load allocations from all nonpoint sources, including air deposition and natural background levels.

An encouraging example of improved water quality is seen in Lake Erie. Although widely regarded as "dead" in the 1960s, the lake today is promoted as the "walleye capital of the world." Bacteria counts and algae blooms have decreased more than 90 percent since 1962. Water that once was murky brown is now clear. Interestingly, part of the improved water quality is due to immense numbers of exotic zebra mussels, which filter the lake water very efficiently. Swimming is now officially safe along 96 percent of the lake's shoreline. Nearly 40,000 nesting pairs of double-crested cormorants nest in the Great Lakes region, up from only about 100 in the 1970s.

Canada's 1970 Water Act has produced comparable results. Seventy percent of all Canadians in towns over 1,000 population are now served by some form of municipal sewage treatment. In Ontario, the vast majority of those systems include tertiary treatment. After ten years of controls, phosphorus levels in the Bay of Quinte in the northeast corner of Lake Ontario have dropped nearly by half, and algal blooms that once turned waters green are less frequent and less intense than they once were. Elimination of mercury discharges from a pulp and paper mill on the Wabigoon-English River system in western Ontario has resulted in a dramatic decrease in mercury contamination. Twenty years ago this mercury contamination was causing developmental retardation in local residents. Extensive flooding associated with hydropower projects has raised mercury levels in fish to dangerous levels elsewhere, however.

**Remaining Problems**  The greatest impediments to achieving national goals in water quality in both the United States and Canada are sediment, nutrients, and pathogens, especially from nonpoint discharges of pollutants (fig. 10.21). These sources are harder to identify and to reduce or treat than are specific point sources. About three-fourths of the water pollution in the United States comes from

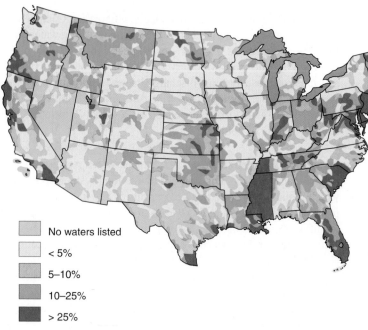

No waters listed
< 5%
5–10%
10–25%
> 25%

**Figure 10.20**  Percent of impaired U.S. rivers in the contiguous 48 states by watershed in 1998. *Source:* Data from U.S. Environmental Protection Agency, 1999.

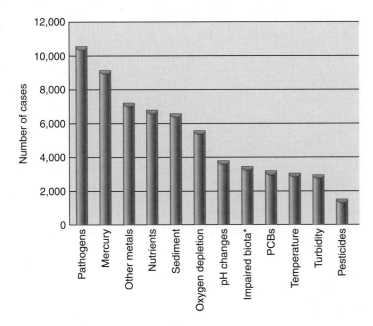

**Figure 10.21** Twelve leading causes of surface-water impairment in the United States. *Undetermined causes. *Source:* Data EPA, 2009.

soil erosion, fallout of air pollutants, and surface runoff from urban areas, farm fields, and feedlots. In the United States, as much as 25 percent of the 46,800,000 metric tons (52 million tons) of fertilizer spread on farmland each year is carried away by runoff.

Cattle in feedlots produce some 129,600,000 metric tons (144 million tons) of manure each year, and the runoff from these sites is rich in viruses, bacteria, nitrates, phosphates, and other contaminants. A single cow produces about 30 kg (66 lbs) of manure per day. Some feedlots have 100,000 animals with no provision for capturing or treating runoff water. Imagine drawing your drinking water downstream from such a facility. Pets also can be a problem. It is estimated that the wastes from about a half million dogs in New York City are disposed of primarily through storm sewers and therefore do not go through sewage treatment.

Loading of both nitrates and phosphates in surface water have decreased from point sources but have increased about four-fold since 1972 from nonpoint sources. Fossil fuel combustion has become a major source of nitrates, sulfates, arsenic, cadmium, mercury, and other toxic pollutants that find their way into water. Carried to remote areas by atmospheric transport, these combustion products now are found nearly everywhere in the world. Toxic organic compounds, such as DDT, PCBs, and dioxins, also are transported long distances by wind currents.

## Developing countries often have serious water pollution

Japan, Australia, and most of western Europe also have improved surface-water quality in recent years. Sewage treatment in the wealthier countries of Europe generally equals or surpasses that in the United States. Sweden, for instance, serves 98 percent of its population with at least secondary sewage treatment (compared with 70 percent in the United States), and the other 2 percent have primary treatment. Poorer countries have much less to spend on sanitation. Spain serves only

18 percent of its population with even primary sewage treatment. In Ireland, it is only 11 percent, and in Greece, less than 1 percent of the people have even primary treatment. Most of the sewage, both domestic and industrial, is dumped directly into the ocean.

The fall of the "iron curtain" in 1989 revealed appalling evironmental conditions in much of the former Soviet Union and its satellite states in eastern and central Europe. The countries closest geographically and socially to western Europe, the Czech Republic, Hungary, East Germany, and Poland, have made massive investments and encouraging progress toward cleaning up environmental problems. Parts of Russia itself, however, along with former socialist states in the Balkans and Central Asia, remain some of the most polluted places on earth. In Russia, for example, only about half the tap water is fit to drink. In cities like St. Petersburg, even boiling and filtering isn't enough to make municipal water safe.

As we saw earlier in this chapter, at least 200 million Chinese live in areas without sufficient fresh water. Sadly, pollution makes

**Figure 10.22** Half of the water in China's major rivers is too polluted to be suitable for any human use. Although the government has spent billions of yuan in recent years, dumping of industrial and domestic waste continues at dangerous levels.

much of the limited water unusable (fig. 10.22). It's estimated that 70 percent of China's surface water is unsafe for human consumption, and that the water in half the country's major rivers is so contaminated that it's unsuited for any use, even agriculture. The situation in Shanxi Province exemplifies the problems of water pollution in China. An industrial powerhouse, in the north-central part of the country, Shanxi has about one-third of China's known coal resources and currently produces about two-thirds of the country's energy. In addition to power plants, major industries include steel mills, tar factories, and chemical plants.

Economic growth has been pursued in recent decades at the expense of environmental quality. According to the Chinese Environmental Protection Agency, the country's ten worst polluted cities are all in Shanxi. Factories have been allowed to exceed pollution discharges with impunity. For example, 3 million tons of wastewater is produced every day in the province with two-thirds of it discharged directly into local rivers without any treatment. Locals complain that the rivers, which once were clean and fresh, now run black with industrial waste. Among the 26 rivers in the province, 80 percent were rated Grade V (unfit for any human use) or higher in 2006. More than half the wells in Shanxi are reported to have dangerously high arsenic levels. Many of the 85,000 reported public protests in China in 2006 involved complaints about air and water pollution.

However, there is also evidence of progress in pollution control. In 1997 Minamata Bay in Japan, long synonymous with mercury poisoning, was declared officially clean again. Another important success is found in Europe, where one of its most important rivers has been cleaned up significantly through international cooperation. The Rhine, which starts in the rugged Swiss Alps and winds 1,320 km through five countries before emptying through a Dutch delta into the North Sea, has long been a major commercial artery into the heart of Europe. More than 50 million people live in its catchment basin, and nearly 20 million get their drinking water from the river or its tributaries. By the 1970s, the Rhine had become so polluted that dozens of fish species disappeared and swimming was discouraged along most of its length.

Efforts to clean up this historic and economically important waterway began in the 1950s, but a disastrous fire at a chemical warehouse near Basel, Switzerland, in 1986 provided the impetus for major changes. Through a long and sometimes painful series of international conventions and compromises, land-use practices, waste disposal, urban runoff, and industrial dumping have been changed and water quality has significantly improved. Oxygen concentrations have gone up five-fold since 1970 (from less than 2 mg/l to nearly 10 mg/l, or about 90 percent of saturation) in long stretches of the river. Chemical oxygen demand has fallen five-fold during the same period, and organochlorine levels have decreased as much as ten-fold. Many species of fish and aquatic invertebrates have returned to the river. In 1992, for the first time in decades, mature salmon were caught in the Rhine.

The less-developed countries of South America, Africa, and Asia have even worse water quality than do the poorer countries of Europe. Sewage treatment is usually either totally lacking or woefully inadequate. In urban areas, 95 percent of all sewage is discharged untreated into rivers, lakes, or the ocean. Low technological capabilities and little money for pollution control are made even worse by burgeoning populations, rapid urbanization, and the shift of much heavy industry (especially the dirtier ones)

**Figure 10.23** Ditches in this Haitian slum serve as open sewers into which all manner of refuse and waste are dumped. The health risks of living under these conditions are severe.

from developed countries where pollution laws are strict to less-developed countries where regulations are more lenient.

Appalling environmental conditions often result from these combined factors (fig. 10.23). Two-thirds of India's surface waters are contaminated sufficiently to be considered dangerous to human health. The Yamuna River in New Delhi has 7,500 coliform bacteria per 100 ml (37 times the level considered safe for swimming in the United States) *before* entering the city. The coliform count increases to an incredible 24 *million* cells per 100 ml as the river leaves the city! At the same time, the river picks up some 20 million liters of industrial effluents every day from New Delhi. It's no wonder that disease rates are high and life expectancy is low in this area. Only 1 percent of India's towns and cities have any sewage treatment, and only eight cities have anything beyond primary treatment.

In Malaysia, 42 of 50 major rivers are reported to be "ecological disasters." Residues from palm oil and rubber manufacturing, along with heavy erosion from logging of tropical rainforests, have destroyed all higher forms of life in most of these rivers. In the Philippines, domestic sewage makes up 60 to 70 percent of the total volume of Manila's Pasig River. Thousands of people use the river not only for bathing and washing clothes but also as their source of drinking and cooking water.

## Groundwater is especially hard to clean up

About half the people in the United States, including 95 percent of those in rural areas, depend on underground aquifers for their drinking water. This vital resource is threatened in many areas by overuse and pollution and by a wide variety of industrial, agricultural, and domestic contaminants. For decades it was widely assumed that groundwater was impervious to pollution because soil would bind chemicals and cleanse water as it percolated through. Springwater or artesian well water was considered to be the definitive standard of water purity, but that is no longer true in many areas.

One of the serious sources of groundwater pollution throughout the United States is MTBE (methyl tertiary butyl ether), a suspected carcinogen added to gasoline to reduce carbon monoxide and ozone in urban air. Aquifers across the United States have been contaminated—mainly from leaking underground storage tanks at gas stations. In one U.S. Geological Survey (USGS) study, 27 percent of shallow urban wells tested contained MTBE. The additive is being phased out, but plumes of tainted water will continue to move through aquifers for decades to come. Liability for this contamination is a highly contentious issue.

The EPA estimates that every day some 4.5 trillion l (1.2 trillion gal) of contaminated water seep into the ground in the United States from septic tanks, cesspools, municipal and industrial landfills and waste disposal sites, surface impoundments, agricultural fields, forests, and wells (fig. 10.24). The most toxic of these are probably waste disposal sites. Agricultural chemicals and wastes are responsible for the largest total volume of pollutants and area affected. Because deep underground aquifers often have residence times of thousands of years, many contaminants are extremely stable once underground. It is possible, but expensive, to pump water out of aquifers, clean it, and then pump it back.

In farm country, especially in the Midwest's corn belt, fertilizers and pesticides commonly contaminate aquifers and wells. Herbicides such as atrazine and alachlor are widely used on corn and soybeans and show up in about half of all wells in Iowa, for example. Nitrates from fertilizers often exceed safety standards in rural drinking water. These high nitrate levels are dangerous to infants (nitrates combine with hemoglobin in the blood and result in "blue-baby" syndrome).

Every year, epidemiologists estimate that around 1.5 million Americans fall ill from infections caused by fecal contamination. In 1993, for instance, a pathogen called cryptosporidium got into the Milwaukee public water system, making 400,000 people sick and killing at least 100 people. The total costs of these diseases amount to billions of dollars per year. Preventative measures, such as protecting water sources and aquifer recharge zones and updating treatment and distribution systems, would cost far less.

## Ocean pollution has few controls

Although we don't use ocean waters directly, ocean pollution is serious and one of the fastest-growing water pollution problems. Coastal bays, estuaries, shoals, and reefs are often overwhelmed by pollution. Dead zones and poisonous algal blooms are increasingly widespread. Toxic chemicals, heavy metals, oil, sediment, and plastic refuse affect some of the most attractive and productive ocean regions. The potential losses caused by this pollution amount to billions of dollars each year. In terms of quality of life, the costs are incalculable.

Discarded plastic flotsam and jetsam are becoming a ubiquitous mark of human impact on the oceans. Even the most remote beaches of distant islands are likely to have mounds of trash. It's been estimated that 6 million metric tons of plastic bottles, packaging material, and other litter are tossed from ships every year into the ocean, where they ensnare and choke seabirds, mammals, and even fish (fig. 10.25).

Researchers have recently discovered a vast swath of the Pacific Ocean filled with a soup of plastic refuse. Dubbed the "Great Pacific Garbage Patch," this slowly swirling vortex fills two "convergence zones" that collect trash from all over the world. One of these gyres occurs between Hawaii and California; the other one is closer to Japan. Each is larger than Texas. Currents sweep all sorts of refuse into these huge vortices that have been called the world's biggest garbage dumps. Much of this plastic consists of tiny particles suspended at or just below the water surface. The smallest particles may be more dangerous biologically than bigger pieces. Plankton and small fish ingest the plastic bits along with the contaminants to their surface, and introduce them into the marine food chain. See chapter 13 for further discussion of this topic.

Oil pollution affects beaches and open seas around the world. Oceanographers estimate that between 3 million and 6 million metric tons of oil are discharged into the world's oceans each year from oil tankers, fuel leaks, intentional discharges of fuel oil, and

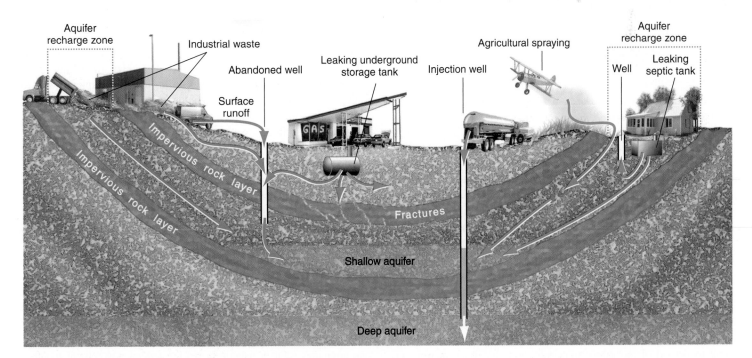

**Figure 10.24** Sources of groundwater pollution. Septic systems, landfills, and industrial activities on aquifer recharge zones leach contaminants into aquifers. Wells provide a direct route for injection of pollutants into aquifers.

(a)

(b)

**Figure 10.25** A deadly necklace. Marine biologists estimate that castoff nets, plastic beverage yokes, and other packing residue kill hundreds of thousands of birds, mammals, and fish each year (a). Oil pollution is an equally serious problem (b). This turtle was caught in the BP *Deepwater Horizon* spill.

coastal industries. About half of this amount is due to maritime transport. Of this portion, most is not from dramatic, headline-making accidents such as the 1989 *Exxon Valdez* spill in Alaska, or even the 2010 British Petroleum spill in the Gulf of Mexico. Rather, routine open-sea bilge pumping and tank cleaning are the primary source. These activities are illegal but very common.

Reports are surfacing of illegal dumping of toxic waste and radioactive trash in the ocean. Dozens of ships have gone down under suspicious circumstances in recent years. Although informers within criminal gangs claim many of these ships were deliberately sunk to get rid of hazardous materials, none has been proven, so far, to have contained illicit cargo. However, it's clear that the profit from this criminal activity could be enormous. It costs thousands

of dollars to properly dispose of a single barrel of toxic or nuclear waste. Crooks can buy or rent an old boat, fill it with hazardous material, scuttle it at sea, and make millions.

Fortunately, awareness of ocean pollution is growing. Oil spill cleanup technologies and response teams are improving, although most oil is eventually decomposed by natural bacteria. Efforts are growing to control waste plastic. Criminals who ship toxic waste to poor countries are being prosecuted. Volunteer efforts also are helping to reduce beach pollution locally: in one day, volunteers in Texas gathered more than 300 tons of plastic refuse from Gulf Coast beaches.

## 10.8 Pollution Control

The cheapest and most effective way to reduce pollution is to avoid producing it or releasing it in the first place. Eliminating lead from gasoline has resulted in a dramatic decrease in the amount of lead in U.S. surface waters. Studies have shown that as much as 90 percent less road deicing salt can be used in many areas without significantly affecting the safety of winter roads. Careful handling of oil and petroleum products can greatly reduce the amount of water pollution caused by these materials. Although we still have problems with persistent chlorinated hydrocarbons spread widely in the environment, the banning of DDT and PCBs in the 1970s has resulted in significant reductions in levels in wildlife.

Industry can reduce pollution by recycling or reclaiming materials that otherwise might be discarded in the waste stream. These approaches usually have economic as well as environmental benefits. Companies can extract valuable metals and chemicals and sell them, instead of releasing them as toxic contaminants into the water system. Both markets and reclamation technologies are improving as awareness of these opportunities grows. In addition, modifying land use is an important component of reducing pollution.

### Nonpoint sources are often harder to control than point sources

Farmers have long contributed a huge share of water pollution, including sediment, fertilizers, and pesticides that flow from fields. Soil conservation practices on farmlands (chapter 7) aim to keep soil and contaminants on fields, where they are needed. Precise application of fertilizer, irrigation water, and pesticides saves money and reduces water contamination. Preserving wetlands which help capture sediment and contaminants, also helps protect surface and groundwaters.

In urban areas, reducing waste that enters storm sewers is essential. It is getting easier for city residents to recycle waste oil and to properly dispose of paint and other household chemicals that they once dumped into storm sewers or the garbage. Urbanites can also minimize use of fertilizers and pesticides. Regular street sweeping greatly reduces nutrient loads (from decomposing leaves and debris) in rivers and lakes.

The tremendous challenge of managing these sources is seen in Chesapeake Bay, America's largest estuary. Once fabled for its abundant oysters, crabs, shad, striped bass, and other valuable fisheries, the bay had deteriorated seriously by the early 1970s. Citizens' groups, local communities, state legislatures, and the federal government together established an innovative pollution-control program that made the bay the first estuary in America targeted for protection and restoration.

Among the principal objectives of this plan is reducing nutrient loading through land-use regulations in the bay's six watershed states to control agricultural and urban runoff. Pollution-prevention measures, such as banning phosphate detergents, also are important, as are upgrading wastewater treatment plants and improving compliance with discharge and filling permits. Efforts are underway to replant thousands of hectares of sea grasses and to restore wetlands that filter out pollutants.

Since the 1980s, annual phosphorous discharges into Chesapeake Bay have dropped 40 percent. Nitrogen levels, however, have remained constant or have even risen in some tributaries. Although progress has been made, the goals of reducing both nitrogen and phosphate levels by 40 percent and restoring viable fish and shellfish populations are still decades away. Still, as former EPA Administrator Carol Browner said, it demonstrates the "power of cooperation" in environmental protection. (See related story "Watershed Protection in the Catskills" at www.mhhe.com/cunningham6e.)

## How do we treat municipal waste?

Under natural conditions, water purification occurs constantly in soils and water. Bacteria take up and transform nutrients or break down oils. Sand and soil filter water; plant roots and fungi use nutrients in the water and simultaneously capture metals and other components. When water is cool and moving, oxygen from the air mixes in, eliminating stagnant conditions where harmful organisms can grow.

The high population densities of cities, however, produce much more waste than natural systems can process. As we have already seen, human and animal wastes usually create the most serious health-related water pollution problems. More than 500 types of disease-causing (pathogenic) bacteria, viruses, and parasites can travel from human or animal excrement through water.

Most developed countries require that cities and towns build municipal water treatment systems to purify the human and household waste. Most rural households use septic systems, which allow solids to settle in a tank, where bacteria decompose them. Liquids percolate through soil, where soil bacteria presumably purify them. Where population densities are not too high, this can be an effective method of waste disposal. With urban sprawl, however, groundwater pollution often becomes a problem.

## Municipal treatment has three levels of quality

Over the past 100 years, sanitary engineers have developed ingenious and effective municipal wastewater treatment systems to protect human health, ecosystem stability, and water quality (fig. 10.26). This topic is an important part of pollution control, and is a principal responsibility of every municipal government.

**Figure 10.26** In conventional sewage treatment, aerobic bacteria digest organic materials in high-pressure aeration tanks. This is described as secondary treatment.

**Primary treatment** physically separates large solids from the waste stream with screens and settling tanks. Settling tanks allow grit and some dissolved (suspended) organic solids to fall out as sludge. Water drained from the top of settling tanks still carries up to 75 percent of the organic matter, including many pathogens. These pathogens and organics are removed by **secondary treatment**, in which aerobic bacteria break down dissolved organic compounds. In secondary treatment, effluent is aerated, often with sprayers or in an aeration tank, in which air is pumped through the microorganism-rich slurry. Fluids can also be stored in a sewage lagoon, where sunlight, algae, and air process waste more cheaply but more slowly. Effluent from secondary treatment processes is usually disinfected with chlorine, UV light, or ozone to kill harmful bacteria before it is released to a nearby waterway.

**Tertiary treatment** removes dissolved metals and nutrients, especially nitrates and phosphates, from the secondary effluent. Although wastewater is usually free of pathogens and organic material after secondary treatment, it still contains high levels of these inorganic nutrients. If discharged into surface waters, these nutrients stimulate algal blooms and eutrophication. Allowing effluent to flow through a wetland or lagoon can remove nitrates and phosphates. Alternatively, chemicals often are used to bind and precipitate nutrients.

Sewage sludge can be a valuable fertilizer, but it can be unsafe if it contains metals and toxic chemicals. Some cities spread sludge on farms and forest lands, while others convert it to methane (natural gas). Many cities, however, incinerate or landfill sludge, both expensive options. Often, sanitary sewers are connected to storm sewers, which carry contaminated runoff from streets, parking lots, and yards. This allows treatment to remove oil, gasoline, fertilizers, and pesticides. Heavy storms, however, often overload municipal systems, resulting in large volumes of raw sewage and toxic surface runoff being dumped directly into rivers or lakes.

**Conventional Treatment Misses New Pollutants**  In 2002, the USGS released the first-ever study of pharmaceuticals and hormones in streams. Scientists sampled 130 streams, looking for 95 contaminants, including antibiotics, natural and synthetic hormones, detergents, plasticizers, insecticides, and fire retardants (fig 10.27). All these substances were found, usually in low concentrations. One stream had 38 of the compounds tested. Drinking-water standards exist for only 14 of the 95 substances. A similar study found the same substances in groundwater, which is much harder to clean than surface waters. What are the effects of these widely used chemicals on our environment or on people consuming the water? Nobody knows. This study is a first step toward filling huge gaps in our knowledge about their distribution, though.

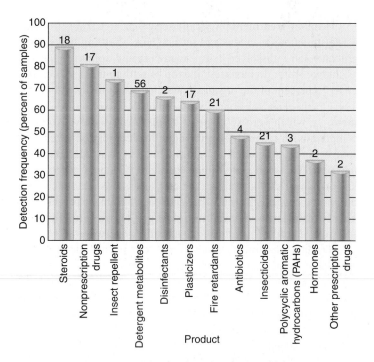

**Figure 10.27** Detection frequency of organic, wastewater contaminants in a recent USGS survey. Maximum concentrations in water samples are shown above the bars in micrograms per liter. Dominant substances included DEET insect repellent, caffeine, and triclosan, which comes from antibacterial soaps.

## Natural wastewater treatment can be an answer

Natural wastewater treatment systems offer a promising alternative to remote locations, developing countries, and small factories that can't afford conventional treatment. These systems are still unfamiliar and unconventional, so they are relatively uncommon, but they offer many advantages. Natural wastewater treatment systems are normally cheaper to build and operate than conventional systems. They use less energy and less chlorine or other purifiers, because gravity moves water, and plants and bacteria do most (or all) disinfection. With fewer pumps and filters to manage, less staff time is needed. Plants remove nutrients, metals, and other contaminants that are not captured by most conventional systems.

**Constructed wetlands** are a complex of artificial marshes designed to filter and decompose waste. One of the best-known of these is in Arcata, California, which was required to build a new and very expensive sewer system upgrade 30 years ago. As an alternative, the city transformed a 65-ha garbage dump into a series of ponds and marshes that serve as a simple, low-cost, waste-treatment facility. Arcata saved millions of dollars and improved its environment simultaneously. The marsh is a haven for wildlife and has become a prized recreation area for the city.

Similar wetland waste treatment systems are now operating in many developing countries. Effluent from these operations can be used to irrigate crops or raise fish for human consumption if care is taken first to destroy pathogens. Usually 20 to 30 days of exposure to sun, air, and aquatic plants is enough to make the water

safe. These systems make an important contribution to human food supplies. A 2,500 ha waste-fed aquaculture facility in Kolkata (Calcutta), for example, supplies about 7,000 metric tons of fish annually to local markets.

Many institutions don't have the space for a constructed wetland. One of these is the Cedar Grove Cheese Factory in southern Wisconsin, which has built a "**Living Machine**,"® a sequence of tanks, bacteria, algae, and small artificial wetlands (fig. 10.28). This system converts factory effluent to nearly pure water and vegetation. It removes 99 percent of the biological oxygen demand, 98 percent of the suspended solids, 93 percent of the nitrogen, and 57 percent of the phosphorus.

Systems like this can be built adjacent to, or even inside of, buildings. Combinations of plants and animals, including algae, rooted aquatic plants, clams, snails, and fish are present, each chosen to provide a particular service in a contained environment. The water leaving such a system is of drinkable quality, and it's cleaner than the water received by the facility. Often the final effluent is used to flush toilets or for irrigation, because most people are squeamish about the idea of drinking treated water. This novel approach can save resources and money, and it can serve as a valuable educational tool.

## Remediation can involve containment, extraction, or biological treatment

Just as there are many sources of water contamination, there are many ways to clean it up. New developments in environmental engineering are providing promising solutions to many water pollution problems. Containment methods keep dirty water from spreading. Many pollutants can be destroyed or detoxified by chemical reactions that oxidize, reduce, neutralize, hydrolyze, precipitate, or otherwise change their chemical composition. Where chemical techniques are ineffective, physical methods may work. Solvents

**Figure 10.28** This Wisconsin cheese factory treats its effluent by passing it through a series of large tanks in which plants bacteria, algae, and other aquatic organisms filter the water and remove organic material, suspended solids, and nutrients.

and other volatile organic compounds, for instance, can be stripped from solution by aeration and then burned in an incinerator.

Often, living organisms can clean contaminated water effectively and inexpensively. We call this **bioremediation**. Restored wetlands, for instance, along stream banks or lake margins can effectively filter out sediment and remove pollutants. Some plants are very efficient at taking up heavy metals and organic contaminants. Bioremediation offers exciting and inexpensive alternatives to conventional cleanup.

# 10.9 Water Legislation

Water pollution control has been among the most broadly popular and effective of all environmental legislation in the United States. It has not been without controversy, however. Table 10.4 describes some of the most important water legislation in the United States.

## The Clean Water Act was ambitious, popular, and largely successful

Passage of the U.S. Clean Water Act of 1972 was a bold, bipartisan step that made clean water a national priority. Along with the Endangered Species Act and the Clean Air Act, this is one of the most significant and effective pieces of environmental legislation

| Table 10.4 | Some Important Water Quality Legislation |
|---|---|

1. *Federal Water Pollution Control Act (1972).* Establishes uniform nationwide controls for each category of major polluting industries.

2. *Marine Protection Research and Sanctuaries Act (1972).* Regulates ocean dumping and established sanctuaries for protection of endangered marine species.

3. *Ports and Waterways Safety Act (1972).* Regulates oil transport and the operation of oil-handling facilities.

4. *Safe Drinking Water Act (1974).* Requires minimum safety standards for every community water supply. Among the contaminants regulated are bacteria, nitrates, arsenic, barium, cadmium, chromium, fluoride, lead, mercury, silver, and pesticides; radioactivity and turbidity also are regulated. This act also contains provisions to protect groundwater aquifers.

5. *Resource Conservation and Recovery Act (RCRA) (1976).* Regulates the storage, shipping, processing, and disposal of hazardous wastes and sets limits on the sewering of toxic chemicals.

6. *Toxic Substances Control Act (TOSCA) (1976).* Categorizes toxic and hazardous substances, establishes a research program, and regulates the use and disposal of poisonous chemicals.

7. *Comprehensive Environmental Response, Compensation, and Liability Act (CERCLA) (1980)* and *Superfund Amendments and Reauthorization Act (SARA) (1984).* Provide for sealing, excavation, or remediation of toxic and hazardous waste dumps.

8. *Clean Water Act (1985) (amending the 1972 Water Pollution Control Act).* Sets as a national goal the attainment of "fishable and swimmable" quality for all surface waters in the United States.

9. *London Dumping Convention (1972).* Calls for an end to all ocean dumping of industrial wastes, tank-washing effluents, and plastic trash. The United States is a signatory to this international convention.

ever passed by the U.S. Congress. It also is an immense and complex law, with more than 500 sections regulating everything from urban runoff, industrial discharges, and municipal sewage treatment to land-use practices and wetland drainage.

The ambitious goal of the Clean Water Act was to return all U.S. surface waters to "fishable and swimmable" conditions. For point sources, the act requires discharge permits and use of the best practicable control technology (BPT). For toxic substances, the act sets national goals of best available, economically achievable technology (BAT) and zero discharge goals for 126 priority toxic pollutants. As discussed earlier, these regulations have had a positive effect on water quality. While not yet swimmable or fishable everywhere, surface-water quality in the United States has significantly improved on average over the past quarter century. Perhaps the most important result of the act has been investment of $54 billion in federal funds and more than $128 billion in state and local funds for municipal sewage treatment facilities.

Opponents of federal regulation have tried repeatedly to weaken or eliminate the Clean Water Act. They regard restriction of their "right" to dump toxic chemicals and wastes into wetlands and waterways to be an undue loss of freedom. They resent being forced to clean up municipal water supplies and call for cost/benefit analysis that places greater weight on economic interests in all environmental planning.

Supporters of the Clean Water Act would like to see a shift away from an "end-of-the-pipe" focus on effluent removal and more attention to changing industrial processes, so that toxic substances aren't produced in the first place. Many people also would like to see stricter enforcement of existing regulations, mandatory minimum penalties for violations, more effective community right-to-know provisions, and increased powers for citizen lawsuits against polluters.

# Conclusion

Water is a precious resource. As human populations grow and climate change affects rainfall patterns, water is likely to become even more scarce in the future. Already, about 2 billion people live in water-stressed countries (where there are inadequate supplies to meet all demands), and at least half those people don't have access to clean drinking water. Depending on population growth rates and climate change, it's possible that by 2050 there could be 7 billion people (about 60 percent of the world population) living in areas with water stress or scarcity. Conflicts over water rights are becoming more common between groups within countries and between neighboring countries that share water resources. This is made more likely by the fact that most major rivers cross two or more countries before reaching the sea, and droughts, such as the one in the southeastern United States, may become more frequent and severe with global warming. Many experts agree with *Fortune* magazine that "water will be to the 21st century what oil was to the 20th."

Forty years ago, rivers in the United States were so polluted that some caught fire while others ran red, black, orange, or other unnatural colors with toxic industrial wastes. Many cities still dumped raw sewage into local rivers and lakes, so that warnings

# Could natural systems treat our wastewater?

**Conventional sewage treatment systems** are designed to treat large volumes of effluent quickly and efficiently. Water treatment is necessary for public health and environmental quality, but it is expensive. Industrial-scale installations, high energy inputs, and caustic chemicals are needed. Huge quantities of sludge must be incinerated or trucked off-site for disposal.

CL 10.2

▲ An aeration tank helps aerobic (oxygen-using) bacteria digest organic compounds.

CL 10.1

**Conventional treatment misses new pollutants.** Pharmaceuticals and hormones, detergents, plasticizers, insecticides, and fire retardants are released freely into surface waters, because these systems are not designed for those contaminants.

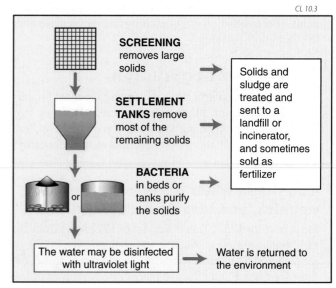

CL 10.3

**SCREENING** removes large solids

**SETTLEMENT TANKS** remove most of the remaining solids

Solids and sludge are treated and sent to a landfill or incinerator, and sometimes sold as fertilizer

**BACTERIA** in beds or tanks purify the solids

The water may be disinfected with ultraviolet light → Water is returned to the environment

▲ The process of conventional sewage treatment

## *Natural  wastewater treatment is unfamiliar but usually cheaper*

We depend on ecological systems—natural bacteria and plants in water and soil—to finish off conventional treatment. Can we use these systems for the entire treatment process? Although they remain unfamiliar to most cities and towns, wetland-based treatment systems have operated successfully for decades—at least as long as the lifetime of a conventional plant. Because they incorporate healthy bacteria and plant communities, there is potential for uptake of novel contaminants and metals as well as organic contaminants. These systems also remove nutrients better than most conventional systems do. These systems can be half as expensive as conventional systems because  they have

- few sprayers, electrical systems, and pumps —> cheaper installation
- gravity water movement —> low energy consumption
- few moving parts or chemicals —> low maintenance
- biotic treatment —> little or no chlorine use
- nutrient uptake —> more complete removal of nutrients, metals, and possibly organic compounds

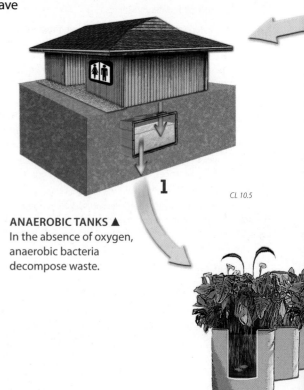

CL 10.5

**ANAEROBIC TANKS ▲** In the absence of oxygen, anaerobic bacteria decompose waste.

**1**

CL 10.4

◀ Drinkable  quality water is produced by a well-designed natural system. This photo shows before and after treatment. Most people are squeamish about the prospect of drinking treated wastewater, so recycled water is generally used for other purposes such as toilets, washing, or irrigation. Since these uses make up about 95% of many municipal water supplies, they can represent a significant savings.

CL 10.6

▲ A constructed wetland outside can be an attractive land-scaping feature that further purifies water.

Where space is available, a larger constructed wetland can serve as recreational space, a wildlife refuge, a living ecosystem, and a recharge area for groundwater or streamflow. ▶

CL 10.7

**Constructed wetland systems** can be designed with endless varieties, but all filter water through a combination of beneficial microorganisms and plants. Here are common components:

1. **Anaerobic (oxygen-free) tanks:** here anaerobic bacteria convert nitrate ($NO_3$) to nitrogen gas ($N_2$), and organic molecules to methane ($CH_4$). In some systems, methane can be captured for fuel.

2. **Aerobic (oxygen-available) tanks:** aerobic bacteria convert ammonium ($NH_4$) to nitrate ($NO_3$); green plants and algae take up nutrients.

3. **Gravel-bedded wetland:** beneficial microorganisms and plants growing in a gravel bed capture nutrients and organic material. In some systems, the wetland provides wildlife habitat and recreational space.

4. **Presumable disinfection:** water is clean leaving the system, but rules usually require that chlorine be added to ensure disinfection. Ozone or ultraviolet light can also be used.

**Can You Explain:**

1. Based on your reading of this chapter, what are the primary contaminants for which water is treated?

2. What is the role of bacteria in a system like this?

3. What factors make conventional treatment expensive?

4. Why is conventional treatment more widely used?

CL 10.8

▲ In this system, after passing through the growing tanks, the effluent water runs over a waterfall and into a small fish pond for additional oxygenation and nutrient removal. This verdant greenhouse is open to the public and adds an appealing indoor space in a cold, dry climate.

**DISINFECTION:** Ozone, chlorine, UV light, or other methods ensure that no harmful bacteria remain. Water can then be reused or released.

DISINFECTION

**4**

**3**

▼ **CONSTRUCTED WETLANDS**
Plants take up remaining nutrients. Remaining nitrate is converted to nitrogen gas.

**2**

◀ **AEROBIC TANKS**
Oxygen is mixed into water, supporting plants and bacteria that further break down and decontaminate waste. Remaining solids settle out.

The growing tanks need to be in a greenhouse or other sunny space to provide light for plants. ▶

CL 10.9

had to be posted to avoid any bodily contact. We've made huge progress since that time. Not all rivers and lakes are "fishable or swimmable," but federal, state, and local pollution controls have greatly improved our water quality in most places.

In rapidly developing countries, such as China and India, water pollution remains a serious threat to human health and eco-system well-being. It will take a massive investment to correct this growing problem. But there are relatively low-cost solutions to many pollution issues. Constructed wetlands for ecological sewage treatment provide low-tech, inexpensive ways to reduce pollution. "Living Machines"® for water treatment in individual buildings or communities also offer hope for better ways to treat our wastes. Perhaps you can use the information you've learned by studying environmental science to plan one for your own community.

## Practice Quiz

1. Describe the path a molecule of water might follow through the hydrologic cycle from the ocean to land and back again.

2. About what percent of the world's water is liquid, fresh, surface water that supports most terrestrial life?

3. What is an *aquifer*? How does water get into an aquifer? Explain the idea of an *artesian well* and a *cone of depression*.

4. What is the difference between water *withdrawal* and *consumption*? Which sector of water use consumes most globally? Overall, has water use increased in the past century? Has efficiency increased or decreased in the three main use sectors?

5. Describe at least one example of the environmental costs of water diversion from rivers to farms or cities.

6. Explain the difference between point and nonpoint pollution. Which is harder to control? Why?

7. Why are nutrients considered pollution? Explain the ideas of *eutrophication* and an *oxygen sag*.

8. Describe primary, secondary, and tertiary water treatment.

9. What are some sources of groundwater contamination? Why is groundwater pollution such a difficult problem?

10. What is a "Living Machine,"® and how does it work?

## Critical Thinking and Discussion Questions

Apply the principles you have learned in this chapter to discuss these questions with other students.

1. What changes might occur in the hydrologic cycle if our climate were to warm or cool significantly?

2. Why does it take so long for deep ocean waters to circulate through the hydrologic cycle? What happens to substances that contaminate deep ocean water or deep aquifers in the ground?

3. If you were a judge responsible for allocating the dwindling water supply in the Colorado River among the various stakeholders, how would you assign water rights? What would be your criteria for needs and rights?

4. Do you think that water pollution is worse now than it was in the past? What considerations go into a judgment such as this? How do your personal experiences influence your opinion?

5. What additional information would you need to make a judgment about whether conditions are getting better or worse? How would you weigh different sources, types, and effects of water pollution?

6. Under what conditions might sediment in water or cultural eutrophication be beneficial? How should we balance positive and negative effects?

# Data Analysis | Graphing Global Water Stress and Scarcity

According to the United Nations, **water stress** is when annual water supplies drop below 1,700 m³ per person. **Water scarcity** is defined as annual water supplies below 1,000 m³ per person. More than 2.8 billion people in 48 countries will face either water stress or scarcity conditions by 2025. Of these countries, 40 are expected to be in West Asia or Africa. By 2050, far more people could be facing water shortages, depending both on population projections and scenarios for water supplies based on global warming and consumption patterns. The following graph in this box shows an estimate for water stress and scarcity in 1995 together with three possible scenarios (high, medium, and low population projections) for 2050. You'll remember from chapter 4 that according to the 2004 UN population revision, the low projection for 2050 is about 7.6 billion, the medium projection is 8.9 billion, and the high projection is 10.6 billion.

1. What are the combined numbers of people who could experience water stress and scarcity under the low, medium, and high scenarios in 2050?

2. What proportion (percentage) of 7.6 billion, 8.9 billion, and 10.6 billion would this be?

3. How does the percentage of the population in these two categories vary in the three estimates?

4. Why is the proportion of people in the scarce category so much larger in the high projection?

5. How many liters are in 1,000 m³? How many gallons?

6. How does 1,000 m³ compare to the annual consumption by the average family of four in the United States? (Hint: Look at table 10.1 and the table of units of measurement conversions at the end of this book).

7. Why isn't the United States (as a whole) considered to be water stressed?

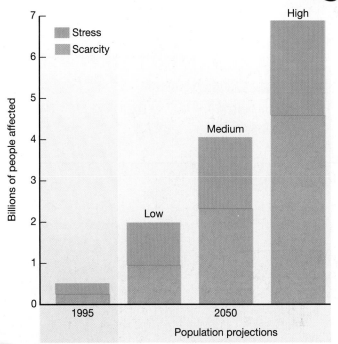

Global water stress and scarcity

**For Additional Help in Studying This Chapter,** please visit our website at www.mhhe.com/cunningham6e. You will find practice quizzes, key terms, answers to end of chapter questions, additional case studies, an extensive reading list, and Google Earth™ mapping quizzes.

connect
| ENVIRONMENTAL SCIENCE

# 11 Environmental Geology and Earth Resources

Hundreds of thousands of buildings collapsed and millions of people were homeless when a magnitude 7.0 earthquake struck the Caribbean island of Haiti in 2010.

*When we heal the earth,*
*we heal ourselves.*

— DAVID ORR

# CASE STUDY

## Earthquake!

Shortly before 5 p.m. on January 12, 2010, a massive earthquake struck the Caribbean island of Haiti. Measuring 7.0 on the Richter scale, the earthquake's epicenter was about 16 km (10 mi) southwest of the capital, Port-au-Prince. It was the worst earthquake in the region in more than two centuries. Huge swaths of the city lay in ruins. Schools, hospitals, commercial buildings, and even the Presidential Palace collapsed. It's estimated that 220,000 people were killed and 300,000 injured. More than 1 million people were homeless, and at least 3 million suffered contaminated water supplies, food shortages, lost jobs, or missing family members. The Inter-American Development Bank estimated the economic losses could be (U.S.)$7 billion to $13 billion.

Port-au-Prince sits on the coastline where two huge geologic features—the Caribbean tectonic plate and the Gonave microplate—slide slowly past each other (fig. 11.1). As the plates grind along what's called a strike-slip fault, strain builds up over many years until they suddenly jerk forward to trigger seismic activity. Two fault systems intersect under Hispaniola, the Caribbean island Haiti shares with the Dominican Republic. The 2010 quake occurred along the Enriquillo-Plantain Garden Fault, an east-west crack in the earth's crust that runs from Hispaniola through Jamaica and the Cayman Islands.

These faults trace their origins to a broader interaction between the North American plate and the Caribbean plate. The North American plate is diving beneath the Caribbean plate, but one piece of the North American plate, called the Bahamas Platform is too buoyant to make the plunge easily. The resulting collision deforms and shakes Hispaniola.

Nearly every island in the Caribbean has experienced earthquakes. Although major quakes occur only every few centuries, they can be catastrophic. In 1692, a 7.5 magnitude megaquake hit the town of Port Royal, Jamaica, which lies on the same fault line as Port-au-Prince. Much of the town, which was unusually rich with pirate plunder, sank below the sea—some say as divine retribution for its wicked ways.

The damage in Haiti in 2010 was especially severe because the quake was close to the city (about 16 km, or 10 mi, southwest of the city center), shallow (only 8 to 10 km below the surface), and more importantly, because many homes and buildings in the economically depressed country weren't constructed to withstand seismic forces. Building codes in Haiti are poorly enforced, and quality supplies are expensive, so most concrete is made with too much sand, too little cement, and not enough reinforcing metal. Furthermore, after the catastrophe occurred, the dysfunctional government was unprepared to offer much assistance to victims. Public services in Haiti are minimal even in the best of times. Port–au-Prince may be the largest city in the world without a public sewer system. With a million people, or more, living in the streets after the quake without shelter, water, or food, looting became widespread and warnings about infectious disease epidemics multiplied. International aid groups had trouble getting into the airport and, once there, were often afraid to go out into the chaotic streets to deliver supplies.

By contrast, a much larger earthquake hit Chile just six weeks after the one in Haiti. With a magnitude of 8.8 on the Richter scale, the Chilean quake was 500 times larger than the one in the Caribbean. But its epicenter was 35 km (21.7 mi) deep, offshore along a relatively remote area of the country, and 105 km (65 mi) from Concepcion, the largest city in the region. Because Chile experiences frequent earthquakes, building codes are far more advanced and more rigorously enforced than they are in Haiti. Only about 700 people died in Chile compared to about 300 times as many in Haiti.

Geologic hazards, such as earthquakes, volcanic eruptions, tsunamis, floods, and landslides represent major threats. Devastating events have altered human history many times in the past, sending geopolitical, economic, genetic, and even artistic repercussions around the planet. The economic costs and benefits of geological resources are equally important in human affairs. In this chapter, we'll look at the processes that shape the earth and how rocks and minerals are formed, as well as what we might do to reduce our risks and the impacts on our environment of acquiring the resources we need.

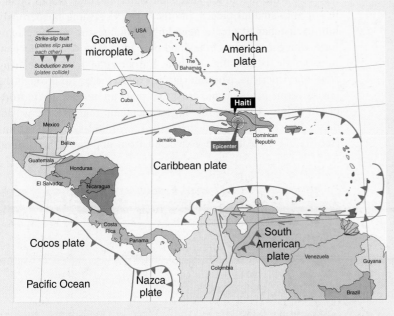

**Figure 11.1** The Gonave microplate is squeezed between its larger neighbors as the North American tectonic plate crashes into and dives under the Caribbean plate.

## 11.1 Earth Processes Shape Our Resources

Many people are exposed to geologic hazards of one type or another, but all of us benefit from the earth's geological resources. Right now you are undoubtedly wearing or using products made from these resources: plastics, of many types are made from petroleum; iron, copper, and aluminum mines produced electrical wiring that brings you power; rare earth metals are essential in your cell phone, your MP3 player, or your computer. All of us also share responsibility for the environmental and social devastation that often results from mining, drilling, and processing materials.

Fortunately, there are many promising solutions to reduce these costs, including recycling and alternative materials. But why are these risks and resources distributed as they are? To understand how and where geological risks and resources are created, we need to learn about the earth's structure and the processes that shape it.

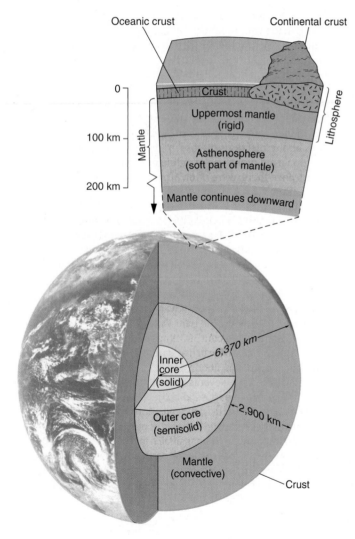

**Figure 11.2** Earth's cross section. Slow convection in the mantle causes the thin, brittle crust to move.

### Earth is a dynamic planet

Although we think of the ground under our feet as solid and stable, the earth is a dynamic and constantly changing structure. Titanic forces inside the earth cause continents to split, move apart, and then crash into each other in slow but inexorable collisions.

The earth is a layered sphere. The **core**, or interior, is composed of a dense, intensely hot mass of metal—mostly iron—thousands of kilometers in diameter (fig. 11.2). Solid in the center but more fluid in the outer core, this immense mass generates the magnetic field that envelops the earth.

Surrounding the molten outer core is a hot, pliable layer of rock called the **mantle**. The mantle is much less dense than the core because it contains a high concentration of lighter elements, such as oxygen, silicon, and magnesium.

The outermost layer of the earth is the cool, lightweight, brittle rock **crust**. The crust below oceans is relatively thin (8–15 km), dense, and young (less than 200 million years old) because of constant recycling. Crust under continents is relatively thick (25–75 km), light, and as old as 3.8 billion years, with new material being added continually. It also is predominantly granitic, while oceanic crust is mainly dense basaltic rock. Table 11.1 compares the composition of the whole earth (dominated by the dense core) and the crust.

### Tectonic processes reshape continents and cause earthquakes

The huge convection currents in the mantle are thought to break the overlying crust into a mosaic of huge blocks called **tectonic plates** (fig. 11.3). These plates slide slowly across the earth's surface like wind-driven ice sheets on water, in some places breaking up into smaller pieces, in other places crashing ponderously into each other to create new, larger landmasses. Ocean basins form where continents crack and pull apart. The Atlantic Ocean, for example, is growing slowly as Europe and Africa move away from the Americas. **Magma** (molten rock) forced up through the cracks forms new oceanic crust that piles up underwater in **mid-ocean ridges**. Creating the largest mountain range in the world, these ridges wind around the earth for 74,000 km (46,000 mi) (see fig. 11.3). Although concealed from our view, this jagged

| Table 11.1 | Eight Most Common Chemical Elements (Percent) in Whole Earth and Crust | | |
|---|---|---|---|
| **Whole Earth** | | **Crust** | |
| Iron | 33.3 | Oxygen | 45.2 |
| Oxygen | 29.8 | Silicon | 27.2 |
| Silicon | 15.6 | Aluminum | 8.2 |
| Magnesium | 13.9 | Iron | 5.8 |
| Nickel | 2.0 | Calcium | 5.1 |
| Calcium | 1.8 | Magnesium | 2.8 |
| Aluminum | 1.5 | Sodium | 2.3 |
| Sodium | 0.2 | Potassium | 1.7 |

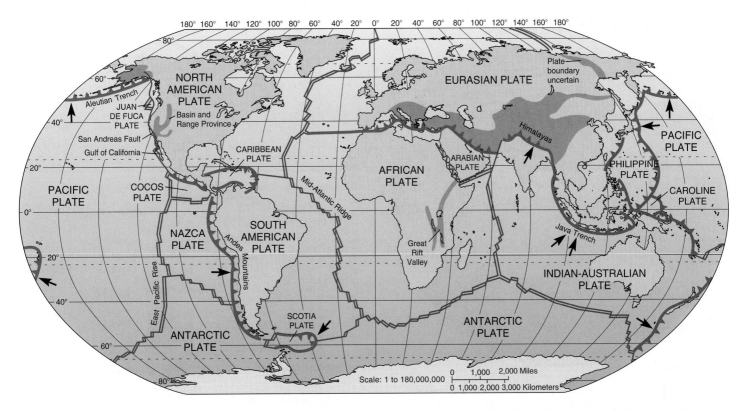

**Figure 11.3** Map of tectonic plates. Plate boundaries are dynamic zones, characterized by earthquakes, volcanism, and the formation of great rifts and mountain ranges. Arrows indicate direction of subduction where one plate is diving beneath another. These zones are sites of deep trenches in the ocean floor and high levels of seismic and volcanic activity. *Sources:* Data from U.S. Department of the Interior and U.S. Geological Survey.

range boasts higher peaks, deeper canyons, and sheerer cliffs than any continental mountains. Slowly spreading from these fracture zones, ocean plates push against continental plates.

Earthquakes, such as the ones that struck Haiti and Chile in 2010, are caused by jerking as plates grind past each other. Mountain ranges like those on the west coasts of North and South America are pushed up at the margins of colliding continental plates. The Himalayas are still rising as the Indian subcontinent collides inexorably with Asia. Southern California is sailing very slowly north toward Alaska. In about 30 million years, Los Angeles will pass San Francisco, if both still exist by then.

When an oceanic plate collides with a continental landmass, the continental plate usually rides up over the seafloor, while the oceanic plate is **subducted**, or pushed down into the mantle, where it melts and rises back to the surface as magma (fig. 11.4). Deep ocean trenches mark these subduction zones, and volcanoes form where the magma erupts through vents and fissures in the overlying crust. Trenches and volcanic mountains ring the Pacific Ocean rim from Indonesia to Japan to Alaska and down the west coast of the Americas, forming a so-called ring of fire where oceanic plates are being subducted under the continental plates. This ring is the source of more earthquakes and volcanic activity than any other region on the earth.

Over millions of years, continents can drift long distances.

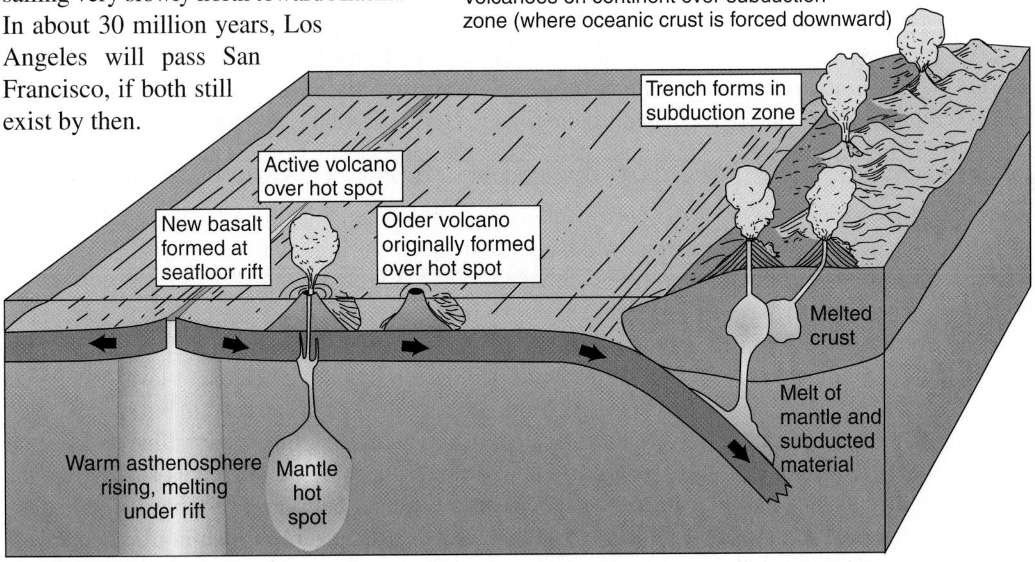

Volcanoes on continent over subduction zone (where oceanic crust is forced downward)

Trench forms in subduction zone

Active volcano over hot spot

New basalt formed at seafloor rift

Older volcano originally formed over hot spot

Melted crust

Melt of mantle and subducted material

Warm asthenosphere rising, melting under rift

Mantle hot spot

**Figure 11.4** Plate tectonic movement. Where thin, oceanic plates diverge, upwelling magma forms midocean ridges. A chain of volcanoes, such as the Hawaiian Islands, may form as plates pass over a hot spot. Where plates converge, melting can cause volcanoes, such as the Cascades.

**Figure 11.5** Pangaea, an ancient supercontinent of 200 million years ago, combined all the world's continents in a single landmass. Continents have combined and separated repeatedly.

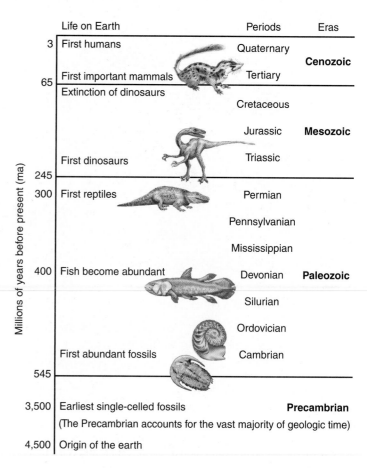

**Figure 11.6** Periods and eras in geologic time, and major life-forms that mark some periods.

Antarctica and Australia once were connected to Africa, for instance, somewhere near the equator and supported luxuriant forests. Geologists suggest that several times in the earth's history most or all of the continents have gathered to form supercontinents, which have ruptured and re-formed over hundreds of millions of years (fig. 11.5). The redistribution of continents has profound effects on the earth's climate and may help explain the periodic mass extinctions of organisms marking the divisions between many major geologic periods (fig. 11.6).

## 11.2 Minerals and Rocks

A **mineral** is a naturally occurring, inorganic solid with a specific chemical composition and a specific internal crystal structure. A mineral is solid; therefore, ice is a mineral (with a distinct composition and crystal structure), but liquid water is not. Similarly molten lava is not crystalline, although it generally hardens to create distinct minerals. Metals (such as iron, copper, aluminum, or gold) come from mineral ores, but once purified, metals are no longer crystalline and thus are not minerals. Depending on the conditions in which they were formed, mineral crystals can be microscopically small, such as asbestos fibers, or huge, such as the tree-size selenite crystals recently discovered in a Chihuahua, Mexico mine.

A **rock** is a solid, cohesive aggregate of one or more minerals. Within the rock, individual mineral crystals (or grains) are mixed together and held firmly in a solid mass. The grains may be large or small, depending on how the rock was formed, but each grain retains its own unique mineral qualities. Each rock type has a characteristic mixture of minerals, grain sizes, and ways in which the grains are mixed and held together. Granite, for example, is a mixture of quartz, feldspar, and mica crystals. Rocks with a granite-like mineral content but much finer crystals are called rhyolite; chemically similar rocks with large crystals are called pegmatite.

### The rock cycle creates and recycles rocks

Although rocks appear hard and permanent, they are part of a relentless cycle of formation and destruction. They are crushed, folded, melted, and recrystallized by dynamic processes related to those that shape the large-scale features of the earth's crust. We call this cycle of creation, destruction, and metamorphosis the **rock cycle** (fig. 11.7). Understanding something of how this cycle works helps explain the origin and characteristics of different types of rocks.

There are three major rock classifications: igneous, metamorphic, and sedimentary. **Igneous rocks** (from *igni*, the Latin word for fire) are solidified from hot, molten magma or lava. Most rock in the earth's crust is igneous. Magma extruded to the surface from volcanic vents cools quickly to make finely crystalline rocks, such as basalt, rhyolite, or andesite. Magma that cools slowly in subsurface chambers or is intruded between overlying layers makes coarsely crystalline rocks, such as gabbro (rich in iron and silica)

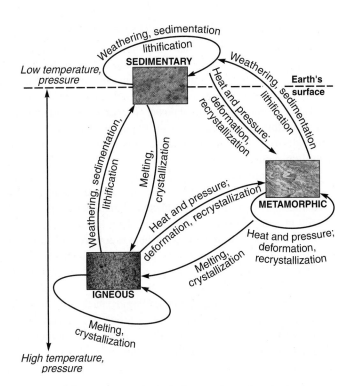

**Figure 11.7** The rock cycle includes a variety of geologic processes that can transform any rock.

or granite (rich in aluminum and silica), depending on the chemical composition of the magma.

**Metamorphic rocks** form from the melting, contorting, and recrystallizing of other rocks. Deep in the ground, tectonic forces squeeze, fold, heat, and recrystallize solid rock. Under these conditions, chemical reactions can alter both the composition and the structure of the component minerals. Metamorphic rocks are classified by their chemical composition and by the degree of recrystallization: some minerals form only under extreme pressure and heat (diamonds or jade, for example); others form under more moderate conditions (graphite or talc). Some common metamorphic rocks are marble (from limestone), quartzite (from sandstone), and slate (from mudstone and shale). Metamorphic rocks often have beautiful colors and patterns left by the twisting and folding that created them.

**Sedimentary rocks** are formed when loose grains of other rocks are consolidated by time and pressure. Sandstone, for example, is solidified from layers of sand, and mudstone consists of extremely hardened mud and clay. Tuff is formed from volcanic ash, and conglomerates are aggregates of sand and gravel. Some sedimentary rocks develop from crystals that precipitate out of extremely salty water. Rock salt, made of the mineral halite, is ground up to produce ordinary table salt (sodium chloride). Salt deposits often form when a body of saltwater dries up, leaving salt crystals behind. Limestone is a rock composed of cemented remains of marine organisms. You can often see the shapes of shells and corals in a piece of limestone. Sedimentary formations often have distinctive layers that show different conditions when they were laid down. Erosion can reveal these layers and inform us of their history (fig. 11.8).

**Figure 11.8** Eons of erosion in Arizona's Grand Canyon reveals many sedimentary layers, and some deep metamorphic rocks.

## Weathering and sedimentation

Most crystalline rocks are extremely hard and durable, but exposure to air, water, changing temperatures, and reactive chemical agents slowly breaks them down in a process called **weathering** (fig. 11.9). Mechanical weathering is the physical breakup of rocks into smaller particles without a change in chemical composition of the constituent minerals. You have probably seen the results of mechanical weathering in rounded rocks in rivers or on shorelines, smoothed by constant tumbling in waves or currents. On a larger scale, mountain valleys are carved by rivers and glaciers.

Chemical weathering is the selective removal or alteration of specific minerals in rocks. This alteration leads to weakening and disintegration of rock. Among the more important chemical

**Figure 11.9** Weathering slowly reduces an igneous rock to loose sediment. Here, exposure to moisture expands minerals in the rock, and frost may also force the rock apart.

weathering processes are oxidation (combination of oxygen with an element to form an oxide or a hydroxide mineral) and hydrolysis (hydrogen atoms from water molecules combine with other chemicals to form acids). The products of these reactions are more susceptible to both mechanical weathering and dissolving in water. For instance, when carbonic acid (formed when rainwater absorbs $CO_2$) percolates through porous limestone layers in the ground, it dissolves the rock and creates caves.

Particles of rock loosened by wind, water, ice, and other weathering forces are carried downhill, downwind, or downstream until they come to rest again in a new location. The deposition of these materials is called **sedimentation**. Water, wind, and glaciers deposit particles of sand, clay, and silt far from their source. Much of the American Midwest, for instance, is covered with hundreds of meters of sedimentary material left by glaciers (till, or rock debris deposited by glacial ice), wind (loess, or fine dust deposits), river deposits of sand and gravel, and ocean deposits of sand, silt, clay, and limestone.

# 11.3 Economic Geology and Mineralogy

The earth is unusually rich in mineral variety. Mineralogists have identified some 4,400 different mineral species, far more, we believe, than any of our neighboring planets. What makes the difference? The processes of plate tectonics and the rock cycle on this planet have gradually concentrated uncommon elements and allowed them to crystalize into new minerals. But this accounts for only about one-third of our geologic legacy. The biggest difference is life. Most of our minerals are oxides, but there was little free oxygen in the atmosphere until it was released by photosynthetic organisms, thus triggering evolution of our great variety of minerals.

Economic mineralogy is the study of resources that are valuable for manufacturing and trade. Most economic minerals are metal ores, minerals with unusually high concentrations of metals. Lead, for example, generally comes from the mineral galena (PbS), and copper comes from sulfide ores, such as bornite ($Cu_5FeS_4$). Nonmetallic geologic resources include graphite, feldspar, quartz crystals, diamonds, and other crystals that are valued for their usefulness or beauty. Metals have been so important in human affairs that major epochs of human history are commonly known by their dominant materials and the technology involved in using those materials (Stone Age, Bronze Age, Iron Age, etc.). The mining, processing, and distribution of these materials have broad implications for both our culture and our environment. Most economically valuable crustal resources exist everywhere in small amounts; the important thing is to find them concentrated in economically recoverable levels.

The United States mining law passed in 1872 encourages mining on public lands as a way of boosting the economy and utilizing natural resources. There have been repeated efforts to update this law and to recover public revenue from publicly owned resources, but powerful friends in Congress together with a tradition of supporting extractive industries in many states have continually blocked these reforms.

## Metals are essential to our economy

Metals are malleable substances that are useful and valuable because they are strong, relatively light, and can be reshaped for many purposes. The availability of metals and the methods to extract and use them have determined technological developments, as well as economic and political power for individuals and nations.

The metals consumed in greatest quantity by world industry include iron (740 million metric tons annually), aluminum (40 million metric tons), manganese (22.4 million metric tons), copper and chromium (8 million metric tons each), and nickel (0.7 million metric tons). Most of these metals are consumed in the United States, western Europe, Japan, and China. They are produced primarily in South America, South Africa, and Russia (fig. 11.10). It is easy to see how these facts contribute to a worldwide mineral trade network that has become crucially important to the economic and social stability of all nations involved. Table 11.2 shows the primary uses of these metals.

The rapid growth of green technologies, such as renewable energy and electric vehicles has made a group of rare earth metals especially important. Worries about impending shortages of these minerals complicate future developments in this sector (see Exploring Science, p. 278).

## Nonmetal mineral resources include gravel, clay, glass, and salts

Nonmetal minerals constitute a broad class that covers resources from gemstones to sand, gravel, salts, limestone, and soils. Sand and gravel production for road and building construction comprise by far the greatest volume and dollar value of all nonmetal mineral resources and a far greater volume than all metal ores. Sand and gravel are used mainly in brick and concrete construction, in paving, as loose road filler, and for sandblasting. High-purity silica sand is our source of glass. These materials usually are retrieved from surface pit mines and quarries, where they were deposited by glaciers, winds, or ancient oceans.

| Table 11.2 | Primary Uses of Some Major Metals | |
|---|---|
| **Metal** | **Use** |
| Aluminum | Packaging foods and beverages (38%), transportation, electronics |
| Chromium | High-strength steel alloys |
| Copper | Building construction, electric and electronic industries |
| Iron | Heavy machinery, steel production |
| Lead | Leaded gasoline, car batteries, paints, ammunition |
| Manganese | High-strength, heat-resistant steel alloys |
| Nickel | Chemical industry, steel alloys |
| Platinum group | Automobile catalytic converters, electronics, medical uses |
| Gold | Medical, aerospace, electronic uses; accumulation as monetary standard |
| Silver | Photography, electronics, jewelry |

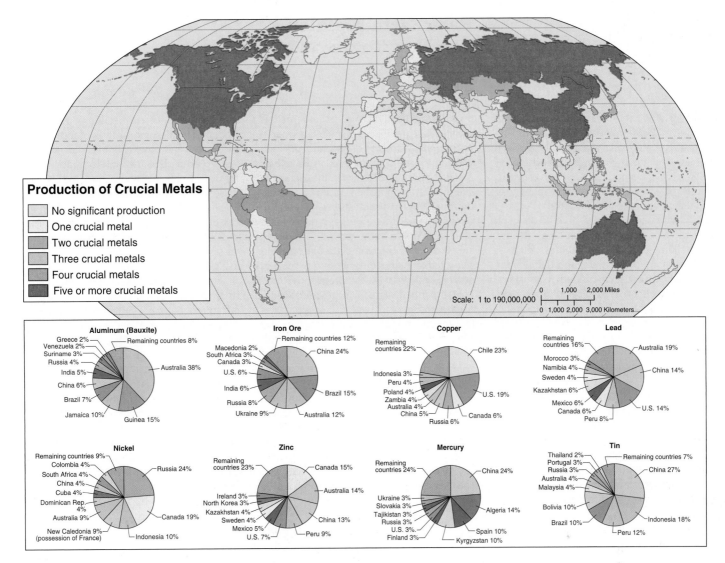

**Figure 11.10** World production of metals most essential for an industrial economy. Principal consumers are the United States, western Europe, Japan, and China.

Limestone, like sand and gravel, is mined and quarried for concrete and crushed for road rock. It also is cut for building stone, pulverized for use as an agricultural soil additive that neutralizes acidic soil, and roasted in lime kilns and cement plants to make plaster (hydrated lime) and cement.

Evaporites (materials deposited by evaporation of chemical solutions) are mined for halite, gypsum, and potash. These are often found at or above 97 percent purity. Halite, or rock salt, is used for water softening and ice melting on winter roads in some northern areas. When refined, it is a source of table salt. Gypsum (calcium sulfate) now makes our plaster wallboard, but it has been used to cover walls ever since the Egyptians plastered their frescoed tombs along the Nile River some 5,000 years ago. Potash is an evaporite composed of a variety of potassium chlorides and potassium sulfates. These highly soluble potassium salts have long been used as a soil fertilizer.

Sulfur deposits are mined mainly for sulfuric acid production. In the United States, sulfuric acid use amounts to more than 200 lbs per person per year, mostly because of its use in industry, car batteries, and some medicinal products.

Durable, highly valuable, and easily portable, gemstones and precious metals have long been a way to store and transport wealth. Unfortunately, these valuable materials also have bankrolled despots, criminal gangs, and terrorism in many countries. In recent years, brutal civil wars in Africa have been financed—and often motivated by—gold, diamonds, tantalum ore, and other high-priced commodities. Much of this illegal trade ends up in the $100 billion per year global jewelry trade, two-thirds of which sells in the United States. Many people who treasure a diamond ring or a gold wedding band as a symbol of love and devotion are unaware that it may have been obtained through slave labor, torture, and environmentally destructive mining and processing methods. Civil rights organizations are campaigning to require better documentation of the origins of gems and precious metals to prevent their use as financing for crimes against humanity.

In 2004 a group of Nobel Peace Laureates called on the World Bank to overhaul its policies on lending for resource extractive

# Rare Earth Metals: The New Strategic Materials

Could shortages of a group of obscure minerals limit the growth of alternative energy supplies and green technology? A recent decision by China to limit exports of rare earth elements is seen by some experts as a serious threat to the global clean tech industry.

"Rare earth" elements are a collection of metallic elements including yttrium, scandium, and 15 lanthanides, such as neodymium, dysprosium, and gadolinium, that are essential in modern electronics. These metals are used in cell phones, high-efficiency lights, hybrid cars, superconductors, high-strength magnets, lightweight batteries, lasers, energy-conserving lamps, and a variety of medical devices. Because of their unusual properties, small amounts of these metals can make motors 90 percent lighter and lights 80 percent more efficient. Without these materials, MP3 players, hybrid vehicles, high-capacity wind turbines, and much other high-tech equipment would be impossible. A Toyota Prius, for example, uses about a kilogram of neodymium and dysprosium for its electric motor and as much as 15 kg of lanthanum for its battery pack.

Despite their name, these elements occur widely in the earth's crust, but commercially viable concentrations are found in only a few locations. China produces about 95 percent of all rare earth metals, an increase from about 30 percent two decades ago. China's dominance in mining these metals results partly because China uses these materials in electronics production, partly because of low labor costs in mining, and partly because the government has been willing to overlook the high environmental costs of extracting these metals from the ground. About half of all Chinese production of rare earth metals occurs in a single mine in Baotou in Inner Mongolia; most of the rest come from small, often unlicensed mines in southern China.

Like gold, silver, and other precious metals, rare earth elements are often separated from ore by crushing ore-bearing rocks and washing the ore in strong acids. Acids release metals from the ore, but when the metals are later separated from the acid slurry, tremendous amounts of toxic wastewater are produced. Often acids are pumped directly into a borehole drilled in the ground, and metals are dissolved from ores in place. The resulting slurry is then pumped to the surface for processing. Acidic wastewater is frequently stored behind earthen dams, which can leak into surface and ground waters. Processing also releases sulfur and radioactive uranium and thorium that frequently occur with rare earth elements. Establishing better control on illegal mines is one reason for China's interest in controlling export and production.

For China, maintaining control of supplies, as well as a near monopoly on production, ensures that domestic electronic needs will be met. Outside of China, there is concern about supplies for both strategic needs (such as military guidance systems), consumer electronics, and alternative energy supplies. Having a near monopoly of rare earth metals production has helped China become a center of technology innovation, and other countries now wonder how to keep up in the high-tech race. Many firms are simply moving to China. The division of General Motors that deals with miniaturized magnet research, for example, shut down its U.S. office and moved its entire staff to China in 2006. The Danish wind turbine company Vestas moved much of its production to China in 2009.

In response to expected shortages and rising prices, several companies are working to reopen mines in North America and Australia. Molycorp Minerals expects to have its mine in Mountain Pass, California, back in production by 2012, meeting perhaps 10 percent of global demand, and Avalon Rare Metals of Toronto is working on a mine in Canada's Northwest Territories. Greenland is also jumping into this new gold rush, with hopes to produce up to 25 percent of rare earth metals from recently discovered ore bodies. It remains to be seen whether new environmental controls will be in place for this coming expansion.

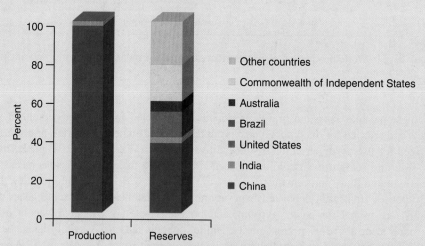

China controls a little more than one-third of known rare earth metals, but currently produces 97 percent of these important materials. *Source:* USGS, 2010.

industries. "War, poverty, climate change, and ongoing violations of human rights—all of these scourges are all too often linked to the oil and mining industries," wrote Archbishop Desmond Tutu, winner of the 1984 Nobel Peace Prize for helping eliminate apartheid in South Africa. In response, the World Bank appointed an Extractive Industries Review headed by former Indonesian Environment Minister Emil Salim. Its final report agreed with many concerns raised by environmental and community organizations.

## Currently, the earth provides almost all our fuel

At present, modern society functions largely on energy produced from geologic deposits of oil, coal, and natural gas. Nuclear energy, which runs on uranium, provides about 20 percent of our electricity. But, as chapter 12 shows, renewable sources, such as sun, wind, hydropower, biomass, and geothermal energy could replace all the fossil fuels and nuclear power we now use while reducing pollution and reducing global climate change.

Oil, coal, and gas are organic, created over millions of years as extreme heat and pressure transformed the remains of ancient organisms. They are not minerals, because they have no crystalline structure, but they can be considered part of economic mineralogy because they are such important geologic resources. In addition to providing energy, oil is the source material for plastics, and natural gas is used to make agricultural fertilizers.

## 11.4 Environmental Effects of Resource Extraction

Each of us depends daily on geologic resources mined or pumped from sites around the world. We use scores of metals and minerals, many of which we've never even heard of, in our lights, computers, watches, fertilizers, and cars. Extracting and purifying these resources can have severe environmental and social consequences. The most obvious effect of mining and well drilling is often the disturbance or removal of the land surface. Farther-reaching effects, though, include air and water pollution. The EPA lists more than 100 toxic air pollutants, from acetone to xylene, released from U.S. mines and wells every year. Nearly 80,000 metric tons of particulate matter (dust) and 11,000 tons of sulfur dioxide are released from nonmetal mining alone. Chemical- and sediment-runoff pollution is a major problem in many local watersheds. Acidic mine runoff has damaged or destroyed aquatic ecosystems in many places (fig. 11.11).

Gold and other metals are often found in sulfide ores that produce sulfuric acid when exposed to air and water. In addition, metal elements often occur in very low concentrations—10 to 20 parts per billion may be economically extractable for gold, platinum, and other metals. Consequently, vast quantities of ore must be crushed and washed to extract metals. Cyanide, mercury, and other toxic

**Figure 11.11** Thousands of abandoned mines on public lands poison streams and groundwater with acid, metal-laced drainage. This old mine in Montana drains into the Blackfoot River, the trout stream featured in Norman Maclean's book *A River Runs through It.*

substances are used to chemically separate metals from the minerals that contain them, and these substances can easily contaminate lakes and streams. Furthermore, a great deal of water is used in washing crushed ore with cyanide and other solutions. In arid Nevada, the USGS estimates that mining consumes about 230,000 m³ (60 million gal) per day. After use in ore processing, much of this water contains sulfuric acid, arsenic, heavy metals, and other contaminants and is unsuitable for any other use.

### Mining and drilling can degrade water quality

There are many techniques for extracting geologic materials. The most common methods are open-pit mining, strip-mining, and underground mining. An ancient method of accumulating gold, diamonds, and coal is placer mining, in which pure nuggets are washed from stream sediments. Since the California gold rush of 1849, placer miners have used water cannons to blast away hillsides. This method, which chokes stream ecosystems with sediment, is still

## Active Learning

### What Geologic Resources Are You Using Right Now?

Make a list of the geologic materials that are found in some of the objects you are using right now. For example, the computer used to write this chapter is made largely of plastic (from oil), silicon chips (sand), and copper wire, and it runs on energy from coal and uranium-powered electric plants.

Start your list with some of the following items: glasses, chair, table, pencil, lightbulb, window, building, wristwatch, coffee cup, tooth fillings.

used in Alaska, Canada, and many other regions. Another ancient and much more dangerous method is underground mining. Ancient Roman, European, and Chinese miners tunneled deep into tin, lead, copper, coal, and other mineral seams. Mine tunnels occasionally collapse, and natural gas in coal mines can explode. Water seeping into mine shafts also dissolves toxic minerals. Contaminated water seeps into groundwater; it is also pumped to the surface, where it enters streams and lakes.

A current controversy in the United States involves extraction of methane gas from coal deposits that are too deep or too disperse for mining. Vast deposits of coal-bearing shale underlie both the Rocky Mountains and the Appalachian Mountains. Because the gas doesn't migrate easily through tight shales, it often takes many closely spaced wells to extract this methane (fig. 11.12). In Wyoming's Powder River basin, for example, 140,000 wells have been proposed for methane extraction. Together with the vast network of roads, pipelines, pumping stations, and service facilities, this industry is having serious impacts on ranching, wildlife, and recreation in formerly remote areas.

Perhaps even worse, is the effect on water supplies. Each well produces up to 75,000 liters of salty water per day. Dumping this toxic waste into streams causes widespread pollution. To boost well output, mining companies rely on hydraulic fracturing (or "fracking"). A mixture of water, sand, and potentially toxic chemicals is pumped into the ground and rock formations at extremely high pressure. The pressurized fluid cracks sediments and releases the gas. This often disrupts aquifers, however, and contaminates wells.

For decades, coal-bed methane extraction was a problem only in western states, but this controversial technology is now moving to the East Coast as well. The Marcellus and Devonian Shales underlie parts of ten eastern states ranging from northern Georgia to Upstate New York. It has long been recognized that methane can be extracted from these formations, but estimates of recoverable amounts were relatively small. New developments in horizontal drilling and hydraulic fracturing along with increased exploratory drilling have now made this deposit a potentially "super-giant gas field." The U.S.

Geological Survey now estimates that the Marcellus/Devonian formation may contain 500 trillion ft$^3$ (13 trillion m$^3$) of methane. If all of it were recoverable, it would make a 100-year supply for the U.S. at current consumption rates. But the same issues, concerning a multitude of wells, water pollution, and threats to water supplies on which millions of people depend, raise thorny problems.

Open-pit mines are used to extract massive beds of metal ores and other minerals. The size of modern open pits can be hard to comprehend. The Bingham Canyon mine, near Salt Lake City, Utah, is 800 m (2,640 ft) deep and nearly 4 km (2.5 mi) wide at the top. More than 5 billion tons of copper ore and waste material have been removed from the hole since 1906. A chief environmental challenge of open-pit mining is that groundwater accumulates in the pit. In metal mines, a toxic soup results. No one yet knows how to detoxify these lakes, which endanger wildlife and nearby watersheds.

Half the coal used in the United States comes from strip mines. Since coal is often found in expansive, horizontal beds, the entire land surface can be stripped away to cheaply and quickly expose the coal. The overburden, or surface material, is placed back into the mine, but usually in long ridges called spoil banks. Spoil banks are very susceptible to erosion and chemical weathering. Because the spoil banks have no topsoil (the complex organic mixture that supports vegetation—see chapter 7), revegetation occurs very slowly.

The 1977 federal Surface Mining Control and Reclamation Act (SMCRA) requires better restoration of strip-mined lands, especially where mines replaced prime farmland. Since then, the record of strip-mine reclamation has improved substantially. Complete mine restoration is expensive, often more than $10,000 per hectare. Restoration is also difficult because the developing soil is usually acidic and compacted by the heavy machinery used to reshape the land surface.

Bitter controversy has grown recently over mountaintop removal, a coal mining method practiced mainly in Appalachia. Long, sinuous ridge-tops are removed by giant, 20-story-tall shovels to expose horizontal beds of coal (fig. 11.13). Up to 215 m (700 ft) of

**Figure 11.12** There could be huge deposits of shale-bed methane in North America, but the costs of extracting this gas could be unacceptable in many areas.

**Figure 11.13** Mountaintop removal mining is a relatively new, and deeply controversial, method of extracting Appalachian coal.

ridge-top may be pulverized and dumped into adjacent river valleys. The debris can be laden with selenium, arsenic, coal, and other toxic substances. At least 900 km (560 mi) of streams have been buried in West Virginia alone. Hundreds of thousands of hectares of Appalachian mountains have been leveled by this practice. In 2010, the U.S. EPA issued new restrictions on valley filling because it violates the Clean Water Act (chapter 10). Industry representatives claimed this will mean the end of mountaintop removal. Coal-state residents are deeply divided about this ruling because they live in affected stream valleys but also depend on a coal economy.

The Mineral Policy Center in Washington, D.C. estimates that 19,000 km (12,000 mi) of rivers and streams in the United States are contaminated by mine drainage. The EPA estimates that cleaning up impaired streams, along with 550,000 abandoned mines in the United States, may cost $70 billion. Worldwide, mine closing and rehabilitation costs are estimated in the trillions of dollars. Because of the volatile prices of metals and coal, many mining companies have gone bankrupt before restoring mine sites, leaving the public responsible for cleanup.

In 2002 more than 500 leading mine executives and their critics convened at the Global Mining Initiative, a meeting in Toronto aimed at improving the sustainability of mining. Executives acknowledged that in the future they will increasingly be held liable for environmental damages, and they said they were seeking ways to improve the industry's social and environmental record. Jay Hair, secretary general of the International Council on Mining and Metals, stated that "environmental protection and social responsibility are important" and that mining companies were interested in participating in sustainable development. Mine executives also recognized that, increasingly, big cleanup bills will cut into company values and stock prices. Finding creative ways to keep mines cleaner from the start will make good economic sense, even if it's not easy to do.

## Processing contaminates air, water, and soil

Metals are extracted from ores by heating or by using chemical solvents. Both processes release large quantities of toxic materials that can be even more environmentally hazardous than mining. **Smelting**—roasting ore to release metals—is a major source of air pollution. One of the most notorious examples of ecological devastation from smelting is a wasteland near Ducktown, Tennessee. In the mid-1800s, mining companies began excavating the rich copper deposits in the area. To extract copper from the ore, they built huge, open-air wood fires, using timber from the surrounding forest. Dense clouds of sulfur dioxide released from sulfide ores poisoned the vegetation and acidified the soil over a 50 mi$^2$ (13,000 ha) area. Rains washed the soil off the denuded land, creating a barren moonscape.

Sulfur emissions from Ducktown smelters were reduced in 1907 after Georgia sued Tennessee over air pollution. In the 1930s the Tennessee Valley Authority (TVA) began treating the soil and replanting trees to cut down on erosion. Recently, upwards of $250,000 per year has been spent on this effort. While the trees and other plants are still spindly and feeble, more than two-thirds of the

area is considered "adequately" covered with vegetation. Similarly, smelting of copper-nickel ore in Sudbury, Ontario, a century ago caused widespread ecological destruction that is slowly being repaired following pollution-control measures (see fig. 9.25).

Chemical extraction is used to dissolve or mobilize pulverized ore, but it uses and pollutes a great deal of water. A widely used method is **heap-leach extraction**, which involves piling crushed ore in huge heaps and spraying it with a dilute alkaline-cyanide solution. The solution percolates through the pile and dissolves gold. The gold-containing solution is then pumped to a processing plant that removes the gold by electrolysis. A thick clay pad and plastic liner beneath the ore heap is supposed to keep the poisonous cyanide solution from contaminating surface or groundwater, but leaks are common.

Once all the gold is recovered, mine operators may simply walk away from the operation, leaving vast amounts of toxic effluent in open ponds behind earthen dams. A case in point is the Summitville Mine near Alamosa, Colorado. After extracting $98 million in gold, the absentee owners declared bankruptcy in 1992, abandoning millions of tons of mine waste and huge, leaking ponds of cyanide. The Environmental Protection Agency may spend more than $100 million trying to clean up the mess and keep the cyanide pool from spilling into the Alamosa River.

# 11.5 Conserving Geologic Resources

Conservation offers great potential for extending our supplies of economic minerals and reducing the effects of mining and processing. The advantages of conservation are significant: less waste to dispose of, less land lost to mining, and less consumption of money, energy, and water resources.

## Recycling saves energy as well as materials

Some waste products already are being exploited, especially for scarce or valuable metals. Aluminum, for instance, must be extracted from bauxite by electrolysis, an expensive, energy-intensive process. Recycling waste aluminum, such as beverage cans, on the other hand, consumes one-twentieth of the energy of extracting new aluminum. Today, nearly two-thirds of all aluminum beverage cans in the United States are recycled, up from only 15 percent 20 years ago. The high value of aluminum scrap ($650 a ton versus $60 for steel, $200 for plastic, $50 for glass, and $30 for paperboard) gives consumers plenty of incentive to deliver their cans for collection. Recycling is so rapid and effective that half of all the aluminum cans now on a grocer's shelf will be made into another can within two months. Table 11.3 shows the energy cost of extracting other materials.

Platinum, the catalyst in automobile catalytic exhaust converters, is valuable enough to be regularly retrieved and recycled from used cars. Other commonly recycled metals are gold, silver, copper, lead, iron, and steel. The last four are readily available in a pure and massive form, including copper pipes, lead batteries,

| Table 11.3 | Energy Requirements in Producing Various Materials from Ore and Raw Source Materials | |
| --- | --- | --- |
| **ENERGY REQUIREMENT (MJ/KG)[1]** | | |
| **Product** | **New** | **From Scrap** |
| Glass | 25 | 25 |
| Steel | 50 | 26 |
| Plastics | 162 | n.a.[2] |
| Aluminum | 250 | 8 |
| Titanium | 400 | n.a.[2] |
| Copper | 60 | 7 |
| Paper | 24 | 15 |

[1] Megajoules per kilogram.
[2] Not available.

*Source:* Data from E. T. Hayes, *Implications of Materials Processing,* 1997.

and steel and iron auto parts. Gold and silver are valuable enough to warrant recovery, even through more difficult means. Nearly all scrapped automobiles and car batteries are now recycled in the United States (fig. 11.14).

While total U.S. steel production has fallen in recent decades—largely because of inexpensive supplies from new and efficient Japanese steel mills—a new type of mill subsisting entirely on a readily available supply of scrap/waste steel and iron is a growing industry. **Minimills**, which remelt and reshape scrap iron and steel, are smaller and cheaper to operate than traditional integrated mills that perform every process from preparing raw ore

to finishing iron and steel products. Minimills take less than half as much energy per ton of steel produced as integrated mill furnaces. Minimills now produce about half of all U.S. steel. Some minimills use as much as 90 percent recycled iron and steel. Now that all new steel made in North America must contain at least 28 percent recycled contents, iron and steel recycling in the United States reached 83 percent in 2010.

## New materials can replace mined resources

Mineral and metal consumption can be reduced by new materials or new technologies developed to replace traditional uses. This is a long-standing tradition; for example, bronze replaced stone technology, and iron replaced bronze. More recently, the introduction of plastic pipe has decreased our consumption of copper, lead, and steel pipes. In the same way, the development of fiber-optic technology and satellite communication reduces the need for copper telephone wires.

Iron and steel have been the backbone of heavy industry, but we are now moving toward other materials. One of our primary uses for iron and steel has been machinery and vehicle parts. In automobile production, steel is being replaced by polymers (long-chain organic molecules similar to plastics), aluminum, ceramics, and new high-technology alloys. All of these reduce vehicle weight and cost, while increasing fuel efficiency. Some of the newer alloys that combine steel with titanium, vanadium, or other metals wear much better than traditional steel. Ceramic engine parts provide heat insulation around pistons, bearings, and cylinders, keeping the rest of the engine cool and operating efficiently. Plastics and glass fiber–reinforced polymers are used in body parts and some engine components.

Electronics and communications (telephone) technology, once major consumers of copper and aluminum, now use ultrahigh-purity glass cables to transmit pulses of light, instead of metal wires carrying electron pulses. Once again, this technology has been developed for its greater efficiency and lower cost, but it also affects consumption of our most basic metals (see A Closer Look, p. 284).

## 11.6 Geologic Hazards

Earthquakes, such as the one described in the opening case study for this chapter, along with volcanoes, floods, and landslides are normal earth processes, events that have made our earth what it is today. However, when they affect human populations, their consequences can be among the worst and most feared disasters that befall us.

### Earthquakes are frequent and deadly hazards

The 2010 earthquake in Haiti wasn't the world's worst geologic disaster. A much larger earthquake and tsunami in 2004 just off the coast of Banda Aceh, Indonesia, killed over 230,000 people and caused damage as far away as Africa. A far larger toll is thought to have been caused by a 1976 earthquake in Tangshan, China. Government

**Figure 11.14** The richest metal source we have—our mountains of scrapped cars—offers a rich, inexpensive, and ecologically beneficial resource that can be "mined" for a number of metals.

**Figure 11.15** Earthquakes are most devastating where building methods cannot withstand shaking. The 2010 earthquake in Haiti is thought to have killed 200,000 people. Collapsed buildings, food and water shortages, infectious diseases, and exposure to the elements contributed to the death toll.

officials reported 655,000 deaths, although some geologists doubt it was that high.

**Earthquakes** are sudden movements in the earth's crust that occur along faults (planes of weakness), where one rock mass slides past another one. When movement along faults occurs gradually and relatively smoothly, it is called creep, or seismic slip, and may be undetectable to the casual observer. When friction prevents rocks from slipping easily, stress builds up until it is finally released with a sudden jerk. The point on a fault at which the first movement occurs during an earthquake is called the epicenter.

Earthquakes have always seemed mysterious, sudden, and violent, coming without warning and leaving ruined cities and dislocated landscapes in their wake. Cities such as Port-au-Prince, Haiti, parts of which which were built on poorly consolidated alluvial soil, often suffer the greatest damage from earthquakes (fig. 11.15). Water-saturated soil can liquefy when shaken. Buildings sometimes sink out of sight or fall down like a row of dominoes under these conditions.

Earthquakes frequently occur along the edges of tectonic plates, especially where one plate is being subducted, or pushed down, beneath another. Earthquakes also occur in the centers of continents, however. In fact, the largest earthquake in recorded history in North America was one of an estimated magnitude 8.8 that struck the area around New Madrid, Missouri, in 1812 (fig. 11.16). Fortunately, few people lived there at the time, and the damage was minimal.

Modern building codes in earthquake zones attempt to prevent damage and casualties by constructing buildings that can withstand tremors. The primary methods used are heavily reinforced structures, strategically placed weak spots in the building that can absorb vibration from the rest of the structure, and pads or floats beneath the building on which it can shift harmlessly with ground motion.

One of the most notorious effects of earthquakes is the **tsunami** (Japanese for "harbor wave.") These giant sea swells, such as the one originating in Banda Aceh, Indonesia, in 2004, can move at 1,000 kph (600 mph), or faster, away from the center of an earthquake. When these swells approach the shore, they can create breakers as high as 65 m (nearly 200 ft). Tsunamis also can be caused by underwater volcanic explosions or massive seafloor slumping.

There's evidence that human activities can trigger earthquakes. Raising and lowering water levels in reservoirs behind large dams often correlates with increased seismic activity. Chinese geologists, for example, suspect that the 2008 earthquake that killed 69,000 people in Sichuan province may have been triggered by recent building of the Zipingpu dam on the Min River only a few kilometers from the earthquake epicenter. Similarly, injection of fluids into deep wells also correlates with increased earth tremors. In 2009, two geothermal deep well projects—one in Switzerland and the other in California—were abruptly canceled when earthquakes in the immediate vicinity suddenly intensified.

## Volcanoes eject deadly gases and ash

**Volcanoes** and undersea magma vents are the sources of most of the earth's crust. Over hundreds of millions of years, gaseous emissions from these sources formed the earth's earliest oceans and atmosphere. Many of the world's fertile soils are weathered volcanic materials. Volcanoes have also been an ever present threat to human populations (fig. 11.17). One of the most famous historic volcanic eruptions was that of Mount Vesuvius in southern Italy, which buried the cities of Herculaneum and Pompeii in A.D. 79. The mountain had been showing signs of activity before it erupted, but many citizens chose to stay and take a chance on survival. On August 24, the mountain buried the two towns in ash. Thousands were killed by the dense, hot, toxic gases that accompanied the ash flowing down from the volcano's mouth. It continues to erupt from time to time.

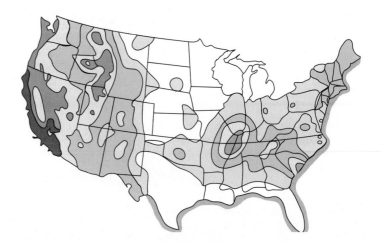

**Figure 11.16** A seismic map of the lower 48 states shows the risk of earthquakes. Greatest risks are along the Pacific coast, but high potential also exists along the Mississippi around New Madrid, Missouri. Colors indicate potential earth movement, in cm/s/s: > 200 (red), 20 (yellow), < 2 (white). *Source:* USGS 2010.

# Where does your cell phone come from?

Mobile phones, computers, and other electronic gadgets have transformed our lives, but few of us think about the geologic resources that went into making those devices. We enjoy these items for their useful lives, but we're always eager to trade up to the next newer and better models. While each individual gadget may be small and contain only tiny amounts of precious metals, rare earths, fossil fuels, and other materials, collectively they make a big impact.

Currently, there are at least 1 billion personal computers and 5 billion mobile phones in use around the world, and the numbers are climbing rapidly. In the United States, most people change their cell phone every 18 to 24 months. Computers last only 2 to 3 years, contributing to the mountains of eWaste discarded in the U.S. every year.

**Here are a few examples of the many source areas that contribute to our cell phones.**

CL 11.1

We depend increasingly on electronics, but where do they originate?

CL 11.2

Although they may be tiny, cell phones contain a surprising amount of metal that could be recycled, and yet hundreds of millions are thrown away every year or lie unused in drawers and cupboards. A typical cell phone can contain gold, silver, copper, palladium, platinum, lead, zinc, mercury, chromium, cadmium, rhodium, beryllium, arsenic, and lithium among other metals and chemical compounds.

Specialized lightweight metals are often mined in remote, hard-to-monitor locations. One of these is "coltan" an ore containing the metals columbium, tantalum, and niobium, which are essential in many electronics, including cell phones. Congo contains 80 percent of the world's supply of coltan. Inhumane conditions and child labor have been involved, and sales of these metals have helped finance wars in central Africa.

Child labor mining coltan          CL 11.3

Depending on the ore quality, a metric ton of ore may yield only 0.3 g of gold, and the miners may have to move 2 to 5 tons of overburden (unwanted rock) to get to that ore.

Abandoned mines often leak strong acids laced with arsenic, mercury, and other toxic metals into local groundwater and surface waters. By some calculations, humans now move more earth than the glaciers did.

Open-pit copper mine

CL 11.4

As we've seen elsewhere in this chapter, supplies of rare earth metals, such as neodymium, dysprosium, lanthanum, and yttrium are also critical for modern electronics. Monopolies in the sources of some of these materials, together with adverse environmental impacts in their extraction and purification, could constrain some technologies.

CL 11.5

Oil refineries produce our plastics from oil.

eWaste collection and monitoring is increasingly important.

CL 11.6

An offshore oil well provides energy and plastics.

CL 11.7

The plastic case for your phone or computer is made from petroleum. Energy is also used to manufacture and ship all the gadgets we use. Extracting, shipping, and refining fossil fuels are among our biggest geologic impacts. Obtaining the 20 billion barrels of petroleum or the 7 billion short tons of coal we use globally every year has uncalculated environmental, social, and economic impacts.

Every year, billions of cell phones and computers are discarded around the world. Added to the piles of refrigerators, air conditioners, TV sets, and other unwanted appliances, disposal of electronic waste is a huge problem. In the United States, where 3 million tons of electronics are tossed out every year, 70 percent of the heavy metals in landfills are from eWaste. Increasingly, this electronic garbage is shipped to developing countries where scavengers disassemble it under dangerous conditions in an effort to recover valuable metals. Modern recycling facilities can recover 99 percent of the contents much more safely and efficiently.

CL 11.8

Gold smelter

Smelting (extracting metals from ore by baking it) takes a huge amount of energy and often releases large amounts of air and water pollution, especially in countries where environmental regulation is weak.

## Can You Explain:

1. If each cell phone contains 0.03 g of gold, how much would be in 5 billion phones?

2. List 15 of the elements or earth materials found in cell phones.

3. Do we have an ethical responsibility for what happens to our waste once we're through with it?

Mudflows  Dust and ash  Nuées ardentes

**Figure 11.17** Lava and ashflow spill down the slopes of Mayon volcano in the Philippines in this September 23, 1984, image. Because more than 73,000 people evacuated danger zones, this eruption caused no casualties.

*Nuees ardentes* (French for "glowing clouds") are deadly, denser-than-air mixtures of hot gases and ash like those that inundated Pompeii and Herculaneum. Temperatures in these clouds may exceed 1,000°C, and they move at more than 100 kph (60 mph). *Nuees ardentes* destroyed the town of St. Pierre on the Caribbean island of Martinique on May 8, 1902. Mount Pelee released a cloud of *nuees ardentes* that rolled down through the town, killing between 25,000 and 40,000 people within a few minutes. All of the town's residents died except for a single prisoner being held in the town dungeon.

Disastrous mudslides are also associated with volcanoes. The 1985 eruption of Nevado del Ruíz, 130 km (85 mi) northwest of Bogotá, Colombia, caused mudslides that buried most of the town of Armero and devastated the town of Chinchina. An estimated 25,000 people were killed. Heavy mudslides also accompanied the eruption of Mount St. Helens in Washington in 1980. Sediments mixed with melted snow destroyed roads, bridges, and property, but because of sufficient advance warning, there were few casualties. Geologists worry that similar mudflows from an eruption at Mount Rainier would threaten much larger populations (fig. 11.18).

Volcanic eruptions often release large volumes of ash and dust into the air. Mount St. Helens expelled 3 km³ of dust and ash, causing ash fall across much of North America. This was only a minor eruption. An eruption in a bigger class of volcanoes was that of Tambora in Indonesia in 1815, which expelled

175 km³ of dust and ash, more than 58 times that of Mount St. Helens. These dust clouds circled the globe and reduced sunlight and air temperatures enough so that 1815 was known as the year without a summer.

It is not just a volcano's dust that blocks sunlight. Sulfur emissions from volcanic eruptions combine with rain and atmospheric moisture to produce sulfuric acid ($H_2SO_4$). Droplets of $H_2SO_4$ interfere with solar radiation and can significantly cool the world climate. In 1991 Mount Pinatubo in the Philippines emitted 20 million tons of sulfur dioxide aerosols, which remained in the stratosphere for two years. This thin haze cooled the entire earth by 1°C for about two years. It also caused a 10 to 15 percent reduction in stratospheric ozone, allowing increased ultraviolet light to reach the earth's surface.

## Floods are part of a river's land-shaping processes

Like earthquakes and volcanoes, **floods** are normal events that cause damage when people get in the way. As rivers carve and shape the landscape, they build broad **floodplains**, level expanses that are periodically inundated. Large rivers, such as the Mississippi, can have huge floodplains. Many cities have been built on these flat, fertile plains, which are so convenient to the river. Floodplains that flood very irregularly may appear safe for many years, but eventually, most floodplains do flood. The severity of floods can be described by the height of water above the normal stream banks or by how frequently a similar

**Figure 11.18** Volcanic activity at Mount Rainier has produced at least 12 large mudflows in the past 6,000 years (*brown areas*). Future flows could threaten large populations now in the area. *Source:* Data from T. W. Sisson, USGS Open File Report 95–642.

**Figure 11.19** The overflowing Cedar River filled most of downtown Cedar Rapids, Iowa during the 2008 floods. More than 40,000 people were forced from their homes in Iowa, and economic losses were estimated to be in the billions of dollars. Are human-caused environmental changes partly to blame for the severity of disasters such as this?

event normally occurs—on average—for a given area. Note that these are statistical averages over long time periods. A "10-year flood" would be expected to occur once in every ten years; a "100-year flood" would be expected to occur once every century. But two 100-year floods can occur in successive years or even in the same year.

Among direct natural disasters, floods take the largest number of human lives and cause the most property damage. A flood on the Yangtze River in China in 1931 killed 3.7 million people, making it the most deadly natural disaster in recorded history. In another flood on China's Yellow River in 1959, about 2 million people died, mostly due to famine and disease. Torrential rains in June 2008 caused massive flooding across the American Midwest. Many cities in Iowa, Wisconsin, Illinois, and Indiana experienced their highest water levels in more than a century. In Cedar Rapids, Iowa, for example, almost the entire downtown was inundated by the overflowing Cedar River (fig. 11.19).

The 2008 floods in the Mississippi River basin caused billions of dollars in property damage. The biggest economic loss from floods is usually not the buildings and property they wash away, but rather the contamination they cause. Virtually everything floodwaters touch in a house—carpets, furniture, drapes, electronics, even drywall and insulation—must be removed and discarded because of the sewage, toxic chemicals, farm waste, dead animals, and smelly mud carried by the water. In some cases, sediment left behind by floods has completely buried whole towns.

In 2008, more than 2 million ha (5 million acres) of rich farmland was inundated in the heart of America's corn (maize) and soybean producing area. The USDA estimates that this will result in loss of 200 million bushels (about 5 million metric tons) of corn and 40 million bushels of soybeans at a time when these commodities are already at record high prices. These losses are likely to exacerbate worldwide food shortages.

Are these floods related to global climate change? Many climate scientists predict that global warming will cause more extreme weather events, including both severe droughts in some places and more intense rainfall in others. In addition, many other human activities increase both the severity and frequency of floods. Covering the land with hardened surfaces, such as roads, parking lots, and building roofs, reduces water infiltration into the soil and speeds the rate of runoff into streams and lakes. Clearing forests for agriculture and destroying natural wetlands also increases both the volume and rate of water discharge after a storm. In Iowa, for example, at least 99 percent of the natural wetlands that existed before settlement have been filled for farmland and urban development.

Even more than development, though, flood-control structures have separated floodplains from rivers. Levees and flood walls are built to contain water within riverbanks, and river channels are dredged and deepened to allow water to recede faster. Every flood-control structure simply transfers the problem downstream, however. The water has to go somewhere. If it doesn't soak into the ground upstream, it will simply exacerbate floods somewhere downstream—leading to more levee development, and then to more flooding farther downstream, and so on.

**Flood Control** More than $25 billion of river-control systems have been built on the Mississippi and its tributaries. These systems have protected many communities over the past century. In the major floods of 1993, however, this elaborate system helped turn a large flood into a major disaster. Deprived of the ability to spill out over floodplains, the river is pushed downstream to create faster currents and deeper floods until eventually a levee gives way somewhere. Hydrologists calculate that the floods of 1993 were about 3 m (10 ft) higher than they would have been, given the same rainfall in 1900 before the flood-control structures were in place.

Under current rules, the government is obligated to finance most levees and flood-control structures. Many people think that it would be much better to spend this money to restore wetlands, replace groundcover on water courses, build check dams on small streams, move buildings off the floodplain, and undertake other nonstructural ways of reducing flood danger. According to this view, floodplains should be used for wildlife habitat, parks, recreation areas, and other uses not susceptible to flood damage.

The National Flood Insurance Program administered by the Federal Emergency Management Agency (FEMA) was intended to aid people who cannot buy insurance at reasonable rates, but its effects have been to encourage building on the floodplains by making people feel that, whatever happens, the government will take care of them. Many people would like to relocate homes and businesses out of harm's way after the recent floods or to improve them so they will be less susceptible to flooding, but owners of damaged property can collect only if they rebuild in the same place and in the same way as before. This perpetuates problems rather than solves them.

**Figure 11.20** Mass wasting includes the collapse of unstable hill slopes, such as this one in Laguna Beach, California. Land clearing and building can accelerate this natural process.

## Mass wasting includes slides and slumps

Gravity constantly pulls downward on every material everywhere on earth. Hillsides, beaches, even relatively flat farm fields can lose material to erosion. Often water helps mobilize loose material, and catastrophic slumping, beach erosion, and gully development can occur in a storm. A general term for downhill slides of earth is "mass wasting."

**Landslides** are sudden collapses of hillsides. In the United States alone, landslides and related mass wasting cause over $1 billion in property damage every year. When unconsolidated sediments on a hillside are saturated by a storm or exposed by logging, road building, or house construction, slopes are especially susceptible to sudden landslides (fig. 11.20).

Often people are unaware of the risks they face by locating on or under unstable hillsides. Sometimes they simply ignore clear and obvious danger. In southern California, where land prices are high, people often build expensive houses on steep hills and in narrow canyons. Most of the time, this dry environment appears quite stable, but in fact, steep hillsides slip and slump frequently. Especially when soil is exposed or rainfall is heavy, mudslides and debris flows can destroy whole neighborhoods. In developing countries, mudslides have buried entire villages in minutes. **Soil creep**, on the other hand, moves material inexorably downhill at an imperceptibly slow pace.

## Erosion destroys fields and undermines buildings

Gullying is the development of deep trenches on relatively flat ground. Especially on farm fields, which have a great deal of loose soil unprotected by plant roots, rainwater running across the surface can dig deep gullies. Sometimes land becomes useless for farming because gullying is so severe and because erosion has removed the fertile topsoil. Agricultural soil erosion has been described as an invisible crisis. Erosion has reduced the fertility of millions of acres of prime farmland in the United States alone.

Beach erosion occurs on all sandy shorelines because the motion of the waves is constantly redistributing sand and other sediments. One of the world's longest and most spectacular sand beaches runs down the Atlantic coast of North America from New England to Florida and around the Gulf of Mexico. Much of this beach lies on some 350 long, thin **barrier islands** that stand between the mainland and the open sea. Behind these barrier islands lie shallow bays or brackish lagoons fringed by marshes or swamps.

Early inhabitants recognized that exposed, sandy shores were hazardous places to live, and they settled on the bay side of barrier islands or as far upstream on coastal rivers as was practical. Modern residents, however, place a high value on living where they have an ocean view and ready access to the beach. And they assume that modern technology makes them immune to natural forces. The most valuable and prestigious property is closest to the shore. Over the past 50 years, more than 1 million acres (400,000 ha) of estuaries and coastal marshes have been filled to make way for housing or recreational developments.

Construction directly on beaches and barrier islands can cause irreparable damage to the whole ecosystem. Under normal circumstances, fragile vegetative cover holds the shifting sand in place. Damaging this vegetation with construction, building roads, and breaching dunes with roads can destabilize barrier islands. Storms then wash away beaches or even whole islands. Hurricane Katrina in 2005 caused $100 billion in property damage along the Gulf coast of the United States mostly from the storm washing over barrier islands and coastlines (fig. 11.21). FEMA estimates that 25 percent of all coastal homes in the United States will have the ground washed out from under them by 2060 as intensified storms and rising sea levels caused by global warming make barrier islands and low-lying areas even riskier places to live.

Cities and individual property owners often spend millions of dollars to protect beaches from erosion and repair damage after storms. Sand is dredged from the ocean floor or hauled in by the truckload, only to wash away again in the next storm. Building artificial barriers, such as groins or jetties, can trap migrating sand and build beaches in one area, but they often starve downstream beaches and make erosion there even worse.

As is the case for inland floodplains, government policies often encourage people to build where they probably shouldn't. Subsidies for road building and bridges, support for water and sewer projects, tax exemptions for second homes, flood insurance, and disaster relief are all good for the real estate and construction businesses but invite people to build in risky places. Flood insurance typically costs

**Figure 11.21** The aftermath of Hurricane Katrina on Dauphin Island, Alabama. Since 1970, this barrier island at the mouth of Mobile Bay has lost 20 million yd³ (15 million m³) of sand to storms. Some beach houses have been rebuilt, mostly at public expense, five times in the past two decades. Does it make sense to keep rebuilding in such an exposed place?

$400 per year for $100,000 of coverage. In 2005 FEMA paid out $17 billion in disaster claims, 80 percent of which were flood-related. Settlement usually requires that structures be rebuilt exactly where and as they were before. There is no restriction on how many claims can be made, and policies are rarely canceled, no matter what the risk. Some beach houses have been rebuilt—at public expense—five times in two decades. The General Accounting Office reports that 2 percent of federal flood policies are responsible for 30 percent of all claims.

The Coastal Barrier Resources Act of 1982 prohibited federal support, including flood insurance, for development on sensitive islands and beaches. In 1992, however, the U.S. Supreme Court ruled that ordinances forbidding floodplain development amount to an unconstitutional "taking," or confiscation, of private property.

## Conclusion

Geologic hazards, including earthquakes, volcanic eruptions, tsunamis, floods, and landslides represent major threats. Devastating events have altered human history many times in the past, sending geopolitical, economic, genetic, and even artistic repercussions around the planet. But the same processes that cause threats to humans also create resources, such as fossil fuels, metals, and building materials. The study of geology has allowed us to predict where these threats and resources will occur. The extraction of earth resources often carries severe environmental costs, however, including water contamination, habitat destruction, and air pollution.

The earth's surface is shaped by shifting pieces of crust, which split and collide slowly but continuously. Earthquakes, volcanoes, and mountains occur on plate margins. Rocks are composed of minerals, and rocks can be described according to their origins in molten material (igneous rocks), eroded or deposited sediments (sedimentary rocks), or materials transformed by heat and pressure deep in the earth (metamorphic rocks).

Earth resources, including oil, gas, and coal, are the foundation of our economy. Metals are expensive to extract, but they are extremely valuable because they are ductile (bendable) yet strong, and because they carry electricity (e.g., copper). Mining and refining of metals and other geologic resources can cause severe environmental damage. In some cases, land can be restored to something close to its original state, but when you dig a mile-deep hole in the ground, or lop the whole top off a mountain and dump the waste into a nearby valley, it's unlikely that the damage will ever be undone.

Many materials can be recycled, saving money, energy, and environmental quality. Recycling aluminum consumes one-twentieth of the energy to extract new aluminum, for example, and recycling copper takes about one-eighth as much energy. We can also save energy and resources by replacing traditional materials with newer, more efficient ones. Fiber-optic communication lines have replaced much of our copper wiring, adding speed and efficiency while saving copper use.

Understanding the forces and processes that create both geologic hazards and resources is important for human existence. As the famous geologist Louis Agassiz said, "Learn geology or die."

# Practice
# Quiz

1. How does tectonic plate movement create ocean basins, mid-ocean ridges, and volcanoes?
2. What is the "ring of fire"?
3. Describe the processes and components of the rock cycle.
4. What is the difference between metals and nonmetal mineral resources?
5. What is a *mineral* and a *rock*? Why are pure metals not minerals?
6. Which countries are the single greatest producers of our major metals?
7. Describe some of the mining, processing, and drilling methods that can degrade water or air quality.
8. Compare the different mining methods of underground, open-pit, strip, and placer mining, as well as mountaintop removal.
9. What resources, aside from minerals themselves, can be saved by recycling?
10. Describe the most deadly risks of volcanoes.
11. What is *mass wasting*? Give three examples and explain why they are a problem.
12. Why is building on barrier islands risky?
13. What is a *floodplain*? Why is building on floodplains controversial?
14. Describe the processes of chemical weathering and mechanical weathering. How do these processes contribute to the recycling of rocks?
15. The Mesozoic period begins and ends with the appearance and disappearance of dinosaurs. What fossils mark the other geologic eras?

# Critical Thinking and Discussion Questions

Apply the principles you have learned in this chapter to discuss these questions with other students.

1. Understanding and solving the environmental problems of mining are basically geologic problems, but geologists need information from a variety of environmental and scientific fields. What are some of the other sciences (or disciplines) that could contribute to solving mine contamination problems?

2. Geologists are responsible for identifying and mapping mineral resources, but mineral resources are buried below the soil and covered with vegetation. How do you suppose geologists in the field find clues about the distribution of rock types?

3. If you had an igneous rock with very fine crystals and another with very large crystals, which would you expect to have formed deep in the ground, and why?

4. Heat and pressure tend to help concentrate metal ores. Explain why such ores might often occur in mountains such as the Andes in South America.

5. The idea of tectonic plates shifting across the earth's surface is central to explanations of geologic processes. Why is this idea still called the "theory" of plate tectonic movement?

6. Geologic data from fossils and sediments provided important evidence for past climate change. What sorts of evidence in the rocks and landscape around you suggest that the place where you live once looked much different than it does today?

# Data Analysis | Exploring Recent Earthquakes

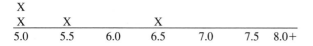

Go to the USGS Earthquake Center (http://earthquake.usgs.gov/eqcenter/). This is a rich source of global earthquake information.

1. Look at the U.S.A. map of earthquakes. Where are the greatest concentrations of earthquakes? Can you explain why those locations have lots of earthquakes?

2. Find the worldwide list of earthquakes, and click on Magnitude 5+. Where was the largest recent earthquake? What was its magnitude? Its depth? Are listed quakes clustered in a few regions? Where are those regions?

3. Still looking at the worldwide list of large earthquakes, make a graph showing the frequency of different magnitudes for listed earthquakes: On a piece of paper, draw a line with earthquake magnitude classes, then mark an X for each earthquake over the appropriate size class, like this:

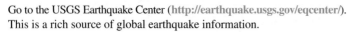

```
X
X      X          X
5.0    5.5   6.0  6.5   7.0    7.5   8.0+
```

This kind of graph is called a frequency distribution graph, or a histogram. Would you describe earthquake sizes as mostly small, evenly distributed, mostly large, or mostly in the middle of the range?

## Understanding Volcanoes

USGS Hawaii Volcano Observatory is one of the most important places for studying and understanding volcanoes. Visit the observatory's website at http://hvo.wr.usgs.gov/.

1. Which of the volcanoes discussed at this website is the largest in the world? Which is the most active?

2. Why are earthquakes discussed on this volcano website?

3. What are the major hazards to people from these volcanoes?

For a good collection of volcano images, go to the USGS Cascades Volcano Observatory at http://vulcan.wr.usgs.gov/Photo/framework.html.

## Evaluating Erosion on Farmland

The Natural Resources Conservation Service (NRCS), part of the U.S. Department of Agriculture, is the agency that monitors agricultural resources and conditions. Among its data-gathering efforts, the NRCS produces a Natural Resources Inventory (NRI), with maps of farmland conditions across the mainland United States and around the world. Visit the NRCS/NRI website at http://www.nrcs.usda.gov/technical/NRI/maps/.

Find the list of "Soil Erosion" maps. Look at several of the maps. First identify the meaning of the colors. Then identify the major concentration of high and low erosion rates.

1. Where is wind erosion worst both for the U.S. and in other countries? Where is water erosion worst both for the U.S. and in other countries?

2. Where are the largest areas of highly erodible cropland? What kind of physical features might occur there?

For Additional Help in Studying This Chapter, please visit our website at www.mhhe.com/cunningham6e. You will find practice quizzes, key terms, answers to end of chapter questions, additional case studies, an extensive reading list, and Google Earth™ mapping quizzes.

ENVIRONMENTAL SCIENCE

# 12 Energy

Photovoltaic cells mounted on tracking frames that follow the sun sit in the desert at Nellis Air Force Base in Navada. Wind, water, and solar power could provide 100 percent of the world's energy and completely replace all fossil fuels by 2030 if we make a commitment to clean technologies.

*We are not only responsible
for what we do, but also
for what we do not do.*

— MOLIERE

# CASE STUDY

## Renewable Energy in China

From ground level, Rizhao looks like any other midsized Chinese city. Located in Shandong Province about halfway between Beijing and Shanghai, Rizhao sits on the coastal plain with its back to the mountains. Rows of traditional houses alternate with high-rise apartments and office buildings. But from above, Rizhao shows a different face. More than 1 million gleaming solar collectors decorate the rooftops of this city of 2.8 million residents (fig. 12.1). More than 99 percent of all households get hot water and space heating from renewable energy.

In 2008, Rizhao became carbon neutral, one of the first four cities in the world to reach this milestone, a remarkable accomplishment in a developing country. Already, Rizhao has cut its per capita carbon emissions by half, compared to a decade ago, and its energy use by one-third. Generous subsidies for property owners, low-cost loans, and regulations that require renewable energy for all new construction have created mass markets for equipment that brings costs down, cleans the air, saves money, and creates thousands of local jobs. A solar water heater currently costs about (U.S.)$230 in Rizhao—about one tenth the cost in the United States—and pays for itself in just a few years.

Fortunately, Rizhao isn't an isolated case. China is well on its way to becoming the world's leader in renewable energy. For the past several years, China has controlled more than half the global market in solar panels. And in 2009, China passed Denmark, Germany, and Spain to become the world's largest producer of wind turbines. The prospect of rapidly falling prices for renewable energy as China develops its technology and mass markets is great news for our global environment, but not such a happy prospect for American manufacturers.

In his 2010 State of the Union address, President Obama said, "I do not accept a future where the jobs and industries of tomorrow take root beyond our borders." But that seems to be what's happening. China's push to dominate renewable energy technology raises the prospect that the United States and Europe may be trading their dependence on Middle Eastern oil for reliance on solar panels, wind turbines, and other energy supplies made in China. China already employs more than a million workers in clean-tech occupations, and is adding about 100,000 new jobs in this area every year.

China has several advantages in the race to produce sustainable energy. Around 250 million people have moved from the country to the city since 1990, and an equal number are expected to become urbanized in the next few decades, providing a huge market for new housing, electricity, and technology. To meet growing energy demand in just the next ten years, China will need to add about nine times as much electric generating capacity as the United States. Where utility managers are adding so much new equipment anyway, it isn't hard to make some of it solar or wind. American and European utilities, on the other hand, may have to abandon some existing technology to move in a meaningful way to renewables.

China also benefits from low labor and raw material costs. Already, Chinese companies produce the lowest priced solar panels in the world. Polysilicon, the main ingredient in solar photovoltaics, cost about $400 per kg in 2008. China can now produce it for $45 per kg, and expects to drive prices down even further in coming years. Furthermore, China has a near monopoly on several rare earth elements, such as dysprosium and terbium, essential in green technology (see chapter 11). Solar power stations and wind farms are built with relative ease in China, meeting little of the public resistance that hampers Western developers. And government officials in China can simply order utilities to switch to renewable power.

The rapid emergence of China as a world leader in green technology is big news for both our global environment and world economy. Many people have wondered how China will provide jobs, housing, and energy for its huge population. Progress in renewable energy and the jobs it provides may show a way, not only for China, but also for other developing countries, to reduce their dependence on environmentally damaging fossil fuels and move toward sustainability. In this chapter, we'll look at world energy resources as well as how we currently obtain the energy we use, and what our options are for finding environmentally and socially sustainable ways to meet our energy needs.

**Figure 12.1** China already has more than 40 million rooftop solar collectors and is well on its way to becoming the world's leader in renewable energy.

## 12.1 Energy Resources and Uses

Fire was probably the first external energy source used by humans. Charcoal from fires has been found at sites occupied by our early ancestors 1 million years ago. Muscle power provided by domestic animals has been important at least since the dawn of the Neolithic age 10,000 years ago. Wind and water power have been used nearly as long. The invention of the steam engine, together with diminishing supplies of wood in industrializing countries, caused a switch to coal as the major energy source at the beginning of the nineteenth century. Coal, in turn, was replaced by oil in the twentieth century due to the ease of shipping and burning liquid fuels. As easily accessible petroleum supplies have been depleted, however, we look increasingly to remote places, such as deep-ocean formations and the Arctic, for the oil on which we have become dependent.

Currently, **fossil fuels** (petroleum, natural gas, and coal) supply about 88 percent of the world's commercial energy needs (fig. 12.2). The dependence—some would say addiction—to fossil fuels causes critical geopolitical and economic problems. The United States, for example, spends about $400 billion every year on imported oil, not counting the costs of maintaining armed forces to ensure access to those resources. And the huge amounts of fossil fuels we now burn to support our lifestyles are now causing unsustainable environmental impacts ranging from mountaintop removal for coal extraction, water pollution from extracting tar sands, or air pollution and global climate change from burning all those carbon-based fuels.

We urgently need to break our fossil fuel habit. Fortunately, that seems to be happening. As the opening case study for this chapter shows, China is currently leading the way in developing renewable energy. This is great news in many ways. As the world's largest emitter of carbon dioxide, what happens in China over the next few decades will have a tremendous impact on our global climate. Furthermore, China's progress may show the way for other developing countries to leapfrog over the mistakes and problems associated with industrialization in Europe and the United States.

Could we get all the power we need from renewable sources? Yes we can. As you'll learn in more detail later in this chapter, the total global potential for wind and solar energy is approximately 8,200 TW (terawatts). Even though much of that supply is far out to sea or other inaccessible places, the easily available power from renewable resources is more than 50 times our current global energy consumption.

### How do we measure energy?

To understand the magnitude of energy use, it is helpful to know the units used to measure it. **Work** is the application of force over distance, and we measure work in **joules** (table 12.1). **Energy** is the capacity to do work. **Power** is the rate of energy flow or the rate of work done: for example, one **watt** (W) is one joule per second. If you use a 100-watt light bulb for 10 hours, you have used 1,000 watt-hours, or one kilowatt-hour (kWh). Most American households use about 11,000 kWh per year (table 12.2).

### Fossil fuels supply most of our energy

Like most other industrialized nations, the United States gets a vast majority of its energy from fossil fuels. Oil makes up 37 percent of this supply, while natural gas (24 percent) and coal (23 percent) follow close behind (fig. 12.3). Perhaps the most important fact about fossil fuel use is that the 20 richest countries consume nearly 80 percent of the natural gas, 65 percent of the oil, and 50 percent of the coal produced each year. Although these countries make up less than one-fifth of the world's population, they dominate more than one-half of the commercial energy supply. The United States, for instance, constitutes only about 4.5 percent of the world's population but consumes about one-quarter of all fossil fuels.

| Table 12.1 | Energy Units |
|---|---|
| 1 joule (J) = work needed to accelerate 1 kg 1 m/sec$^2$ for 1 m (or 1 amp/sec flowing through 1 ohm resistance) | |
| 1 watt (W) = 1 J per second<br>1 terawatt (TW) = 1 trillion watts | |
| 1 kilowatt hour (kWh) = 1,000 W exerted for 1 hour (or 3.6 million J) | |
| 1 megawatt (MW) = 1 million (10$^6$) W | |
| 1 gigajoule (GJ) = 1 billion (10$^9$) J | |
| 1 standard barrel (bbl) of oil = 42 gal (160 liters) | |

| Table 12.2 | Energy Uses | |
|---|---|
| **Uses** | **kWh/year*** |
| Computer | 100 |
| Television | 125 |
| 100 W light bulb | 250 |
| 15 W fluorescent bulb | 40 |
| Dehumidifier | 400 |
| Dishwasher | 600 |
| Electric stove/oven | 650 |
| Clothes dryer | 900 |
| Refrigerator | 1,100 |

*Averages shown; actual rates vary greatly.

*Source:* U.S. Department of Energy.

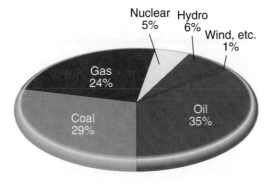

**Figure 12.2** Worldwide commercial energy consumption. This does not include energy collected for personal use or traded in informal markets.

*Source:* Date from British Petroleum, 2010.

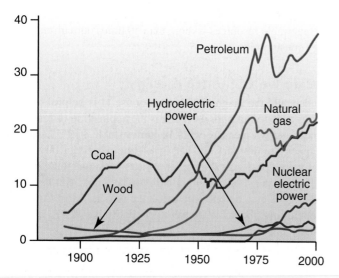

**Figure 12.3** Although the relative importance of various fuels has shifted over the past century, fossil fuels supply about 84 percent of all energy used currently in the United States, and petroleum makes up the largest share of that total. Furthermore, all energy sources, except wood and hydropower, surged to remarkable levels in the past 50 years. *Source:* U.S. DOE, 2010.

Renewable sources—solar, wind, geothermal, and hydroelectricity—make up about 7 percent of U.S. commercial power (but hydro and biomass account for almost all of that). While growing rapidly, solar, wind, and geothermal power still make up less than 1 percent of the U.S. energy supply. Wood, charcoal and other biomass sources provide the primary energy source for at least a billion people in developing countries. This is important in the lives of poor people but can be a serious cause of forest destruction (chapter 6).

Nuclear power is slightly greater than renewables (about 9 percent of all U.S. energy), but it provides about 20 percent of all electricity. There's enough nuclear fuel to produce power for a long time, but as we discuss later in this chapter, safety concerns and waste storage problems make this option unacceptable to most people.

How much energy do you use every year? Most of us don't think about it much, but maintaining the lifestyle we enjoy requires an enormous energy input. On average, each person in the United States and Canada uses more than 300 gigajoules (GJ) (equivalent to about 60 barrels of oil) per year. By contrast, in some of the poorest countries of the world, such as Ethiopia, Nepal, and Bhutan, each person generally consumes less than 1 GJ per year. This means that each of us consumes, on average, almost as much energy in a single day as a person in one of these countries consumes in a year.

Clearly, energy consumption is linked to the comfort and convenience of our lives. Those of us in the richer countries enjoy many amenities not available to most people in the world. The link isn't absolute, however. Several European countries, including Sweden, Denmark, and Finland, have higher standards of living than does the United States by almost any measure but use about half as much energy.

## How do we use energy?

The largest share of the energy used in the United States is consumed by industry (fig. 12.4). Mining, milling, smelting, and forging of primary metals consume about one-quarter of that industrial energy share. The chemical industry is the second largest industrial user of fossil fuels, but only half of its use is for energy generation. The remainder is raw material for plastics, fertilizers, solvents, lubricants, and hundreds of thousands of organic chemicals in commercial use. The manufacture of cement, glass, bricks, tile, paper, and processed foods also consumes large amounts of energy. While coal provides about one-quarter of our total energy in the United States, it supplies about half our electricity.

Residential and commercial customers use roughly 41 percent of the primary energy consumed in the United States, mostly for space heating, air conditioning, lighting, and water heating. Transportation requires about 28 percent of all energy used in the United States each year. About 98 percent of that energy comes from petroleum products refined into gasoline and diesel fuel, and the remaining 2 percent is provided by natural gas and electricity.

Almost three-quarters of all transport energy is used by motor vehicles. Nearly 3 trillion passenger miles and 600 billion ton miles of freight are carried annually by motor vehicles in the United States. About 75 percent of all freight traffic in the United States is carried by trains, barges, ships, and pipelines, but because they are very efficient, they use only 12 percent of all transportation fuel.

Producing and transporting energy also consumes and wastes energy. About half of all the energy in primary fuels is lost during conversion to more useful forms, while being shipped to the site of end use, or during use. Electricity is generally promoted as a clean, efficient source of energy because, when it is used to run a resistance heater or an electrical appliance, almost 100 percent of its energy is converted to useful work and no pollution is given off.

What happens, however, before electricity reaches us? Coal-fired power plants supply about half our electrical energy, and large amounts of pollution are released during mining and burning of that coal. Furthermore, nearly two-thirds of the energy in the coal was lost in thermal conversion in the power plant. About 10 percent more is lost during transmission and stepping down to household voltages.

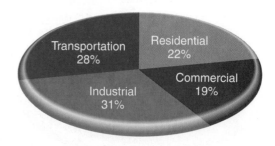

**Figure 12.4** Fossil fuels supply 84 percent of the energy used in the United States, and oil (three-quarters of it imported) makes up the largest share. Industry is the largest energy use sector. Transportation, however, uses about two-thirds of all oil. *Source:* Data from U.S Department of Energy, 2010.

## 12.2 Fossil Fuels

Fossil fuels are organic (carbon-based) compounds derived from decomposed plants, algae, and other organisms buried in rock layers for hundreds of millions of years. Most of the richest deposits date to about 286 million to 360 million years ago (the Mississippian, Pennsylvanian, and Permian periods: see chapter 11), when the earth's climate was much warmer and wetter than it is now.

### Coal resources are vast

World coal deposits are vast, ten times greater than conventional oil and gas resources combined. Almost all the world's coal is in North America, Europe, and Asia (fig. 12.5), and just three countries, the United States, Russia, and China, account for two-thirds of all proven reserves. Coal seams can be 100 m thick and can extend across tens of thousands of square kilometers that were vast, swampy forests in prehistoric times. The total resource is estimated to be 10 trillion metric tons. If all this coal could be extracted, and we could find environmentally benign ways to use it, this would amount to several thousand years' supply. Economically feasible reserves are generally a small fraction of a total resource (fig. 12.6).

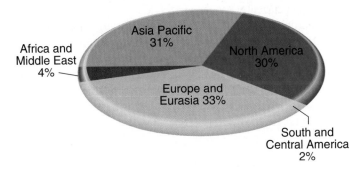

**Figure 12.5** Proven-in-place coal reserves by region, 2008.
*Source:* British Petroleum, 2010.

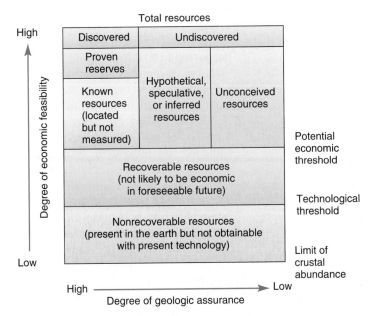

**Figure 12.6** Categories of natural resource according to economic and technological feasibility, as well as geologic assurance.

**Figure 12.7** Mountaintop removal is an extremely destructive method of coal mining.

But do we really want to use all of the coal? Coal mining is a dirty, dangerous activity. Underground mines are notorious for cave-ins, explosions, and lung diseases, such as black lung suffered by miners. Surface mines (called strip mines, where large machines scrape off overlying sediment to expose coal seams) are cheaper and generally safer for workers than tunneling, but leave huge holes where coal has been removed and vast piles of discarded rock and soil.

An especially damaging technique employed in Appalachia is called mountaintop removal. Typically, the whole top of a mountain ridge is scraped off to access buried coal (fig. 12.7). In 2010, the EPA announced regulations that should end this practice by banning "valley fill," in which waste rock is pushed into nearby valleys (see chapter 11 for further discussion of mining). Mine reclamation is now mandated in the United States, but efforts often are only partially successful.

Coal burning releases huge amounts of air pollution. Global climate change caused by carbon dioxide ($CO_2$) emissions is the biggest problem associated with coal. Every year the roughly 1 billion tons of coal burned in the United States (83 percent for electric power generation) releases close to a trillion metric tons of ($CO_2$). This is about half of the industrial $CO_2$ released by the United States each year.

Coal also contains toxic impurities, such as mercury, arsenic, chromium, and lead, which are released into the air during combustion. The coal burned every year in the United States releases 18 million metric tons of sulfur dioxide ($SO_2$), 5 million metric tons of nitrogen oxides ($NO_x$), 4 million metric tons of airborne particulates, 600,000 metric tons of hydrocarbons and carbon monoxide, and 40 tons of mercury. This is about three-quarters of the $SO_2$, and one-third of the $NO_x$ released by the United States each year. Sulfur and nitrogen oxides combine with water in the air to form sulfuric and nitric acid, making coal burning the largest single source of acid rain in many areas (chapter 9).

It's possible to make either gas or liquid fuels out of coal, but these processes are even dirtier and more expensive than burning the coal directly. Both coal to liquid or coal to gas are environmentally disastrous.

Another problem with coal combustion was revealed in 2009 when an earthen dam broke in eastern Tennessee and released a billion gallons (3.8 billion l) of coal ash sludge into a tributary of the Tennessee River. The ash contained dangerous levels of arsenic, mercury, and toxic hydrocarbons. After the spill, the U.S. EPA revealed that this impoundment was only one of hundreds of equally risky coal ash dumps across the country.

## New plants could be cleaner

Because coal causes so much air pollution, a great deal of effort has been invested in developing clean coal plants. While the initial cost of these plants is higher than older technology, they can pay for themselves over time. One of these systems is **integrated gasification combined cycle (IGCC)**, a technology that could produce zero-emissions electricity from coal. Power plants using this system could generate electricity while capturing and permanently storing carbon dioxide and other pollutants. An IGCC plant has been operating successfully for the past decade just outside of Tampa, Florida. Every day, the Polk power plant converts 2,400 tons of coal into 250 megawatts (MW) of electricity, or enough power for about 100,000 homes. Unlike conventional coal-fired power plants, an IGCC doesn't actually burn the coal. It converts the coal into gas and then burns the gas in a turbine (fig. 12.8). To do this, the coal is first ground into a fine powder and mixed with water to create a slurry. The slurry is pumped at high pressure into a gasification chamber, where it mixes with 96 percent pure oxygen, and is heated to 1,370°C (2,500°F). The coal doesn't burn; instead it reacts with the oxygen and breaks down into a variety of gases, mostly hydrogen and carbon dioxide. The gases are cooled, separated, and converted into easily managed forms.

After purification, the synthetic hydrogen gas (or syngas) is pumped to the combustion turbine, which spins a huge magnet to produce electricity. Superheated gases from the turbine are fed into a steam generator that drives another turbine to produce more electrical current. Combining these two turbines makes an IGCC about 15 percent more efficient than a normal coal-fired power plant. Perhaps even better is that the hydrogen gas could power fuel cells if they become commercially feasible.

Contaminants, such as sulfur dioxide ($SO_2$), ash, and mercury, that often go up the smokestack in a normal coal-burning plant, are captured and sold to make the IGCC cleaner and more economical. Sulfur is marketed as fertilizer; ash and slag are sold to cement companies. Mercury removal is an important public health benefit. All the slurry water is recycled to the gasifier; there is no waste water and very little solid waste. Because of these efficiencies, the Polk plant produces the cheapest electricity in the whole Tampa system. It doesn't now capture carbon dioxide, because it isn't required to, but it could easily do so. If we had $CO_2$ emission limits, IGCC plants could either pump it into deep wells for storage, or use it to enhance oil and natural gas recovery.

Despite the success of the Polk facility, only a few of the 80 or so new coal-fired power plants planned for construction over the next decade are slated to be IGCC, largely because of construction costs. While an IGCC can be very economical to operate, it costs 15 to 20 percent more to build than a conventional design. If industries were required to either sequester their $CO_2$ or pay a tax for not doing so, clean coal technology would be much more attractive, and our contributions to global warming would be far lower. Although the Tampa plant is the only one in the United States, Japan currently has about 18 IGCC plants.

China and India, both of which have very large coal resources, now burn about half of all coal mined annually in the world. Both of these countries have been increasing coal production greatly in the recent past to fuel their rapidly growing economies. Continuing to do so could cause run-away global climate change, so it's very good news that China, at least, seems determined to move quickly to renewable energy.

## Have we passed peak oil?

In the 1940s Dr. M. King Hubbert, a Shell Oil geophysicist, predicted that oil production in the United States would peak in the 1970s, based on estimates of U.S. reserves at the time. Hubbert's predicted peak was correct, and subsequent calculations have estimated a similar peak in global oil production in about 2005–2010 (fig. 12.9). While global production has not yet slowed significantly, many oil experts expect that we will pass this peak in the next few years.

About half of the world's original 4 trillion bbl (600 billion metric tons) of liquid oil are thought to be ultimately recoverable. (The rest is too diffuse, too tightly bound in rock formations, or too deep to be extracted.) Of the 2 trillion recoverable barrels, roughly 1.26 trillion bbl are in proven reserves (defined in fig. 12.6). We have already used more than 0.5 trillion bbl—almost half of proven reserves—and the remainder is expected to last 41 years at current consumption rates of 30.7 billion bbl per year. Middle Eastern countries have more than half of world supplies (fig. 12.10).

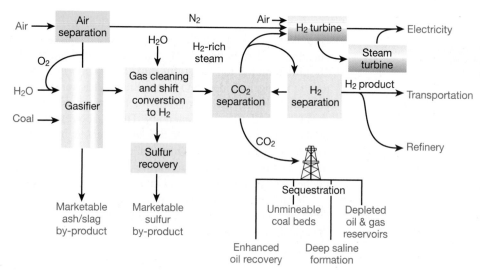

**Figure 12.8** Clean coal technology could contribute to energy independence, while also reducing our greenhouse gas emissions.

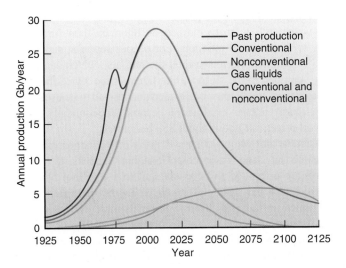

Figure 12.9 Worldwide production of crude oil with predicted Hubbert production. Gb = billion barrels. *Source:* Jean Laherrere, www.hubbertpeak.org.

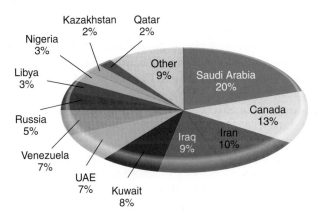

**Figure 12.10** Proven oil reserves. Twelve countries (eight of them in the Greater Middle East) account for 91 percent of all known, economically recoverable oil. *Source:* Data from U.S. DOE, 2008.

Consumption rates continue to climb, however, both in developed countries, and in the fast-growing economies such as China, India, and Brazil. China's energy demands have more than tripled in the past 35 years (much of this energy is used to produce goods for the U.S. and European markets), and China anticipates another doubling of energy demands in the next 15 years. Although renewables are supplying a growing share of China's energy, it's clear that competition is growing for global oil and gas supplies. Oil prices have been highly unstable recently, ranging from about $15 per barrel in 1993 to more than $150 per barrel in 2008.

The instability of global oil prices makes it difficult to establish conservation practices and renewable technologies. When oil is expensive, people are more likely to invest in alternative energy sources or change their lifestyle choices. When oil prices come tumbling back down, however, most people return to wasteful ways. China has an advantage in developing renewable resources in that the government can simply order homeowners and businesses to install solar collectors or to buy wind power. Currently, the Chinese government charges a renewable energy fee to all electricity users. This fee raises billions of yuan annually to help subsidize alternative energy supplies.

## Domestic oil supplies are limited

The United States has used more than half of its technically recoverable petroleum resources. About 30.7 billion barrels are proven in place. At 2010 U.S. rates of consumption (20 million bbl/day), that's enough for about 4.2 years, if we were to stop all imports. Most of the remaining potential for new oil supplies are in coastal waters, Alaska's far north, or other remote areas that provide wildlife habitat, valuable fisheries, and are difficult or dangerous for drilling.

The catastrophic explosion and well blowout in the Gulf of Mexico in 2010 provides a dire warning of the dangers of our addiction to oil. The well was being drilled in 5,000 ft (1,500 m) of water and had just reached a huge oil deposit about 17,000 ft (5,200 m) beneath the ocean floor when a bubble of explosive methane gas surged up the drill pipe and exploded into a massive fire ball (fig. 12.11). Eleven workers were killed and 17 were wounded. The drill rig sank and the oil began gushing out of the ruptured well.

Officials estimated the spill at 5,000 barrels (800,000 liters) per day, but some experts warned that the actual amount could be 30 times as much. To put this in perspective, the Gulf disaster could be discharging as much oil every two days as the total *Exxon Valdez* spill in Alaska in 1989.

As the oil contaminated beaches along the entire eastern Gulf Coast and spread toward Florida's coral reefs, it threatened fragile coastal marshes, valuable barrier islands, bird colonies, aquatic life, and some of the world's richest fishing grounds. Thousands of

**Figure 12.11** In 2010, the oil drilling rig Deepwater Horizon exploded and sank in the Gulf of Mexico. Ruptured pipelines gushed up to 6 million gallons (23 million liters) of crude oil per day for more than a month, contaminating hundreds of kilometers of Gulf Coast beaches and wetlands and killing untold numbers of birds, turtles, fish, and other aquatic creatures.

# Active Learning

jobs in fishing and tourism and billions of dollars in the regional economy are at stake in this terrible tragedy, which could well be the worst environmental calamity in American history.

The Gulf disaster renewed demands for an offshore drilling ban and a switch to renewable energy sources. Conservation can make a big difference in stretching oil supplies. Transportation accounts for over 40 percent of U.S. energy use, and oil (refined to produce gasoline or diesel fuel) provides over 90 percent of energy in transportation. So vehicle efficiency can have a substantial influence in our overseas oil dependence (see Active Learning, p. 298).

## Oil shales and tar sands contain huge amounts of petroleum

Estimates of our recoverable oil supplies usually don't account for the very large potential from unconventional resources. The World Energy Council estimates that oil shales, tar sands, and other unconventional deposits contain ten times as much oil as liquid petroleum reserves. **Tar sands** are composed of sand and shale particles coated with bitumen, a viscous, tarlike mixture of long-chain hydrocarbons. Shallow tar sands are excavated and mixed with hot water and steam to extract the bitumen, then fractionated to make useful products. For deeper deposits, superheated steam is injected to melt the bitumen, which can then be pumped to the surface, like liquid crude. Once the oil has been retrieved, it still must be cleaned and refined to be useful. This costly, energy-intensive extraction becomes economically justified when oil prices rise above about $50 per barrel.

Canada and Venezuela have the world's largest and most accessible tar sand resources. Canadian deposits in northern Alberta are estimated to be equivalent to 1.7 trillion bbl of oil, and Venezuela has nearly as much. Together, these deposits are three times as large as all conventional liquid oil reserves. By 2010 Alberta produced some 2 million bbl per day, or twice the maximum projected output of the Alaska's controversial Arctic National Wildlife Refuge (ANWR). Furthermore, because Athabascan tar sand beds are 40 times larger and much closer to the surface than ANWR oil, the Canadian resource will last longer and may be cheaper to extract. Canada is already the largest supplier of oil to the United States, having surpassed Saudi Arabia in 2000.

There are severe environmental costs, however, in producing this oil. A typical plant producing 125,000 bbl of oil per day creates about 15 million $m^3$ of toxic sludge, releases 5,000 tons of greenhouse gases, and consumes or contaminates billions of liters of water each year. Surface mining in Canada could destroy millions of hectares of boreal forest. Native Cree, Chipewyan, and Metis people worry about effects on traditional ways of life if forests are destroyed and wildlife and water are contaminated. Many Canadians dislike becoming an energy colony for the United States, and environmentalists argue that investing billions of dollars to extract this resource simply makes us more dependent on fossil fuels.

**Oil shales** are fine-grained sedimentary rock rich in solid organic material called kerogen. Like tar sands, the kerogen can be heated, liquefied, and pumped out like liquid crude oil. Oil shale beds up to 600 m (1,800 ft) thick underlie much of Colorado, Utah, and Wyoming. If these deposits could be extracted at a reasonable price and with acceptable environmental impacts, they might yield the equivalent of several trillion barrels of oil. Mining and extraction of oil shale—like tar sands—uses vast amounts of water (a scarce resource in the arid western United States), releases much more carbon dioxide than burning an equivalent amount of coal, and creates enormous quantities of waste. The rock matrix expands when heated, resulting in two or three times the volume that was dug out of the ground. Billions of dollars were spent in the 1980s on pilot projects to produce shale oil. When oil prices dropped, these schemes were abandoned. With rapidly rising crude oil prices in recent years, interest in this resource has rekindled. The Bureau of Land Management currently has several dozen active leases and pilot projects on oil shale extraction.

## Natural gas is growing in importance

Natural gas is the world's third largest commercial fuel, making up 24 percent of global energy consumption. Because natural gas produces only half as much $CO_2$ per unit of energy as coal, substitution could help reduce global warming (chapter 9).

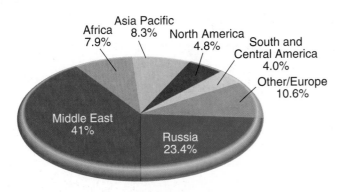

Figure 12.12 Proven natural gas reserves by region, 2008 *Source:* Data from British Petroleum, 2010.

Figure 12.13 As domestic supplies of natural gas dwindle, the United States is turning increasingly to shipments of liquefied gas in specialized ships, such as this one at an Australian terminal. An explosion of one these ships would release about as much energy as a medium-size atomic bomb.

Russia has nearly one-quarter of known natural gas reserves (mostly in Siberia and the Central Asian republics) and accounts for about 35 percent of all global production. Both Eastern and Western Europe depend on gas from these wells. Figure 12.12 shows the distribution of proven natural gas reserves in the world.

The total ultimately recoverable natural gas resources are estimated to be 10,000 trillion ft$^3$, corresponding to about 80 percent as much energy as the recoverable reserves of crude oil. The proven global reserves of natural gas are 6,200 trillion ft$^3$ (176 trillion metric tons). Because gas consumption rates are only about half of those for oil, current gas reserves represent roughly a 60-year supply at present usage rates. Proven reserves in the United States are about 185 trillion ft$^3$, or 3 percent of the world total. This is about a ten-year supply at current rates of consumption. Known reserves are more than twice as large.

Large amounts of methane are released from coal deposits. The Rocky Mountain front in Colorado, Wyoming, and Montana could have 10 percent of the total world methane supply. Drilling thousands of coal-bed methane wells in Wyoming and Utah, for example, has raised protests about water pollution and land damage. Other states could face similar problems. The Marcellus and Devonian Shales, which underlie much of the Appalachian Mountains from New York to Tennessee, may contain as much natural gas as western formations. Of particular concern is the process of fracturing (or fracking) rocks to release the gas. This can contaminate groundwater supplies with toxic chemicals.

World consumption of natural gas is growing by about 2.2 percent per year, considerably faster than either coal or oil. Much of this increase is in the developing world, where concerns about urban air pollution encourage the switch to cleaner fuel. Gas can be shipped easily and economically through buried pipelines. The United States has been fortunate to have abundant gas resources accessible by an extensive pipeline system. It is difficult and dangerous, however, to ship and store gas between continents. To make the process economical, gas is compressed and liquefied. At −160°C (−260°F) the liquid takes up about one-six-hundredth the volume of gas. Special refrigerated ships transport liquefied natural gas (LNG) (fig. 12.13). LNG weighs only about half as much as water, so the ships are very buoyant.

Finding sites for terminals to load and unload these ships is difficult. Many cities are unwilling to accept the risk of an explosion of the volatile cargo. A fully loaded LNG ship contains about as much energy as a medium-size atomic bomb. Furthermore, huge amounts of seawater are used to warm and re-gasify the LNG. This can have deleterious effects on coastal ecology. To override local objections, the federal government has assumed jurisdiction over LNG terminal siting.

## 12.3 Nuclear Power

In 1953 President Dwight Eisenhower presented his "Atoms for Peace" speech to the United Nations. He announced that the United States would build nuclear-powered electrical generators to provide clean, abundant energy. He predicted that nuclear energy would fill the deficit caused by predicted shortages of oil and natural gas. It would provide power "too cheap to meter" for continued industrial expansion of both the developed and the developing world. Today there are about 440 reactors in use worldwide, 104 of these in the United States (fig. 12.14). Half of the U.S. plants (52) are more than 30 years old and are thus approaching the end of their expected operational life. Cracking pipes, leaking valves, and other parts increasingly require repair or replacement as a plant ages. Nuclear power now amounts to about 9 percent of U.S. energy supply (almost twice the world average). All of it is used to generate electricity.

Rapidly increasing construction costs, safety concerns, and the difficulty of finding permanent storage sites for radioactive waste have made nuclear energy less attractive than promoters expected in the 1950s. Of the 140 reactors on order in 1975, 100 were subsequently canceled. The costs of decommissioning old reactors is a serious concern, because demolishing a worn-out plant may cost ten times as much as building it in the first place. Ten nuclear reactors have been shut down in the United States and deconstruction of most of them is now underway. Although these plants were generally small, costs have averaged several hundred million dollars each.

**Figure 12.14** Two nuclear reactors (domes) at the San Onofre Nuclear Generating Station sit between the beach and Interstate 5, the major route between Los Angeles and San Diego.

About half the existing nuclear reactors in the United States have had their licenses renewed for an additional 20 years beyond their original 40-year design, and several new plants are now on the drawing board. The nuclear power industry has been campaigning for greater acceptance, arguing that reactors don't release greenhouse gases that cause global warming. That's true during ordinary operation of the reactor, but mining, processing, and shipping of nuclear fuel together with decommissioning of old reactors and perpetual storage of wastes result in up to 25 times more carbon emissions than an equal amount of wind energy.

Nevertheless, a number of prominent environmentalists have endorsed nuclear power as a solution to global climate change. In 2010 President Obama approved $8 billion in loan guarantees for two new nuclear reactors to be built in Georgia by the Southern Company. This will be the first new nuclear power plant built in three decades in the United States. However, worries about accidents and susceptibility to terrorist attacks make many people fearful of this solution.

## How do nuclear reactors work?

The most commonly used fuel in nuclear power plants is $U^{235}$, a naturally occurring radioactive isotope of uranium. Uranium ore must be purified to a concentration of about 3 percent $U^{235}$, enough to sustain a chain reaction in most reactors. The uranium is then formed into cylindrical pellets slightly thicker than a pencil and about 1.5 cm long. Although small, these pellets pack an amazing amount of energy. Each 8.5 g pellet is equivalent to a ton of coal or 4 bbl of crude oil.

The pellets are stacked in hollow metal rods approximately 4 m long. About 100 of these rods are bundled together to make a **fuel assembly**. Thousands of fuel assemblies containing about 100 tons of uranium are bundled in a heavy steel vessel called the reactor core. Radioactive uranium atoms are unstable—that is,

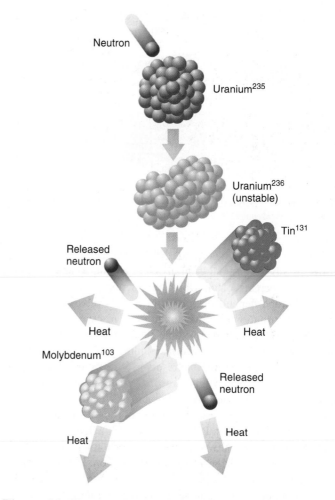

**Figure 12.15** The process of nuclear fission is carried out in the core of a nuclear reactor. In the sequence shown here, the unstable isotope uranium-235 absorbs a neutron and splits to form tin-131 and molybdenum-103. Two or three neutrons are released per fission event and continue the chain reaction. The total mass of the reaction product is slightly less than the starting material. The residual mass is converted to energy (mostly heat).

when struck by a high-energy subatomic particle called a neutron, they undergo **nuclear fission** (splitting), releasing energy and more neutrons. When uranium is packed tightly in the reactor core, the neutrons released by one atom will trigger the fission of another uranium atom and the release of still more neutrons (fig. 12.15). Thus, a self-sustaining **chain reaction** is set in motion, and vast amounts of energy are released.

The chain reaction is moderated (slowed) in a power plant by a neutron-absorbing cooling solution that circulates between the fuel rods. In addition, **control rods** of neutron-absorbing material, such as cadmium or boron, are inserted into spaces between fuel assemblies to shut down the fission reaction or are withdrawn to allow it to proceed. Water or some other coolant is circulated between the fuel rods to remove excess heat. The greatest danger in one of these complex machines is a cooling system failure. If the pumps fail or pipes break during operation, the nuclear fuel quickly overheats, and a "meltdown" can result that releases deadly radioactive material. Although nuclear power plants cannot explode like a nuclear bomb, the radioactive releases from a worst-case disaster, such as the meltdown of the Chernobyl reactor in the Soviet Ukraine in 1986, are just as devastating as a bomb. (See related story on Chernobyl at www.mhhe.com/cunningham6e.)

## Nuclear reactor design

Seventy percent of the world's nuclear plants are pressurized water reactors (PWR). Water circulates through the core, absorbing heat as it cools the fuel rods (fig. 12.16). This primary cooling water is heated to 317°C (600°F) and reaches a pressure of 2,235 psi. It then is pumped to a steam generator, where it heats a secondary water-cooling loop. Steam from the secondary loop drives a high-speed turbine generator that produces electricity. Both the reactor vessel and the steam generator are contained in a thick-walled, concrete-and-steel containment building that prevents radiation from escaping and is designed to withstand high pressures and temperatures in case of accidents.

Overlapping layers of safety mechanisms are designed to prevent accidents, but these fail-safe controls make reactors both expensive and complex. A typical nuclear power plant has 40,000 valves, compared with only 4,000 in a fossil fuel-fired plant of similar size. In some cases, the controls are so complex that they confuse operators and cause accidents, rather than prevent them. Under normal operating conditions, however, a PWR releases very little radioactivity and is probably less dangerous for nearby residents than a coal-fired power plant.

The Chernobyl plant that exploded and burned in Ukraine in 1986 used a graphite cooling design. Graphite has a high capacity for both capturing neutrons and dissipating heat. Designers

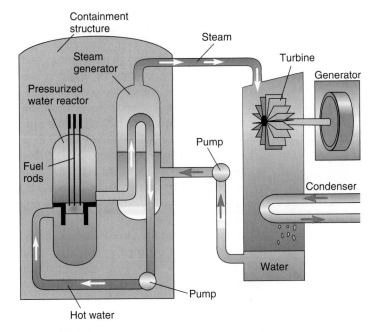

**Figure 12.16** Pressurized water nuclear reactor. Water is super-heated and pressurized as it flows through the reactor core. Heat is transferred to non-pressurized water in the steam generator. The steam drives the turbogenerator to produce electricity.

Courtesy of Northern States Power Company. Minneapolis, MN.

claimed that these reactors couldn't possibly run out of control; unfortunately, they were proven wrong. The small cooling tubes are quickly blocked by steam if the cooling system fails, and the graphite core burns when exposed to air. Burning graphite in the Chernobyl nuclear plant made the fire much more difficult to control than it might have been in another reactor design. Radioactive particles spread across much of northern Europe before fires were put out. Fortunately, such catastrophes have been rare.

## We lack safe storage for radioactive waste

One of the most difficult problems associated with nuclear power is the disposal of wastes produced during mining, fuel production, and reactor operation. How these wastes are managed may ultimately be the overriding obstacle to nuclear power.

Enormous piles of mine wastes and abandoned mill tailings in uranium-producing countries represent another serious waste disposal problem. Production of 1,000 tons of uranium fuel typically generates 100,000 tons of tailings and 3.5 million liters of liquid waste. There now are approximately 200 million tons of radioactive waste in piles around mines and processing plants in the United States. This material is carried by the wind or washes into streams, contaminating areas far from its original source. Canada has even more radioactive mine waste on the surface than does the United States.

In addition to the leftovers from fuel production, the U.S. has about 100,000 tons of low-level waste (contaminated tools, clothing, building materials, etc.) and about 77,000 tons of high-level (very radioactive) wastes. The high-level wastes consist mainly of spent fuel rods from commercial nuclear power plants and assorted wastes from nuclear weapons production. While they're still intensely radioactive, spent fuel assemblies are being stored in deep, water-filled pools at the power plants. These pools were originally intended only as temporary storage until the wastes were shipped to reprocessing centers or permanent disposal sites.

In 1987 the U.S. Department of Energy announced plans to build the first high-level waste repository on a barren desert ridge under Yucca Mountain in Nevada. Waste was to be buried deep in the ground, where it was hoped it would remain unexposed to groundwater and earthquakes for the thousands of years required for the radioactive materials to decay to a safe level. But continuing worries about the stability of the site led the Obama administration to cut off funding for the project in 2009 after 20 years of research and $100 billion in exploratory drilling and development.

For the foreseeable future, the high-level wastes that were to go to Yucca Mountain will be held in temporary surface storage facilities located at 131 sites in 39 states (fig. 12.17). But local residents living near these sites fear casks will leak. Most nuclear power plants are built near rivers, lakes, or seacoasts. Radioactive materials could spread quickly over large areas if leaks occur. A hydrogen gas explosion and fire in 1997 in a dry storage cask at Wisconsin's Point Beach nuclear plant intensified opponents' suspicions about this form of waste storage.

**Figure 12.17** Spent fuel is being stored temporarily in large, above ground "dry casks" at many nuclear power plants.

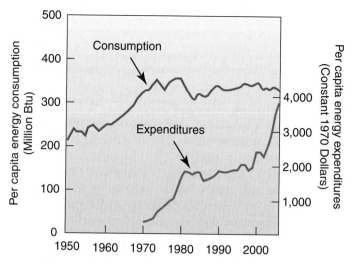

**Figure 12.18** Per capita energy consumption in the United States rose rapidly in the 1960s. Price shocks in the 1970s encouraged conservation. Although GDP continued to grow in the 1980s and 90s, higher efficiency kept per capita consumption relatively constant. Expenditures per person, however have risen sharply. *Sources:* Data from U.S. Department of Energy, 2010.

If the owners of nuclear facilities had to pay the full cost for fuel, waste storage, and insurance against catastrophic accidents, no one would be interested in this energy source. Rather than be too cheap to meter, it would be too expensive to matter.

## 12.4 Energy Conservation

One of the best ways to avoid energy shortages and to relieve environmental and health effects of our current energy technologies is simply to use less (see What Can You Do? p. 302). Much of the energy we consume is wasted. Our ways of using energy are so inefficient that most potential energy in fuel is lost as waste heat, becoming a form of environmental pollution. Conservation involves technology innovation as well as changes in behavior, but we have met these challenges in the past.

Oil price shocks in the 1970s led to rapid improvements in industrial and household energy use. Although population and GDP have continued to grow since then, the **energy intensity,** or amount of energy needed to provide goods and services has declined while prices have risen sharply (fig. 12.18). In response to federal regulations and high gasoline prices, automobile gas-mileage averages in the United States more than doubled from 13 mpg in 1975 to 28.8 mpg in 1988. Unfortunately, the oil glut and falling fuel prices of the 1990s discouraged further conservation. By 2004 the average slipped to only 20.4 mpg. In 2010, however, the Obama administration mandated an average fleet fuel efficiency of 35.5 mpg (14.6 km/l) for cars and light trucks by 2016.

But you don't have to wait until 2016. High-efficiency automobiles are already available. Low-emission, hybrid gas-electric vehicles get up to 30.3 km/liter (72 mpg) on the highway. And walking, biking, or taking public transport can lower your personal energy footprint far more. Amory B. Lovins of Colorado's Rocky Mountain Institute estimates that raising the average fuel efficiency of the U.S. car and light-truck fleet 1 mpg will cut oil consumption about 295,000 bbl per day. In one year, this would equal the total amount the U.S. Department of the Interior estimates might be extracted from the Arctic National Wildlife Refuge in Alaska.

Many improvements in domestic energy efficiency also have occurred in recent decades. Today's average new home uses one-half the fuel required in a house built in 1974, but much more can be done. Reducing air infiltration is usually the cheapest, quickest, and most effective way of saving energy because it is the largest source of losses in a typical house. It doesn't take much skill or investment to caulk around doors, windows, foundation joints, electrical outlets, and other sources of air leakage. Mechanical ventilation is

**Steps to Save Energy and Money**

1. Live close to work and school, or near transit routes, so you can minimize driving.
2. Ride a bicycle, walk, and use stairs instead of elevators.
3. Keep your thermostat low in winter and high in summer. Fans are cheaper to run than air conditioners.
4. Buy fewer disposable items: producing and shipping them costs energy.
5. Turn off lights, televisions, computers, and other appliances when not needed.
6. Line-dry your laundry.
7. Recycle.
8. Cut back on meat consumption: if every American ate 20 percent less meat, we would save as much energy as if everyone used a hybrid car.
9. Buy some of your food locally to reduce energy in shipping.

needed to prevent moisture buildup in tightly sealed homes. Household energy losses can be reduced by one-half to three-fourths by using better insulation, installing double- or triple-glazed windows, purchasing thermally efficient curtains or window coverings, and sealing cracks and loose joints.

## Green building can cut energy costs by half

Innovations in "green" building have been stirring interest in both commercial and household construction. Much of the innovation has occurred in large commercial structures, which have larger budgets—and more to save through efficiency—than most homeowners have. Elements of green building are evolving rapidly, but they include extra insulation in walls and roofs, coated windows to keep summer heat out and winter heat in, and recycled materials, which save energy in production. Orienting windows toward the sun, or providing roof overhangs for shade, are important for comfort as well as for saving money.

Many appliances, such as dishwashers and coffee makers, already have timers you can program to operate at specific times. Suppose your whole house or apartment had similar capacities. Several utilities are experimenting with **smart metering**, in which you get information not only on how much energy any particular appliance is using at a given time, but also the source of that energy and how much it costs. Using one of these systems, you might program your water heater to operate only after midnight when electricity is cheapest or surplus wind power is available. These systems can be controlled remotely. You might turn on your heating system or air conditioning with with your telephone as you're on your way home. Or the utility might turn off those same systems for short periods to avoid bringing expensive peak power on-line.

New houses can also be built with extra-thick, superinsulated walls and roofs. Windows can be oriented to let in sunlight, and eaves can be used to provide shade. Double-glazed windows that have internal reflective coatings and that are filled with an inert gas (argon or xenon) have an insulation factor of R11, the same as a standard 4-inch-thick insulated wall, or ten times as efficient as a single-pane window (fig. 12.19). Superinsulated houses now being built in Sweden require 90 percent less energy for heating and cooling than the average American home. President Obama's "Cash for Caulkers" initiative hopes to retrofit 100 million American homes and generate a million green jobs while cutting greenhouse gas emissions 5 percent over the next 20 years.

Improved industrial design has also cut our national energy budget. More efficient electric motors and pumps, new sensors and control devices, advanced heat-recovery systems, and material recycling have reduced industrial energy requirements significantly. In the early 1980s, U.S. businesses saved $160 billion per year through conservation. When oil prices collapsed, however, many businesses returned to wasteful ways.

Cities can make surprising contributions to energy conservation. New York City has become a leader in this effort, replacing 11,000 traffic signals with more-efficient LEDs (light-emitting diodes), and 180,000 old refrigerators with energy-saving models. Ann Arbor, Michigan, replaced 1,000 streetlights with LED

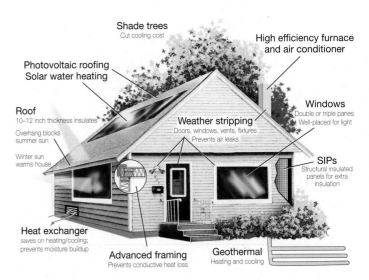

**Figure 12.19** Energy-efficient building can lower energy costs dramatically. Many features can be added to older structures. New buildings that start with energy-saving features (such as SIPs or advanced framing) can save even more money.

models. These lights saved the city over $80,000 in the first year, and will pay for themselves in just over two years.

## Cogeneration makes electricity from waste heat

One of the fastest growing sources of new energy is **cogeneration,** the simultaneous production of both electricity and steam or hot water in the same plant. By producing two kinds of useful energy in the same facility, the net energy yield from the primary fuel is increased from 30–35 percent to 80–90 percent. In 1900 half the electricity generated in the United States came from plants that also provided industrial steam or district heating. As power plants became larger, dirtier, and less acceptable as neighbors, they were forced to move away from their customers. Waste heat from the turbine generators became an unwanted pollutant to be disposed of in the environment. Furthermore, long transmission lines, which are unsightly and lose up to 20 percent of the electricity they carry, became necessary.

By the 1970s, cogeneration had fallen to less than 5 percent of our power supplies, but interest in this technology is growing. District heating systems are being rejuvenated, and the EPA estimates that cogeneration could produce almost 20 percent of U.S. electrical use, or the equivalent of 400 coal-fired plants.

## 12.5 Energy from Biomass

Plants capture immense amounts of solar energy by storing it in the chemical bonds of plant cells. Firewood is probably our original fuel source. As recently as 1850, wood supplied 90 percent of the heat used in the United States. For more than a billion people in developing countries, burning biomass remains the principal energy source for heating and cooking. An estimated 1,500 m$^3$ of

**Figure 12.20** A charcoal market in Ghana. Firewood and charcoal provide the main fuel for billions of people. Forest destruction results in wildlife extinction, erosion, and water loss.

**Figure 12.21** This Michigan power plant uses wood chips to fuel its boilers. Where wood supplies are nearby, this is a good choice both economically and environmentally.

fuelwood is gathered each year globally. This amounts to half of all wood harvested. In urban areas of developing countries, wood is often sold in the form of charcoal (fig. 12.20). Wood gathering and charcoal burning are important causes of forest depletion in many rural areas—although commercial logging and conversion to farms and plantations are more rapid and widespread causes of forest loss globally. In some countries, such as Mauritania, Rwanda, and Sudan, firewood demand is ten times the sustainable yield.

In developed countries, where we depend on fossil fuels for most energy, wood burning is a minor heat source. Inefficient burning in stoves and fireplaces makes wood burning an important source of air pollution, especially soot and hydrocarbons, in some areas. However, biomass burning provides an important fuel source for many medium-sized power plants, which produce steam for both heating and electricity. Many of these plants burn waste material such as urban tree clippings, which makes them an efficient, local, carbon-neutral source of energy (fig. 12.21).

## Ethanol and biodiesel can contribute to fuel supplies

**Biofuels**, ethanol and biodiesel, are by far the biggest recent news in biomass energy. Globally, production of these two fuels is booming, from Brazil (which uses sugarcane) to Southeast Asia (oil palm fruit) to the United States and Europe (corn, soybeans, rape seed). In the United States, both farm policies and energy policies have promoted biofuel crops. The energy bill passed by the U.S. Congress in 2007 required a four-fold increase in ethanol production, from 9 billion to 36 billion gallons (34 billion to 136 billion liters) per year, in just 13 years. This rule provided an enormous boon to corn growers in the Midwest, where falling corn prices have plagued farmers for decades.

In 2007 alone, the U.S. ethanol industry grew by 40 percent, corn production grew by 25 percent, and corn prices rose to historic highs above $5 per bushel. Still more important, the bill requires

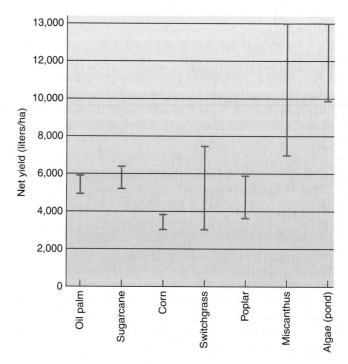

**Figure 12.22** Proven biofuel sources include oil palms, sugarcane, and corn grain (maize). Other experimental sources may produce better yields, however. *Source:* Data from E. Marris, 2006. *Nature* 444:670–678.

development of biofuels from inedible, woody parts of whole plants (cellulose), rather than the corn kernels currently used in most U.S. ethanol production. This change is important because corn is a relatively low-efficiency source of biomass (fig. 12.22), but most research and development have focused, until recently, on corn (see Exploring Science, p. 305).

Small amounts of ethanol have been added to gasoline for years, because oxygen-rich ethanol molecules help gasoline burn (oxidize) more completely. Ethanol helps reduce carbon monoxide

# Can Biofuels Be Sustainable?

**B**iofuels (alcohol refined from plant material or diesel fuel made from vegetable oils or animal fats) might be the answer to both our farm crisis and our fuel needs. But do these crops represent a net energy gain? Or does it take more fossil fuel energy to grow, harvest, and process crop-based biofuels than you get back in the finished product? The answer depends on the assumptions you make in calculating net energy yields. How much energy does it take to grow crops, and what harvest can you expect? What return do you assume for fermentation, and what credit do you assign for recycled heat or useful by-products?

For years, David Pimental from Cornell University has published calculations showing a net energy loss in biofuels. In 2005, he was joined by Tad Patzek from the University of California-Berkeley, in claims that it takes 29 percent more energy to refine ethanol from corn than it yields. Soy-based biodiesel is equally inefficient, these authors maintain, and cellulose-based biofuels are even worse. Switchgrass and woodchips take at least 50 percent more energy than they produce as ethanol, according to their calculations.

A counter argument came from Bruce Dale of Michigan State University and John Sheehan from the U.S. National Renewable Energy Laboratory, who maintain that biofuels produced by modern techniques represent a positive energy return. They say that Pimental and Patzek used outdated data and unreasonably pessimistic assumptions in making their estimates. Dramatic improvements in farming productivity, coupled with much greater efficiency in ethanol fermentation now yield about 35 percent more energy in ethanol from corn than is consumed in growing and harvesting the crop. A major difference between the outcomes is how far back you assign costs. Is the energy used to manufacture farm equipment included, or only that which is needed

for fermentation and purification? Pimental and Patzek assume this energy comes from fossil fuels, but Dale and Sheehan argue that fermentation waste can be burned to make manufacturing more efficient, as is already being done in Brazil.

A valuable addition to this debate comes from the work of ecologist David Tilman and his colleagues at the Cedar Creek Natural History Area in Minnesota. This group studies the effects of biodiversity on ecosystem resilience. They have shown that plots with high species diversity have greater net productivity than species grown in a monoculture. Tilman suggests that diverse mixtures of native perennial plants could grow on marginal land with far lower inputs of water and nutrients, and less fossil fuels for planting, cultivation, and weed control than grains such as soy or corn. Tilman and his colleagues calculate a corn-based ethanol net energy ratio of 1.2, while cellulosic ethanol from prairie species can yield about 5.4 times as much energy as it takes to grow, harvest, and process the crop.

In 2009, Tilman joined with economist Steven Polasky and others to compare a broader set of environmental and health considerations for different biofuels. They calculated the climate-change and health costs of different crops. An important assumption in this study is that diversion of food crops, such as soy and corn, to biofuel production results in prairie and forest destruction when food shortages and rising prices force people in developing countries to seek new land for agriculture. This land conversion creates a carbon debt that can take centuries to balance against the higher efficiency of the biofuel.

The greatest debt, according to these authors, is from

palm oil grown on tropical peatlands, which would take 423 years to repay. Corn ethanol, in these calculations, would take 93 years to repay if its cultivation results in conversion of existing grasslands. Prairie grasses grown on marginal land with minimal inputs, according to this study, would have no carbon debt. When Tilman and his colleagues add up health costs (from fine particulate materials released during processing) and climate costs (from release of greenhouse gases), they calculate that a billion-gallon increase in fuel consumption (about the U.S. growth between 2006 and 2007) would cost $469 million for gasoline, between $472 million and $952 million for corn ethanol (depending on biorefinery technology and heat source), but only $123 million to $208 million for cellulosic ethanol. These conclusions were immediately challenged by Adam Liska and his colleagues from the University of Nebraska, who claim that Tilman and his colleagues also used outdated data for their net energy yields. Modern refineries, this group claims, produce 1.8 times as much energy in corn ethanol as the crop inputs. They didn't address other health or environmental effects, however.

Obviously, there are many assumptions in all these studies. If you were asked to calculate the yields and effects of various biofuels, where would you start?

## Biomass Fuel Efficiency

| Fuel | Outputs (GJ/ha) | Inputs (GJ/ha) | Net Energy Ratio |
|---|---|---|---|
| Corn ethanol | 75.0 | 93.8 | 1.2 |
| Soy ethanol | 15.0 | 28.9 | 1.9 |
| Cellulosic electricity | 4.0 | 22.0 | 5.5 |
| Cellulosic ethanol | 4.0 | 21.8 | 5.4 |
| Cellulosic synfuel | 4.0 | 32.4 | 8.1 |

Source: Tilman, et al. 2006. Science 314:1598.

(CO) emissions, by converting it to carbon dioxide ($CO_2$). Ethanol is made by adding yeast to a liquid mix of water and ground grain, then fermenting it to produce alcohol.

One drawback to producing ethanol from biomass is that it takes about 3 to 5 liters of water for every liter of fuel produced.

And if the energy crops are irrigated, it can take up to 600 liters of water for every liter of ethanol created. In arid regions, there simply isn't enough water for both food and energy. Some studies have calculated that because of the inherent efficiencies of electric vehicles compared to internal combustion engines, you get twice as many vehicle miles by burning biomass and producing electricity than you do by turning that biomass into ethanol.

Biodiesel, derived from organic oils, can be burned in normal diesel engines, and it can be much cheaper to produce than ethanol because it requires no fermentation. Just about anything organic, from turkey entrails and cow dung to soybeans, can be used as a source. Currently, most biodiesel is being made from either soybeans or rape seed (Canola), which compete with food production, or from palm oil grown in the tropics where creation of new palm plantations is causing massive deforestation.

## Grasses and algae could grow fuel

Expanding markets for ethanol have spurred research into new fuel sources. Switchgrass (*Panicum virgatum*), a tall grass native to the Great Plains, has been one focus of attention. Switchgrass is a perennial species, with deep roots that store carbon (and thus capture atmospheric greenhouse gases). Perennial plants also hold soil in place, unlike annual corn crops, which leave fields bare for much of the year. Fewer trips through the field with a tractor or cultivator require much less fuel and improve net energy yield (fig. 12.22).

An even better biofuel crop may be *Miscanthus x giganteus*, a perennial grass from Asia. Often called elephant grass (although this name is also used for other species), *Miscanthus* is a sterile hybrid that grows 3 or 4 meters in a single season (fig. 12.23). Europeans have been experimenting with this crop for several decades, but it has only recently been introduced to the United States. *Miscanthus* can produce at least five times as much dry biomass per hectare as corn. Where using corn to replace 20 percent of U.S. gasoline consumption would take about one-quarter of all curent U.S. cropland out of food production, *Miscanthus* could produce the same amount on less than half that much area, and it wouldn't need to be prime farm fields. *Miscanthus* can grow on marginal soil with far less fertilizer than corn need. In the fall *Miscanthus* moves nutrients into underground rhizomes. This means that the standing stalks are almost entirely cellulose and next year's crop needs very little fertililzer.

**Figure 12.23** *Miscanthus x giganteus* is a perennial grass that can grow 3 or 4 meters in a single season. It thrives on marginal land with little fertilizer or water and can produce five times as much biomass as corn.

Some studies suggest that mixed fields of perennial, native grasses could provide biofuels and wildlife habitat at the same time. While switchgrass is a native plant, a monoculture of this one species is little different for wildlife than other monocultures. One study from Minnesota found that mixed prairie grasses provided a biomass yield, and potential ethanol yield, comparable to switchgrass but with more drought resistance, because in a mixed field, different species flourish under different weather conditions.

Algae could be an extremely efficient source of oil, or biodiesel, although this source remains experimental. Researchers have found strains of algae that grow rapidly under hot and saline conditions, producing abundant lipids (oils) that could be converted to biodiesel. Algae could be grown with recycled water, in containment ponds or chambers built on land that cannot be farmed. The U.S. Department of Energy has proposed that algae ponds could be built near existing power plants. Flue gases bubbled through these ponds could provide $CO_2$ for algae growth, while preventing the escape of $CO_2$ to the atmosphere. Thus, algae could be a very cheap form of carbon capture. Although this technology has not been developed on a large scale, it shows great promise.

Many other potential sources of biomass exist, including urban sewage, waste products from meat packing plants, orange peels from Florida citrus growers, and sawdust from lumber mills. New plants built for these sources are among the more than 100 facilities now in development.

## Effects on food and environment are uncertain

Will biofuel production affect food costs? Yes, but the seriousness of the problem depends on where you look. Since a $3 box of cereal contains only about one penny's worth of corn, a doubling of corn prices shouldn't affect the price of corn flakes much. Corn and soy costs, however, can make up 40–50 percent of meat prices. Many low-income Americans can ill afford steep price increases, but most people in wealthy countries spend only about 10 percent of their income on food. So most people could absorb somewhat higher food costs.

In developing countries, more than 50 percent of household income may be spent on food. Higher costs of cooking oil and grain can be devastating for family budgets. Regions dependent on food aid have seen supplies dwindling and prices rising. (For some farmers in developing countries, however, who have been struggling to compete with cheap imported corn from the United States, rising grain prices may be a blessing.) Gary Becker, a Nobel laureate in economics, calculates that a 30 percent rise in food prices would reduce living standards in rich countries by about 3 percent; in developing countries, living standards would drop by 20 percent.

Although ethanol and biodiesel are renewable fuels, they are not necessarily friendly to the environment. That depends on what kinds of plants are used and where they are grown. Algae or mixed prairie grasses could provide a sustainable, wildlife-friendly feed source with almost no soil erosion or water pollution, but these fuel sources are still hypothetical and experimental. In many areas, biofuel production has led to intensive cropping on erodible soils, as well as rapid clearing of grasslands and forests for crop fields. Accelerating soil erosion and plummeting biodiversity result. In Indonesia, conversion to oil palm plantations has become an important threat to primary rainforest habitat. In Brazil, grasslands and forests have been replaced with soy and sugarcane. Fertilizer-intensive crops, including corn and sugarcane, also increase nutrient runoff in rivers. Water shortages are also a concern. With current technology, 3 to 6 liters of water is needed to produce 1 liter of ethanol. In many farming states, there isn't enough water for both agriculture and food production. Plans for some new processing facilities have been scaled back because of water shortages.

## Methane from biomass is efficient and clean

Just about any organic waste, but especially sewage and manure, can be used to produce methane. Methane gas, the main component of natural gas, is produced when anaerobic bacteria (bacteria living in an oxygen-free space) digest organic matter (fig. 12.24). The main by-product of this digestion, $CH_4$, has no oxygen atoms because no oxygen was available in digestion. But this molecule oxidizes, or burns, easily, producing $CO_2$ and $H_2O$ (water vapor). Consequently, methane is a clean, efficient fuel. Today, as more cities struggle to manage urban sewage and feedlot manure, methane could be a rich source of energy. In China, in addition to solar and wind power, more than 6 million households use methane, also known as biogas, for cooking and lighting. Two large municipal facilities in Nanyang, China, provide fuel for more than 20,000 families.

Methane is a promising resource, but it has not been adopted as widely as it could be. Gas is harder to store than liquid fuels like ethanol, and low prices for natural gas and other fuels have reduced incentives for building methane production systems.

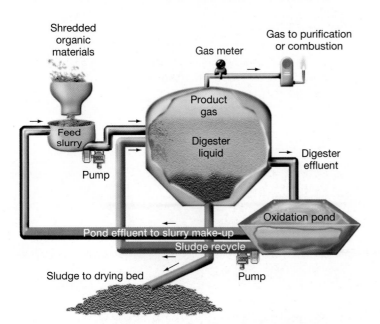

**Figure 12.24** Continuous unit for converting organic material to methane by anaerobic fermentation. One kilogram of dry organic matter will produce 1–1.5 $m^3$ of methane, or 2,500–3,600 million calories per metric ton.

However, concerns about greenhouse gases may lead to further development, because methane is a powerful agent of atmospheric warming (chapter 9). Especially around livestock facilities, such as poultry or hog barns, large lagoons of liquid manure release a constant flow of methane to the atmosphere. These lagoons are also a threat to water bodies, because they occasionally overflow. But trapping this methane would provide energy, save money, and reduce atmospheric impacts. City sewage treatment plants and landfills also offer rich, and mostly untapped, potential for methane generation.

# 12.6 Wind and Solar Energy

Renewable sources could supply all the energy we need (see A Closer Look, p. 308). In China's efforts to reduce dependence on fossil fuels (opening case study), wind power has been the principal focus, followed by solar thermal (heat) systems. Relative to other alternative sources, wind is cheap and available almost everywhere. Although wind turbines are highly visible, they have a small footprint, so they don't displace farming and other land uses. How people feel about the visibility of a wind farm depends on whether they are enthusiastic about energy alternatives, whether it earns money for their community, and which particular view is obstructed by the turbines.

Solar energy can be converted to heat (thermal energy), as well as electricity. The sun is an almost inconceivably rich source of energy. The average amount that reaches the earth's surface is some 10,000 times greater than all commercially sold energy used each year. However, this energy is diffuse and low in intensity. Innovations in recent years have produced new strategies for concentrating solar energy to make it useful for more purposes.

## Wind is our fastest growing energy source

Although China installed the largest amount (10,000 MW) of new wind generating capacity in the world in 2009, the United States still leads the world with 35,000 MW of total installed capacity. Texas is the U.S. wind power leader, with 9,400 MW of wind farms, followed by Iowa, California, and Minnesota. Denmark gets the largest fraction (22 percent) of its electricity from wind power of any country. Wind power is the fastest growing energy source in the United States. Together with natural gas, wind accounted for more than 80 percent of all new electric generating capacity in 2009.

Potential for wind development is immense. The World Meteorological Organization has estimated that wind could produce about 50 times the total capacity of all nuclear power plants now in operation. In the 1980s the state of California was the world's top wind power producer, with 90 percent of all existing wind power generators. Some 17,000 windmills marched across windy mountain ridges at Altamont, Tehachapi, and San Gorgonio Passes. Poor management, technical flaws, and overdependence on subsidies, however, led to bankruptcy of major corporations, including Kenetech, once the largest turbine producer in the United States.

Now Chinese wind machines are capturing the rapidly growing world market. In 2010, the largest wind farm under construction

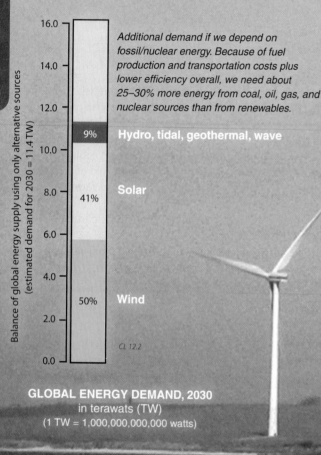

# How realistic is alternative energy?

It's very realistic, according to studies from Stanford University and the University of California at Davis.* With existing technology, renewable sources could provide all the energy we need, including the fossil fuels we use now. And we could save money at the same time. **Land-based wind, water power, and solar potential exceed all global energy consumption.** Renewable energy supplies over the oceans are even larger, since oceans cover two-thirds of the earth's surface. Many studies suggest that renewables could meet future demand more economically and more safely than fossil-based energy plans. How would this energy future look?

*Additional demand if we depend on fossil/nuclear energy. Because of fuel production and transportation costs plus lower efficiency overall, we need about 25–30% more energy from coal, oil, gas, and nuclear sources than from renewables.*

Balance of global energy supply using only alternative sources (estimated demand for 2030 = 11.4 TW)

- 9% Hydro, tidal, geothermal, wave
- 41% Solar
- 50% Wind

CL 12.2

**GLOBAL ENERGY DEMAND, 2030**
in terawats (TW)
(1 TW = 1,000,000,000,000 watts)

**1. Wind** could supply 50 percent of our energy, according to this plan. It would take 3.8 million large wind turbines to supply electricity to the whole world. Isn't that an impossible task? Not necessarily: we build that many cars and trucks every year worldwide.  *Background image, CL 12.1*

**2. Solar energy** could provide 41 percent of our total energy supply. It would take 1.7 billion rooftop photovoltaic systems and nearly 100,000 concentrated solar power plants to provide 4.6 TW. Rooftop collectors can be located where energy is used, so they don't lose energy in transmission and don't compete with other land uses.

**3. Hydropower (dams, tidal, geothermal, wave energy)** could supply about 9 percent of our energy. Most major rivers are already dammed, but underwater turbines in rivers and tidal areas could be effective. Deep wells could tap geothermal energy, but there are worries about triggering earthquakes and contaminating aquifers.

CL 12.3

◄ Solar thermal collectors already are price competitive with fossil fuels, but they generally can't be located close to consumers, and they may require scarce cooling water in arid lands where sunshine is plentiful.

Geothermal plant ▼

CL 12.4

*For more information: see Jacobson, M. Z., and M. A. Delucchi. 2009. A path to sustainable energy. *Scientific American* 301(5) 58–65.

## But wouldn't we have problems with unreliable supplies and a need for expensive storage?

Fortunately, the wind blows more at night to complement sunshine during the day. By balancing renewable sources, we can have just as reliable supplies as we now have with fossil fuels. Renewable sources ▶ also have a much better service record. Coal-burning power plants are out of production 46 days per year for maintenance. Solar panels and wind turbines average only 7 days down for repairs per year.

Solar, wind, and water power also solve two of our most pressing global problems: (1) the problem of climate change, perhaps the most serious and costly problem we face currently, as water shortages, crop failures, and refugee migrations destabilize developing regions; and (2) political conflict over fuel supplies, as in the oil fields of Iraq, Nigeria, and Ecuador, or nuclear fuel processing in Iran.

## What would renewable energy cost?

By 2020, wind and hydroelectricity should cost about half as much as fossil fuels or nuclear power, and because renewable energy sources are inherently more efficient than fossil fuels, it should take about one-third less energy to supply the same services with sun, wind, and water.

CL 12.5

**PEAK DEMAND (Summer)**

Power (1,000 MW) — Time of day

Hydro / Solar / Wind / Geothermal

In addition to the energy we can obtain from renewable sources, conservation measures could save up to half the energy we now use. Mass transit, weather-proofing, urban in-fill, and efficient appliances are among the available strategies that can save money in the near term and in the long term.

Light rail ▼

CL 12.6

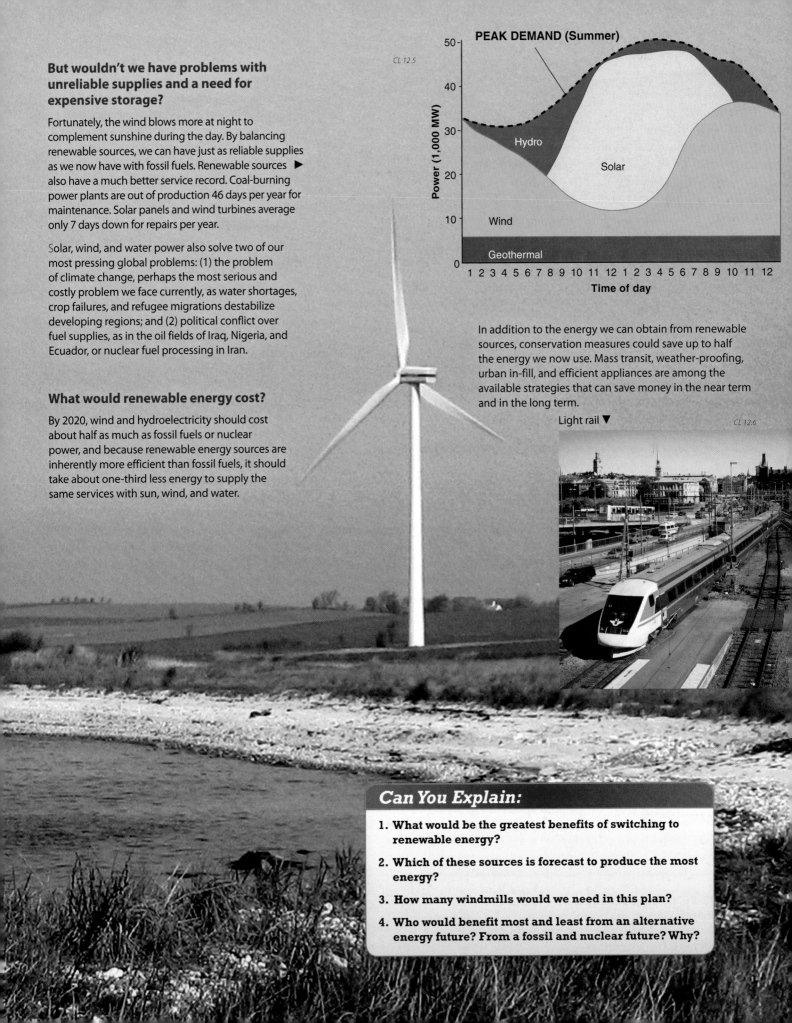

### Can You Explain:

1. What would be the greatest benefits of switching to renewable energy?

2. Which of these sources is forecast to produce the most energy?

3. How many windmills would we need in this plan?

4. Who would benefit most and least from an alternative energy future? From a fossil and nuclear future? Why?

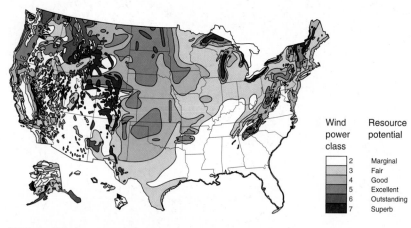

**Figure 12.25** United States wind resource map. Mountain ranges and areas of the High Plains have the highest wind potential, but much of the country has fair to good wind supply. *Source:* Data from U.S. Department of energy.

| Wind power class | Resource potential |
|---|---|
| 2 | Marginal |
| 3 | Fair |
| 4 | Good |
| 5 | Excellent |
| 6 | Outstanding |
| 7 | Superb |

The World Energy Council predicts that wind could account for 400,000 MW of electricity by 2020, depending on how seriously politicians take global warming and how many older fossil plants and nuclear reactors go offline. One thousand megawatts meets the energy needs of about 50,000 typical U.S. households or is equivalent to about 6 million bbl of oil. Shell Oil suggests that half of all the world's energy could be wind and solar generated by the middle of this century.

**Wind farms** are large concentrations of wind generators producing commercial electricity (fig. 12.26). Do wind turbines have negative impacts? Often they're built where wind and weather make homes or other development unattractive. But they can interrupt the view in remote areas and destroy a sense of isolation and natural beauty. Bird and bat kills have been reported in some places. Careful placement of wind farms outside of migration corridors, however, and the addition of warning devices can greatly reduce wildlife problems. As wind turbines have proliferated, neighbors who live close by often complain about noise and flickering shadows from the blades. We may need land-use ordinances about how close turbines can be to homes.

Wouldn't wind power take up a huge land area if we were to depend on it for a major part of our energy supply? As table 12.3 shows, the actual space taken up by towers, roads, and other structures on a wind farm is only about one-third as much as would be consumed by a coal-fired power plant or solar thermal energy system to generate the same amount of energy over a 30 year period. Furthermore, the land around wind towers is more easily used for grazing or farming than is a strip-mined coal field or land under solar panels. Farmers are finding wind energy to be a lucrative crop. A single tower sitting on 0.1 ha (0.25 acre) can pay $100,000 per year to an owner-operator.

in the United States was a $1.5 billion project in Texas, where a Chinese company, A-Power Systems, using Chinese wind turbines and financing by Chinese banks, was building a 600 MW wind farm to supply electricity to about 180,000 Texas homes. Ironically, the project was subsidized by the American Recovery and Reinvestment Act, which was intended to revive the American economy.

The 158,000 MW of installed wind power currently in operation worldwide demonstrates the economy of wind turbines. Theoretically up to 60 percent efficient, windmills typically produce about 35 percent efficiency under field conditions. Where conditions are favorable, wind power is now cheaper than any other new energy source, with electric prices now as low as 4¢ per kilowatt-hour in places with steady winds averaging at least 24 kph (15 mph). Large areas of western North America meet this requirement (fig. 12.25). Some energy experts have called North America's Great Plains the Saudi Arabia of wind power. By 2020, it's expected that wind energy will cost about half as much as fossil fuel or nuclear power.

When a home owner or community builds their own wind turbine, what can they do with excess power? Storing electricity in batteries is expensive. Many experts believe the best use for excess power is to sell it to the public utility grid. In states that require utilities to offer feed-in tariffs or net energy pricing, you sell excess electricity from wind or solar systems back to a local utility at a fixed price.

The 1978 Public Utilities Regulatory Policies Act required utilities to buy power generated by small hydro, wind, solar, cogeneration

**Figure 12.26** Renewable energy sources, such as wind, solar energy, geothermal power, and biomass crops, could eliminate our dependence on fossil fuels and prevent extreme global climate change, if we act quickly.

| Table 12.3 | Jobs and Land Required for Alternative Energy Sources | |
|---|---|---|
| Technology | Land Use (m² per gigawatt-hour for 30 years) | Jobs (per terawatt-hour per year) |
| Coal | 3,642 | 116 |
| Photovoltaic | 3,237 | 175 |
| Solar thermal | 3,561 | 248 |
| Wind | 1,335 | 542 |

*Source:* Data from Lester R. Brown, et al. Saving the Planet. 1991. W. W. Norton & Co., Inc.

(simultaneous production of useful heat and electricity), and other privately owned technologies at a fair price. Not all utilities yet comply, but some—notably in California, Oregon, Maine, and Vermont—are purchasing significant amounts of private energy.

Isn't wind intermittent? What would we do for electricity when the wind dies? It's true that at any particular place the wind doesn't blow constantly, but studies have shown that interconnected wind farms only a few hundred kilometers apart can smooth out fluctuations in supply. Furthermore, wind turbines are down for maintenance far less than coal-burning power plants. The average coal plant shuts down for maintenance 46 days per year, while wind turbines now average only 7 days per year of downtime. Furthermore, in most places, the wind blows most strongly at night, while solar energy is available (obviously) during the day. A mix of solar, wind, hydro, and geothermal sources could completely replace fossil fuels.

Some other strategies for storing energy involve pumped storage facilities. Water, for example, can be pumped from a low reservoir to a higher one when excess electricity is available. Later, when energy demand rises, the water runs back downhill, reversing turbines and generating electricity. Similarly, air can be pumped into caves or abandoned mines as an energy storage method. Some pumped storage facilities have been in use for decades and the technology is well proven. A more speculative suggestion is that we could use excess electrical power to electrolyze water (split it into hydrogen and oxygen molecules). These gases could be stored and transported more easily than electricity, and turned back into useful energy in a fuel cell where and when it's needed.

## Solar energy is diffuse but abundant

The sun is a giant nuclear furnace in space, constantly bathing our planet with a free energy supply. Solar heat drives winds and the hydrologic cycle. All biomass, as well as fossil fuels and our food (both of which are derived from biomass), results from conversion of light energy (photons) into chemical bond energy by photosynthetic bacteria, algae, and plants.

Until recently, this tremendous infusion of energy has been too diffuse and low in intensity to be of much use except for environmental heating and photosynthesis. Now, fortunately, we're finding ways to make it more accessible. Figure 12.27 shows solar energy levels over the United States for typical summer and winter days.

## Passive solar absorbs heat; active solar pumps heated fluids

The opening case study shows the value of solar energy for water and space heating. In Rizhao and many other Chinese cities, solar collectors already produce most heated water for household use. Similarly, in Greece, Italy, Israel, Australia, and other countries where sunshine is abundant and energy is expensive, up to 70 percent of domestic hot water comes from solar collectors.

Massive heat storage has been used to capture solar energy for thousands of years. Thick adobe or stone walls absorb daytime heat and release it gradually at night. This **passive solar absorption** has been updated in modern homes with massive,

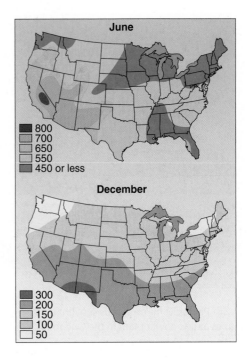

**Figure 12.27** Average daily solar radiation in the United States in June and December. One Langley, the unit for solar radiation, equals 1 cal/cm$^2$ of earth surface (3.69 Btu/ft$^2$). *Source:* Data from National Weather Bureau, U.S. Department of Commerce.

heat-absorbing floors and walls, or with glass-walled "sun spaces" on the south side of a building.

**Active solar systems,** like those in Rizhao, generally pump a heat-absorbing fluid medium (air, water, or an antifreeze solution) through a relatively small collector, rather than passively collecting heat in a stationary medium, such as masonry. Active collectors can be located adjacent to or on top of buildings, rather than being built into the structure.

A flat, black surface sealed with a double layer of glass makes a good solar collector. A fan circulates air over the hot surface and into the house through ductwork of the type used in standard forced-air heating. Alternatively, water can be pumped through dark tubes within the collector to pick up heat for space heating or to provide hot water.

Sunshine doesn't reach us all the time, of course. How can solar energy be stored for times when it is needed? A number of options are available for homeowners. In a climate where sunless days are rare and seasonal variations are small, a small, insulated water tank is a good solar energy storage system. In areas where clouds block the sun for days at a time or where energy must be stored for winter use, a large, insulated bin containing a heat-storing mass, such as stone, water, or clay, provides solar energy storage. During the summer months, a fan blows heated air from the collector into the storage medium. In the winter, a similar fan at the opposite end of the bin blows the warm air into the house.

During the summer, the storage mass is cooler than the outside air, and it helps cool the house by absorbing heat. During the winter, it is warmer and acts as a heat source by radiating stored heat. In many areas, six or seven months' worth of thermal energy can be stored in 10,000 gal of water or 40 tons of gravel, about the

**Figure 12.28** Parabolic mirrors focus sunlight on steam-generating tubes at this power plant in the California desert.

**Figure 12.29** In a power tower, hundreds or thousands of tracking mirrors, called heliostats, focus sunlight on a heat absorber at the top of the central tower where a concentrated salt solution can reach 1,000 degrees F (538 C). A heat exchanger then generates steam, which produces electricity in a standard steam turbine.

amount of water in a small swimming pool or the gravel in two average-size dump trucks.

## Concentrating solar power generates electricity

Solar thermal energy can also be used to generate electricity. Concentrating trough systems use long rows of parabolic mirrors (fig. 12.28) to heat a transfer fluid to temperatures as high as 400°C. The hot liquid is pumped to a central plant, where it turns water into steam that spins a turbine to produce electricity. California's Mojave Desert has had solar thermal facilities for decades and now has over 300 MW of installed capacity. Abengoa Solar, a Spanish company, is building a $1.5 billion complex near Phoenix that will cover 770 ha (1,900 acres) of desert with parabolic troughs to generate 280 MW of electricity.

Another type of concentrating solar power uses thousands of heliostats—mirrors that track the sun—to focus sunlight on a boiler sitting atop a tower. Steam from the boiler drives a turbine as do other thermal systems (fig. 12.29). BrightSource recently signed a contract with Southern California Edison to build more than 1,300 MW of solar electric capacity in the Mojave desert over the next decade. Although some people regard the desert as a useless wasteland, many ecologists argue that it's as unique and biologically interesting as a forest or grassland. They'd like to see large blocks of desert land protected from any development—including solar energy.

China also is investing in concentrating solar power. In 2010, several American companies signed contracts to build power towers in China. The first of these is to be a 92 MW facility in Mongolia. An even more ambitious project is being discussed in Africa. A coalition of German companies is pooling resources in design, finance, and manufacturing to build Desertech, a (U.S.)$400 billion network of power towers and high-voltage transmission lines, to supply electricity to Europe. Just 0.3 percent of the sunlight falling on the Sahara and Middle Eastern deserts, they calculate, could supply all the electricity currently used in Europe.

## Photovoltaic cells generate electricity directly

**Photovoltaic cells** capture solar energy and convert it directly to electrical current by separating electrons from their parent atoms and accelerating them across a one-way electrostatic barrier formed by the junction between two different types of semiconductor material (fig. 12.30). The first photovoltaic cells were made by slicing thin wafers from giant crystals of extremely pure silicon.

Over the past 25 years, the efficiency of energy captured by photovoltaic cells has increased from less than 1 percent of incident light to more than 10 percent under field conditions and over 75 percent in the laboratory. Promising experiments are underway using exotic metal alloys, such as gallium arsenide, and semiconducting polymers of polyvinyl alcohol, which are more efficient in energy conversion than silicon crystals.

One of the most promising developments in photovoltaic cell technology in

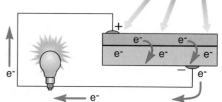

**Figure 12.30** The operation of a photovoltaic cell. Boron impurities incorporated into the upper silicon crystal layers cause electrons (e⁻) to be release when solar radiation hits the cell. The released electrons move into the lower layer of the cell, thus creating a shortage of electrons, or a positive charge, in the upper layer and an oversupply of electrons, or negative charge, in the lower layer. The difference in charge creates an electric current in a wire connecting the two layers.

recent years is the invention of **amorphous silicon collectors**. First described in 1968 by Stanford Ovshinky, these noncrystalline silicon semiconductors can be made into lightweight, paper-thin sheets that require much less material than conventional crystalline silicon cells. They also are much cheaper to manufacture and can be made in a variety of shapes and sizes, permitting ingenious applications. Roof tiles with amorphous silicon collectors layered on their surface already are available. Even flexible films can be coated with these materials. Photovoltaic cells already are providing power to places where conventional power is unavailable, such as lighthouses, mountaintop microwave repeater stations, villages on remote islands, and ranches in the Australian outback.

In 2010, thin-film photovoltaic cells finally broke the $1-per-watt barrier, a price that begins to make them competitive with fossil fuels and nuclear power in many situations. As further research improves their efficiency and lifespan, industry experts believe they could produce electricity for less than 10¢ per kilowatt-hour by 2020.

Although concentrating thermal systems are currently the cheapest form of solar collectors, they tend to be located in deserts far from the places we live. It will take a massive reconstruction of the electrical distribution grid to deliver either wind or concentrating solar power to markets. Systems that generate electricity closer to the end user, on the other hand, have many advantages. Mounting a photovoltaic system in your yard or on your rooftop delivers electricity without the losses inherent in long-distance distribution.

A photovoltaic array of about 30–40 m² will generate enough electricity for an efficient house (fig. 12.31). There's a huge potential for rooftop solar energy. One study estimated that more than 1,000 mi² (2,590 km²) of roofs suitable for photovoltaic systems in the United States could generate about three-quarters of present electrical consumption. In 2010, Southern California Edison started construction of photovoltaic arrays on roofs of warehouses and big-box retail stores. Over the next five years, the utility expects to install a total of 250 MW of solar voltaic power. Overall, the 1 million solar roofs project aims to install

**Figure 12.31** Solar roof tiles (*shiny area*) can generate enough electricity for a house full of efficient appliances. On sunny days, this array can produce a surplus to sell back to the utility company, making it even more cost-efficient.

3,000 MW of photovoltaic energy on homes and apartments in California by 2016. More than $2.8 billion in incentives are available to homeowners to cover costs.

Innovative financing programs are helping make this dream a reality. First introduced in Berkeley, California, Property Assessed Clean Energy (PACE) uses city bonds to pay for renewable energy and conservation expenses. The bonds are paid off through a 20-year assessment on property taxes. Decreased utility bills often offset tax increases, so that switching to renewable energy is relatively painless for the property owner.

Some other financing arrangements that help overcome the high up-front costs of renewable energy are power purchasing agreements and solar leasing programs. In both cases an investor builds a certain amount of solar or wind energy in return for a contract to buy the energy produced at a specific rate for a fixed length of time. This frees property owners from large capital expenses, while giving investors a secure return on their investment. Feed-in tariffs that require utilities to buy excess power from homeowners at a fair price also help make solar photovoltaics economically feasible.

An intriguing option for storing electricity is in plug-in hybrid vehicles, which could provide an enormous, distributed battery array. You'd recharge your auto battery at night when power plants have excess generating capacity. During the day, your car would be plugged into a smart meter that could sell electricity back to your utility if prices rise. A few million mobile battery arrays could greatly help smooth out power peaks and valleys.

## 12.7 Water Power

Falling water is one of our oldest power sources. In early American settlements, water-powered gristmills and sawmills were essential, and most early industrial cities were built where falling water could run mills. The invention of water turbines in the nineteenth century greatly increased the efficiency of hydropower dams (fig. 12.32). By 1925 falling water generated 40 percent of the world's electric power. Since then, hydroelectric production capacity has grown 15-fold, but fossil fuel use has risen so rapidly that water power is now only one-quarter of total electrical generation. Still, many countries produce most of their electricity from falling water. Norway, for instance, depends on hydropower for 99 percent of its electricity; Brazil, New Zealand, and Switzerland all produce at least three-quarters of their electricity with water power. Canada is the world's leading producer of hydroelectricity, running 400 power stations with a combined capacity exceeding 60,000 MW. First Nations people protest, however, that their rivers are being diverted and lands flooded to generate electricity, most of which is sold to the United States.

The total world potential for hydropower is estimated to be about 3 million MW. If all of this capacity were put to use, the available water supply could provide between 8 and 10 terawatt hours ($1,0^{12}$ watt-hours) of electrical energy. Currently, we use only about 10 percent of the potential hydropower supply. The energy derived from this source in 1994 was equivalent to about 500 million tons of oil, or 8 percent of the total world commercial energy consumption.

**Figure 12.32** Hydropower dams produce clean renewable energy but can be socially and ecologically damaging.

## Most hydropower comes from large dams

Much of the hydropower development since the 1930s has focused on enormous dams. There is a certain efficiency of scale in giant dams, and they bring pride and prestige to the countries that build them, but they can have unwanted social and environmental effects that spark protests in many countries. China's Three Gorges Dam on the Yangtze River, for instance, spans 2.0 km (1.2 mi) and is 185 m (600 ft) tall. The reservoir it creates is 644 km (400 mi) long and has displaced more than 1 million people (see related story "Three Gorges Dam" at www.mhhe.com/cunningham6e).

In warm, dry climates, large reservoirs often suffer enormous water losses. Lake Nasser, behind the Aswan High Dam in Egypt, loses 15 billion m$^3$ each year to evaporation and seepage. Unlined canals lose another 1.5 billion m$^3$. Together, these losses represent one-half of the Nile River flow, or enough water to irrigate 2 million ha of land. The silt trapped by the Aswan High Dam formerly fertilized farmland during seasonal flooding and provided nutrients that supported a rich fishery in the delta region. Farmers now must buy expensive chemical fertilizers, and the fish catch has dropped almost to zero. Schistosomiasis, spread by snails that flourish in the reservoir, is an increasingly serious problem.

Large dams also destroy biodiversity. In 2010, Brazil announced approval of a controversial Belo Monte Dam on the Xingu River (a major tributary of the Amazon) in Para State. The $17 billion dam would be the third largest in the world. It will fuel development in this remote area, and flood 250 km$^2$ (96.5 mi$^2$) of tropical rainforest. Indigenous Kayapo people protested the loss of traditional hunting lands.

Dam promoters claim that the area to be flooded is less than the 5,000 km2 originally planned, and equal to the forest flooded every year during the rainy season. Dam opponents, on the other hand, point out that the seasonally flooded forest is a unique ecosystem in which plants and animals are exquisitely adapted to changing water levels. The reservoir created by the dam will irreversibly change local ecology and eliminate many endemic species. Furthermore, decaying vegetation in the drowned forest will emit methane that could cause more global climate change than burning an equivalent amount of coal.

## Unconventional hydropower comes from tides and waves

Ocean tides and waves also contain enormous amounts of energy that can be harnessed to do useful work. A tidal station works like a hydropower dam, with its turbines spinning as the tide flows through them. A high-tide/low-tide differential of several meters is required to spin the turbines. Unfortunately, variable tidal periods often cause problems in integrating this energy source into the electric utility grid. Nevertheless, some of these plants have operated for many decades.

Ocean wave energy can easily be seen and felt on any seashore. The energy that waves expend as millions of tons of water are picked up and hurled against the land, over and over, day after day, can far exceed the combined energy budget for both insolation (solar energy) and wind power in localized areas. Captured and turned into useful forms, that energy could make a substantial contribution to meeting local energy needs.

Dutch researchers estimate that 20,000 km of ocean coastline are suitable for harnessing wave power. Among the best places in the world for doing this are the west coasts of Scotland, Canada, the United States (including Hawaii), South Africa, and Australia. Wave energy specialists rate these areas at 40 to 70 kW per meter of shoreline. Altogether, it's calculated, if the technologies being studied today become widely used, wave power could amount to as much as 16 percent of the world's current electrical output.

Some of the designs being explored include oscillating water columns that push or pull air through a turbine, as well as a variety of floating buoys, barges, and cylinders that bob up and down as waves pass, using a generator to convert mechanical motion into electricity. However, it's difficult to design a mechanism that can survive the worst storms.

An interesting new development in this field is the Pelamis wave-power generator developed by the Scottish company Ocean Power Delivery (fig. 12.33). The first application of this technology is now in operation 5 km off the coast of Portugal, with

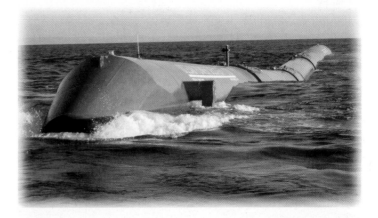

**Figure 12.33** The Pelamis wave converter (named after a sea snake) is a 125 m long and 3.5 m diameter tube, tube, hinged so it undulates as ocean swells pass along it. This motion drives pistons that turn electrical generators. Energy experts calculate that capturing just 1 to 2 percent of global wave power could supply at least 16 percent of the world's electrical demand.

three units producing 2.25 MW of electricity, or enough to supply 1,500 Portuguese households. Another 28 units are currently being installed. Each of the units consists of four cylindrical steel sections linked by hinged joints. Anchored to the seafloor at its nose, the snakelike machine points into the waves and undulates up and down and side to side as swells move along its 125 m length. This motion pumps fluid to hydraulic motors that drive electrical generators to produce electricity, which is carried to shore by underwater cables. Portugal considers wave energy one of its most promising sources of renewable energy.

Pelamis's inventor, Richard Yemm, says that survivability is the most important feature of a wave-power device. Being offshore, the Pelamis isn't exposed to the pounding breakers that destroy shore-based wave-power devices. If waves get too steep, the Pelamis simply dives under them, much as a surfer dives under a breaker. These wave converters lie flat in the water and are positioned far offshore, so they are unlikely to stir up as much opposition as do the tall towers of wind generators.

## Geothermal heat, tides, and waves could supply substantial amounts of energy in some places

The earth's internal temperature can provide a useful source of energy in some places. High-pressure, high-temperature steam fields exist below the earth's surface. Around the edges of continental plates or where the earth's crust overlays magma (molten rock) pools close to the surface, this **geothermal energy** is expressed in the form of hot springs, geysers, and fumaroles. Yellowstone

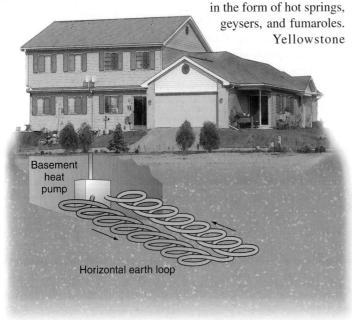

**Figure 12.34** Geothermal energy can cut heating and cooling costs by half in many areas. In summer (*shown here*), warm water is pumped through buried tubing (*earth loops*), where it is cooled by constant underground temperatures. In winter, the system reverses and the relativity warm soil helps the house. Where space is limited, earth loops can be vertical. If more space is available, the tubing can be laid in shallow horizontal trenches, as shown here.

National Park is the largest geothermal region in the United States. Iceland, Japan, and New Zealand also have high concentrations of geothermal springs and vents.

Depending on the shape, heat content, and access to groundwater, these sources produce wet steam, dry steam, or hot water. Iceland, which sits on a midocean ridge (chapter 1), has abundant geothermal energy. Iceland has ambitious plans to be the first carbon-neutral country, largely because the earth's heat provides steam for heat and electric energy. Even places that don't naturally have geysers or hot springs may have hot spots close enough to the surface to be tapped by deep wells. In 2010, however, two large deep well projects in Switzerland and California were shut down abruptly when evidence surfaced that they might trigger earthquakes.

While few places have geothermal steam, the earth's warmth can help reduce energy costs nearly everywhere. Pumping water through deeply buried pipes can extract enough heat so that a heat pump will operate more efficiently. Similarly, the relatively uniform temperature of the ground can be used to augment air conditioning in the summer (fig. 12.34).

## 12.8 Fuel Cells

Rather than store and transport energy, another alternative is to generate it locally, on demand. **Fuel cells** are devices that use ongoing electrochemical reactions to produce an electrical current. They are very similar to batteries except that, rather than recharging them with an electrical current, you add more fuel for the chemical reaction. Depending on the environmental costs of input fuels, fuel cells can be a clean energy source for office buildings, hospitals, or even homes.

All fuel cells consist of a positive electrode (the cathode) and a negative electrode (the anode) separated by an electrolyte, a material that allows the passage of charged atoms, called ions, but is impermeable to electrons (fig. 12.35). In the

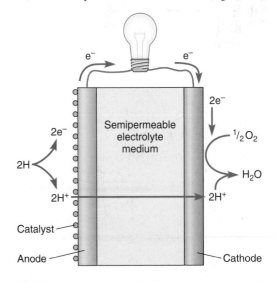

**Figure 12.35** Fuel cell operation. Electrons are removed from hydrogen atoms at the anode to produce hydrogen ions (protons) that migrate through a semipermeable electrolyte medium to the cathode, where they reunite with electrons from an external circuit and oxygen atoms to make water. Electrons flowing through the circuit connecting the electrodes create useful electrical current.

most common systems, hydrogen or a hydrogen-containing fuel is passed over the anode, while oxygen is passed over the cathode. At the anode, a reactive catalyst, such as platinum, strips an electron from each hydrogen atom, creating a positively charged hydrogen ion (a proton). The hydrogen ion can migrate through the electrolyte to the cathode, but the electron is excluded. Electrons flow through an external circuit, and the electrical current generated by their passage can be used to do useful work. At the cathode, the electrons and protons are reunited and combined with oxygen to make water.

Fuel cells provide direct-current electricity as long as they are supplied with hydrogen and oxygen. For most uses, oxygen is provided by ambient air. Hydrogen can be supplied as a pure gas, but storing hydrogen gas is difficult and dangerous because of its explosive nature. An alternative is a device called a **reformer** or converter that strips hydrogen from fuels such as natural gas, methanol, ammonia, gasoline, ethanol, or even vegetable oil. Even methane effluents from landfills and wastewater treatment plants can be used as a fuel source. Or, hydrogen gas could be provided by solar, wind, or geothermal facilities that use electricity to hydrolyze water.

A fuel cell that runs on pure oxygen and hydrogen produces no waste products except drinkable water and radiant heat. Other fuels create some pollutants (most commonly carbon dioxide), but the levels are typically far less than conventional fossil fuel combustion in a power plant or an automobile engine. Although the theoretical efficiency of electrical generation of a fuel cell can be as high as 70 percent, the actual yield is closer to 40 or 45 percent. The quiet, clean operation and variable size of fuel cells make them useful in certain places (fig. 12.36), such as buildings where waste heat can be captured for water heating or space heating. A 45-story office building at 4 Times Square, for example, has two 200 kW fuel cells that provide both electricity and heat. The same building has photovoltaic panels on its façade, natural lighting, fresh-air intakes to reduce air conditioning, and a number of other energy conservation features.

## Utilities are promoting renewable energy

Utility restructuring currently being planned in the United States could include policies to encourage conservation and alternative energy sources. Among the proposed policies are (1) "distributional surcharges" in which a small per kilowatt-hour charge is levied on all utility customers to help finance renewable energy research and development, (2) "renewables portfolio" standards to require power suppliers to obtain a minimum percentage of their energy from sustainable sources, and (3) **green pricing** that allows utilities to profit from conservation programs and charge premium prices for energy from renewable sources.

Some states already are pursuing these policies. For example, Iowa has a Revolving Loan Fund supported by a surcharge on investor-owned gas and electric utilities. This fund provides low-interest loans for renewable energy and conservation. Several states have initiated green pricing programs as a way to encourage a transition to sustainable energy. One of the first was in Colorado, where 1,000 customers agreed to pay $2.50 per month above their regular electric rates to help finance a 10 MW wind farm on the Colorado–Wyoming border. Buying a 100 kW "block" of wind power provides the same environmental benefits as planting a half acre of trees or not driving an automobile 4,000 km (2,500 mi) per year.

## 12.9 What's Our Energy Future?

In 2008, former Vice President Al Gore issued a bold and inspiring challenge to the United States. Currently, he said, "We're borrowing money from China to buy oil from the Persian Gulf to burn in ways that destroy the planet." He urged America to repower itself with 100 percent carbon-free electricity within a decade. Doing so, he proposed, would solve the three biggest crises we face—environmental, economic, and security—simultaneously. This ambitious project could create millions of jobs, spur economic development, and eliminate our addiction to imported fossil fuels.

But could we get all our electricity from renewable, environmentally friendly sources in such a short time? Mark Jacobson from Stanford University and Mark Delucchi from the University of California-Davis believe we can. Moreover, they calculate that currently available wind, water, and solar technologies could supply 100 percent of the world's energy by 2030 and completely eliminate all our use of fossil fuels. They calculate that it would take 3.8 million large wind turbines (each rated at 5 MW), 1.7 billion rooftop photovoltaic systems, 720,000 wave converters, half a million tidal turbines, 89,000 concentrated solar power plants and industrial-sized photovoltaic arrays, 5,350 geothermal plants, and 900 hydroelectric plants, worldwide.

Wouldn't it be an overwhelming job to build and install all that technology? It would be a huge effort, but it's not impossible. Jacobson and Delucchi point out that society has achieved massive transformations before. In 1956 the United Sates began building

**Figure 12.36** The Long Island Power Authority has installed 75 stationary fuel cells to provide reliable backup power.

the Interstate Highway System, which now extends 47,000 mi (75,600 km) and has changed commerce, landscapes, and society. And every year roughly 60 million new cars and trucks are added to the world's highways.

Is there enough clean energy to meet our needs? Yes, there is. As we've already seen, the readily available wind, solar, and water power sources are at least 100 times larger than our current power consumption. Even allowing for growth as residents in the developing world improve their standard of living, there's more than enough environmentally friendly energy for everyone.

Interestingly, it would take about 30 percent less total energy to meet our needs with sun, wind, and water than to continue using fossil fuels. That's because electricity is a more efficient way to use energy than burning dead plants and animals. For example, only about 20 percent of the energy in gasoline is used to move a vehicle (the rest is wasted as heat). An electric vehicle, on the other hand, uses about three-quarters of the energy in electricity for motion. Furthermore, much of the energy from renewable sources could often be produced closer to where it's used, so there are fewer losses in transmission and processing.

Won't it be expensive to install so much new technology? Yes it will be, but the costs of continuing our current dependence on fossil fuels would be much higher. It's estimated that investing $700 billion per year now in clean energy will avoid twenty times that much in a few decades from the damages of climate change.

One of the biggest challenges in moving to clean energy is that the wind doesn't blow all the time and the sun doesn't always shine in a given location. But a smart balance of sources can even out shortages (fig. 12.37). We'll need a large investment in the electric transmission grid—including some high-voltage interchange lines—to tie together the areas with abundant sun and wind with the cities where most people live. A smart grid that transmits energy more efficiently and safely is a good investment in any case.

As you've learned in the opening case study for this chapter, China is taking bold steps to develop and employ wind, hydro, and solar energy. Let's hope that other developing countries follow their lead. Even some richer countries may see the benefits of this path. A decade ago it wasn't clear that clean energy would be technically or economically feasible. Now that it is, we all need to work to make it politically feasible as well. The energy choices we make now will have profound effects in the future on our lives and our environment.

## Conclusion

Conventional resources, especially oil, coal, and natural gas, remain our dominant energy sources, for now. Coal is extremely abundant, especially in North America, but extracting and burning coal have been major causes of environmental damage and air pollution. Clean-burning coal plants that use integrated gasification combined cycle (IGCC) technology together with carbon capture and storage might help minimize global climate change, but it would be even better to simply move to renewable energy sources. Oil (petroleum) currently provides most of our transportation energy. The United States has consumed over half of its recoverable oil resources, and the remaining supply (including controversial sources in the Arctic) would last about three years if we stopped all imports.

Natural gas is more abundant than oil and cleaner than coal, so its importance has been increasing. The main drawback of gas is the risk of shipping and storing this highly combustible material. And, although it produces less $CO_2$ than coal or oil, it still contributes to climate change. Nuclear power supplies a significant proportion of the electricity in some countries. Nuclear power doesn't create $CO_2$ while operating, but mining, processing, and shipping fuel together with perpetual storage of wastes results in 25 times more greenhouse gases than does wind energy. Furthermore, storing the highly dangerous waste from uranium mining, processing, and reactor operation remains an expensive and unresolved problem.

Conservation is a key factor in a sustainable energy future. New designs in housing, office buildings, industrial production, and transportation can all save huge amounts of energy. Transportation consumes over 40 percent of the U.S. energy budget, so more-efficient vehicles can have a substantial effect on our energy impacts.

Biofuels including ethanol and oil (biodiesel) vary greatly in their net energy yield and environmental effects. Cellulosic ethanol could provide useful energy in some areas. Hydropower is now our principal renewable resource. Hydro can be clean and reliable, but a focus on huge dams has led to many environmental and social problems. Rapid innovations in solar, wind, wave power, and other renewable energy sources now make it possible to get all our energy from clean technologies. The choices we make about our energy sources and uses will have profound effects on our environment and society.

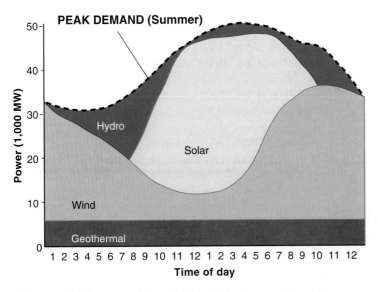

**Figure 12.37** The wind doesn't blow all the time, nor is sunshine always available, but a mix of renewable resources could supply all the energy we need, especially if distant facilities are linked together. This graph shows hypothetical energy supplies for a typical July day in California.

## Practice Quiz

1. Where is Rizhao, and how does it supply its energy needs?
2. Define *energy*, *power*, and *kilowatt-hour* (kWh).
3. What are the major sources of global commercial energy?
4. How does energy consumption in the United States compare to that in other countries?
5. Why don't we want to use all the coal in the ground?
6. Where is most liquid oil located? How long are supplies likely to last?
7. What are *tar sands* and *oil shales*? What are the environmental costs of their extraction?
8. How are nuclear wastes now being stored?
9. Explain active and passive solar energy.
10. How do photovoltaic cells work?

# Critical Thinking and Discussion Questions

Apply the principles you have learned in this chapter to discuss these questions with other students.

1. If you were the energy czar of your state or country, where would you invest your budget? Why?
2. We have discussed a number of different energy sources and energy technologies in this chapter. Each has advantages and disadvantages. If you were an energy policy analyst, how would you compare such different problems as the risk of a nuclear accident versus air pollution effects from burning coal?
3. If your local utility company were going to build a new power plant in your community, what kind would you prefer? Why?
4. The nuclear industry is placing ads in popular magazines and newspapers, claiming that nuclear power is environmentally friendly because it doesn't contribute to the greenhouse effect. How do you respond to that claim?
5. How would you evaluate the debate about net energy loss or gain in biofuels? What questions would you ask the experts on each side of this question? What worldviews or hidden agendas do you think might be implicit in this argument?
6. It clearly will cost a lot of money to switch from fossil fuels to renewables. How would you respond to someone who says that future costs from climate change are no concern of theirs?

# Data Analysis | Personal Energy Use

For many college students, a car and a computer are life essentials. Suppose you were to buy a very efficient car, such as the Honda Insight, rather than a sport utility vehicle, such as a Ford Excursion. How much energy would that save, and how long could you run your computer with that energy?

These calculations are not hard, but you'll need some key numbers to start with:

1. A Honda Insight gets about 75 mpg, while an Excursion gets about 12 mpg.
2. A typical American drives about 15,000 miles per year.
3. A gallon of gasoline contains the equivalent energy of about 3,400 kilowatt-hours (kWh).
4. A computer uses about 100 W of electricity.

Use the previous numbers to figure out the following:

1. How much gasoline would you save in an Insight, compared with an Excursion?
   a. Excursion:
      15,000 mi/yr ÷ 12 mpg = _____ gal/yr
   b. Insight:
      15,000 mi/yr ÷ 75 mpg = _____ gal/yr
   c. Gasoline savings (a − b) = _____ gal/yr
   d. Energy savings:
      (gal × 3,400 kWh) = _____ kWh/yr
2. How much energy does a computer use if it is left on continuously? (You really should turn it off at night or when it isn't in use, but we'll simplify the calculations.)
   100 watt/h × 24 h/day × 365 days/yr = _____ kWh/yr
3. How long would the energy saved run your computer?
   kWh/yr saved by Insight ÷ kWh/yr consumed by computer = _____

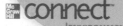

# 13 Solid and Hazardous Waste

A crane unloads a garbage barge at Fresh Kills on Staten Island, the world's largest landfill before it closed in 2001.

## Learning Outcomes

*After studying this chapter, you should be able to answer the following questions:*

- What are the major components of the waste stream?
- How does a sanitary landfill operate? Why are we searching for alternatives to landfills?
- Why is ocean dumping a problem?
- What are the "three Rs" of waste reduction, and which is most important?
- How can biomass waste be converted to natural gas?
- What are toxic and hazardous waste? How do we dispose of them?
- What is bioremediation?
- What is the Superfund, and has it shown progress?

# The New Alchemy: Creating Gold from Garbage

Most people think of recycling in terms of newspapers, plastic bottles, and other household goods. Your daily household recycling is the bedrock of recycling programs, but another growing and exciting area of recycling is done at commercial and industrial scales. The 230 million tons of garbage the United States produces each year includes some knotty problems: old furniture and carpeting, appliances and computers, painted wood, food waste. It's no wonder that we've simply dumped it all in landfills as long as we could. But landfills are becoming more scarce and more difficult to site (fig. 13.1).

Incinerators are a common alternative, but they are expensive to build and operate, and they can produce dangerous air contaminants, including dioxins from burned plastics, and heavy metals.

One of our largest sources of waste is construction and demolition debris—the rubble left over when a building is torn down, remodeled, or built. Construction and demolition account for over 140 million tons of waste per year, about 1.5 kg per person per day—on top of the 230 million tons per year of municipal solid waste. All this mixed debris is normally trucked to landfills, but alternatives have emerged in recent years.

A slowly growing number of cities and companies are sending their waste, including construction debris, to commercial recyclers. One of these recyclers is Taylor Recycling, based in Montgomery, New York. Starting as a tree removal business, Taylor has expanded to construction and demolition waste and now operates in four states. The company recycles and sells 97 percent of the mixed debris it receives, well above the industry average of 30 to 50 percent. Trees are ground and converted to mulch for landscaping. Dirt from stumps is screened and sold as clean garden soil. Mixed materials are sorted into recyclable glass, metals, and plastics. Construction debris is sorted and ground: broken drywall is ground to fresh gypsum, which is sold to drywall producers; wood is composted or burned; bricks are crushed for fill and construction material. Organic waste that can't be separated, such as food-soaked paper, is sent to a gassifier.

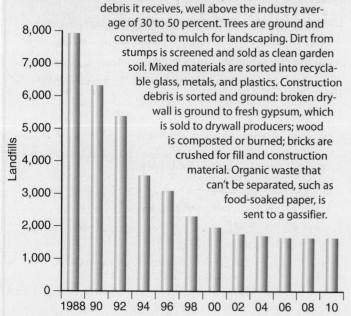

**Figure 13.1** The number of landfills in the United States has fallen by nearly 80 percent over the past two decades, but the total capacity has remained relatively constant because landfills are now much larger than in the past. *Source:* Data from Environmental Protection Agency, 2010.

The gassifier is like an enclosed, oxygen-free pressure cooker, which converts biomass to natural gas. The gas runs electric generators for the plant, and any extra gas can be sold. Waste heat warms the recycling facility. The 3 percent of incoming waste that doesn't get recycled is mainly mixed plastics, which are currently landfilled.

From their base outside of New York City, recycling is clearly a good idea. New York has used up most of its landfill space and now ships garbage to Virginia, Ohio, Pennsylvania, and South Carolina. Fuel and trucking costs alone drive up disposal costs, and with landfill capacity shrinking, tipping fees are climbing. Every day, roughly 1,000 garbage trucks leave New York City, carrying garbage to other states. The average round trip is 300 miles, at less than 4 miles per gallon of fuel.

## The Story of Garbage Is Changing Globally

In Western Europe and Japan, there is a rapidly growing industry in composting municipal solid waste. The Swiss company Kompogas, a leader in the industry, uses giant anaerobic (oxygen-free) tanks to compost organic waste. The methane produced can be burned as natural gas in cars, trucks, and electricity generators. Selling this gas adds to company profits. The sterile compost is an ideal fertilizer for gardeners and farmers.

In Europe this industry is aided by new laws that make it illegal to dispose of organic waste in landfills. Those laws protect dwindling open space. They also protect the global climate, since decaying garbage in landfills produces abundant volumes of methane, one of our most important greenhouse gases.

China has also had a recycling revolution. Hungry for all kinds of industrial materials, Chinese manufacturers have found rich resources in American and European discarded paper and other waste. Garbage has long been one of the United States' largest exports. Now, growing volumes of recycling are traveling to China in otherwise-empty shipping containers, then returning as new packaging for goods and electronics.

Recycling is a rapidly growing industry because it makes money coming and going. Recyclers are paid to haul away waste, which they turn into marketable products.

You might not think of it often, but waste management is an exciting and innovative industry. Companies such as Taylor Recycling and Kompogas provide huge social and economic benefits while making money. Often when we discuss environmental problems, it seems businesses are part of the problem, but these examples show that business owners can be just as excited as anybody about environmental quality.

How big a part of waste management do these stories represent? In this chapter we'll examine this question. We'll also look at our other waste management methods, the composition of our waste, and some of the differences between solid waste and hazardous waste.

# 13.1 What Waste Do We Produce?

Waste is everyone's business, even though we don't think about it every day. We all produce unwanted by-products in nearly everything we do. According to the Environmental Protection Agency (EPA), the United States produces 11 billion tons of solid waste each year. That's roughly 3.6 tons per person. Nearly half of that amount consists of agricultural waste, such as crop residues and animal manure, which are generally recycled into the soil on the farms where they are produced. Agricultural wastes provide groundcover to reduce erosion, and they nourish new crops, but they also constitute the single largest source of nonpoint air and water pollution in the country. Another one-third of all solid wastes are mine tailings, overburden from strip mines, smelter slag, and other industrial waste from mining and metal processing. Much of this material is stored in or near its source of production. Improper disposal practices, however, can result in serious and widespread pollution.

Industrial waste—other than mining and mineral production—amounts to some 400 million metric tons per year in the United States. Most of this material is recycled, converted to other forms, or disposed of in private landfills or deep injection wells. About 60 million metric tons of industrial waste fall in a special category of hazardous and toxic waste, which we will discuss later in this chapter.

**Municipal solid waste**, the garbage we produce in our houses, offices, and cities, accounts for a small percentage of total waste by weight, but it is one of our most important challenges in waste management. Municipal solid waste is hard to reuse and recycle because it contains many different kinds of materials, yet it amounts to about 250 million metric tons per year in the United States (fig. 13.2). That's just over 2 kg (4.6 lbs) per person per day—twice as much per capita as Europe or Japan, and five to ten times as much as most developing countries.

Despite considerable progress in the past 20 years, we recycle only about 30 percent of our glass bottles and jars, less than 50 percent of aluminum drink cans, and less than 7 percent of our plastic food and beverage containers. We could save money, energy, land, and many other resources if we could improve on this rate.

## The waste stream is everything we throw away

What kinds of materials are in all that waste? There are organic materials, such as yard and garden wastes, food wastes, and sewage sludge from sewage treatment plants; junked cars; worn-out furniture; and consumer products of all types. Newspapers, magazines, packaging, and office refuse make paper one of our major wastes (fig. 13.3).

The **waste stream** is a term that describes the steady flow of varied wastes that we all produce, from domestic garbage and yard wastes to industrial, commercial, and construction refuse. Many of the materials in our waste stream would be valuable resources if they were not mixed with other garbage. Unfortunately,

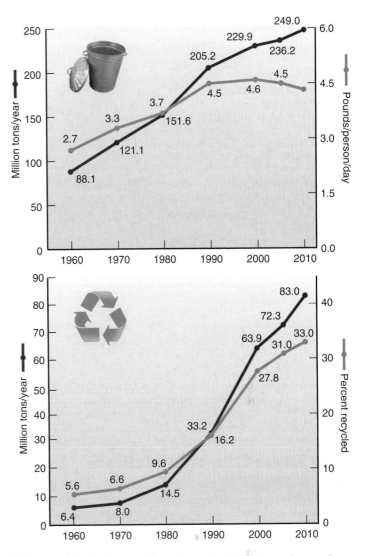

**Figure 13.2** Bad news and good news in solid waste production. Per capita waste has risen steadily to more than 2 kg per person per day. Recycling rates are also rising, however. Recycling data include composting.
*Source:* Data from U.S. Environmental Protection Agency, 2010.

our collecting and dumping processes mix and crush everything together, making separation an expensive and sometimes impossible task. In a dump or incinerator, much of the value of recyclable materials is lost.

When hazardous materials get mixed into the waste stream, they get dispersed through thousands of tons of miscellaneous garbage. This mixing makes the disposal or burning of what might have been rather innocuous stuff a difficult, expensive, and risky business. Spray-paint cans, pesticides, batteries (zinc, lead, or mercury), cleaning solvents, smoke detectors containing radioactive material, and plastics that produce dioxins and PCBs (polychlorinated biphenyls) when burned are mixed with paper, table scraps, and other nontoxic materials. The best thing to do with household toxic and hazardous materials is to separate them for safe disposal or recycling, as we will see later in this chapter.

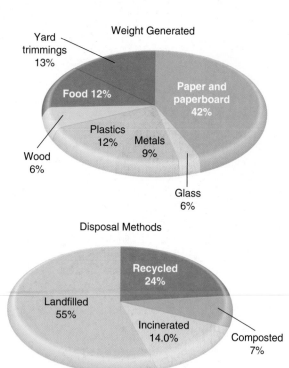

**Weight Generated**

Yard trimmings 13%

Food 12%

Paper and paperboard 42%

Plastics 12%

Metals 9%

Wood 6%

Glass 6%

**Disposal Methods**

Recycled 24%

Landfilled 55%

Incinerated 14.0%

Composted 7%

**Figure 13.3** Composition of municipal solid waste in the United States by weight, before recycling, and disposal methods. *Source:* Data from U.S. Environmental Protection Agency Office of Solid Waste Management, 2009.

**Figure 13.4** Trash disposal has become a crisis in the developing world, where people have adopted cheap plastic goods and packaging but lack good recycling or disposal options.

## 13.2 Waste Disposal Methods

Where do our wastes go now? In this section, we will examine some historic methods of waste disposal, as well as some future options. We begin with the least desirable but most commonly used methods. We'll end with the the most important strategies, the "three Rs" of Reduction, Reuse, and Recycling.

### Open dumps release hazardous substances into the air and water

Often people dispose of waste by simply dropping it someplace. Open, unregulated dumps are still the predominant method of waste disposal in most developing countries, where government infrastructure, including waste collection, has difficulty serving growing populations. Giant megacities in the developing world have enormous garbage problems (fig. 13.4). Mexico City, one of the largest cities in the world, generates some 10,000 tons of trash each day. Until recently, most of this torrent of waste was left in giant piles, exposed to the wind and rain, as well as rats, flies, and other vermin. Manila, in the Philippines, has at least ten huge open dumps. The most notorious is called "Smoky Mountain" because of its constant smoldering fires. Thousands of people live and work on this 30 m high heap of refuse. They spend their days sorting through the garbage for edible or recyclable materials. Health conditions are abysmal, but these people have nowhere else to go, and the city has no current alternatives for waste disposal.

Most developed countries forbid open dumping, at least in urban areas, but illegal dumping is still a problem. You have

undoubtedly seen trash accumulating along roadsides and in vacant, weedy lots. Is this just an aesthetic problem? No. Much of this trash washes into sewers and then into the ocean (see next section). Often illegally dumped garbage includes waste oil and solvents. An estimated 200 million liters of waste motor oil are poured into the sewers or allowed to soak into the ground every year in the United States. This is about five times as much as was spilled by the *Exxon Valdez* in Alaska in 1989! No one knows the volume of solvents and other chemicals disposed of by similar methods.

Increasingly, these toxic chemicals are showing up in groundwater, on which nearly half of Americans depend for drinking (chapter 10). An alarmingly small amount of oil or other solvents can pollute large quantities of drinking or irrigation water. One liter of gasoline, for instance, can make a million liters of water undrinkable.

### Ocean dumping is mostly uncontrolled

The oceans are vast, but they're not large enough to absorb our waste without harm. Every year some 25,000 metric tons (55 million lbs) of packaging, including millions of bottles, cans, and plastic containers, are dumped at sea. Even in remote regions, beaches are littered with the nondegradable flotsam and jetsam (fig. 13.5a). About 150,000 tons (330 million lbs) of fishing gear—including more than 1,000 km (660 mi) of nets—are lost or discarded at sea each year. An estimated 50,000 northern fur seals are entangled in this refuse and drown or starve to death every year in the North Pacific alone.

Until recently, many cities in the United States dumped municipal refuse, industrial waste, sewage, and sewage sludge into the ocean. Federal legislation now prohibits this dumping. New York City, the last to stop offshore sewage sludge disposal, finally ended this practice in 1992.

Plastic debris is a growing problem in all the world's oceans. Millions of tons of plastic drink bottles, bottle caps, plastic shopping bags, and other debris end up at sea. Most is probably

(a)

(b)

**Figure 13.5** (a) Plastic trash dumped on land and at sea ends up on remote beaches. (b) and in the bellies of young seabirds. Here the open belly of a Laysan albatross shows plastics its parents accidentally swallowed and then regurgitated to feed the chick. *Source: NOAA.*

carelessly disarded litter and uncontained garbage, but there is also deliberate disposal at sea, especially from cruise ships and container ships. All this debris, floating just below the surface, accumulates in vast regions of slowly swirling ocean currents.

The **Great Parcific Garbage Patch**, discovered in 1997 by sailing captain Charles Moore, is the best known of these plastic debris fields. In all the world's oceans, vast circulating currents known as gyres are driven by the earth's rotation. These currents collect floating plastic debris, much of it tiny fragments, in regions thousands of km wide. The North Pacific gyre has captured at least 100 million tons of plastic. An estimated 80 percent of this debris originates from improper or accidental disposal of plastics on land. The remaining 20 percent is dumped or lost by ships at sea.

All this plastic flotsam outweighs the living biomass in large parts of the Pacific and Atlantic oceans. Fish have been found with stomachs full of plastic fragments. Seabirds gulp down plastic debris, then regurgitate it for their chicks. With stomachs blocked by undigestible bottle caps, disposable lighters, and other fragments, chicks slowly starve to death. In one study of Laysan albatrosses, 90 percent of the carcasses of dead albatross chicks contained plastic (fig. 13.5b).

Oceanographers are trying to find ways of collecting or controlling this debris that is slowly starving ocean ecosystems. In 2010 the *Plastiki*, a catamaran built from discarded plastic drink bottles, did a worldwide tour to promote ocean conservation and publicize the problem of uncontrolled plastic waste. Most material is too fine-grained to capture easily in nets, and it is distributed widely around the world's oceans. Growing awareness, however, is a first step toward resolving the problem. You can learn more by searching online for information on *Plastiki* or on the Pacific garbage gyre.

## Landfills receive most of our waste

Currently, landfills receive 54 percent of all municipal solid waste in the United States, 33 percent is recycled, and 13 percent is incinerated. While we have a long way to go in controlling waste, this is a dramatic change from 1960, when 94 percent was landfilled and only 6 percent was recycled.

A modern **sanitary landfill** is designed to contain waste. Operators are required to compact the refuse and cover it every day with a layer of dirt, to decrease smells and litter and to discourage insects and rats. This method helps control pollution, but the dirt fill also takes up as much as 20 percent of landfill space. Since 1994, all operating landfills in the United States have been required to control such hazardous substances as oil, chemical compounds, and toxic metals, that seep through piles of waste along with rain water. To prevent leakage to groundwater and streams, landfills require an impermeable clay and/or plastic lining (fig. 13.6). Drainage systems are installed in and around the liner to catch drainage and to help monitor chemicals that leak out. Modern municipal solid waste landfills now have many of the safeguards of hazardous waste repositories described later in this chapter.

Sanitary landfills also must manage methane, a greenhouse gas produced when organic material decomposes in the anaerobic conditions deep inside a landfill. Landfills are the single largest anthropogenic source of methane in the United States. Globally, landfills are estimated to produce more than 700 million metric tons of methane annually. Because methane is 20 times as potent at absorbing heat as $CO_2$, this represents about 12 percent of all greenhouse gas emissions. Until recently, almost all this landfill methane was simply vented into the air. Now about half of all landfill gas in the United States is either flared (burned) on site or is collected and used as fuel for electrical generation. Methane recovery in the United States produces 440 trillion Btu per year, and is equivalent

# Active Learning

## Life Cycle Analysis

One step toward understanding your place in the waste stream is to look at the life cycle of the materials you buy. Here is a rough approximation of the process. With another student, choose one item that you use regularly. On paper, list your best guess for the following: (1) a list of the major materials in it; (2) the original sources (geographic locations and source materials) of those materials; (3) the energy needed to extract/convert the materials; (4) the distances the materials traveled; (5) the number of businesses involved in getting the item to you; (6) where the item will go when you dispose of it; (7) what kinds of reused/recycled products could be made from the materials in it.

**Figure 13.6** A plastic liner being installed in a sanitary landfill. This liner and a bentonite clay layer below it prevent leakage to groundwater. Trash is also compacted and covered with earth fill every day.

to removing 25 million vehicles from the highway. Some landfill operators are deliberately pumping water to their waste as a way of speeding up production of this valuable fuel.

Historically, landfills were convenient and cheap. This was because we had much less waste to deal with—we produced only a third as much in 1960 as today—and because there were few regulations about disposal sites and methods. Since 1984, when stricter financial and environmental protection requirements for landfills took effect, roughly 90 percent of landfills in the United States have closed. Most all of those landfills lacked environmental controls to keep toxic materials from leaking into groundwater and surface waters. Many areas now suffer groundwater and stream contamination from decades-old unregulated dump sites.

With new rules for public health protection, landfills are becoming fewer, larger, and more expensive (see fig. 13.1). Cities often truck their garbage hundreds of miles for disposal, as noted in the opening case study. The United States now spends about $10 billion per year to dispose of trash. A decade from now, it may cost us $100 billion per year to dispose of our trash and garbage. On the other hand, rising landfill costs make it more economical to pursue alternatives strategies, including waste reduction and recycling.

## We often export waste to countries ill-equipped to handle it

Most industrialized nations agreed to stop shipping hazardous and toxic waste to less-developed countries in 1989, but the practice still continues. In 2006, for example, 400 tons of toxic waste were illegally dumped at 14 open dumps in Abidjan, the capital of the Ivory Coast. The black sludge—petroleum wastes containing hydrogen sulfide and volatile hydrocarbons—killed ten people and injured many others. At least 100,000 city residents sought medical treatment for vomiting, stomach pains, nausea, breathing difficulties, nosebleeds, and headaches. The sludge—which had been refused entry at European ports—was transported by an Amsterdam-based multinational company on a Panamanian-registered ship and handed over to an Ivorian firm (thought to be connected to corrupt government officials) to be dumped in the Ivory Coast. The Dutch company agreed to clean up the waste and pay the equivalent of (U.S.)$198 million to settle claims.

Most of the world's obsolete ships are now dismantled and recycled in poor countries. The work is dangerous, and old ships often are full of toxic and hazardous materials, such as oil, diesel fuel, asbestos, and heavy metals. On India's Alang Beach, for example, more than 40,000 workers tear apart outdated vessels using crowbars, cutting torches, and even their bare hands. Metal is dragged away and sold for recycling. Organic waste is often simply burned on the beach, where ashes and oily residue wash back into the water.

Discarded electronics, or **e-waste**, is one of the greatest sources of toxic material currently going to developing countries. There are at least 2 billion television sets and personal computers in use globally. Televisions often are discarded after only about five years, while computers, play-stations, cellular telephones, and other electronics become obsolete even faster. It's estimated that 50 million tons of e-waste are discarded every year worldwide. Only about 20 percent of the components are currently recycled. The rest generally goes to open dumps or landfills. This waste stream contains at least 2.5 billion kg of lead, as well as mercury, gallium, germanium, nickel, palladium, beryllium, selenium, arsenic, and valuable metals, such as gold, silver, copper, and steel.

Until recently, most of this e-waste went to China, where villagers, including young children, would break it apart to retrieve valuable metals. Often, this scrap recovery was done under primitive conditions where workers had little or no protective gear (fig. 13.7a). Health risks in this work are severe, especially for growing children. Soil, groundwater, and surface-water contamination at these sites is extremely high. Food grown in contaminated soils often contains toxic levels of lead and other metals.

Shipping e-waste to China is now officially banned, but illegal smuggling continues. With tighter regulation in China, informal e-waste recycling has shifted to India, Congo, and other areas with weak environmental regulation. Adding to the difficulty of this problem, these developing areas will soon be producing more e-waste than wealthier countries with better regulation (fig. 13.7b). Will those developing areas be able to defend public health with this increase in waste production?

(a)

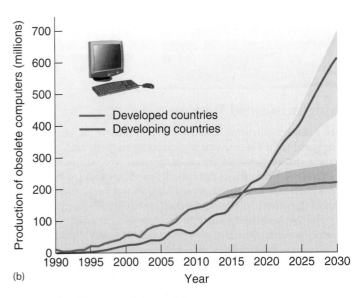

(b)

**Figure 13.7** A Chinese woman breaks up e-waste to extract valuable metals. (a) This kind of unprotected demanufacturing is hazardous to workers and the environment, but production of e-waste is rising in both developed and developing areas. (b) The graph shows expected trends and the estimated range of likely increases. *Source: Modified from Yu, et al. 2010. Environmental Science and Technology.*

The Basel Action Network is an international network of activists seeking better controls on global trade in toxic materials. This group, named after the city where an interenational agreement was made banning the practice, tracks international e-waste shipments and working conditions. Exporting waste to poor communities also occurs within countries (see What Do You Think? p. 326).

## Incineration produces energy from trash

Faced with growing piles of garbage and a lack of available landfills at any price, many cities have built waste incinerators to burn municipal waste. Another term commonly used for this technology is **energy recovery**, or waste-to-energy, because the heat derived from incinerated refuse is a useful resource. Burning garbage can produce steam used directly for heating buildings or generating electricity. Internationally, well over 1,000 waste-to-energy plants in Brazil, Japan, and Western Europe generate much-needed energy while reducing the amount that needs to be landfilled. In the United States more than 110 waste incinerators burn 45,000 metric tons of garbage daily. Some of these are simple incinerators; others produce steam and/or electricity.

Municipal incinerators are specially designed burning plants capable of burning thousands of tons of waste per day. In some plants, refuse is sorted as it comes in to remove unburnable or recyclable materials before combustion. This is called **refuse-derived fuel** because the enriched burnable fraction has a higher energy content than the raw trash. Another approach, called **mass burn**, is to dump everything smaller than sofas and refrigerators into a giant furnace and burn as much as possible (fig. 13.8). This technique avoids the expensive and unpleasant job of sorting, but it produces more unburned ash and often produces more air pollution as plastics, batteries, and other mixed substances are burned.

The cost-effectiveness of garbage incinerators is the subject of heated debates. Initial construction costs are high—usually

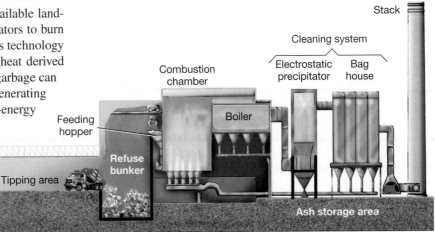

**Figure 13.8** A diagram of a municipal "mass burn" garbage incinerator. Steam produced in the boiler can be used to generate electricity or to heat nearby buildings.

# What Do YOU Think?

## Environmental Justice

When a new landfill, petrochemical factory, incinerator, or other unwanted industrial facility is proposed for a minority neighborhood, charges of environmental racism often are raised by those who oppose this siting. Everyday experiences tell us that minority neighborhoods are much more likely to have high pollution levels and facilities that you wouldn't want to live near than are middle- or upper-class white neighborhoods. But does this prove that land-use decisions are racist, or just that minorities are less politically powerful than middle- or upper-class residents? Could it be that land prices are simply cheaper and public resistance to locating a polluting facility in a place that's already polluted is less than putting it in a cleaner environment? Or does this distinction matter? Perhaps showing that a disproportionate number of minorities live in dirtier places is evidence enough of racism. How would you decide?

One of the first systematic studies showing this inequitable distribution of environmental hazards based on race in the United States was conducted by Robert D. Bullard in 1978. Asked for help by a predominantly black community in Houston that was slated for a waste incinerator, Bullard discovered that all five of the city's exist-

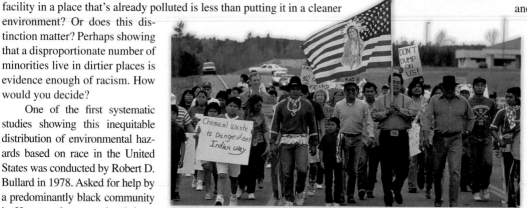

Native Americans march in protest of toxic waste dumping on tribal lands.

ing landfills and six of eight incinerators were located in African-American neighborhoods. In a book entitled *Dumping on Dixie*, Bullard showed that this pattern of risk exposure in minority communities is common throughout the United States. Among his findings are:

- Three of the five largest commercial hazardous waste landfills, accounting for about 40 percent of all hazardous waste disposal in the United States, are located in predominantly African-American or Hispanic communities.

- Sixty percent of African Americans and Latinos and nearly half of all Asians, Pacific Islanders, and Native Americans live in communities with uncontrolled toxic waste sites.

- The average percentage of the population made up by minorities in communities without a hazardous waste facility is 12 percent.

By contrast, communities with one hazardous waste facility have, on average, twice as high (24 percent) a minority population, while those with two or more such facilities average three times as high a minority population (38 percent) as those without one.

But does this prove that race, not class or income, is the strongest determinant of who is exposed to environmental hazards? What additional information might you look for to make this distinction? One of the lines of evidence Dr. Bullard raises is the fact that the discrepancy between the pollution exposure of middle-class blacks and that of middle-class whites is even greater than the difference between poorer whites and blacks. While upper-class whites can "vote with their feet" and move out of polluted and dangerous neighborhoods, Bullard argues, minorities are restricted by color barriers and prejudice to less desirable locations.

Some additional evidence uncovered by this research is variation in the way toxic waste sites are cleaned up and how polluters are punished in different neighborhoods. White communities see faster responses and get better results once toxic wastes are discovered than do minority communities. For instance, the EPA takes 20 percent longer to place a hazardous waste site in a minority community on the Superfund National Priority List than it does for one in a white community. Penalties assessed against polluters of white communities average six times higher than those against polluters of minority communities. Cleanup is more thorough in white communities as well. Most toxic wastes in white communities are treated—that is, removed or destroyed. By contrast, waste sites in minority neighborhoods are generally only "contained" by putting a cap over them, leaving contaminants in place to potentially resurface or leak into groundwater at a later date.

How would you evaluate these findings? Do they convince you that racism is at work, or do you think that other explanations might be equally likely? Which of these arguments do you find most persuasive, or what other evidence would you need to make a reasoned judgment about whether or not environmental racism is a factor in determining who gets exposed to pollution and who enjoys a cleaner, more pleasant environment?

---

between $100 million and $300 million for a typical municipal facility. Tipping fees at an incinerator (the fee charged to haulers for each ton of garbage dumped) are often much higher than those at a landfill. Ironically, one worry about incinerators is whether enough garbage will be available to feed them. Incinerators also compete with recyclers for high-energy paper and plastics. Cities usually have contracts guaranteeing certain amounts of waste daily. Some communities in which recycling has been really successful have had to buy garbage from neighbors to meet contractual obligations to waste-to-energy facilities.

**Incinerators Can Produce Health Risks** Incinerators produce considerable amounts of ash and airborne emissions that are hard to monitor. Residual ash and unburnable residues representing 10 to 20 percent of the original volume are usually taken to a landfill for disposal. Because the volume of burned garbage is reduced by 80 to 90 percent, disposal is a smaller task. However, the residual ash usually contains a variety of toxic components. The EPA has found alarmingly high levels of dioxins, furans, lead, and cadmium in incinerator ash. These toxic materials are more concentrated in the fly ash (lighter, airborne particles capable of penetrating deep into the lungs) than in heavy bottom ash. All of the incinerators on one EPA study exceeded cadmium standards, and 80 percent exceeded lead standards. Proponents of incineration argue that, if they are run properly and equipped with appropriate pollution-control devices, incinerators are safe for the general public. Opponents counter that neither public officials nor pollution-control equipment can be trusted to keep the air clean. They argue that recycling and source reduction efforts are better ways to deal with waste.

The EPA, which generally supports incineration, acknowledges the health threat of incinerator emissions but holds that the danger is very slight. The EPA estimates that dioxin emissions from a typical municipal incinerator may cause one death per million people in 70 years of operation. Critics of incineration claim that a more accurate estimate is 250 deaths per million in 70 years.

One way to reduce these dangerous emissions is to remove batteries containing heavy metals and plastics containing chlorine before wastes are burned. Increasingly, European cities are banning plastics from incinerator waste and requiring households to separate plastics from other garbage. This is expected to eliminate nearly all dioxins and other combustion by-products. Separation also prevents the expense of installing costly pollution-control equipment that otherwise would be necessary to keep the burners operating. Keeping items such as batteries and compact fluorescent light bulbs out of waste is also essential to minimize mercury and other metals in incinerator emissions.

## 13.3 Shrinking the Waste Stream

Compared to landfilling and incineration, recycling saves money, energy, raw materials, and land space, and it reduces pollution. **Recycling**, as the term is used in solid waste management, is the reprocessing of discarded materials into new products (fig. 13.9). Sometimes the same products are remade: old aluminum cans and glass bottles are usually melted and recast into new cans and bottles,

**Figure 13.9** In some systems, residents sort recyclables, which are then transported in trucks with multiple compartments. In other systems, everything is mixed together for transport and then sorted by workers or complex machines at a recycling center.

lead from car batteries can be made into new batteries. Sometimes entirely new products are made. Old tires, for instance, are shredded and turned into rubberized playground or road surfacing. Newspapers become cellulose insulation, and steel cans become new automobiles and construction materials.

There have been some dramatic successes in recycling in recent years. Nationally, the United States recycles or composts one-third of municipal solid waste. Minneapolis and Seattle claim a 60 percent recycling rate, something thought unattainable a decade ago. San Francisco is aiming for 100 percent recycling. Residents are now required to separate recyclables, compostables, or trash, in order to aid this effort. All this recyling makes good environmental sense, but it also saves San Francisco the cost of waste disposal.

### Recycling Continues to Face Challenges

Aluminum is probably the easiest and most valuable material to recycle. The lightweight, high-value scrap can be reused for thousands of purposes. Still, only half of aluminum cans are recycled in the United States. This rate is up from only 15 percent 20 years ago, but Americans still throw away nearly 350,000 metric tons of aluminum beverage containers each year. That is enough to make 3,800 Boeing 747 airplanes. This is especially unfortunate because producing new aluminum is extraordinarily energy intensive, while recycling is relatively easy.

Wild fluctuations in commodity prices are a challenge in developing a market for recycled materials. Newsprint, for example, cost $160 a ton in 1995; by 1999 it dropped to just $42 per ton and then climbed to $650 per ton in 2009 (fig. 13.10).

Low prices for new materials is also an obstacle. New plastic, made from oil, is usually cheaper than the cost of collecting and transporting used

**Figure 13.10** Creating a stable, economically viable market for recycled products is essential for recycling success. Consumers can help by buying recycled products.

plastics (when the cost of disposal and other expenses are not considered). Consequently, less than 7 percent of the United States' 30 million tons of plastic waste is recycled each year. Contamination is a major obstacle in plastics recycling. Most plastic soft drink bottles are made of PET (polyethylene terphthalate), which can be remanufactured into carpet, fleece clothing, plastic strapping, and nonfood packaging. However, even a trace of vinyl—a single PVC (polyvinyl chloride) bottle in a truckload, for example—can make PET useless. Because single-use beverage containers are so costly to recycle, they have been outlawed in Denmark and Finland.

The growing popularity of bottled water is producing a serious waste disposal problem. Of the 300 billion bottles of water consumed each year globally, less than 20 percent are recycled. It takes around 75 billion liters (500 million barrels) of oil to manufacture and ship these bottles. In most American cities, tap water is safe and is subjected to more rigorous testing than bottled water. The best way to control this problem is through bottle deposits. States with deposit laws recover about 78 percent of all beverage containers, while those without generally have recycling rates of 20 percent or less.

**Recycling Saves Money, Energy, and Space** Curbside pickup of recyclables costs around $35 per ton, as opposed to the $80 paid to dispose of them at an average metropolitan landfill. Many recycling programs cover their own expenses with materials sales and may even bring revenue to the community. Recycling also encourages individual awareness and responsibility for the refuse produced (fig. 13.11).

Recycling drastically reduces pressure on landfills and incinerators. Philadelphia is investing in neighborhood collection centers that will recycle 600 tons a day, enough to eliminate the need for a previously planned, high-priced incinerator. New York City, down to one available landfill but still producing 27,000 tons of garbage a day, set a target of 50 percent waste reduction to be accomplished by recycling office paper and household and commercial waste. In 2002 Mayor Michael Bloomberg discontinued most recycling, arguing that the program was too expensive. The city quickly found that disposing of waste was more expensive than recycling, and most programs were reinstated.

Japan probably has the most successful recycling program in the world. Half of all household and commercial wastes in Japan are recycled, while the rest are about equally incinerated or landfilled. The country has begun a push to increase recycling, because incineration costs almost as much. Some communities have raised recycling rates to 80 percent, and others aim to reduce waste altogether by 2020. This level of recycling takes a high level of participation and commitment. In Yokohama, a city of 3.5 million, there are now 10 categories of recyclables, including used clothing and sorted plastics. Some communities have 30 or 40 categories for sorting recyclables.

Recycling lowers demand for raw resources (fig. 13.12). The United States cuts down 2 million trees every day to produce newsprint and paper products, a heavy drain on its forests. Recycling the print run of a single Sunday issue of the *New York Times* would spare 75,000 trees. Every piece of plastic made in the United States reduces the reserve supply of petroleum and makes the country more dependent on foreign oil. Recycling 1 ton of aluminum saves 4 tons of bauxite (aluminum ore) and 700 kg of petroleum coke and pitch, as well as keeping 35 kg of aluminum fluoride out of the air.

Recycling also reduces energy consumption and air pollution. Plastic bottle recycling could save 50 to 60 percent of the energy

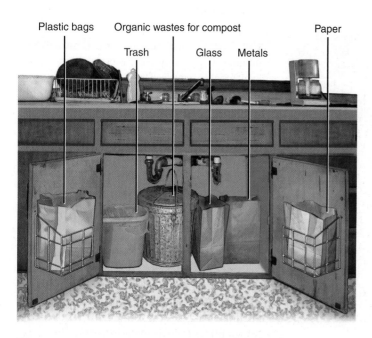

**Figure 13.11** Source separation in the kitchen—the first step in a strong recycling program.

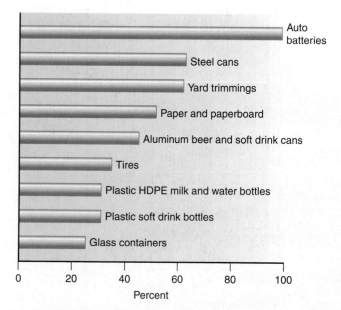

**Figure 13.12** Recycling rates for selected materials in the United States. Battery recycling, which is required by law, is very successful. Other materials, even though valuable for reuse, have mixed recycling success.
*Source:* Data from Environmental Protection Agency, 2007.

needed to make new ones. Making new steel from old scrap offers up to 75 percent energy savings. Producing aluminum from scrap instead of bauxite ore cuts energy use by 95 percent, yet the United States still throws away more than a million tons of aluminum every year. If aluminum recovery were doubled worldwide, more than a million tons of air pollutants would be eliminated every year (see A Closer Look, p. 330).

Reducing litter is an important benefit of recycling. Ever since disposable paper, glass, metal, foam, and plastic packaging began to accompany nearly everything we buy, these discarded wrappings have collected on our roadsides and in our lakes, rivers, and oceans. Litter is a costly as well as unsightly problem. Americans pay an estimated 32¢ for each piece of litter picked up by crews along state highways, which adds up to $500 million every year. "Bottle bills" requiring deposits on bottles and cans have reduced littering in many states.

## Composting recycles organic waste

Pressed for landfill space, many cities have banned yard waste from municipal garbage. Rather than bury this valuable organic material, they are turning it into a useful product through **composting**: biological degradation or breakdown of organic matter under aerobic (oxygen-rich) conditions. The organic compost resulting from this process makes a nutrient-rich soil amendment that aids water retention, slows soil erosion, and improves crop yields.

Many cities and counties provide centralized composting, to help people keep compostables out of the municipal waste stream. You can also compost your own organic waste. All you need to do is to pile up lawn clippings, vegetable waste, fallen leaves, wood chips, or other organic matter in an out-of-the way place, keep it moist, and turn it over every week or so (fig. 13.13). Within a few months, naturally occurring microorganisms will decompose the organic material into a rich, pleasant-smelling compost that you can use to enrich your yard or garden.

As noted in the opening case study, some composting systems produce methane fuel. Worldwide, at least one-fifth of municipal waste is organic kitchen and garden refuse. In developing countries

**Figure 13.13** Composting is a good way to convert yard waste, vegetable scraps, and other organic materials into useful garden mulch.

**Figure 13.14** Reusing discarded products is a creative and efficient way to reduce wastes. This recycling center in Berkeley, California, is a valuable source of used building supplies and a money saver for the whole community.

up to 85 percent of the waste stream is food, textiles, vegetable matter, and other biodegradable materials.

Methane is captured from this material at many landfills, but it's much more efficient to convert organic waste to methane in a contained, anaerobic digester. Germany and Switzerland now have at least 30 municipal-scale waste-to-methane plants. Anaerobic digestion also can be done on a small scale. Millions of household methane generators provide fuel for cooking and lighting for homes in China and India (chapter 12). In the United States some farmers produce all the fuel they need to run their farms—both for heating and for running trucks and tractors—by generating methane from animal manure.

## Reuse is even better than recycling

Even better than recycling or composting is cleaning and reusing materials in their present form, thus saving the cost and energy of remaking them into something else. We do this already with some specialized items. Auto parts are regularly sold from junkyards, especially for older car models. In some areas stained-glass windows, brass fittings, fine woodwork, and bricks salvaged from old houses bring high prices. Some communities sort and reuse a variety of materials received in their dumps (fig. 13.14).

# Garbage: Liability or resource?

**Municipal solid waste includes all our mixed refuse.** Most of us don't spend much time thinking about where our waste ends up, but as you know from the principle of conservation of matter (chapter 2), materials are never destroyed or created, they're just transformed from one shape to another. Elements in our waste such as aluminum, lead, carbon, or nitrogen don't disappear. They may sit in a landfill for centuries, or they may be incinerated and emitted into the atmosphere, or they may be recycled and transformed into another useful object. The question is which of these is the most efficient use of our resources and environment.

Materials in our municipal waste stream have been hard to extract and reuse because they're usually all mixed together, although new sorting and recycling systems can separate mixed waste. Waste can be a liability or a resource. It all depends on how much we produce, how much we landfill and incinerate, and how much we recycle.

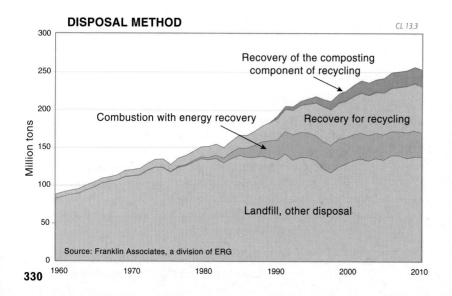

*CL 13.1*

## What are the major types of waste we produce, and how much do we recycle?

**We produce far more waste than our grandparents did.**

The EPA has tracked overall production of municipal solid waste in the United States since 1960. Disposable paper and plastic products have grown most dramatically in the past 50 years. Recovery rates are worst for plastics (because mixed waste contaminates plastics and new plastic is inexpensive) and food products (because these are relatively hard to store and transport to central recycling facilities). Metals, glass, and yard compost have relatively high recycling rates. ▶

**Where does it all go?**

As the available landfills decline, we are recycling and incinerating more municipal waste. ▼

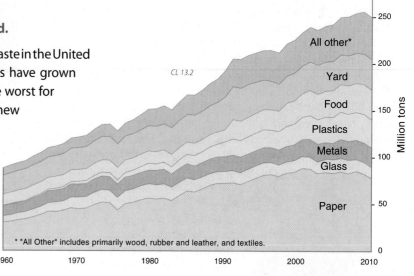

**WASTE PRODUCTION**

*CL 13.2*

- All other*
- Yard
- Food
- Plastics
- Metals
- Glass
- Paper

Million tons
250 — 200 — 150 — 100 — 50 — 0

* "All Other" includes primarily wood, rubber and leather, and textiles.

1960   1970   1980   1990   2000   2010

*CL 13.4*

### DISPOSAL METHOD

*CL 13.3*

Million tons
300
250
200
150
100
50
0

Recovery of the composting component of recycling

Combustion with energy recovery

Recovery for recycling

Landfill, other disposal

Source: Franklin Associates, a division of ERG

1960   1970   1980   1990   2000   2010

## YARD WASTE
CL 13.5

*Generation*

*Recovery*

Million tons (y-axis: 0, 5, 10, 15, 20, 25, 30, 35, 40)
x-axis: 1960, 1970, 1980, 1990, 2000, 2010

Recycling rate = Yard waste: 65%
Food scraps: negligible

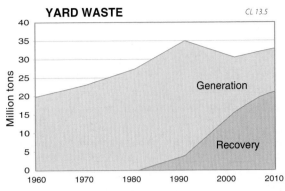
CL 13.8

Recycling rate = negligible (all plastics)
PET bottles: 27%
HDPE bottles: 29%

## PLASTICS
CL 13.7

*Generation*

*Recovery*

Million tons (y-axis: 0, 4, 8, 12, 16, 20, 24, 28, 32)
x-axis: 1960, 1970, 1980, 1990, 2000, 2010

## METALS
CL 13.9

*Generation*

*Recovery*

Million tons (y-axis: 0, 2, 4, 6, 8, 10, 12, 14, 16, 18, 20, 22)
x-axis: 1960, 1970, 1980, 1990, 2000, 2010

Recycling rate = 35%
(Aluminum: 21%
Iron/steel: 34%
Other metals: 69%)

CL 13.10

## GLASS
CL 13.11

*Generation*

*Recovery*

Million tons (y-axis: 0, 2, 4, 6, 8, 10, 12, 14, 16, 18)
x-axis: 1960, 1970, 1980, 1990, 2000, 2010

Recycling rate = 23%

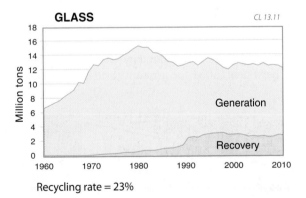

## PAPER AND PAPERBOARD
CL 13.12

*Generation*

*Recovery*

Million tons (y-axis: 0, 10, 20, 30, 40, 50, 60, 70, 80, 90, 100)
x-axis: 1960, 1970, 1980, 1990, 2000, 2010

Recycling rate = 56%

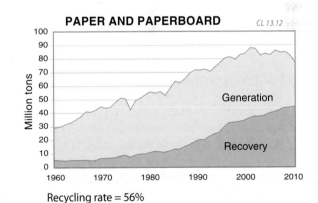

### Can You Explain:

1. Which of these materials has the highest rate of recovery? Which is lowest?

2. Is there an approximate year in which recovery and recycling began to increase?

3. Why is recycling less common for plastics than for metals?

4. In the plot of production, which factors have increased most from 1960 to 2008? Roughly what is the ratio of total production in 2008 to total production in 1960?

CL 13.13

In many cities, glass and plastic bottles are routinely returned to beverage producers for washing and refilling. The reusable, refillable bottle is the most efficient beverage container we have. It is better for the environment than remelting and more profitable for local communities. A reusable glass container makes an average of 15 round-trips between factory and customer before it becomes so scratched and chipped that it has to be recycled. Reusable containers also favor local bottling companies and help preserve regional businesses.

Since the advent of cheap, lightweight, disposable food and beverage containers, many small, local breweries, canneries, and bottling companies have been forced out of business by huge national conglomerates. These big companies can afford to ship food and beverages thousands of miles, as long as it is a one-way trip. National companies favor recycling rather than refilling because they prefer to operate a few very large plants and don't want to be responsible for collecting and reusing containers.

In many less-affluent nations, reusing manufactured goods is an established tradition. If manufactured products are expensive and labor is cheap, it pays to salvage, clean, and repair products. Cairo, Manila, Mexico City, and many other cities have large populations of poor people who make a living by scavenging. Entire ethnic populations may survive on scavenging, sorting, and reprocessing scraps from city dumps. Is this the best way to manage waste? What alternatives might there be in a developing country?

## Reducing waste is often the cheapest option

Most of our attention in waste management focuses on recycling, but slowing the production of throw-away products is by far the most effective way to save energy, materials, and money. Among the "three Rs"—reduce, reuse, recycle—the most important strategy is the first. Industries are increasingly finding that reducing saves money. Soft-drink makers use less aluminum per can than they did 20 years ago, and plastic bottles use less plastic. 3M has saved over $500 million in the past 30 years by reducing its use of raw materials, reusing waste products, and increasing efficiency. Individual action is essential, too (see What Can You Do? p. 332).

In recent decades, we have greatly increased our waste production rather than reducing it. As consumer goods have multiplied and as global economies have grown, all of us have done our part for the economy by consuming, and discarding, more things (fig. 13.15). Moreover, as developing countries become wealthier they are catching up with the high levels of waste production in wealthier countries. Adopting better strategies for reducing waste clearly deserves our attention (see A Closer Look, p. 330).

Excessive packaging of food and consumer products is one of our greatest sources of unnecessary waste. Paper, plastic,

glass, and metal packaging material makes up 50 percent of our domestic trash by volume. Much of that packaging is primarily for marketing and has little to do with product protection. Manufacturers and retailers can reduce these practices if consumers ask for products with less packaging. Canada's National Packaging Protocol (NPP) recommends that packaging minimize depletion of virgin resources and production of toxins in manufacturing. The preferred hierarchy is (1) no packaging, (2) minimal packaging, (3) reusable packaging, and (4) recyclable packaging. This plan sets an ambitious target of 50 percent reduction in excess packaging.

In 2008, China banned ultrathin (less than 0.025 mm thick) plastic bags and called for a return to reusable cloth bags for

**Figure 13.15** How much more do we need? Where will we put what we already have? JIM BORGMAN © Cincinnati Enquirer. Reprinted with permission of UNIVERSAL UCLICK. All rights reserved.

shopping. This could eliminate up to 3 billion plastic bags used every day in China. Japan, Ireland, South Africa, and Taiwan also have discouraged single-use plastic bags through taxes or prohibitions. In 2007, San Francisco became the first American city to outlaw petroleum-based plastic grocery bags.

Where disposable packaging is necessary, we still can reduce the volume of waste in our landfills by using materials that are compostable or degradable. **Photodegradable plastics** break down when exposed to ultraviolet radiation. **Biodegradable plastics** incorporate such materials as cornstarch that microorganisms can decompose. Several states have introduced legislation requiring biodegradable or photodegradable six-pack beverage yokes, fast-food packaging, and disposable diapers. These degradable plastics often don't decompose completely, however; many kinds only break down to small particles that remain in the environment.

## 13.4 Hazardous and Toxic Wastes

The most dangerous aspect of the waste stream is that it often contains highly toxic and hazardous materials that are injurious to both human health and environmental quality (fig. 13.16). We now produce and use a vast array of flammable, explosive, caustic, acidic, and highly toxic chemical substances for industrial, agricultural, and domestic purposes. According to the EPA, U.S. industries generate about 900 million metric tons of officially classified hazardous wastes each year, about 3 metric tons for each person in the country. In addition, considerably more toxic and hazardous waste material is generated by industries or processes not regulated by the EPA. Shockingly, at least 40 million metric tons (22 billion lbs) of toxic and hazardous wastes are released into the air, water, and land in the United States each year. The biggest sources of these toxins are the chemical and petroleum industries (fig. 13.17).

### Hazardous waste includes many dangerous substances

Legally, a **hazardous waste** is any discarded material, liquid or solid, that contains substances known to be (1) fatal to humans or laboratory animals in low doses; (2) toxic, carcinogenic, mutagenic,

**Figure 13.16** Hazardous waste is dangerous even with small exposure. Here a worker tests for radioactive soil.

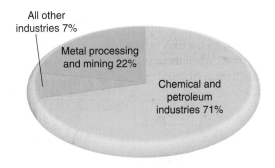

**Figure 13.17** Producers of hazardous wastes in the United States. *Source:* Data from the U.S. Environmental Protection Agency, 2006.

or teratogenic to humans or other life-forms; (3) ignitable with a flash point less than 60°C; (4) corrosive; or (5) explosive or highly reactive (undergoes violent chemical reactions either by itself or when mixed with other materials). Notice that this definition includes both toxic and hazardous materials, as defined in chapter 8. Certain compounds are exempt from regulation as hazardous waste if they are accumulated in less than 1 kg (2.2 lbs) of commercial chemicals or 100 kg of contaminated soil, water, or debris. Even larger amounts (up to 1,000 kg) are exempt when stored at an approved waste treatment facility for the purpose of being beneficially used, recycled, reclaimed, detoxified, or destroyed.

Most hazardous waste is recycled, converted to nonhazardous forms, stored, or otherwise disposed of on-site by the generators—chemical companies, petroleum refiners, and other large industrial facilities—so that it doesn't become a public problem. Still, the hazardous waste that does enter the waste stream or the environment represents a serious environmental problem. And orphan wastes left behind by abandoned industries remain a serious threat to both environmental quality and human health. For years little attention was paid to this material. Wastes stored on private property, buried, or allowed to soak into the ground were considered of little concern to the public. An estimated 5 billion metric tons of highly poisonous chemicals were improperly disposed of in the United States between 1950 and 1975 before regulatory controls became more stringent.

## Federal legislation regulates hazardous waste

Two important federal laws regulate hazardous waste management and disposal in the United States. The Resource Conservation and Recovery Act (RCRA, pronounced "rickra") of 1976 is a comprehensive program that requires rigorous testing and management of toxic and hazardous substances. At every step, generators, shippers, users, and disposers of these materials must keep account of everything they handle and what happens to it from generation (cradle) to ultimate disposal (grave) (fig. 13.18).

The Comprehensive Environmental Response, Compensation, and Liability Act (CERCLA or Superfund Act), passed in 1980, is aimed at rapid containment, cleanup, or remediation of abandoned toxic waste sites. The act establishes a National Priority List (NPL) of sites most in need of remediation. In 2010 there were approximately 1,280 sites on the list, with 60 waiting for a decision and over 1,000 sites designated as "completed." CERCLA authorizes the EPA to take emergency actions when there is a threat that toxic material could leak into the environment. The EPA also is empowered to sue responsible parties for the recovery of treatment costs.

About 30 percent of sites on the NPL are "orphan" sites, whose owners have disappeared or gone out of business. For these, CERCLA established a "Superfund," a pool of money to cover remediation costs until responsible parties can be located.

The government does not have to prove that anyone violated a law or what role he or she played in a Superfund site. Rather, liability under CERCLA is "strict, joint, and several," meaning that anyone associated with a site can be held responsible for the entire cost of cleaning it up, no matter how much of the mess they made. In some cases property owners have been assessed millions of dollars for removal of wastes left there years earlier by previous owners. This strict liability has been a headache for the real estate and insurance businesses.

CERCLA was amended in 1995 to make some of its provisions less onerous. In cases where treatment is unavailable or too costly and it is likely that a less costly remedy will become available within a reasonable time, interim containment is now allowed. The EPA also now has the discretion to set site-specific cleanup levels, rather than adhere to rigid national standards.

CERCLA was modified in 1984 by the Superfund Amendments and Reauthorization Act (SARA). SARA also established a community "right to know," the notion that the public had a right to know about production, use, or transportation of toxic materials where they live. A key part of public information and emergency planning is the **Toxic Release Inventory**, a listing of addresses where regulated materials are handled. This inventory requires 20,000 manufacturing facilities to report annually on releases of more than 300 toxic materials. The EPA publishes this list, and from it you can find specific information in the inventory about what is in your neighborhood.

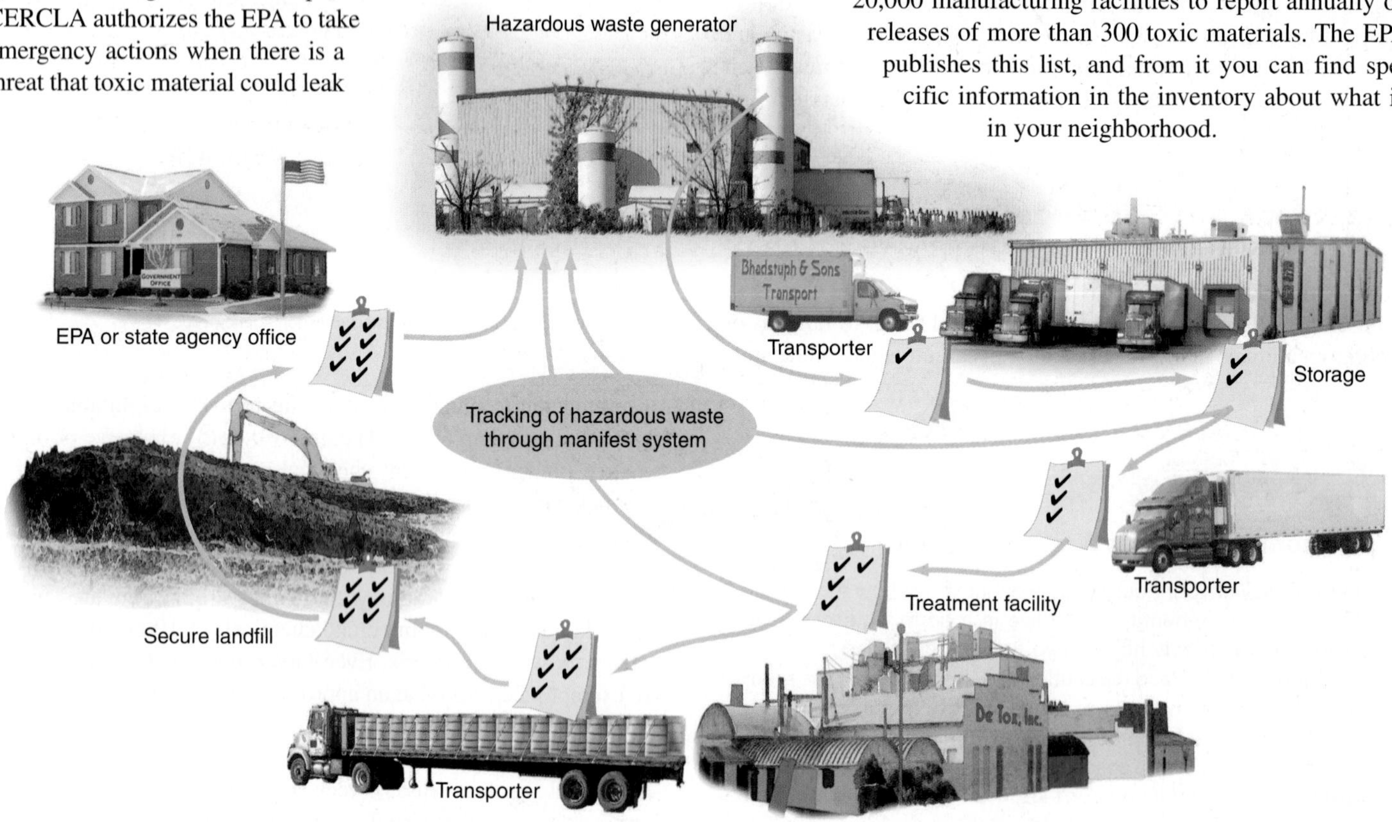

**Figure 13.18** Toxic and hazardous wastes must be tracked from "cradle to grave" by detailed shipping manifests.

## Superfund sites are listed for federal cleanup

The EPA estimates that there are at least 36,000 seriously contaminated sites in the United States. The General Accounting Office (GAO) places the number much higher, perhaps more than 400,000 when all are identified. Originally, about 1,671 sites were placed on the National Priority List for cleanup with financing from the federal Superfund program. The **Superfund** is a revolving pool designed to (1) provide an immediate response to emergency situations that pose imminent hazards, and (2) to clean up or remediate abandoned or inactive sites. Without this fund, sites would languish for years or decades while the courts decided who was responsible for paying for the cleanup (fig. 13.19). Originally a $1.6 billion pool, the fund peaked at $3.6 billion. From its inception, the fund was financed by taxes on producers of toxic and hazardous wastes. Industries opposed this "polluter pays" tax, because current manufacturers are often not the ones responsible for the original contamination. In 1995 Congress agreed to let the tax expire. Since then the Superfund has dwindled, and the public has picked up an increasing share of the bill. In the 1980s the public covered less than 20 percent of the Superfund. Since 2004, however, general revenues (public tax dollars) have paid the entire cost off a greatly reduced program, and the industry share has been zero. President Barack Obama has proposed reducing the public tax burden by reinstating the "polluter pays" tax.

Total costs for hazardous waste cleanup in the United States are estimated to be between $370 billion and $1.7 trillion, depending on how clean sites must be and what methods are used. For years, Superfund money was spent mostly on lawyers and consultants, and cleanup efforts were often bogged down in disputes over liability and best cleanup methods. During the 1990s, however, progress improved substantially, with a combination of rule adjustments and administrative commitment to cleanup. By 2004, more than half (over 1,000) of the original NPL sites were listed as completed in cleanup or containment.

What qualifies a site for the NPL? These sites are considered to be especially hazardous to human health and environmental quality because they are known to be leaking or have a potential for leaking supertoxic, carcinogenic, teratogenic, or mutagenic materials (chapter 8). The ten substances of greatest concern or most commonly detected at Superfund sites are lead, trichloroethylene, toluene, benzene, PCBs, chloroform, phenol, arsenic, cadmium, and chromium. These and other hazardous or toxic materials are known to have contaminated groundwater at 75 percent of the sites now on the NPL. In addition, 56 percent of these sites have contaminated surface waters, and airborne materials are found at 20 percent of the sites. Seventy million Americans, including 10 million children, live within 6 km of a Superfund site.

Where are these thousands of hazardous waste sites, and how did they get contaminated? Old industrial facilities, such as smelters, mills, petroleum refineries, and chemical manufacturing plants, are highly likely to have been sources of toxic wastes. Regions of the country with high concentrations of aging factories, such as the "rust belt" around the Great Lakes or the Gulf Coast petrochemical centers, have large numbers of Superfund sites (fig. 13.20). Mining districts also are prime sources of toxic and hazardous waste. Within cities, factories and places such as railroad yards, bus repair barns, and filling stations, where solvents, gasoline, oil, and other petrochemicals were spilled or dumped on the ground, often are highly contaminated.

Some of the most infamous toxic waste sites were old dumps where many different materials were mixed together indiscriminately. For instance, Love Canal in Niagara Falls, New York, was an open dump that both the city and nearby chemical factories used as a disposal site. More than 20,000 tons of toxic chemical waste were buried under what later became a housing development. Another infamous example occurred in Hardeman County, Tennessee, where about a quarter of a million barrels of chemical waste were buried in shallow pits that subsequently leaked toxins into the groundwater.

**Figure 13.19** Modern society produces large amounts of toxic and hazardous waste.

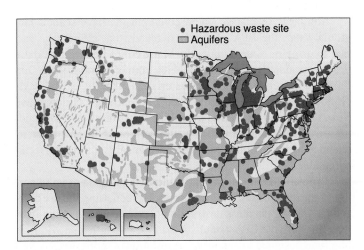

**Figure 13.20** Some of the hazardous waste sites on the EPA priority cleanup list. Sites located on aquifer recharge zones represent an especially serious threat. Once groundwater is contaminated, cleanup is difficult and expensive. In some cases, it may not be possible.
*Source:* Environmental Protection Agency.

## Brownfields present both liability and opportunity

Among the biggest problems in cleaning up hazardous waste sites are questions of liability and the degree of purity required. In many cities, these problems have created large areas of contaminated properties, known as **brownfields**, that have been abandoned or are not being used to their potential because of real or suspected pollution. Up to one-third of all commercial and industrial sites in the urban core of many big cities fall in this category. In heavy industrial corridors the percentage typically is higher.

For years no one was interested in redeveloping brownfields because of liability risks. Who would buy a property, knowing that they might be forced to spend years in litigation and negotiations and be forced to pay millions of dollars for pollution they didn't create? Even if a site has been cleaned to current standards, there is a worry that additional pollution might be found in the future or that more stringent standards might be applied.

In many cases, property owners complain that unreasonably high levels of purity are demanded in remediation programs. Consider the case of Columbia, Mississippi. For many years a 35-ha (81-acre) site in Columbia was used for turpentine and pine tar manufacturing. Soil tests showed concentrations of phenols and other toxic organic compounds exceeding federal safety standards. The site was added to the Superfund NPL, and remediation was ordered. Some experts recommended that the best solution was to simply cover the surface with clean soil and enclose the property with a fence to keep people out. The total costs would have been about $1 million. Instead, the EPA ordered Reichhold Chemical, the last known property owner, to excavate more than 12,500 tons of soil and haul it to a commercial hazardous waste dump in Louisiana at a cost of some $4 million. The intention is to make the site safe enough to be used for any purpose, including housing—even though no one has proposed building anything there. According to the EPA, the dirt must be clean enough for children to play in—even eat—without risk.

Similarly, in places where contaminants have seeped into groundwater, the EPA generally demands that cleanup be carried to drinking-water standards. Many critics believe that these pristine standards are unreasonable. Former Congressman Jim Florio, a principal author of the original Superfund Act, says, "It doesn't make any sense to clean up a rail yard in downtown Newark so it can be used as a drinking water reservoir." Depending on where the site is, what else is around it, and what its intended uses are, much less stringent standards may be perfectly acceptable.

Brownfield redevelopment is increasingly seen as an opportunity for rebuilding cities, creating jobs, increasing the tax base, and preventing needless destruction of open space at urban margins. In 2002 the EPA established a new brownfields revitalization fund designed to encourage restoration of more sites, as well as more kinds of sites. In some communities former brownfields are being turned into "eco-industrial parks" that feature environmentally friendly businesses and bring in much-needed jobs to inner-city neighborhoods (chapter 14).

## Hazardous waste must be processed or stored permanently

What shall we do with toxic and hazardous wastes? In our homes, we can reduce waste generation and choose less toxic materials. Buy only what you need for the job at hand. Use up the last little bit, or share leftovers with a friend or neighbor. Many common materials that you probably already have make excellent alternatives to commercial products.

**Produce Less Waste** As with other wastes, the safest and least expensive way to avoid hazardous waste problems is to avoid creating the wastes in the first place. Manufacturing processes can be modified to reduce or eliminate waste production. In Minnesota, the 3M Company reformulated products and redesigned manufacturing processes to eliminate more than 140,000 metric tons of solid and hazardous wastes, 4 billion liters (1 billion gal) of wastewater, and 80,000 metric tons of air pollution each year. It frequently found that these new processes not only spared the environment but also saved money by using less energy and fewer raw materials.

Recycling and reusing materials also eliminates hazardous wastes and pollution. Many waste products of one process or industry are valuable commodities in another. Already, about 10 percent of the wastes that would otherwise enter the waste stream in the United States are sent to surplus material exchanges, where they are sold as raw materials for use by other industries. This figure could probably be raised substantially with better waste management. In Europe at least one-third of all industrial wastes are exchanged through clearinghouses, where beneficial uses are found. This represents a double savings: the generator doesn't have to pay for disposal, and the recipient pays little, if anything, for raw materials.

**Convert to Less Hazardous Substances** Several processes are available to make hazardous materials less toxic. *Physical treatments* tie up or isolate substances. Charcoal or resin filters absorb toxins. Distillation separates hazardous components from aqueous solutions. Precipitation and immobilization in ceramics, glass, or cement isolate toxins from the environment, so that they become essentially nonhazardous. One of the few ways to dispose of metals and radioactive substances is to fuse them in silica at high temperatures to make a stable, impermeable glass that is suitable for long-term storage. Plants, bacteria, and fungi can also concentrate or detoxify contaminants (see Exploring Science, p. 337).

*Incineration* is applicable to mixtures of wastes. A permanent solution to many problems, it is quick and relatively easy, but not necessarily cheap—nor always clean—unless done correctly. Wastes must be heated to over 1,000°C (2,000°F) for a sufficient period of time to complete destruction. The ash resulting from thorough incineration is reduced in volume up to 90 percent and often is safer to store in a landfill or another disposal site than the original wastes.

*Chemical processing* can transform materials to make them nontoxic. Included in this category are neutralization, removal of metals or halogens (chlorine, bromine, etc.), and oxidation. The Sunohio Corporation of Canton, Ohio, for instance, has developed a process called PCBx, in which chlorine in such molecules as PCBs is replaced with other ions that render the compounds less

# Bioremediation

Cleaning up the thousands of hazardous waste sites at factories, farms, and gas stations is an expensive project. In the United States alone, waste cleanup is projected to cost at least $700 billion. Usually hazardous waste remediation (cleanup) involves digging up soil and incinerating it, potentially releasing toxins into the air, or trucking it to a secure landfill. Contaminated groundwater is frequently pumped out of the ground; hopefully, contaminants are retrieved at the same time.

How do plants, bacteria, and fungi do all this? Many of the biophysical details are poorly understood, but in general, plant roots are designed to efficiently extract nutrients, water, and trace minerals from soil and groundwater. The mechanisms involved may aid extraction of metallic and organic contaminants. Some plants also use toxic elements as a defense against herbivores: locoweed, for example, selectively absorbs elements such as selenium, concentrating toxic levels in its leaves. Absorption can be extremely effective. Bracken fern growing in Florida has been found to contain arsenic at concentrations more than 200 times higher than in the soil in which it was growing.

Genetically modified plants are also being developed to process toxins. Poplars have been developed to process toxins, using a gene borrowed from bacteria that transforms a toxic compound of mercury into a safer form. In another experiment, a gene for producing mammalian liver enzymes, which specialize in breaking down toxic organic compounds, was inserted into tobacco plants. The plants succeeded in producing the liver enzymes and breaking down toxins absorbed through their roots.

These remediation methods are not without risks. Insects could consume leaves containing concentrated substances, allowing contaminants to enter the food chain. Some absorbed contaminants are volatilized, or emitted in gaseous form, through pores in plant leaves. Once contaminants are absorbed into plants, the plants themselves are usually toxic and must be landfilled. But the cost of phytoremediation can be less than half the cost of landfilling or treating toxic soil, and the volume of plant material requiring secure storage is a fraction of the volume of the contaminated dirt.

Cleaning up hazardous and toxic waste sites will be a big business for the foreseeable future, in North America and around the world. Innovations such as bioremediation offer promising prospects for business development, as well as for environmental health and saving taxpayer money.

A promising alternative to these methods involves **bioremediation**, or biological waste treatment. Microscopic bacteria and fungi can absorb, accumulate, and detoxify a remarkable variety of toxic compounds. They can also accumulate heavy metals, and some have been developed that can metabolize (break down) PCBs. Aquatic plants such as water hyacinths and cattails can also be used to purify contaminated effluent.

Recently, an increasing variety of plants have been used in phytoremediation (cleanup using plants). Some types of mustard can extract lead, arsenic, zinc, and other metals from contaminated soil. Radioactive strontium and cesium have been extracted from soil near the Chernobyl nuclear power plant using common sunflowers. Poplar trees can absorb and break down toxic organic chemicals. Natural bacteria in groundwater, when provided with plenty of oxygen, can neutralize contaminants in aquifers. Experiments have shown that pumping air *into* groundwater can be a more effective cleanup method than pumping water *out*.

---

toxic. A portable unit can be moved to the location of the hazardous wastes, eliminating the need for shipping them.

**Store Permanently** Inevitably, there are some materials we can't destroy, make into something else, or otherwise eliminate. We will have to store them out of harm's way (fig. 13.21).

**Permanent retrievable storage** involves placing waste storage containers in a secure place such as a salt mine or bedrock cavern, where they can be inspected periodically and retrieved if necessary. This approach is expensive because it requires monitoring, but it has the advantage that we don't completely lose control of highly toxic substances that could eventually leak into groundwater if they were buried in a landfill. If we learn someday that our disposal methods were bad, we can retrieve waste and treat it more effectively. Retrieving waste from storage in a mine is much cheaper and more effective than digging up and remediating buried pollutants from a landfill.

**Secure landfills** are the most popular solutions for hazardous waste disposal, however. Although many landfills have been environmental disasters, newer techniques make it possible to create safe, secure modern landfills that can contain many hazardous wastes. As with a modern solid waste landfill, the first line of defense in a secure

**Figure 13.21** Hazardous substances we can't decontaminate must be catalogued, contained, and stored permanently. Here workers retrieve buried waste from the Hanford nuclear site.

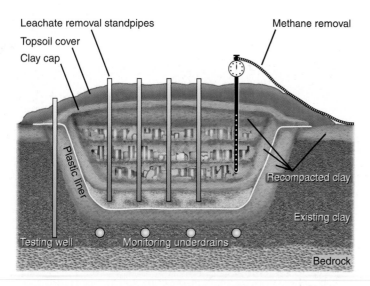

Leachate removal standpipes

Topsoil cover

Clay cap

Methane removal

Plastic liner

Recompacted clay

Existing clay

Testing well

Monitoring underdrains

Bedrock

**Figure 13.22** A secure landfill for toxic waste. A thick plastic liner and two or more layers of impervious compacted clay enclose the landfill. A gravel bed between the clay layers collects any leachate, which can then be pumped out and treated. Well samples are tested for escaping contaminants and methane is collected for combustion.

landfill is a thick bottom cushion of compacted clay that surrounds the pit like a bathtub (fig. 13.22). Moist clay is flexible and resists cracking if the ground shifts. It is impermeable to groundwater and will safely contain wastes. A layer of gravel is spread over the clay liner, and perforated drainpipes are laid in a grid to collect any seepage that escapes from the stored material. A thick polyethylene liner, protected from punctures by soft padding materials, covers the gravel bed. A layer of soil or absorbent sand cushions the inner liner, and the wastes are packed in drums, which then are placed into the pit, separated into small units by thick berms of soil or packing material.

When the landfill has reached its maximum capacity, a cover much like the bottom sandwich of clay, plastic, and soil—in that order—caps the site. Vegetation stabilizes the surface and improves its appearance. Sump pumps collect any liquids that filter through the landfill, either from rainwater or leaking drums. This leachate is treated and purified before being released. Monitoring wells check groundwater around the site to ensure that no toxins have escaped.

Most landfills are buried below ground level to be less conspicuous; however, in areas where the groundwater table is close

to the surface, it is safer to build aboveground storage. The same protective construction techniques are used as in a buried pit. An advantage to such a facility is that leakage is easier to monitor because the bottom is at ground level.

Transportation of hazardous wastes to disposal sites is of concern because of the risk of accidents. Emergency-preparedness officials conclude that the greatest risk in most urban areas is not nuclear war or natural disaster but crashes involving trucks or trains carrying hazardous chemicals through densely packed urban corridors. Another worry is who will bear financial responsibility for abandoned waste sites. Hazardous wastes remain toxic long after the businesses that created them are gone. As is the case with nuclear wastes (chapter 12), we may need new institutions for perpetual care of these wastes.

## Conclusion

In many traditional societies, people reuse nearly everything because they can't afford to discard useful resources. Modern society, however, produces a prodigious amount of waste. Government policies and economies of scale make it cheaper and more convenient to extract virgin raw materials to make new consumer products rather than to reuse or recycle items that still have useful life. We're now beginning to recognize the impacts of this wasteful lifestyle. We see the problems associated with waste disposal as well as the impacts of energy and material resource extraction. The increasing toxicity of modern products makes waste reduction even more urgent. The mantra of reduction, reuse, and recycle is becoming more widely accepted.

A first step toward reducing our waste production is to understand how much we produce. Another key step is to make our waste disposal more visible. Paying attention to recycling, re-use, and reducing both household and hazardous waste can greatly improve our awareness of our environmental responsibilities.

There are increasing opportunities to exchange materials with others who can use them, or to recycle them into other products. A big market for used construction supplies and surplus chemicals allows salvage of stuff that would otherwise go to landfills. Vehicles, electronics, and other complex products are demanufactured to reclaim valuable metals. Paint, used carpet, food and beverage containers, and many other unwanted consumer products are transformed into new merchandise. Organic matter can be composted into beneficial soil amendments. Some pioneers in sustainability find they can live comfortably while producing no waste at all if they practice reduction, reuse, and recycling faithfully.

## Practice Quiz

1. List some items that can be recycled from construction and demolition waste.

2. What are *solid wastes* and *hazardous wastes*? What is the difference between them?

3. Describe the difference between an open dump, a sanitary landfill, and a modern, secure, hazardous waste disposal site.

4. Describe some concerns about waste incineration.

5. List some benefits and drawbacks of recycling wastes. What are the major types of materials recycled from municipal waste, and how are they used?

6. What is *e-waste*? How is most of it disposed of, and what are some strategies for improving recycling rates?

7. What is *composting*, and how does it fit into solid waste disposal?

8. What materials are most recycled in the United States?

9. What are *brownfields*, and why do cities want to redevelop them?

10. What are *bioremediation* and *phytoremediation*? What are some advantages to these methods?

# Critical Thinking and Discussion Questions

Apply the principles you have learned in this chapter to discuss these questions with other students.

1. A toxic waste disposal site has been proposed for the Pine Ridge Indian Reservation in South Dakota. Many tribal members oppose this plan, but some favor it because of the jobs and income it will bring to an area with 70 percent unemployment. If local people choose immediate survival over long-term health, should we object or intervene?

2. Should industry officials be held responsible for dumping chemicals that were legal when they did it but are now known to be extremely dangerous? At what point can we argue that they should have known about the hazards involved?

3. Suppose that your brother or sister has decided to buy a house next to a toxic waste dump because it costs $20,000 less than a comparable house elsewhere. What do you say to him or her?

4. Is there a fundamental difference between incinerating municipal, medical, or toxic industrial waste? Would you oppose an incinerator in your neighborhood for one type of waste but not others? Why or why not?

5. Some scientists argue that permanent retrievable storage of toxic and hazardous wastes is preferable to burial. How can we be sure that material that will be dangerous for thousands of years will remain secure? If you were designing such a repository, how would you address this question?

## Data Analysis | How Much Waste Do You Produce, and How Much Do You Know How to Manage?

As people become aware of waste disposal problems in their communities, more people are recycling more materials. Some things are easy to recycle, such as newsprint, office paper, or aluminum drink cans. Other things are harder to classify. Most of us give up pretty quickly and throw things in the trash if we have to think too hard about how to recycle them.

1. Take a poll to find out how many people in your class know how to recycle the items in the table at right. Once you have taken your poll, convert the numbers to percentages: divide the number who know how to recycle each item by the number of students in your class, and then multiply by 100.

2. Now find someone on your campus who works on waste management. This might be someone in your university/college administration, or it might be someone who actually empties trash containers. (You might get more interesting and straightforward answers from the latter.) Ask the following questions: (1) Can this person fill in the items your class didn't know about? (2) Is there a college/university policy about recycling? What are some of the points on that policy? (3) How much does the college spend each year on waste disposal? How many tuition payments does that total? (4) What are the biggest parts of the waste stream? (5) Does the school have a plan for reducing that largest component?

| Item | Percentage Who Know How to Recycle |
|---|---|
| Newspapers | |
| Paperboard (cereal boxes) | |
| Cardboard boxes | |
| Cardboard boxes with tape | |
| Plastic drink bottles | |
| Other plastic bottles | |
| Styrofoam food containers | |
| Food waste | |
| Plastic shopping bags | |
| Plastic packaging materials | |
| Furniture | |
| Last year's course books | |
| Left-over paint | |

For Additional Help in Studying This Chapter, please visit our website at www.mhhe.com/cunningham6e. You will find practice quizzes, key terms, answers to end of chapter questions, additional case studies, an extensive reading list, and Google Earth™ mapping quizzes.

# 14 Economics and Urbanization

Car-free roads provide a cleaner, safer, healthier environment for residents of Vauban, Germany.

*What kind of world do you want to live in? Demand that your teachers teach you what you need to know to build it.*

— PETER KROPOTKIN

## Learning Outcomes

*After studying this chapter, you should be able to answer the following questions:*

- How have the size and location of the world's largest cities changed over the past century?
- Define *slum* and *shantytown*, and describe the conditions you might find in them.
- What is urban sprawl? How have automobiles contributed to sprawl?
- What are some principles of smart growth and new urbanism?
- Describe sustainable development and why it's important.
- What value do we get from free ecological services?
- What's the difference between GNP and GPI?
- What do we mean by internalizing external costs?

# CASE STUDY

## Vauban: A Car-free Suburb

What would it be like to live in a suburb without automobiles? Residents in the German town of Vauban are forging a new lifestyle that may serve as a model for other areas. Although cars aren't strictly banned in this affluent suburb of Freiburg near the German/Swiss border (fig. 14.1), people mostly go about their lives on foot, by bicycles, or on public transportation.

To make it convenient to live in Vauban without a car, the city is designed using "smart growth" principles with stores, banks, schools and restaurants mixed with homes so everything is within easy walking distance. Jobs and office space are available in the village, and a trolley with frequent connections to Freiburg runs down the main street and around the periphery of the village. Residential streets are narrow and vehicle free, making a great place for bicycles and playing children. Car ownership is allowed, but you have to park in a large municipal ramp at the edge of town, and buying a space there costs $40,000. Consequently, nearly three-quarters of Vauban's families don't own a car, and more than half sold their car to move there.

Fewer vehicles mean less air pollution and greater safety for pedestrians, but most families moved to Vauban, not for environmental reasons, but because they believe a car-free lifestyle is healthier for children. The narrow row houses put everything close together. Children can play outside or walk to school without having to cross busy streets. Outdoor cafés don't have to worry about the noise and fumes from passing traffic. For family vacations or moving furniture, a car-sharing service and rentals are available at the municipal garage.

Community events and shared spaces encourage humane, healthy lifestyles and community ties. Child-care services, entertainment and sports facilities were planned for when the community was designed. In most American cities, parking and transportation take up as much as one-third of all land. Think of what could be done with that space if it weren't devoted to automobiles.

Free-standing homes are prohibited in Vauban. Instead, housing is provided in stylish row houses designed to conserve energy but maximize quality of life. Clever use of space, lots of built-ins, beautiful woodwork, large balconies, and large, superinsulated windows make homes feel spacious while maintaining a small footprint. Just having shared walls minimizes energy losses. Many houses are so efficient that they don't need a heating system at all. Owning and operating a vehicle in Germany is expensive, so living a car-free lifestyle saves much money that can be put to use elsewhere.

Similar projects are being built across Europe and even in some developing countries, such as China. On Dongtan Island in the mouth of the Yangtze River near Shanghai, the Chinese government is planning an eco-city for 50,000 people that is expected to be energy, water, and food self-sufficient. In the United States, the Environmental Protection Agency is promoting "car reduced" communities. In California, for example, developers are planning a Vauban-like community called Quarry Village on the outskirts of Oakland, accessible to the Bay Area Rapid Transit system and to the California State University's campus in Hayward.

Decades of advertisements and government policies in the United States have persuaded most people that the dream home is a single-family residence on a spacious lot in the suburbs, where a car—regardless of the costs in energy use, insurance, accidents, or land consumption—is essential for every trip no matter how short the distance. Whether we can break those patterns remains to be seen.

Vauban illustrates a number of ways that we might live sustainably with our environment and our neighbors. In this chapter, we'll look at other aspects of city planning and urban environments as well as some principles of ecological economics that help us understand the nature of resources and the choices we face both as individuals and communities.

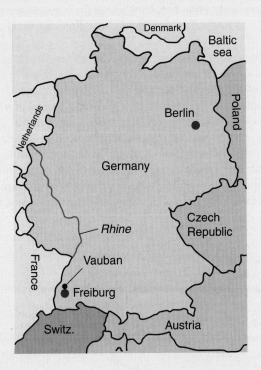

**Figure 14.1** Vauban is a suburb of Freiburg, Germany.

# 14.1 Cities Are Places of Crisis and Opportunity

More than half of humans now live in cities, and in the next quarter century that number will approach three-quarters of us. This is a dramatic change from all previous human history, in which most humans lived by hunting and gathering, farming, or fishing. Since the beginning of the industrial revolution about 300 years ago, cities have grown rapidly in both size and power (fig. 14.2). In 1950, 38 percent of the world's population lived in cities; by 2030 that proportion will nearly double (table 14.1).

The vast majority of urban growth will occur in less-developed countries (fig. 14.3). Populations in these cities are expanding far faster than infrastructure, including roads and transportation, housing, water supplies, sewage treatment, and schools, can possibly grow. Building new infrastructure is especially hard in poor countries, where incomes are low and tax collection is insufficient to support public services. Despite these challenges, cities are also places where innovation occurs. Ideas mix and experimentation

| Table 14.1 | Urban Share of Total Population (Percentage) | | |
|---|---|---|---|
| | **1950** | **2000** | **2030\*** |
| Africa | 18.4 | 40.6 | 57.0 |
| Asia | 19.3 | 43.8 | 59.3 |
| Europe | 56.0 | 75.0 | 81.5 |
| Latin America | 40.0 | 70.3 | 79.7 |
| North America | 63.9 | 77.4 | 84.5 |
| Oceania | 32.0 | 49.5 | 60.7 |
| World | 38.3 | 59.4 | 70.5 |

\*Projected.

*Source:* Data from United Nations Population Division, 2003.

happens in urban areas. Diverse employment opportunities and new economies arise in cities, as well as concentrations of poverty. Huge **urban agglomerations** (merging of multiple municipalities) are forming throughout the world. Some have become **megacities** (with populations over 10 million people). While these cities pave over vast landscapes and consume inconceivable amounts of resources, they are also relatively efficient in resource use. Environmental degradation would probably be much worse if that many people were spread across the countryside. Cities, for all their ills, are one of the places where we can learn new ways to live sustainably. New York City, one of the largest in the world, has established new codes for "green" building, for water conservation, and for recycling. More New Yorkers use public transportation and walk to work than in any other major American city.

Cities can be engines of economic progress and social reform. Some of the greatest promise for innovation comes from cities like Vauban, where innovative leaders can focus knowledge and resources on common problems. Cities can be efficient places to live, where mass transportation can move people around and goods and services are more readily available than in the country. Concentrating people in urban areas leaves open space available for farming and biodiversity. But cities can also be dumping grounds for poverty, pollution, and unwanted members of society. Providing

**Figure 14.2** In less than 20 years, Shanghai, China, has built Pudong, a new city of 1.5 million residents and 500 skyscrapers on former marshy farmland across the Huang Pu River from the historic city center. This kind of rapid urban growth is occurring in many developing countries.

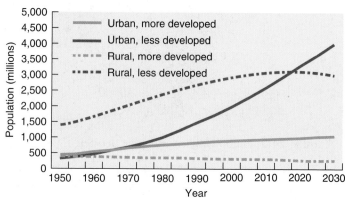

**Figure 14.3** Growth of urban and rural populations in more-developed regions and in less-developed regions. *Source:* United Nations Population Division. *World Urbanization Prospects*, 2004.

food, housing, transportation, jobs, clean water, and sanitation to the 2 or 3 billion new urban residents expected to crowd into cities—especially those in the developing world—in this century may be one of the preeminent challenges of this century.

As Vauban shows, there is much we can do to make our cities more livable. But what of poorer countries? What hope is there for them? Urban planning in the developing world represents one of the most important issues we face.

## Large cities are expanding rapidly

You can already see the dramatic shift in size and location of big cities. In 1900 only 13 cities in the world had populations over 1 million (table 14.2). All of those cities except Tokyo and Peking were in Europe or North America. London was the only city in the world with more than 5 million residents. By 2007, there were at least 300 cities—100 of them in China alone—with more than 1 million residents. Of the 13 largest of these metropolitan areas, none are in Europe. Only New York City and Los Angeles are in a developed country. By 2025, it's expected that at least 93 cities will have populations over 5 million, and three-fourths of those cities will be in developing countries (fig. 14.4). In just the next 25 years, Mumbai, India; Delhi, India; Karachi, Pakistan; Manila, Philippines; and Jakarta, Indonesia, all are expected to grow by at least 50 percent.

China represents the largest demographic shift in human history. Since the end of Chinese collectivized farming and factory work in 1986, around 250 million people have moved from rural areas to cities. And in the next 25 years an equal number is expected to join this vast exodus. In addition to expanding existing cities, China plans to build 400 new urban centers with populations of at least 500,000 over the next 20 years. Already at least

| Table 14.2 | The World's Largest Urban Areas (Populations in Millions) | | |
|---|---|---|---|
| **1900** | | **2015**** | |
| London, England | 6.6 | Tokyo, Japan | 31.0 |
| New York, USA | 4.2 | New York, USA | 29.9 |
| Paris, France | 3.3 | Mexico City | 21.0 |
| Berlin, Germany | 2.4 | Seoul, Korea | 19.8 |
| Chicago, USA | 1.7 | São Paulo, Brazil | 18.5 |
| Vienna, Austria | 1.6 | Osaka, Japan | 17.6 |
| Tokyo, Japan | 1.5 | Jakarta, Indonesia | 17.4 |
| St. Petersburg, Russia | 1.4 | Delhi, India | 16.7 |
| Philadelphia, USA | 1.4 | Los Angeles, USA | 16.6 |
| Manchester, England | 1.3 | Beijing, China | 16.0 |
| Birmingham, England | 1.2 | Cairo, Egypt | 15.5 |
| Moscow, Russia | 1.1 | Manila, Philippines | 13.5 |
| Peking, China* | 1.1 | Buenos Aires, Argentina | 12.9 |

*Now spelled Beijing.
**Projected.

*Source:* Data from T. Chandler, *Three Thousand Years of Urban Growth*, 1974, Academic Press; and *World Gazetter*, 2003.

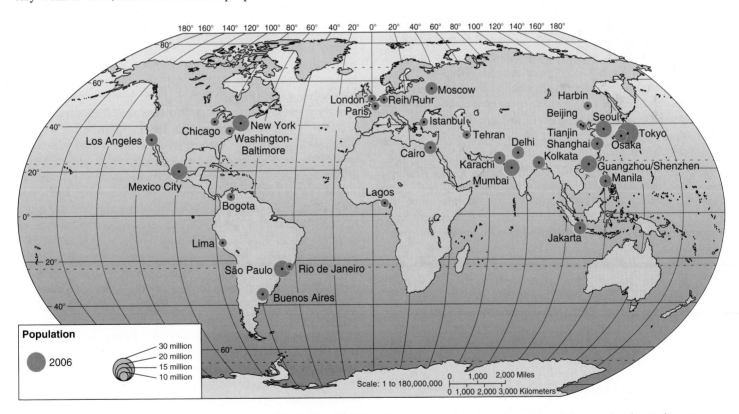

**Figure 14.4** Some of the world's largest urban agglomerations in 2006. Sizes of many of these metropolitan areas are only educated guesses. As much as half the population of some cities in developing countries can be undocumented migrant workers or shantytown residents who are difficult to count. Most population growth in this century is expected to be in the megacities of the developing world.

half of the concrete and one-third of the steel used in construction around the world each year is consumed in China.

Consider Shanghai, for example. In 1985, the city had a population of about 10 million. It's now about 19 million—including at least 4 million migrant laborers. In the past decade, Shanghai has built 4,000 skyscrapers (buildings with more than 25 floors). The city already has twice as many tall buildings as Manhattan, and proposals have been made for 1,000 more. The problem is that most of this growth has taken place in a swampy area called Pudong, across the Huang Pu River from the historic city center (see fig. 14.2). Pudong is now sinking about 1.5 cm per year due to groundwater drainage and the weight of so many buildings.

Other Chinese cities have plans for similar massive building projects to revitalize blighted urban areas. Harbin, a city of about 9 million people and the capital of Heilongjiang Province, for example, recently announced plans to relocate across the Songhua River on 740 km² (285 mi², or roughly the size of New York City) of former farmland. Residents hope these new towns will be both more livable for their residents and more ecologically sustainable than the old cities they're replacing. In 2005, the Chinese government signed a long-term contract with a British engineering firm to build at least five "eco-cities," each the size of a large Western capital. Plans call for these cities to be self-sufficient in energy, water, and most food products, with the aim of zero emissions of greenhouse gases from transportation.

## Immigration is driven by push and pull factors

People migrate to cities for many reasons. In China over the past 20 years—or in America during the twentieth century—mechanization eliminated jobs and drove people off the land. Where cropland is owned by a minority of wealthy landlords, as is the case in many developing countries, subsistence farmers are often ejected when new cash crops or cattle grazing become economically viable. Many people also move to the city because of the opportunities and independence offered there. Cities offer jobs, better housing, entertainment, and freedom from the constraints of village traditions. Possibilities exist in the city for upward social mobility, prestige, and power not ordinarily available in the country. Cities support specialization in arts, crafts, and professions for which markets don't exist elsewhere.

Government policies often favor urban over rural areas in ways that both push and pull people into cities. Developing countries commonly spend most of their budgets on improving urban areas (especially around the capital city, where leaders live). This gives the major cities a virtual monopoly on new jobs, housing, education, and finance, all of which bring in rural people searching for a better life. Lima, for example, has only 20 percent of Peru's population, but has 50 percent of the national wealth, 60 percent of the manufacturing, 65 percent of the retail trade, 73 percent of the industrial wages, and 90 percent of all banking in the country. Similar statistics pertain to many national capitals.

## Congestion, pollution, and water shortages plague many cities

First-time visitors to a supercity—particularly in a developing country—often are overwhelmed by the immense crush of pedestrians and vehicles of all sorts jostling for space in the streets. The noise,

**Figure 14.5** Motorized rickshaws, motor scooters, bicycles, street vendors, and pedestrians all vie for space on the crowded streets of Jakarta. The heat, noise, smells, and sights are overpowering. In spite of the difficulties of living here, people work hard and have hope for the future.

congestion, and confusion of traffic make it seem suicidal to venture onto the street. Jakarta, Indonesia, for instance, is one of the most densely populated cities in the world (fig. 14.5). Traffic is chaotic almost all the time. People often spend three or four hours each way commuting to work from outlying areas.

Pollution from burgeoning traffic and from unregulated factories degrades air quality in many urban areas. China's spectacular economic growth has resulted in a flood of private automobiles mainly in cities. Beijing, for instance, has doubled the number of cars on its streets in just the past five years to 4 million. China is now the world's largest producer of greenhouse gases, and the World Bank warns that it is home to 16 of the world's 20 cities with the worst air pollution. Chinese health authorities say that a third of the country's urban residents are exposed to harmful air pollution levels. They blame this pollution for more than 400,000 premature deaths each year.

Few cities in developing countries can afford to build modern waste treatment systems for their rapidly growing populations. The World Bank estimates that only one-third of urban residents in developing countries have satisfactory sanitation services. The 2010 earthquake in Haiti reminded us that Port au Prince is the largest city in the world with no sewer system. In Egypt, Cairo's sewer system was built about 50 years ago to serve a population of 2 million people. It's now being overwhelmed by more than five times that many residents. Less than 1 percent of India's 500,000 towns and villages have even partial sewage systems or water treatment facilities.

It's often difficult to find clean drinking water for urban areas. According to Qiu Baoxing, Chinese minister of construction, 70 percent of his country's surface water is so polluted by industrial

# What Do YOU Think?

## People for Community Recovery

The Lake Calumet Industrial District on Chicago's far South Side is an environmental disaster area. A heavily industrialized center of steel mills, oil refineries, railroad yards, coke ovens, factories, and waste disposal facilities, much of the site is now a marshy wasteland of landfills, toxic waste lagoons, and slag dumps, around a system of artificial ship channels.

At the southwest corner of this degraded district sits Altgeld Gardens, a low-income public housing project built in the late 1940s by the Chicago Housing Authority. The 2,000 units of "The Gardens" or "The Projects," as they are called by the largely minority residents, are low-rise row-houses, many of which are vacant or in poor repair. But residents of Altgeld Gardens are doing something about their neighborhood. People for Community Recovery (PCR) is a grassroots citizen's group organized to work for a clean environment, better schools, decent housing, and job opportunities for the Lake Calumet neighborhood.

PCR was founded in 1982 by Mrs. Hazel Johnson, an Altgeld Gardens resident whose husband died from cancer that may have been pollution-related. PCR has worked to clean up more than two dozen waste sites and contaminated properties in their immediate vicinity. Often this means challenging authorities to follow established rules and enforce existing statutes. Public protests, leafleting, and community meetings have been effective in public education about the dangers of toxic wastes and have helped gain public support for cleanup projects. PCR's efforts successfully blocked construction of new garbage and hazardous waste landfills, transfer stations, and incinerators in the Lake Calumet district. Pollution prevention programs have been established at plants still in operation. And PCR helped set up a community monitoring program to stop illegal dumping and to review toxic inventory data from local companies.

Education is an important priority for PCR. An environmental education center administered by community members organizes workshops, seminars, fact sheets, and outreach for citizens and local businesses. A public health education and screening program has been set up to improve community health. Partnerships have been established with nearby Chicago State University to provide technical assistance and training in environmental issues.

PCR also works on economic development. Environmentally responsible products and services are now available to residents. Jobs are being created as green businesses are brought into the community. Wherever possible, local people and minority contractors from the area are hired to clean

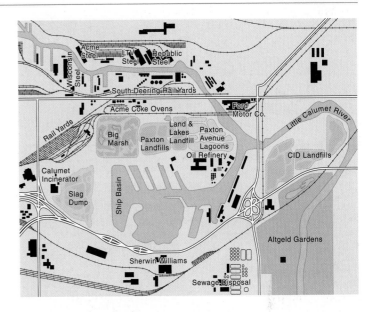

The Calumet industrial district in South Chicago.

up waste sites and restore abandoned buildings. Job training for youth and adults as well as retraining for displaced workers is a high priority.

In the 1980s, a young community organizer named Barack Obama worked with PCR on jobs creation, housing issues, and education. He credits the lessons he learned there for much of his subsequent political successes. In his best-selling memoir, *Dreams from My Father,* Obama devotes more than 100 pages to his formative experiences at Altgeld Gardens and other nearby neighborhoods.

PCR and Mrs. Johnson have received many awards for their fight against environmental racism and despair. In 1992, PCR was the recipient of the President's Environmental and Conservation Challenge Award. PCR is the only African-American grassroots organization in the country to receive this prestigious award.

Although Altgeld Gardens is far from clean, much progress has been made. Perhaps the most important accomplishment is community education and empowerment. Residents have learned how and why they need to work together to improve their living conditions. Could these same lessons be useful in your city or community? What could you do to help improve urban environments where you live?

---

toxins, human waste, and agricultural chemicals that it is unsuited for human consumption. One hundred of China's 660 cities face severe water shortages, he reported. Worldwide, according to the United Nations, at least 1.1 billion people don't have safe drinking water, and twice that many don't have adequate sanitation. It may not be so bad to have primitive sanitation if you live in a sparsely populated rural area, but imagine what it's like to live in a densely crowded megacity, such as Jakarta, with 10 million people, fewer than half of whom are served by a municipal sanitary system.

Pollution isn't limited to the developing world, however. Many cities in industrialized countries have a tragic heritage

of pollution and abandoned factories (see What Do You Think? on this page). But community organizing can make a difference.

## Many cities lack sufficient housing

The United Nations estimates that at least 1 billion people live in crowded, unsanitary slums of the central cities or in the vast shantytowns and squatter settlements that ring the outskirts of most major cities in the developing world. Around 100 million people have no home at all. In Mumbai (formerly Bombay), India, for example, it's estimated that half a million people sleep on the

**Figure 14.6** In Mumbai, India, as many as half a million people sleep on the streets because they have no other place to live. Ten times as many live in crowded, dangerous slums and shantytowns throughout the city.

**Figure 14.7** Shantytowns called *favelas* perch on hillsides above Rio de Janeiro.

streets, sidewalks, and traffic circles because they can find no other place to live (fig. 14.6).

**Slums** are generally legal but inadequate multifamily tenements or rooming houses, often converted from some other use. Families live crowded in small rooms with inadequate ventilation and sanitation. Often these structures are rickety and unsafe. In 1999, for example, a 7.4 magnitude earthquake hit eastern Turkey, killing more than 14,000 people when shoddy, poorly built apartments collapsed.

**Shantytowns**, with shacks built of corrugated metal, discarded packing crates, brush, plastic sheets, and other scavenged materials, grow on the outskirts of many cities in the developing world. They can house millions of people but generally lack clean water, sanitation, or safe electrical power. Shantytowns are usually illegal, but they quickly fill in the empty space in towns where squatters can build shelters close to jobs. With little or no public services, shantytowns often fill with trash and debris. Many governments try to clean out illegal settlements by torching or bulldozing the huts and sending riot police to drive out residents, but people either move back in or relocate to another shantytown. In 2005, the government of Zimbabwe destroyed the homes of some 700,000 people in shantytowns around the capital of Harare.

Families were evicted in the middle of the night during the coldest weather of the year, often with only minutes to gather their belongings. President Robert Mugabe justified this blitzkreig as necessary to control crime, but critics claimed it was mainly to remove political opponents.

Two-thirds of the population of Kolkata are thought to live in unplanned squatter settlements, and nearly half the 25 million residents of Mexico City occupy the unauthorized *colonias* around the city. Often, shantytowns occupy the most polluted, dangerous parts of cities where no one else wants to live. In Bhopal, India, and Mexico City, for example, squatter settlements were built next to deadly industrial sites. In Brazil, shantytowns called *favelas* perch on steep hillsides unwanted for other building (fig. 14.7). As desperate and inhumane as conditions are in these slums and shantytowns, many people do more than merely survive there. They work hard, raise families, educate their children, and often improve their living standard little by little as they make some money.

Many countries are recognizing that the only way they can house all their citizens is to cooperate with shantytown dwellers. Recognizing land rights, providing financing for home improvements, and supporting community efforts to provide water, sewers, and power can greatly improve living conditions for many poor people.

## 14.2 Urban Planning

How can we live together in cities in ways that are environmentally sound, socially just, and economically sustainable? Starting with Greek cities thousands of years ago, planners have debated the best ways for us to organize ourselves.

### Transportation is crucial in city development

Most of the world's major cities grew up around a port, a river crossing, a railroad hub, or some other focal point for transportation. Often, those original reasons for city placement no longer apply, and a location that made sense for a small, backwoods community no longer works for a major metropolitan center.

Getting people around within a large urban area has become one of the most difficult problems that many city officials face. A century ago, most American cities were organized around transportation corridors. First horse-drawn carriages, then electric streetcars provided a way for people to get to work, school, and shops. Everyone, rich or poor, wanted to live as close to the city center as possible, and within easy walking distance of the trolley or streetcar line. When Henry Ford introduced the first affordable, mass-produced automobile, it allowed people to build houses on larger lots in areas served only by streets. Freeway construction, which began in America in the 1950s, allowed people to move even farther out into the country. Cities that were once compact began to spread over the landscape, consuming space and wasting resources. This pattern of development is known as **sprawl**. While there is no universally accepted definition of the term, sprawl generally includes the characteristics outlined in table 14.3.

In most American metropolitan areas, the bulk of new housing is in large, tract developments that leapfrog out beyond the city edge in a search for inexpensive rural land with few restrictions on land use or building practices (fig. 14.8). The U.S. Department of Housing and Urban Development estimates that urban sprawl consumes some 200,000 ha (roughly 500,000 acres) of farmland and open space every year. Although the price of

**Figure 14.8** Huge houses on sprawling lots consume land, alienate us from our neighbors, and make us ever more dependent on automobiles. © 2003 Regents of the University of Minnesota. All rights reserved. Used with permission of the Design Center for American Urban Landscape.

tract homes often is less than comparable urban property, there are external costs in the form of new roads, sewers, water mains, power lines, schools, shopping centers, and other infrastructure required by this low-density development. Ironically, people who move to the country to escape from urban problems such as congestion, crime, and pollution often find that they have simply brought those problems with them.

Because many Americans live far from where they work, shop, or recreate, they consider it essential to own a private automobile. The average U.S. driver spends 443 hours per year behind a steering wheel, or the equivalent of one full 8-hour day per week in an automobile. The freeway system was designed to allow drivers to travel at high speeds from source to destination without ever having to stop (fig 14.9). As more and more vehicles clog highways, however, the reality is far different. In Los Angeles, for example, which has the worst congestion in the United States, the average speed in 1982 was 58 mph (93 kph), and the average driver spent less than 4 hours per year in traffic jams. In 2004, the average speed was only 35.6 mph (57.3 kph), and the typical driver spent 97 hours in bumper-to-bumper traffic.

Altogether, it's estimated that traffic congestion costs the United States $78 billion per year in wasted time and fuel. Some people argue that the existence of traffic jams in cities shows that more highways are needed. Often, however, building more traffic lanes simply encourages more people to drive farther and put more cars on the road. Meanwhile, about one-third of Americans are too young, too old, or too poor to drive. For these people, car-oriented development causes isolation and makes daily tasks like grocery shopping difficult. Parents spend long hours transporting young children. Teenagers and aging grandparents are forced to drive, often presenting a hazard on public roads.

As the opening case study for this chapter shows, it's possible to build cities without private autos. Most European urban areas have good mass transit systems that have allowed them to preserve historic city centers and remain relatively compact while avoiding the sprawl engendered by an American-style freeway system.

| Table 14.3 | Characteristics of Urban Sprawl |
| --- |
| 1. Unlimited outward extension |
| 2. Low-density residential and commercial development |
| 3. Leapfrog development that consumes farmland and natural areas |
| 4. Fragmentation of power among many small units of government |
| 5. Dominance of freeways and private automobiles |
| 6. No centralized planning or control of land uses |
| 7. Widespread strip-malls and "big-box" shopping centers |
| 8. Great fiscal disparities among localities |
| 9. Reliance on deteriorating older neighborhoods for low-income housing |
| 10. Decaying city centers as new development occurs in previously rural areas |

*Source:* Data from PlannersWeb, Burlington, Vermont, 2001.

**Figure 14.9** Freeways give us the illusion of speed and privacy, but they consume land, encourage sprawl, and create congestion as people move farther from the city to get away from traffic and then have to drive to get anywhere.

Many American cities are now rebuilding the public transportation systems that were abandoned in the 1950s (fig. 14.10). Consider how different your life might be if you lived an automobile-free life in a city with good mass transit.

Vehicle fleets are expanding rapidly, however, in many developing countries and traffic accidents have become the third largest cause of years of lost life worldwide. For example, the number of vehicles increased eight-fold in Nigeria and six-fold in Pakistan between 1980 and 2000, while the road network in those countries expanded by only 10 to 20 percent in the same time. The recent introduction of the Tata Nano in India raises nightmares for both urban planners and energy experts. Costing less than $2,000 brand new, these tiny vehicles put car ownership within reach for millions who could never afford it before. But they will probably increase petrol consumption greatly and result in huge traffic jams as inexperienced drivers take to the road for the first time.

A famous example of successful mass transit is found in Curitiba, Brazil. High-speed, bi-articulated buses, each of which can carry 270 passengers, travel on dedicated roadways closed to all other vehicles. These bus-trains are linked to 340 feeder routes extending throughout the city. Everyone in the city is within walking distance of a bus stop that has frequent, convenient,

affordable service. Curitiba's buses carry some 1.9 million passengers per day or about three-quarters of all personal trips within the city. Working with existing roadways for the most part, the city was able to construct this system for one-tenth the cost of a light rail system or freeway system, and one-hundredth the cost of a subway.

## We can make our cities more livable

Are there alternatives to unplanned sprawl and wasteful resource use? One option proposed by many urban planners is **smart growth**, which makes effective use of land resources and existing infrastructure by encouraging in-fill development that avoids costly duplication of services and inefficient land use (table 14.4). Smart growth aims to provide a mix of land uses to create a variety of affordable housing choices and opportunities. It also attempts to provide a variety of transportation choices, including pedestrian-friendly neighborhoods. This approach to planning also seeks to maintain a unique sense of place by respecting local cultural and natural features.

By making land-use planning open and democratic, smart growth makes urban expansion fair, predictable, and cost-effective. All stakeholders are encouraged to participate in creating a vision for the city and to collaborate with rather than confront each other. Goals are established for staged and managed growth in urban transition areas with compact development patterns. This approach is not opposed to growth. It recognizes that the goal is not to block growth but to channel it to areas where it can be sustained over the long term. Smart growth strives to enhance access to equitable public and private resources for everyone and to promote the safety, livability, and revitalization of existing urban and rural communities.

Smart growth protects environmental quality. It tries to reduce traffic and to conserve farmlands, wetlands, and open space. As cities

**Figure 14.10** Many American cities are now rebuilding light rail systems that were abandoned in the 1950s when freeways were built. Light rail is energy efficient and popular, but it can cost up to $100 million per mile ($60 million per kilometer).

| Table 14.4 | Goals for Smart Growth |
| --- |
| 1. Create a positive self-image for the community. |
| 2. Make the downtown vital and livable. |
| 3. Alleviate substandard housing. |
| 4. Solve problems with air, water, toxic waste, and noise pollution. |
| 5. Improve communication between groups. |
| 6. Improve community member access to the arts. |

*Source:* Data from Vision 2000, Chattanooga, Tennessee.

grow and transportation and communications enable more community interaction, the need for regional planning becomes greater and more pressing. Community and business leaders must make decisions based on a clear understanding of regional growth needs and how infrastructure can be built most efficiently and for the greatest good.

One of the best examples of successful urban land-use planning in the United States is Portland, Oregon, which has rigorously enforced a boundary on its outward expansion, requiring instead that development be focused on in-filling unused space within the city limits. Because of its many urban amenities, Portland is considered one of the best cities in America. Between 1970 and 1990 the Portland population grew by 50 percent, but its total land area grew only 2 percent. During this time, Portland property taxes decreased 29 percent and vehicle miles traveled increased only 2 percent. By contrast, Atlanta, which had similar population growth, experienced an explosion of urban sprawl that increased its land area three-fold, drove up property taxes 22 percent, and increased traffic miles by 17 percent. A result of this expanding traffic and increasing congestion was that Atlanta's air pollution increased by 5 percent, while Portland, which has one of the best public transit systems in the nation, saw a decrease of 86 percent.

## New urbanism incorporates smart growth

Rather than abandon the cultural history and infrastructure investment in existing cities, a group of architects and urban planners is attempting to redesign metropolitan areas to make them more appealing, efficient, and livable. Vauban, Germany, described in the opening case study for this chapter follows many of these principles of green design and smart growth. Other European cities such as Stockholm, Sweden; Helsinki, Finland; Leichester, England; and Neerlands, the Netherlands, have a long history of innovative urban planning. In the United States, Andres Duany, Elizabeth Plater-Zyberk, Peter Calthorpe, and Sym Van Der Ryn have been leaders in this movement. Using what is sometimes called a neo-traditionalist approach, these designers attempt to recapture some of the best features of small towns and livable cities of the past. They are designing urban neighborhoods that integrate houses, offices, shops, and civic buildings. Ideally, no house should be more than a five-minute walk from a neighborhood center with a convenience store, a coffee shop, a bus stop, and other amenities. A mix of apartments, townhouses, and detached houses in a variety of price ranges ensures that neighborhoods will include a diversity of ages and income levels (see A Closer Look, p. 350). Some design principles of this movement include:

- Limit city size or organize cities in modules of 30,000 to 50,000 people—large enough to be a complete city but small enough to be a community.

- Maintain greenbelts in and around cities. These provide recreational space and promote efficient land use, as well as help ameliorate air and water pollution.

- Determine in advance where development will take place. This protects property values and prevents chaotic development. Planning can also protect historical sites, agricultural resources, and ecological services of wetlands, clean rivers, and groundwater replenishment.

- Locate everyday shopping and services so people can meet daily needs with greater convenience, less stress, less automobile dependency, and less use of time and energy (fig. 14.11). This might be accomplished by encouraging small-scale commercial development in or close to residential areas.

- Encourage walking or the use of small, low-speed, energy-efficient vehicles (microcars, motorized tricycles, bicycles, etc.) for many local trips now performed in full-size automobiles. Creating special traffic lanes, reducing the number or size of parking spaces, and closing shopping streets to big cars might encourage such alternatives.

- Promote more diverse, flexible housing as an alternative to conventional detached, single-family houses. In-fill building between existing houses saves energy, reduces land costs, and might help provide a variety of living arrangements. Allowing single-parent families or groups of unrelated adults to share housing and to use facilities cooperatively also provides alternatives to those not living in a traditional nuclear family.

**Figure 14.11** This walking street in Queenstown, New Zealand, provides opportunities for shopping, dining, and socializing in a pleasant outdoor setting.

# What makes a city green?

CL 14.1

**Efficiency.** Over half of humans now live in cities. Environmental scientists have often criticized cities for expanding into farmland (▶) and for their tremendous consumption of energy, water, food, concrete, and land. But the environmental cost per person is usually lower for urban living than for suburban or rural living, especially in wealthy countries. Because they are compact, cities require fewer miles of roads, water and sewer lines, less heating, and fewer private cars per household. Because distances are shorter, roads and utility infrastructure are shared, apartments or row houses share heat, and public transportation reduces the need for driving to work.

Polluted cities can be unhealthy, but well organized cities can provide cultural resources and preserve environmental resources in many beneficial ways.

**Here are 10 features that make cities healthy for people and the environment.**

CL 14.2

## 1. Public transit

◀ High-density areas can afford to support reliable, efficient transit systems, where many riders share the cost of getting around, such as this bus-rapid transit system in Curitiba, Brazil. Public transit uses far less space, energy, and materials than does private travel.

CL 14.3a

## 2. Safe walking and bike routes

Freedom from dependence on cars increases mobility for young people, old people, and others without cars. Cities with separated walk-ways and bikeways are friendly for children and families; they also provide exercise and save money. ▶

CL 14.3b

## 3. Compact building

CL 14.4

A compact urban design greatly increases efficiency of land use, reduces transit distances, and increases heating or cooling efficiency, as buildings share walls. Reduced dependence on cars, and car sharing, can help control the problem of parking shortages.

◀ *Amsterdam's row houses give the city its historic identity as well as efficiency.*

CL 14.6

## 4. Mixed-use planning

CL 14.5

Integrating housing with shopping, entertainment, and office space provides jobs and services where people live. These neighborhoods can encourage walking and build community, as people spend less time in travel to shopping and work.

◀ *A used bookstore and cafe share space with housing in the historic city center of Trondheim, Norway.*

## 10. Farmland conservation

Sprawling suburbs gobble up farmland, woodlands, and wetlands. This is the fastest type of land-use change in most developing countries. Compact cities minimize destruction of farmland, habitat, recreational space, and watersheds. ▼

CL 14.8

CL 14.7

## 9. Local food

Local farm economies are more viable if farmers can sell direct to consumers—something that is much easier where there are lots of buyers in one place. Cities have become an essential income source for many produce farmers.

*The St. Johnsbury, Vermont farmer's market provides fresh, locally grown food for urban residents.* ▲

CL 14.9

## 8. Energy efficiency

Alternative energy is easier to use right at the source. Rooftop solar energy, district heating, and other strategies aid efficiency.

◄ *This biomass-burning plant in Copenhagen, and others like it, provide nearly all heating for Denmark's major cities.*

CL 14.10

## 7. Green infrastructure

New techniques moderate the impact of impervious surfaces, including permeable pavement, green roofs, and better building design.

*A "green" parking lot in Chengdu, China supports both traffic and vegetation, allowing rainfall to percolate into the ground.* ▶

CL 14.11

## 6. Recycling programs

Recycling collection is easiest where transportation is minimal and where recyclable materials are abundant.

*These bins in Kuala Lumpur, Malaysia accept all kinds of recyclables.* ▶

## 5. Green space

Recreational space has physical and emotional benefits for urban residents. Living vegetation and soils cool the local microclimate, store nutrients and moisture, and provide habitat for birds and other wildlife.

◄ *Here a visitor watches skaters in New York's Central Park.*

### Can You Explain:

1. What factors can make per capita energy use low in urban areas?

2. Which of the green factors listed would be easiest to enhance where you live? Why?

3. Which do you find most and least appealing? Why?

**Figure 14.12** Many cities have large amounts of unused open space that could be used to grow food. Residents often need help decontaminating soil and gaining access to the land.

- Make cities more self-sustainable by growing food locally, recycling wastes and water, using renewable energy sources, reducing noise and pollution, and creating a cleaner, safer environment. Encourage community gardening (fig. 14.12). Reclaimed inner-city space or a greenbelt of agricultural and forestland around the city provides food and open space, and also contributes valuable ecological services, such as purifying air, supplying clean water, and protecting wildlife habitat and recreation land.

- Equip buildings with "green roofs" or rooftop gardens that improve air quality, conserve energy, reduce stormwater runoff, reduce noise, and help reduce urban heat island effects. Intensive gardens can include large trees, shrubs, flowers, and may require regular maintenance (fig. 14.13). Extensive gardens require less soil, add less weight to the building, and usually have simple plantings of prairie plants or drought-resistant species, such as sedum, that require minimum care. They can last twice as long as conventional roofs. In Europe more than 1 million $m^2$ of green roofs are installed every year. Urban roofs are also a good place for solar collectors or wind turbines.

- Plan cluster housing, or open-space zoning, which preserves at least half of a subdivision as natural areas, farmland, or other forms of open space. Studies have shown that people who move to the country don't necessarily want to live miles from the nearest neighbor; what they most desire is long views across an interesting landscape and an opportunity to see wildlife. By carefully clustering houses on smaller lots, a conservation subdivision can provide the same number of buildable lots as a conventional subdivision and still preserve 50 to 70 percent of the land as open space (fig. 14.14). This not only reduces development costs (less distance to build roads, lay telephone lines, sewers, power cables, etc.), but also helps to foster a greater sense of community among new residents.

- Preserve urban habitat. It can make a significant contribution toward saving biodiversity as well as improving mental health and giving us access to nature.

These planning principles aren't just a matter of aesthetics. Dr. Richard Jackson, former director of the National Center for Environmental Health in Atlanta, points out a strong association between urban design and our mental and physical health. As our cities have become ever more spread out and impersonal, we have fewer opportunities for healthful exercise and socializing. Chronic diseases, such as cardiovascular diseases, asthma, diabetes, obesity, and depression, are becoming the predominant health concerns in the United States.

"Despite common knowledge that exercise is healthful," Dr. Jackson says, "fewer than 40% of adults are regularly active, and 25% do no physical activity at all. The way we design our communities makes us increasingly dependent on automobiles for the shortest trip, and recreation has become not physical but observational." Long commutes and a lack of reliable mass transit and walkable neighborhoods mean that we spend more and more time in stressful road congestion. "Road rage" isn't imaginary. Every commuter can describe unpleasant encounters with rude drivers. Urban design that offers the benefits of more walking, more social contact, and surroundings that include water and vegetation can provide healthful physical exercise and psychic respite.

## 14.3 Economics and Sustainable Development

Like many of our environmental issues, improving urban conditions will ultimately be decided by economics and policy decisions. We'll discuss policy in chapter 15. In the next half of this chapter, we'll review some of the principles of environmental economics.

**Figure 14.13** This award-winning green roof on the Chicago City Hall is functional as well as beautiful. It reduces rain runoff by about 50 percent, and keeps the surface as much as 30°F cooler than a conventional roof on hot summer days.

**Figure 14.14** This conservation development clusters houses on one-third of its property, and the rest is preserved as native prairie and oak woodland. Being close together, neighbors develop a sense of community, yet everyone has expansive views and access to open space.

## Can development be sustainable?

By now it is clear that security and living standards for the world's poorest people are inextricably linked to environmental protection. One of the most important questions in environmental science is how we can continue improvements in human welfare within the limits of the earth's natural resources. *Development* means improving people's lives. *Sustainability* means living on the earth's renewable resources without damaging the ecological processes that support us all. **Sustainable development** is an effort to marry these two ideas. A popular definition describes this goal as "meeting the needs of the present without compromising the ability of future generations to meet their own needs."

But is this possible? As you've learned elsewhere in this book, many people argue that our present population and economic levels are exhausting the world's resources. There's no way, they insist, that more people can live at a higher standard without irreversibly degrading our environment. Others claim that there's enough for everyone if we just share equitably and live modestly. Let's look a little deeper into this important debate.

## Our definitions of resources shape how we use them

To understand the problems and promise of sustainability, you need to understand the different kinds of resources we use. The way we treat resources depends largely on how we view and define them. **Classical economics**, developed in the 1700s by philosophers such as Adam Smith (1723–1790) and Thomas Malthus (1766–1834), assumes that natural resources are finite—that resources such as iron, gold, water, and land exist in fixed amounts. According to this view, as populations grow, scarcity of these resources reduces quality of life, increases competition, and ultimately causes populations to fall again. In a free market, where fully informed buyers and

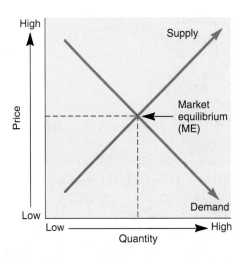

**Figure 14.15** Classic supply/demand curves. When price is low, supply is low and demand is high. As prices rise, supply increases but demand falls. Market equilibrium is the price at which supply and demand are equal.

sellers make free, independent decisions to buy and sell, the price of a pound of butter depends on the supply of available butter (it is cheap when plenty is available) and the demand for butter (buyers pay more when they must compete to get the resource, fig. 14.15).

This price mechanism has been modified by the idea of **marginal costs**. Buyers and sellers evaluate the added return for buying (or making and selling) slightly more of a product, or the marginal cost of slightly greater production or purchase. If the return is greater than the marginal cost, then a sale is made.

The nineteenth-century economist John Stuart Mill assumed that most resources are finite, but he developed the idea of a **steady-state economy**. Rather than boom-and-bust cycles of population and resource use, as envisioned by Malthus, Mill proposed that economies can achieve an equilibrium of resource use and production. Intellectual and moral development continues, he argued, once this stable, secure state is achieved.

**Neoclassical economics**, developed in the nineteenth century, expanded the idea of resources to include labor, knowledge, and capital. Labor and knowledge are resources because they are necessary to create goods and services; they are not finite because every new person can add more labor and energy to an economy. **Capital** is any form of wealth that contributes to the production of more wealth. Money can be invested to produce more money. Mineral resources can be developed and manufactured into goods that return more money. Economists distinguish several kinds of capital:

1. Natural capital: goods and services provided by nature
2. Human capital: knowledge, experience, human enterprise
3. Manufactured (built) capital: tools, buildings, roads, technology

To this list some social theorists would add social capital, the shared values, trust, cooperation, and organization that can develop in a group of people but cannot exist in one individual alone.

Because the point of capital is the production of more capital (that is, wealth), neoclassical economics emphasizes the idea of growth. Growth results from the flow of resources, goods, and services

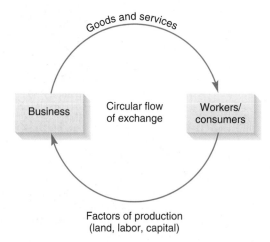

**Figure 14.16** The neoclassical model of the economy focuses on the flow of goods, services, and factors of production (land, labor, capital) between business and individual workers/consumers. The social and environmental consequences of these relationships are irrelevant in this view.

(fig. 14.16). Continued growth is always necessary for continued prosperity, according to this view. Natural resources contribute to production and growth, but they are not critical supplies that limit growth. They are not limiting because resources are considered to be interchangeable and substitutable. As one resource becomes scarce, neoclassical economics predicts that a substitute will be found.

Since production of wealth is central to neoclassical economics, an important measure of growth and wealth is consumption. If a society consumes more oil, more minerals, and more food, it is presumably becoming wealthier. This idea has extended to the idea of *throughput*, the amount of resources a society uses and discards. More throughput is a measure of greater consumption and greater wealth, according to this view. Throughput is commonly measured in terms of **gross national product (GNP)**, the sum of all products and services bought and sold in an economy. Because GNP includes activities of offshore companies, economists sometimes prefer **gross domestic product (GDP)**, which more accurately reflects the local economy by accounting for only those goods and services bought and sold locally.

**Natural resource economics** extends the neoclassical viewpoint to treat natural resources as important waste sinks (absorbers), as well as sources of raw materials. Natural capital (resources) is considered more abundant, and therefore cheaper, than built or human-made capital.

## Ecological economics incorporates principles of ecology

**Ecological economics** applies ecological ideas of system functions and recycling to the definition of resources. This school of thought also recognizes efficiency in nature, and it acknowledges the importance of ecosystem functions for the continuation of human economies and cultures. In nature, one species' waste is another's food, so that nothing is wasted. We need an economy that recycles materials and uses energy efficiently, much as a biological community does. Ecological economics also treats the natural environment as part of

**Table 14.5 | Important Ecological Services**

We depend on our environment to continually provide:

1. A regulated global energy balance and climate; chemical composition of the atmosphere and oceans; water catchment and groundwater recharge; production and recycling of organic and inorganic materials; maintenance of biological diversity.

2. Space and suitable substrates for human habitation, crop cultivation, energy conversion, recreation, and nature protection.

3. Oxygen, fresh water, food, medicine, fuel, fodder, fertilizer, building materials, and industrial inputs.

4. Aesthetic, spiritual, historic, cultural, artistic, scientific, and educational opportunities and information.

*Source:* Data from R. S. de Groot, *Investing in Natural Capital*, 1994.

our economy, so that natural capital becomes a key consideration in economic calculations. Ecological functions, such as absorbing and purifying wastewater, processing air pollution, providing clean water, carrying out photosynthesis, and creating soil, are known as **ecological services** (table 14.5). These services are free: we don't pay for them directly (although we often pay indirectly when we suffer from their absence). Therefore, they are often excluded from conventional economic accounting, a situation that ecological economists attempt to rectify (fig. 14.17).

Many ecological economists also promote the idea of a steady-state economy. As with John Stuart Mill's original conception of steady states, these economists argue that economic health can be maintained without constantly growing consumption and throughput. Instead, efficiency and recycling of resources can allow steady prosperity where there is little or no population growth. Low birth rates and death rates (like *K*-adapted species, see chapter 3), political and social stability, and reliance on renewable energy would characterize such a steady-state economy. Like Mill, these economists argue that human and social capital—knowledge, happiness, art, life expectancies, and

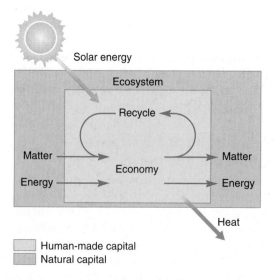

**Figure 14.17** An ecological economics view considers natural capital and recycling integral to the economy. Human-made capital is created using limited supplies of natural capital. *Source:* Data from Herman Daly in A. M. Jansson et al., *Investing in Natural Capital*, ISEE.

cooperation—can continue to grow even without constant expansion of resource use.

Both ecological economics and neoclassical economics distinguish between renewable and nonrenewable resources. **Nonrenewable resources** exist in finite amounts: minerals, fossil fuels, and also groundwater that recharges extremely slowly are all fixed, at least on a human timescale. **Renewable resources** are naturally replenished and recycled at a fairly steady rate. Fresh water, living organisms, air, and food resources are all renewable (fig. 14.18).

These categories are important, but they are not as deterministic as you might think. Nonrenewable resources, such as iron and gold, can be extended through more efficient use: cars now use less steel than they once did, and gold is mixed in alloys to extend its use. Substitution also reduces demand for these resources: car parts once made of iron are now made of plastic and ceramics; copper wire, once stockpiled to provide phone lines, is now being replaced with cheap, lightweight fiber-optic cables made from silica (sand). Recycling also extends supplies of nonrenewable resources. Aluminum, platinum, gold, silver, and many other valuable metals are routinely recycled now, further reducing the demand for extracting new sources. The only limit to recycling is usually the relative costs of extracting new resources compared with collecting used materials. Recoverable sources of nonrenewable resources are also expanded by technological improvements. New methods make it possible to mine very dilute metal ores, for example. Gold ore of extremely low concentrations is now economically recoverable—that is, you can make money on it—even though the price of gold has fallen because of greater efficiency, more discoveries, and resource substitution. Scarcity of resources, seen by classical economists as the trigger for conflict and suffering, can actually provide the impetus for much of the innovation that leads to substitution, recycling, and efficiency.

On the other hand, renewable resources can become exhausted if they are managed badly. This is especially apparent in biological resources, such as the passenger pigeon, American bison, and Atlantic cod. All these species once existed in extraordinary numbers, but within a few years, each was brought to the brink of extinction (or eliminated entirely) by overharvesting.

## Scarcity can lead to innovation

Are we about to run out of essential natural resources? It stands to reason that, if we consume a fixed supply of nonrenewable resources at a constant rate, we'll eventually use up all the economically recoverable reserves. There are many warnings in the environmental literature that our extravagant depletion of nonrenewable resources sooner or later will result in catastrophe, misery, and social decay. Models for exploitation rates of nonrenewable resources—called Hubbert curves after Stanley Hubbert, who developed them—often closely match historic experience for natural resource depletion (fig. 14.19).

Many economists, however, contend that human ingenuity and enterprise often allow us to respond to scarcity in ways that postpone or alleviate dire effects of resource use. The question of whether this view is right has to do with the important theme of **limits to growth**.

In the early 1970s an influential study of resource limitations was funded by the Club of Rome, an organization of wealthy business owners and influential politicians. The study was carried out by a team of scientists, from the Massachusetts Institute of Technology, headed by Donnela Meadows. The results of this study were published in the 1972 book *Limits to Growth*. A complex computer model of the world economy was used to examine various scenarios of different resource depletion rates, growing population, pollution, and industrial output. Given the Malthusian assumptions built into this model, catastrophic social and environmental collapse seemed inescapable.

**Figure 14.18** Biological resources are renewable in that they replace themselves by reproduction, but if overused or misused, populations die. If a species is lost, it cannot be re-created. It is permanently lost as a component of its ecosystem and as a resource to humans.

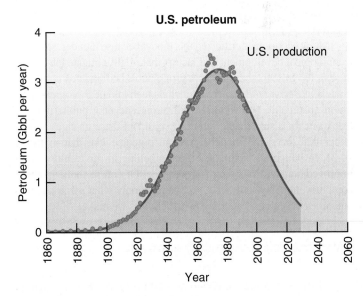

**Figure 14.19** U.S. petroleum production. Dots indicate actual production. The bell-shaped curve is a theoretical Hubbert curve for a nonrenewable resource. The shaded area under the curve, representing 220 Gbbl (Gbbl [equals] Gigabarrels or billions of standard 42-gallon barrels), is an estimate of the total economically recoverable resource.

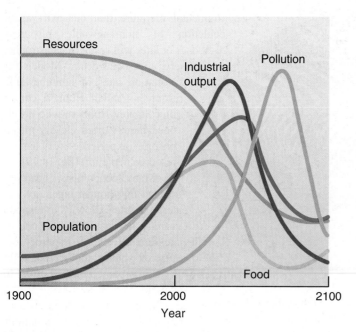

**Figure 14.20** A run of one of the world models in *Limits to Growth*. This model assumes business-as-usual for as long as possible until Malthusian limits cause industrial society to crash. Notice that pollution continues to increase well after industrial output, food supplies, and population have all plummeted.

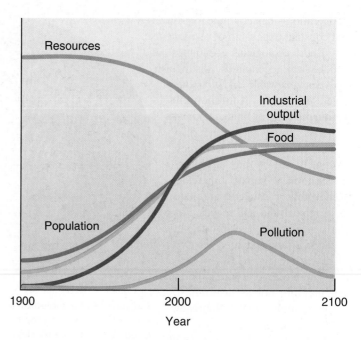

**Figure 14.21** A run of the world model from *Beyond the Limits*. This model assumes that population and consumption are curbed, new technologies are introduced, and sustainable environmental policies are embraced immediately, rather than after resources are exhausted.

Figure 14.20 shows an example of the world model, that is, the output from one run of the model. Food supplies and industrial output rise as population grows and resources are consumed. Once past the carrying capacity of the environment, however, a crash occurs as population, food production, and industrial output all decline precipitously. Pollution continues to grow as society decays and people die, but eventually it also falls. Notice the similarity between this set of curves and the "boom-and-bust" population cycles described in chapter 3.

Many economists criticized this model because it underestimated technological development and factors that might mitigate the effects of scarcity. In 1992 the Meadows group published updated computer models in *Beyond the Limits* that include technological progress, pollution abatement, population stabilization, and new public policies that work for a sustainable future. If we adopt these changes sooner rather than later, the models show an outcome like that in figure 14.21, in which all factors stabilize sometime in this century at an improved standard of living for everyone. Of course, none of these computer models shows what will happen, only what some possible outcomes might be, depending on the choices we make.

## Communal property resources are a classic problem in economics

One of the difficulties of economics and resource management is that there are many resources we all share but nobody owns. Clean air, fish in the ocean, clean water, wildlife, and open space are all natural amenities that we exploit but that nobody clearly controls.

In 1968 biologist Garret Hardin wrote **"The Tragedy of the Commons,"** an article describing how commonly held resources

are degraded and destroyed by self-interest. Using the metaphor of the "commons," or community pastures in colonial New England villages, Hardin theorized that it behooves each villager to put more cows on the pasture. Each cow brings more wealth to the individual farmer, but the costs of overgrazing are shared by all. The individual farmer, then, suffers only part of the cost, but gets to keep all the profits from the extra cows s/he put on the pasture. Consequently, the commons becomes overgrazed, exhausted, and depleted. This dilemma is also known as the "free rider problem." The best solution, Hardin argued, is to either give coercive power to the government or to privatize resources so that a single owner controls resource use.

This metaphor has been applied to many resources, especially to human population growth. According to this view, it benefits poor villagers to produce a few more children, but collectively these children consume all the resources available, making us all poorer in the end. The same argument has been applied to many resource overuse problems, such as depletion of ocean fisheries, pollution, African famines, and urban crime.

Recent critics have pointed out that what Hardin was really describing was not a commons, or collectively owned and managed resource, but an **open access system**, in which there are no rules to manage resource use. The work of Nobel laureate Elinor Ostrom and others shows that many common resources have been managed successfully for centuries by cooperative agreements among users. Native American management of wild rice beds, Swiss village-owned mountain forests and pastures, Maine lobster fisheries, and communal irrigation systems in Spain, Bali, Laos, and many other countries have all remained viable for centuries under communal management.

Each of these "commons," or **communal resource management systems**, shares a number of features: (1) community members have lived on the land or used the resource for a long time and anticipate that their children and grandchildren will as well, thus giving them a strong interest in sustaining the resource and maintaining bonds with their neighbors; (2) the resource has clearly defined boundaries; (3) the community group size is known and enforced; (4) the resource is relatively scarce and highly variable, so that the community is forced to be interdependent; (5) the management strategies appropriate for local conditions have evolved over time and are collectively enforced; that is, those affected by the rules have a say in them; (6) the resource and its use are actively monitored, discouraging anyone from cheating or taking too much; (7) conflict resolution mechanisms reduce discord; and (8) incentives encourage compliance with rules, while sanctions for noncompliance keep community members in line.

Rather than being the only workable solution to problems in common pool resources, privatization and increasing external controls often prove to be disastrous. Where small villages have owned and operated local jointly held forests and fishing grounds for generations, nationalization and commodification of resources generally have led to rapid destruction of both society and ecosystems. Where communal systems once enforced restraint over harvesting, privatization encouraged narrow self-interest and allowed outsiders to take advantage of the weakest members of the community.

## 14.4 Natural Resource Accounting

Decision making about sustainable resource use often entails **cost-benefit analysis (CBA)**, the process of accounting and comparing the costs of a project and its benefits. Ideally, this process assigns values to social and environmental effects of a given undertaking, as well as the value of the resources consumed or produced. However, the results of CBA often depend on how resources are accounted for and measured in the first place. CBA is one of the main conceptual frameworks of resource economics, and it is used by decision makers around the world as a way of justifying the building of dams, roads, and airports, as well as in considering what to do about biodiversity loss, air pollution, and global climate change. CBA is a useful way of rational decision making about these projects. It is also widely disputed because it tends to discount the value of natural resources, ecological services, and human communities, and it is used to justify projects that jeopardize all these resources.

In CBA the monetary value of all benefits of a project are counted up and compared with the monetary costs of the project. Usually, the direct expenses of a project are easy to ascertain: how much will you have to pay for land, materials, and labor? The monetary worth of lost opportunities—to swim or fish in a river or to see birds in a forest—on the other hand, is much harder to appraise, as are inherent values of the existence of wild species or wild rivers. What is a bug or a bird worth, for instance, or the opportunity for solitude or inspiration? Eventually, the decision maker compares all the costs and benefits to see whether the project is justified or whether an alternative action might bring greater benefit at less cost.

Critics of CBA point out its absence of standards, inadequate attention to alternatives, and the placing of monetary values on intangible and diffuse or distant costs and benefits. Who judges how costs and benefits will be estimated? How can we compare things as different as the economic gain from cheap power with loss of biodiversity or the beauty of a free-flowing river? Critics claim that placing monetary values on everything could lead to a belief that only money and profits matter and that any behavior is acceptable as long as you can pay for it. Sometimes speculative or even hypothetical results are given specific numerical values in CBA and then treated as if they were hard facts.

Figure 14.22 shows an example of a cost-benefit analysis for reducing particulate air pollution (soot) in Poland. As you can see, removing the highest 40 percent of particulates is highly cost-effective. Approaching 70 percent particulate removal, however, the costs may exceed benefits. Data such as these can be useful to decision makers. On the other hand, this same study showed that controlling sulfur emissions had high costs and negligible benefits. Might this conclusion result from the ways "benefits" were evaluated?

Values such as wildlife, nonhuman ecological systems, and ecological services can be incorporated with natural resource accounting. In theory this accounting contributes to sustainable resource use because it can put a value on long-term or intangible goods that are necessary but often disregarded in economic decision making. One important part of natural resource accounting is assigning a value to ecological services (table 14.6). The total value of nature's services of $33.3 trillion per year is about half the current annual world GDP. Another is using alternative measures of wealth and development. As mentioned earlier, GDP is a widely used measure of wealth that is based on rates of consumption and throughput. It doesn't account, however, for natural resource depletion or ecosystem damage.

## Active Learning

### Costs and Benefits

Figure 14.22 shows an example of the relative costs and benefits of reducing air pollution in Poland.

1. For the first 30 percent of reduction (on the X-axis), benefits rise rapidly. What are some of the economic benefits that might be represented by this rising curve?

2. What might be some of the nearly free pollution reduction steps represented by the "costs" curve in the first 30 percent reduction?

3. If you were planning a budget, you would want to maximize benefits and minimize costs. For what percentage of pollution reduction would you aim? At what point would you redirect your budget to other priorities?

*Answers:* 1. Benefits include improved health; less damage to buildings, crops, and materials; and improved quality of life. 2. Conservation, improved planning and efficiency in transportation, buildings, and energy production; replacing old, inefficient industrial plants and vehicles. 3. At any reduction up to 70 percent, benefits outweigh costs.

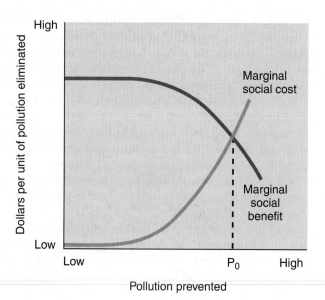

**Figure 14.22** To achieve maximum economic efficiency, regulations should require pollution prevention up to the optimum point ($P_0$) at which the costs of eliminating pollution just equal the social benefits of doing so.

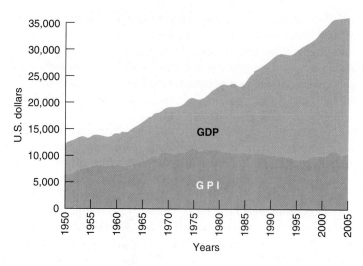

**Figure 14.23** Although per capita GDP in the United States nearly doubled between 1970 and 2000 in inflation-adjusted dollars, a genuine progress index that takes into account natural resource depletion, environmental damage, and options for future generations hardly increased at all. *Source:* Data from *Redefining Progress*, 2006.

The World Resources Institute, for example, estimates that soil erosion in Indonesia reduces the value of crop production about 40 percent per year. If natural capital were taken into account, Indonesian GDP would be reduced by at least 20 percent annually. Similarly, Costa Rica experienced impressive increases in timber, beef, and banana production between 1970 and 1990. But decreased natural capital during this period, represented by soil erosion, forest destruction, biodiversity losses, and accelerated water runoff, added up to at least $4 billion, or about 25 percent of annual

GDP. A number of countries, including Canada and China, now use a "green GDP" that measures environmental costs as part of economic accounting.

## New approaches measure real progress

A number of systems have been proposed as alternatives to GNP that reflect genuine progress and social welfare. In their 1989 book, Herman Daly and John Cobb proposed a **genuine progress index (GPI)**, which takes into account real per capita income, quality of life, distributional equity, natural resource depletion, environmental damage, and the value of unpaid labor. They point out that, while per capita GDP in the United States nearly doubled between 1970 and 2000, per capita GPI increased only 4 percent (fig. 14.23). Some social service organizations would add to this index the costs of social breakdown and crime, which would decrease real progress even further over this time span. Bhutan measures Gross Domestic Happiness as their indicator of progress.

The United Nations Development Programme (UNDP) uses a benchmark called the **human development index (HDI)** to track social progress. HDI incorporates life expectancy, educational attainment, and standard of living as critical measures of development. Gender issues are accounted for in the gender development index (GDI), which is simply HDI adjusted or discounted for inequality or achievement between men and women.

In its annual Human Development Report, the UNDP compares country-by-country progress. As you might expect, the highest development levels are generally found in North America, Europe, and Japan. In 2009 Norway ranked first in the world in both HDI and GDI. Canada was fourth, but subtracting the HDI rank from GDP index placed Canada first in the world on an equity-adjusted basis. The United States ranked thirteenth on the HDI, although it was 62nd in a measure of environmental

| Table 14.6 | Estimated Annual Value of Ecological Services | |
| --- | --- |
| **Ecosystem Services** | **Value (Trillion $ U.S.)** |
| Soil formation | 17.1 |
| Recreation | 3.0 |
| Nutrient cycling | 2.3 |
| Water regulation and supply | 2.3 |
| Climate regulation (temperature and precipitation) | 1.8 |
| Habitat | 1.4 |
| Flood and storm protection | 1.1 |
| Food and raw materials production | 0.8 |
| Genetic resources | 0.8 |
| Atmospheric gas balance | 0.7 |
| Pollination | 0.4 |
| All other services | 1.6 |
| Total value of ecosystem services | 33.3 |

*Source:* Adapted from R. Costanza, et al., "The Value of the World's Ecosystem Services and Natural Capital," in *Nature*, vol. 387, 1997.

## Personally Responsible Consumerism

Each of us can do many things to lower our ecological impacts and support "green" businesses through responsible consumerism and ecological economics.

- Practice living simply. Ask yourself if you really need more material goods to make your life happy and fulfilled.

- Rent, borrow, or barter when you can. Can you reduce the amount of stuff you consume by renting, instead of buying, machines and equipment you actually use only rarely?

- Recycle or reuse building materials: doors, windows, cabinets, appliances. Shop at salvage yards, thrift stores, yard sales, or other sources of used clothes, dishes, appliances, etc.

- Consult the *National Green Pages* from Co-Op America for a list of eco-friendly businesses. Write to companies from which you buy goods or services and ask them what they are doing about environmental protection and human rights.

- Buy "green" products. Look for efficient, high-quality materials that will last and that are produced in the most environmentally friendly manner possible. Subscribe to clean-energy programs if they are available in your area. Contact your local utility and ask that it provide this option if it doesn't now.

- Buy locally grown or locally made products made under humane conditions by workers who receive a fair wage.

- Think about the total life-cycle costs of the things you buy, especially big purchases, such as cars. Try to account for the environmental impacts, energy use, and disposal costs, as well as initial purchase price.

- Stop junk mail. Demand that your name be removed from mass-mailing lists.

- Invest in socially and environmentally responsible mutual funds or "green" businesses when you have money for investment.

### Internalizing external costs

One of the factors that can make resource-exploiting enterprises look good in cost-benefit analysis is externalizing costs. **Externalizing costs** is the act of disregarding or discounting resources or goods that contribute to producing something but for which the producer does not actually pay. Usually, external costs are diffuse and difficult to quantify. Generally, they belong to society at large, not to the individual user. When a farmer harvests a crop in the fall, for example, the value of seeds, fertilizer, and the sale of the crop is tabulated; the values of soil lost to erosion, water quality lost to nonpoint-source pollution, and depleted fish populations are not accounted for. These are most often costs shared by the whole society, rather than borne by the resource user. They are external to the accounting system, and they are generally ignored in cost-benefit analysis—or when the farmer evaluates whether the year was profitable. Larger enterprises, such as dam building, logging, and road building, generally externalize the cost of ecological services lost along the way.

One way to use the market system to optimize resource use is to make sure that those who reap the benefits of resource use also bear all the external costs. This is referred to as **internalizing costs**. Calculating the value of ecological services or diffuse pollution is not easy, but it is an important step in sustainable resource accounting.

protection and governance. The 25 countries with the lowest HDI in 2009 were all in Africa. Haiti ranked the lowest in the Western Hemisphere.

Although poverty remains widespread in many places, encouraging news also can be found in development statistics. Poverty has fallen more in the past 50 years, the UNDP reports, than in the previous 500 years. Child death rates in developing countries as a whole have been more than halved. Average life expectancy has increased by 30 percent, while malnutrition rates have declined by almost a third. The proportion of children who lack primary school has fallen from more than half to less than a quarter. And the share of rural families without access to safe water has fallen from nine-tenths to about one-quarter.

Some of the greatest progress has been made in Asia. China and a dozen other countries with populations that add up to more than 1.6 billion have decreased the proportion of their people living below the poverty line by half. Still, in the 1990s the number of people with incomes less than (U.S.) $1 per day increased by almost 100 million to 1.3 billion—and the number appears to be growing in every region except Southeast Asia and the Pacific. Even in industrial countries, more than 100 million people live below the poverty line and 37 million are chronically unemployed.

## 14.5 Trade, Development, and Jobs

A sustainable society requires some degree of equitable resource distribution: if most wealth is held by just a few people, the misery and poverty of the majority eventually lead to social instability and instability of resource supplies. Accordingly, wealthy industrial nations have worked harder in recent decades to assist in developing the economies in poorer countries.

### International trade can stimulate growth but externalize costs

Expanding trade relations has been promoted as a way to distribute wealth, stimulate economies around the world, and at the same time satisfy the desires of consumers in wealthy countries. According to the economic theory of *comparative advantage*, each place has some sort of goods or services it can make and sell cheaper, or better, than others can. International trade allows us to take advantage of all the best or cheapest products from around the world. If Egypt can produce cotton cheaper than Texas, then we should buy our cotton from Egypt. If Malaysia can

## Loans That Change Lives

Ni Made is a young mother of two children who lives in a small Indonesian village. Her husband is a day laborer who makes only a few dollars per day—when he can find work. To supplement their income, Made goes to the village market every morning to sell a drink she makes out of boiled pandamus leaves, coconut milk, and pink tapioca. A small loan would allow her to rent a covered stall during the rainy season and to offer other foods for sale. The extra money she could make could change her life, but traditional banks consider Made too risky to lend to, and the amounts she needs too small to bother with.

Around the world, billions of poor people find themselves in the same position as Made; they're eager to work to build a better life for themselves and their families, but lack resources to succeed. Now, however, a financial revolution is sweeping around the world. Small loans are becoming available to the poorest of the poor. This new approach was invented by Dr. Muhammad Yunus, professor of rural economics at Chittagong University in Bangladesh. Talking to a woman who wove bamboo mats in a village near his university, Dr. Yunus learned that she had to borrow the few taka she needed each day to buy bamboo and twine. The interest rate charged by the village moneylenders consumed nearly all her profits. Always living on the edge, this woman, and many others like her, couldn't climb out of poverty.

To break this predatory cycle, Dr. Yunus gave the woman and several of her neighbors small loans totaling about 1,000 taka (about $20). To his surprise, the money was paid back quickly and in full. So he offered similar amounts to other villagers with similar results. In 1983, Dr. Yunus started the Grameen (village) Bank to show that "given the support of financial capital, however small, the poor are fully capable of improving their lives." His experiment has been tremendously successful. In 2006, Dr. Yunus won the Nobel Peace Prize for his work. By 2010, the Grameen Bank had more than 8 million customers, 97 percent of them women. It had loaned more than $8.7 billion with 98 percent repayment, nearly twice the collection rate of commercial Bangladesh banks.

The Grameen Bank provides credit to poor people in rural Bangladesh without the need for collateral. It depends, instead, on mutual trust, accountability, participation, and creativity of the borrowers themselves. Microcredit is now being offered by hundreds of organizations in 43 other countries—including the United States. Institutions from the World Bank to religious charities make small loans to worthy entrepreneurs. Wouldn't you like to be part of this movement? Well, now you can. You don't have to own a bank to help someone in need.

A brilliant way to connect entrepreneurs in developing countries with lenders in wealthy countries is offered by Kiva, a San Francisco-based technology start-up. The idea for Kiva, which means unity or cooperation in Swahili, came from Matt and Jessica Flannery. Jessica had worked in East Africa with the Village Enterprise Fund, a California nonprofit that provides training, capital, and mentoring to small businesses in developing countries. Jessica and Matt wanted to help some of the people she had met, but they weren't wealthy enough to get into microfinancing on their own. Joining with four other young people with technology experience, they created Kiva, which uses the power of the Internet to help the poor.

Kiva partners with about 50 development nonprofits with staff in developing countries. The partners identify hardworking entrepreneurs who deserve help. They then post a photo and brief introduction to each one on the Kiva web page. You can browse the collection to find someone whose story touches you. The minimum loan is generally $25. Your loan is bundled with that of others until it reaches the amount needed by the borrower. You make your loan using your credit card (through PayPal, so it's safe and easy). The loan is generally repaid within 12 to 18 months (although without interest). At that point, you can either withdraw the money, or use it to make another loan.

The in-country staff keeps track of the people you're supporting and monitors their progress, so you can be confident that your money will be well used. Loan requests often are on their web page for only a few minutes before being filled. In just four years, Kiva raised more than $122 million from 677,000 lenders to help 305,000 entrepreneurs around the world fulfill their dreams. Wouldn't you like to take part in this innovative person-to-person human development project? Check out Kiva.org.

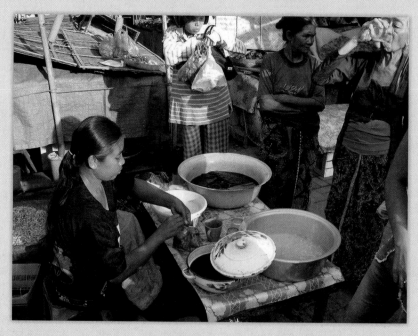

A small amount of seed money would allow this young mother to expand her business and help provide for her family.

manufacture athletic shoes with labor that costs a few cents an hour, then we should buy our shoes from Malaysia. Building factories in Malaysia also stimulates the Malaysian economy, even though workers earn only a small fraction of what a worker in a wealthy country would earn.

A problem with international trade is that it externalizes costs on a grand scale. Tropical hardwood products can be sold extremely cheaply in the United States—as lumber, plywood, shipping pallets, and so on. The environmental costs of producing those hardwood products occur far from the consumer who buys a piece of cheap Brazilian plywood. Making matters worse, the environmental costs of the plywood are usually exported to places where there are few legal controls on pollution and resource extraction. A factory in the United States, for example, is legally bound to minimize its production of air and water pollution.

Pollution control can be expensive, and internalizing this cost makes a factory less profitable. A similar factory in Mexico might have far less responsibility for pollution control, making it cheaper, at least in the short term, to produce goods there than in the United States. Ongoing protests in the United States and elsewhere around the world against the World Trade Organization (WTO) and other forces of globalization have been largely about such exporting and externalizing of environmental and social costs of production.

Another criticism of international trade is that the international banking systems that finance it are set up by and for the wealthy countries. The WTO and the General Agreement on Tariffs and Trade (GATT), for example, regulate 90 percent of all international trade. The WTO and GATT are both made up of relationships and agreements between corporations in a few very wealthy countries. Representatives of less powerful countries often charge that these agreements trap poorer regions into the role of suppliers of natural resources—timber, mineral ores, fruit, and cheap labor. These countries are forced to mine their natural capital for only small returns in wealth.

## Socially responsible development can help people and protect their environment

The World Bank has more influence on the financing and policies of developing countries than any other institution. Of some $25 billion loaned each year for Third World projects by multinational development banks, about two-thirds comes from the World Bank. This institution was founded in 1945 to provide aid to war-torn Europe and Japan. In the 1950s its emphasis shifted to development aid for Third World countries. This aid was justified on humanitarian grounds, but it also conveniently provided markets and political support for growing American and European multinational corporations.

Many World Bank projects have been environmentally destructive and highly controversial. In Botswana, for example, $18 million was provided to increase beef production for export by 20 percent, despite already severe overgrazing on fragile grasslands. The project failed, as had two previous beef production projects in the same area. In Ethiopia, rich floodplains in the Awash River Valley were flooded to provide electric power and irrigation water for cash export crops. More than 150,000 subsistence farmers were displaced, and food production was seriously reduced.

Recently, the World Bank has begun to attempt some environmental and social review of its loans. In part this change comes from demands from the U.S. Congress that projects be environmentally and socially benign. Whether this will improve the World Bank's track record remains to be seen.

The World Bank deals in huge loans for massive projects. These are impressive to investors and to the countries that borrow the money. They are also a huge economic gamble, and on average the economic return on large loans has been quite low.

Recently, smaller, local development programs, often called **microlending**, have begun to develop. These are aimed at small-scale, widespread development, and their results have been very promising. The first of these was Bangladesh's Grameen (village) Bank network (see Exploring Science p. 360 ). These banks make small loans, often just a few dollars, to help poor people buy a sewing machine, a bicycle, a loom, a cow, or some other commodity that will help them start, or improve, a home business. Ninety percent of the customers are women, usually with no collateral or steady income. Still, loan repayment rates are 98 percent—compared with only 30 percent at conventional banks in developing countries. This program enhances dignity, respect, and cooperation in a village community, and it teaches individual responsibility and enterprise.

Comparable programs have now sprung up around the world. In the United States, more than a hundred organizations have begun providing microloans and small grants for training. The Women's Self-Employment Project in Chicago, for instance, teaches job skills to single mothers in housing projects. Similarly, "tribal circle" banks on Native American reservations successfully finance microscale economic development projects.

## Active Learning

### Try Your Hand at Microlending

The best way to observe microlending at work is to try it out. Collect donations of $1–$5 from people in your class, until the total is $25. Go to www.kiva.org, a microlending organization that pools small loans, and select a business to support. You can use PayPal to send the money, and for the next year, you will receive periodic reports on how the business is going. To evaluate whether you're getting a good rate of return, consider that for most stock market investments, about 5–10 percent annual return is reasonable.

1. What is 5–10 percent of $25?

Also poll the class to get these averages:

2. What percentage interest do you earn from your bank accounts?

3. What percentage do you pay to credit card companies?

Answers: 1. $1.25–$2.50, 2, 3. Answers will vary, but probably <2% and <15%.

Table 14.7 | Goals for an Eco-Efficient Economy

- Introduce no hazardous materials into the air, water, or soil.

- Measure prosperity by how much natural capital we can accrue in productive ways.

- Measure productivity by how many people are gainfully and meaningfully employed.

- Measure progress by how many buildings have no smokestacks or dangerous effluents.

- Make the thousands of complex governmental rules that now regulate toxic or hazardous materials unnecessary.

- Produce nothing that will require constant vigilance from future generations.

- Celebrate the abundance of biological and cultural diversity.

- Live on renewable solar income rather than fossil fuels.

## 14.6 Green Business and Green Design

Businesspeople and consumers are increasingly aware of the unsustainability of producing the goods we use every day. Recently, a number of business innovators have tried to develop green businesses, which produce environmentally and socially sound products. Environmentally conscious, or "green," companies, such as the Body Shop, Patagonia, Aveda, Malden Mills, Johnson and Johnson, and others, have shown that operating according to the principles of sustainable development and environmental protection can be good for public relations, employee morale, and sales (table 14.7).

Green business works because consumers are becoming aware of the ecological consequences of their purchases. Increasing interest in environmental and social sustainability has caused an explosive growth of green products. The *National Green Pages* published by Co-Op America currently lists more than 2,000 green companies. You can find eco-travel agencies, telephone companies that donate profits to environmental groups, entrepreneurs selling organic foods, shade-grown coffee, straw-bale houses, paint thinner made from orange peels, sandals made from recycled auto tires, and a plethora of hemp products, including burgers, ale, clothing, shoes, rugs, and shampoo. Although these eco-entrepreneurs represent a tiny sliver of the $7 trillion per year U.S. economy, they often are pioneers in developing new technologies and offering innovative services. Markets also grow over time: organic food marketing has grown from a few funky local co-ops to a $7 billion market segment. Most supermarket chains now carry some organic food choices. Similarly, natural-care health and beauty products reached $2.8 billion in sales in 1999 out of a $33 billion industry. By supporting these products, you can ensure that they will continue to be available and, perhaps, even help expand their penetration into the market.

Corporations committed to eco-efficiency and clean production include such big names as Monsanto, 3M, DuPont, and Duracell. Applying the famous three *R*s—reduce, reuse, recycle—these firms have saved money and gotten welcome publicity (see related story "Eco-Efficient Carpeting" at **www.mhhe.com/cunningham6e**). Savings can be substantial. Pollution-prevention programs at 3M, for example, have saved $857 million over the past 25 years. In a major public relations achievement, DuPont has cut its emissions of airborne cancer-causing chemicals almost 75 percent since 1987. Small operations can benefit as well. Stanley Selengut, owner of three eco-tourist resorts in the U.S. Virgin Islands, attributes $5 million worth of business to free press coverage about the resorts' green building features and sustainable operating practices.

## Green design is good for business and the environment

Architects are starting to get on board the green bandwagon, too. Acknowledging that heating, cooling, lighting, and operating buildings is one of our biggest uses of energy and resources, architects such as William McDonough are designing "green office" projects. Among McDonough's projects are the Environmental Defense Fund headquarters in New York City; the Environmental Studies Center at Oberlin College in Ohio; the European headquarters for Nike in Hilversum, the Netherlands; and the Gap corporate offices in San Bruno, California (fig. 14.24). Each uses a combination of energy-efficient designs and technologies, including natural lighting and efficient water systems.

**Figure 14.24** The award-winning Gap, Inc. corporate offices in San Bruno, California, demonstrate some of the best features of environmental design. A roof covered with native grasses provides insulation and reduces runoff. Natural lighting, an open design, and careful relation to its surroundings make this a pleasant place to work.

## Table 14.8 | McDonough Design Principles

Inspired by the way living systems actually work, Bill McDonough offers three simple principles for redesigning processes and products:

- *Waste equals food.* This principle encourages elimination of the concept of waste in industrial design. Every process should be designed so that the products themselves, as well as leftover chemicals, materials, and effluents, can become "food" for other processes.

- *Rely on current solar income.* This principle has two benefits: First, it diminishes, and may eventually eliminate, our reliance on hydrocarbon fuels. Second, it means designing systems that sip energy rather than gulping it down.

- *Respect diversity.* Evaluate every design for its impact on plant, animal, and human life. What effects do products and processes have on identity, independence, and integrity of humans and natural systems? Every project should respect the regional, cultural, and material uniqueness of its particular place.

The Gap office building, for example, is intended to promote employee well-being and productivity, as well as efficiency. It has high ceilings, abundant skylights, windows that open, a full-service fitness center (including pool), and a landscaped atrium for each office bay that brings the outside in. The roof is covered with native grasses. Warm interior tones and natural wood surfaces (all wood used in the building was harvested by certified sustainable methods) give a friendly feeling. Paints, adhesives, and floor coverings are low-toxicity, and the building is one-third more energy-efficient than strict California laws require. The pleasant environment helps improve employee effectiveness and retention. Gap, Inc., estimates that the increased energy and operational efficiency will have a four- to eight-year payback (table 14.8).

## Environmental protection creates jobs

For years business leaders and politicians have portrayed environmental protection and jobs as mutually exclusive. They claim that pollution control, protection of natural areas and endangered species, and limits on use of nonrenewable resources will strangle the economy and throw people out of work. Ecological economists dispute this claim, however. Their studies show that only 0.1 percent of all large-scale layoffs in the United States in recent years were due to government regulations (fig. 14.25). Environmental protection, they argue, is not only necessary for a healthy economic system; it actually creates jobs and stimulates business.

Green businesses often create far more jobs and stimulate local economies far more than environmentally destructive ones. Wind energy, for example, provides about five times as many jobs per kilowatt-hour of electricity than does coal-fired power (chapter 12).

As chapter 12 shows, China has emerged as the world leader in sustainable energy. Recognizing the multibillion-dollar economic potential of "green" business, China is investing at least $8 billion per year on research and development, and now it is selling about $12 billion worth of equipment and services per year worldwide. Japan, also, is marketing advanced waste incinerators, pollution-control equipment, alternative energy sources, and water treatment systems. Superefficient "hybrid" gas-electric cars are helping Japanese

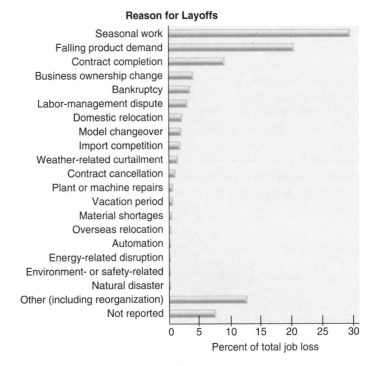

**Figure 14.25** Although opponents of environmental regulation often claim that protecting the environment costs jobs, studies by economist E. S. Goodstein show that only 0.1 percent of all large-scale layoffs in the United States were the result of environmental laws. *Source:* Data from E. S. Goodstein, Economic Policy Institute, Washington, D.C.

automakers flourish, while U.S. corporations that once dominated the world slide into bankruptcy. Unfortunately, the United States has been resisting international pollution-control conventions, rather than recognizing the potential for economic growth and environmental protection in the field of "green" business.

## Conclusion

More than half of us now live in cities, and in a generation three-quarters of us will be urban dwellers. Most of this growth will occur in the large cities of developing countries, where resources are already strained. Cities draw immigrants from the countryside by offering jobs, social mobility, education, and other opportunities unavailable in rural areas. Weak rural economies and a lack of access to land also push people to cities. Shortages of water and housing are especially urgent problems in fast-growing cities of the developing world. Illegal shantytowns often develop as people seek a place to live on the outskirts of cities. Crime and pollution plague residents of these developments, who often have nowhere else to go.

Urban planning tries to minimize the strains of urbanization. Good planning saves money, because providing roads and services to sprawling suburbs is very expensive. Transportation, which is key to our economy, is a critical part of planning because it determines how far-flung urban development will be. Smart growth, cluster development, and improved standards for environmentally conscious building are also important in urban planning.

Economic policies are often at the root of the success or failure of cities. These policies build from some basic sets of assumptions about the nature of resources. Classical economics assumes that resources are finite, so that we compete to control them. Neoclassical economics assumes that resources are based on capital, which can include knowledge and social capital as well as resources, and that constant growth is both possible and essential. Natural resource economics extends neoclassical ideas to internalize the value of ecological services in economic accounting.

The "tragedy of the commons" is a classic description of our inability to take care of public resources. Subsequent explanations have pointed that collective rules of ownership are necessary for the survival of shared resources. Our ability to agree on these rules appears to depend on a number of factors, including the scarcity of the resource and our ability to monitor its use.

Because classic productivity indices count many social and environmental ills as positive growth, alternatives have been proposed, including the genuine progress index (GPI). Measures like the GPI can be used to help ensure fair and responsible growth in developing areas. Microlending is another innovative strategy that promotes equity in economic growth. Green business and green design are fast-growing parts of many economies. These approaches save money by minimizing consumption and waste.

## Practice Quiz

1. How many people now live in urban areas?
2. How many cities were over 1 million in 1900? How many are now?
3. Why do people move to urban areas?
4. What is the difference between a shantytown and a slum?
5. Define *sprawl*.
6. In what ways are cities ecosystems?
7. Define *smart growth*.
8. Describe a "green" roof.
9. Describe a few ways in which Vauban is self-sufficient and sustainable.
10. Define *sustainable development*.
11. Briefly summarize the differences in how neoclassical and ecological economics view natural resources.
12. What is the estimated economic value of all the world's ecological services?
13. How is it that nonrenewable resources can be extended indefinitely, while renewable resources are exhaustible?
14. In your own words, describe what is shown in figure 14.22.
15. What's the difference between open access and communal resource management?
16. Describe the genuine progress index (GPI).
17. What is *microlending*?

# Critical Thinking and Discussion Questions

Apply the principles you have learned in this chapter to discuss these questions with other students.

1. Some people—especially automakers—claim that Americans will never give up their cars. Do you agree? What might persuade you to change to a car-free lifestyle?
2. This chapter presents a number of proposals for suburban redesign. Which of them would be appropriate or useful for your community? Try drawing up a plan for the ideal design of your neighborhood.
3. A city could be considered an ecosystem. Using what you learned in chapters 2 and 3, describe the structure and function of a city in ecological terms.
4. If you were doing a cost-benefit study, how would you assign a value to the opportunity for good health or the existence of rare and endangered species in faraway places? Is there a danger or cost in simply saying some things are immeasurable and priceless and therefore off limits to discussion?
5. What would be the effect on the developing countries of the world if we were to change to a steady-state economic system? How could we achieve a just distribution of resource benefits while still protecting environmental quality and future resource use?
6. When an ecologist warns that we are using up irreplaceable natural resources and an economist rejoins that ingenuity and enterprise will find substitutes for most resources, what underlying premises and definitions shape their arguments?

# Data Analysis | Using a Logarithmic Scale

We've often used very large numbers in this book. Millions of people suffer from common diseases. Hundreds of millions are moving from the country to the city. Billions of people will probably be added to the world population in the next half century. Cities that didn't exist a few decades ago now have millions of residents. How can we plot such rapid growth and such huge numbers? If you use ordinary graph paper, making a scale that goes to millions or billions will run off the edge of the page unless you make the units very large.

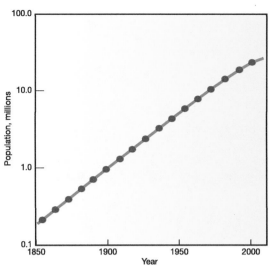

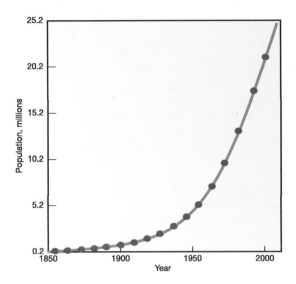

**Figure 1** The growth of Mumbai.

Figure 1, for example, shows the growth of Mumbai, India, over the past 150 years plotted with an **arithmetic scale** (showing constant intervals) for the Y-axis. It looks as if there is very little growth in the first third of this series and then explosive growth during the last few

**Figure 2** The growth of Mumbai.

decades, yet we know that the *rate* of growth was actually greater at the beginning than at the end of this time. How could we display this differently? One way to make the graph easier to interpret is to use a **logarithmic scale.** A logarithmic scale, or "log scale," progresses by factor of 10. So the Y-axis would be numbered 0, 1, 10, 100, 1,000 . . . . The effect on a graph is to spread out the smaller values and compress the larger values. In figure 2, the same data are plotted using a log scale for the Y-axis, which makes it much easier to see what happened throughout this time period.

Do these two graphing techniques give you a different impression of what's happening in Mumbai? How might researchers use one or the other of these scales to convey a particular message or illustrate details in a specific part of the growth curve?

# Appendixes

# Vegetation

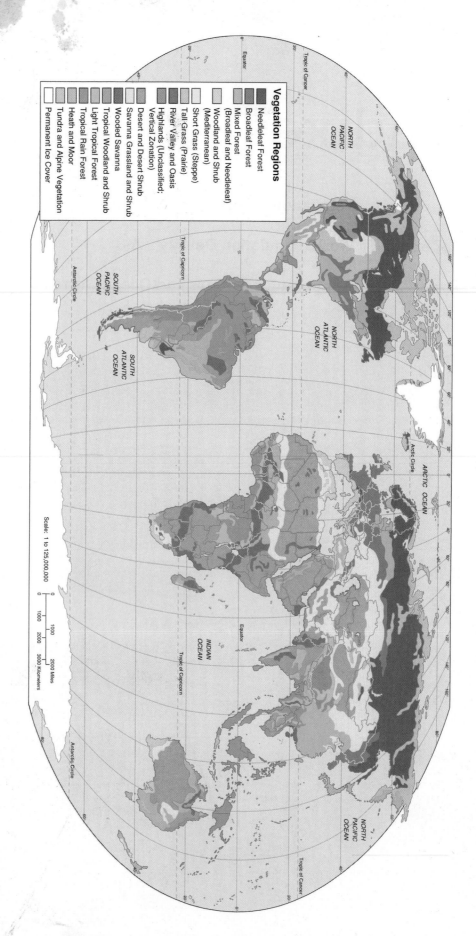

## Vegetation Regions

- Needleleaf Forest
- Broadleaf Forest
- Mixed Forest (Broadleaf and Needleleaf)
- Woodland and Shrub (Mediterranean)
- Short Grass (Steppe)
- Tall-Grass (Prairie)
- River Valley and Oasis
- Highlands (Unclassified; Vertical Zonation)
- Desert and Desert Shrub
- Savanna Grassland and Shrub
- Wooded Savanna
- Tropical Woodland and Shrub
- Light Tropical Forest
- Tropical Rain Forest
- Heath and Moor
- Tundra and Alpine Vegetation
- Permanent Ice Cover

Scale: 1 to 125,000,000

0    1000    2000    3000 Kilometers
0    1000    2000 Miles

Vegetation is the most visible consequence of the distribution of temperature and precipitation. The global distribution of vegetation types and the global distribution of climate are closely related, but not all vegetation types are the consequence of temperature and precipitation or other climatic variables. Many types of vegetation, in many areas of the world, are the consequence of human activities, particularly the grazing of domesticated livestock, burning, and forest clearance.

Appendix 1 Vegetation

# World Population Density

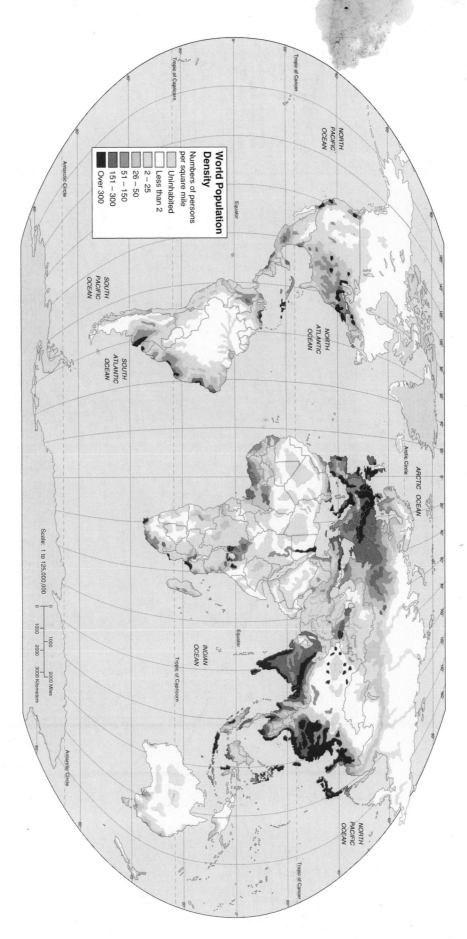

**World Population Density**

Numbers of persons per square mile

- Uninhabited
- Less than 2
- 2 – 25
- 26 – 50
- 51 – 150
- 151 – 300
- Over 300

Scale: 1 to 125,000,000

No feature of human activity is more reflective of environmental conditions than where people live. In the areas of densest population, a mixture of natural and human factors have combined to allow maximum food production, maximum urbanization, and especially concentrated economic activity. Three such great concentrations appear on the map—East Asia, South Asia, and Europe—with a fourth lesser concentration in eastern North America (the "Megalopolis" region of the United States and Canada). The areas of future high density (in addition to those already existing) are likely to be in Middle and South America and Africa, where population growth rates are well above the world average. Population that is extremely dense or growing at an excessive rate when measured against a region's habitability is one of the greatest indicators of environmental deterioration.

# Temperature Regions and Ocean Currents

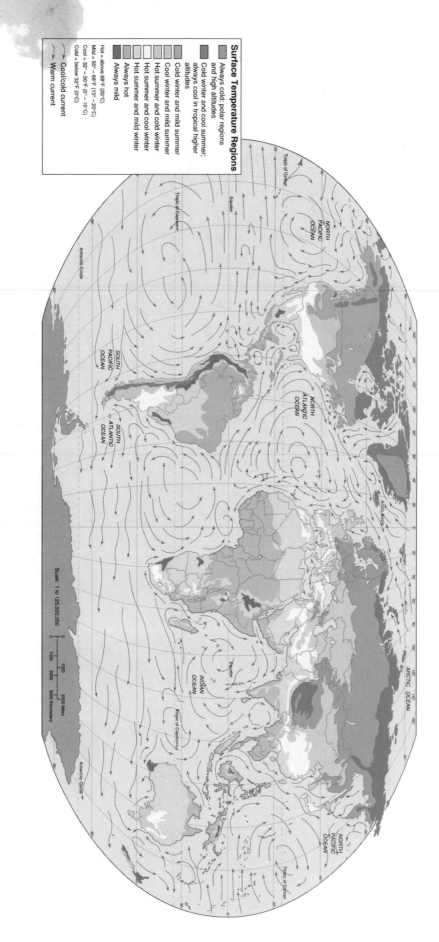

**Surface Temperature Regions**

- Always cold; polar regions and high altitudes
- Cold winter and cool summer; always cool in tropical higher altitudes
- Cold winter and mild summer
- Cool winter and mild summer
- Cool winter and cool winter
- Hot summer and cold winter
- Hot summer and mild winter
- Always hot
- Always mild

→ Cool/cold current
→ Warm current

Scale 1 to 125,000,000

Hot = above 68°F (20°C)
Mild = 50°–68°F (10°–20°C)
Cool = 32°–50°F (0°–10°C)
Cold = below 32°F (0°C)

Along with precipitation, temperature is one of the two most important environmental variables, defining the climatic conditions so essential for the distribution of human activities and the human population. Ocean currents exert a significant influence over the climate of adjacent continents and are the most important mechanism for redistributing surplus heat from the equatorial region into middle and high latitudes.

# Glossary

## A

**abundance**  The number of individuals of a species in an area.

**acid precipitation**  Acidic rain, snow, or dry particles deposited from the air due to increased acids released by anthropogenic or natural resources.

**acids**  Substances that release hydrogen atoms in water.

**active solar systems**  Mechanical systems that use moving substances to collect and transfer solar energy.

**acute effects**  A sudden onset of symptoms or effects of exposure to some factor.

**acute poverty**  Insufficient income or access to resources needed to provide the basic necessities for life, such as food, shelter, sanitation, clean water, medical care, and education.

**adaptation**  Physical changes that allow organisms to survive in a given environment.

**adaptive management**  A management plan designed from the outset to "learn by doing" and to actively test hypotheses and adjust treatments as new information becomes available.

**administrative law**  Executive orders, administrative rules and regulations, and enforcement decisions by administrative agencies and special administrative courts.

**aerosols**  Minute particles or liquid droplets suspended in the air.

**affluenza**  An addiction to spending and consuming beyond one's needs.

**albedo**  A description of a surface's reflective properties.

**allergens**  Substances that activate the immune system and cause an allergic response; may not be directly antigenic themselves but may make other materials antigenic.

**allopatric speciation**  Species that arise from a common ancestor through geographic isolation or some other barrier to reproduction.

**ambient air**  The air immediately around us.

**amorphous silicon collectors**  Photovoltaic cells made from randomly assembled silicon molecules rather than silicon crystals. Amorphous collectors are less efficient but far cheaper than crystalline collectors.

**analytical thinking**  A way of systematic analysis that asks, "How can I break this problem down into its constituent parts?"

**anemia**  Low levels of hemoglobin due to iron deficiency or lack of red blood cells.

**anthropocentric**  Believing that humans hold a special place in nature; being centered primarily on humans and human affairs.

**antigens**  Substances that stimulate the production of, and react with, specific antibodies.

**aquifers**  Porous, water-bearing layers of sand, gravel, and rock below the earth's surface; reservoirs for groundwater.

**arithmetic scale**  A pattern of growth that increases at a constant amount per unit time, such as 1, 2, 3, 4 or 1, 3, 5, 7.

**atmospheric deposition**  Sedimentation of solids, liquids, or gaseous materials from the air.

**atom**  The smallest particle that exhibits the characteristics of an element.

**atomic number**  The characteristic number of protons per atom of an element.

**autotroph**  An organism that synthesizes food molecules from inorganic molecules by using an external energy source, such as light energy.

## B

**barrier islands**  Low, narrow, sandy islands that form offshore from a coastline.

**bases**  Substances that readily bond with hydrogen ions in an aqueous solution.

**Batesian mimicry**  Evolution by one species to resemble another species that is protected from predators by a venomous stinger, bad taste, or some other defensive adaptation.

**benthic**  The bottom of a sea or lake.

**binomials**  Scientific or Latin names that combine the genus and species, e.g., *Zea mays*.

**bioaccumulation**  The selective absorption and concentration of molecules by cells.

**biocentrism**  The belief that all creatures have rights and values; being centered on nature rather than humans.

**biochemical oxygen demand (BOD)**  A standard test for measuring the amount of dissolved oxygen utilized by aquatic microorganisms.

**biodegradable plastics**  Plastics that can be decomposed by microorganisms.

**biodiversity**  The genetic, species, and ecological diversity of the organisms in a given area.

**biofuel**  Fuel made from biomass.

**biogeochemical cycles**  Movement of matter within or between ecosystems; caused by living organisms, geologic forces, or chemical reactions. The cycling of nitrogen, carbon, sulfur, oxygen, phosphorus, and water are examples.

**biological community**  The populations of plants, animals, and microorganisms living and interacting in a certain area at a given time.

**biological controls**  Use of natural predators, pathogens, or competitors to regulate pest populations.

**biomagnification**  Increase in concentration of certain stable chemicals (for example, heavy metals or fat-soluble pesticides) in successively higher trophic levels of a food chain or web.

**biomass**  The accumulated biological material produced by living organisms.

**biomass fuel**  Organic material produced by plants, animals, or microorganisms that can be burned directly as a heat source or converted into a gaseous or liquid fuel.

**biomass pyramid**  A metaphor or diagram that explains the relationship between the amounts of biomass at different trophic levels.

**biomes**  Broad, regional types of ecosystems characterized by distinctive climate and soil conditions and distinctive kinds of biological community adapted to those conditions.

**bioremediation**  Use of biological organisms to remove pollution or restore environmental quality.

**biosphere**  The zone of air, land, and water at the surface of the earth that is occupied by organisms.

**biosphere reserves**  World heritage sites identified by the IUCN as worthy for national park or wildlife refuge status because of high biological diversity or unique ecological features.

**biotic potential**  The maximum reproductive rate of an organism, given unlimited resources and ideal environmental conditions.

**birth control**  Any method used to reduce births, including celibacy, delayed marriage, contraception; devices or medications that prevent implantation of fertilized zygotes and induced abortions.

**blind experiments**  A design in which researchers don't know which subjects were given experimental treatment until after data have been gathered and analyzed.

**bogs**  Areas of waterlogged soil that tend to be peaty; fed mainly by precipitation; low productivity; some bogs are acidic.

**boreal forest**  A broad band of mixed coniferous and deciduous trees that stretches across northern North America (and Europe and Asia); its northernmost edge, the taiga, intergrades with the arctic tundra.

**brownfields**  Abandoned or underused urban areas in which redevelopment is blocked by liability or financing issues related to toxic contamination.

## C

**cancer**  Invasive, out-of-control cell growth that results in malignant tumors.

**cap-and-trade agreement**  A policy to set pollution limits, then allow companies to buy and sell their allotted rights to emit pollutants.

**capital**  Any form of wealth, resources, or knowledge available for use in the production of more wealth.

**carbohydrate**  An organic compound consisting of a ring or chain of carbon atoms with hydrogen and oxygen attached; examples are sugars, starches, cellulose, and glycogen.

**carbon cycle**   The circulation and reutilization of carbon atoms, especially via the processes of photosynthesis and respiration.

**carbon management**   Projects to reduce carbon dioxide emissions from fossil fuel or to ameliorate their effects.

**carbon monoxide**   Colorless, odorless, nonirritating but highly toxic gas produced by incomplete combustion of fuel, incineration of biomass or solid waste, or partially anaerobic decomposition of organic material.

**carbon neutral**   Producing no net carbon dioxide emissions.

**carbon sink**   Places of carbon accumulation, such as in large forests (organic compounds) or ocean sediments (calcium carbonate).

**carcinogens**   Substances that cause cancer.

**carnivores**   Organisms that mainly prey upon animals.

**carrying capacity**   The maximum number of individuals of any species that can be supported by a particular ecosystem on a long-term basis.

**case law**   Precedents from both civil and criminal court cases.

**cell**   Minute compartments surrounded by semipermeable membranes within which the processes of life are carried out by all living organisms.

**cellular respiration**   The process in which a cell breaks down sugar or other organic compounds to release energy used for cellular work; may be anaerobic or aerobic, depending on the availability of oxygen.

**chain reaction**   A self-sustaining reaction in which the fission of nuclei produces subatomic particles that cause the fission of other nuclei.

**chaparral**   A biological community characterized by thick growth of thorny, evergreen shrubs typical of a Mediterranean climate.

**chemical bond**   The force that holds molecules together.

**chemical energy**   Potential energy stored in chemical bonds of molecules.

**chemosynthesis**   Extracting energy for life from inorganic chemicals, such as hydrogen sulfide, rather than from sunlight.

**chlorinated hydrocarbons**   Hydrocarbon molecules to which chlorine atoms are attached. Often used as pesticides and are both highly toxic and long-lasting in the environment.

**chlorofluorocarbons**   Chemical compounds with a carbon skeleton and one or more attached chlorine and fluorine atoms. Commonly used as refrigerants, solvents, fire retardants, and blowing agents.

**chloroplasts**   Chlorophyll-containing organelles in eukaryotic organisms; sites of photosynthesis.

**chronic effects**   Long-lasting results of exposure to a toxin; can be a permanent change caused by a single, acute exposure or a continuous, low-level exposure.

**citizen science**   Projects in which trained volunteers work with scientific researchers to answer real-world questions.

**civil law**   A body of laws regulating relations between individuals or between individuals and corporations concerning property rights, personal dignity and freedom, and personal injury.

**classical economics**   Modern, Western economic theories of the effects of resource scarcity, monetary policy, and competition on supply and demand of goods and services in the marketplace. This is the basis for the capitalist market system.

**clear-cutting**   Cutting every tree in a given area, regardless of species or size; an appropriate harvest method for some species; can be destructive if not carefully controlled.

**climate**   A description of the long-term pattern of weather in a particular area.

**climax community**   A long-lasting, self-sustaining community resulting from ecological succession that is resistant to disturbance.

**closed-canopy**   A forest where tree crowns spread over 20 percent of the ground; has the potential for commercial timber harvests.

**closed system**   A system in which there is no exchange of energy or matter with its surroundings.

**cloud forests**   High mountain forests where temperatures are uniformly cool and fog or mist keeps vegetation wet all the time.

**coevolution**   The process in which species exert selective pressure on each other and gradually evolve new features or behaviors as a result of those pressures.

**cogeneration**   The simultaneous production of electricity and steam or hot water in the same plant.

**coliform bacteria**   Bacteria that live in the intestines (including the colon) of humans and other animals; used as a measure of the presence of feces in water or soil.

**commensalism**   A symbiotic relationship in which one member is benefited and the second is neither harmed nor benefited.

**communal resource management systems**   Resources managed by a community for long-term sustainability.

**community (ecological) structure**   The patterns of spatial distribution of individuals, species, and communities.

**competitive exclusion**   A theory that no two populations of different species will occupy the same niche and compete for exactly the same resources in the same habitat for very long.

**complexity**   The number of species at each trophic level and the number of trophic levels in a community.

**composting**   The biological degradation of organic material under aerobic (oxygen-rich) conditions to produce compost, a nutrient-rich soil amendment and conditioner.

**compound**   Substances composed of different kinds of atoms.

**confidence limits**   Upper and lower values in which the true value (such as a mean) is likely to fall.

**confined animal-feeding operation**   Feeding large numbers of livestock at a high density in pens or barns.

**conifer**   A needle-bearing tree that produces seeds in cones.

**conservation medicine**   Attempts to understand how changes we make in our environment threaten our health as well as that of natural communities on which we depend.

**conservation of matter**   In any chemical reaction, matter changes form; it is neither created nor destroyed.

**conspicuous consumption**   A term coined by economist and social critic Thorstein Veblen to describe buying things we don't want or need to impress others.

**constructed wetlands**   Artificially constructed wetlands.

**consumers**   Organisms that obtain energy and nutrients by feeding on other organisms or their remains. See also *heterotroph*.

**consumption**   The fraction of withdrawn water that is lost in transmission or that is evaporated, absorbed, chemically transformed, or otherwise made unavailable for other purposes as a result of human use.

**contour plowing**   Plowing along hill contours; reduces erosion.

**controlled studies**   Comparisons made between two populations that are identical (as far as possible) in every factor except the one being studied.

**control rods**   Neutron-absorbing material inserted into spaces between fuel assemblies in nuclear reactors to regulate fission reaction.

**convection currents**   Rising or sinking air currents that stir the atmosphere and transport heat from one area to another. Convection currents also occur in water.

**conventional (criteria) pollutants**   The seven substances (sulfur dioxide, carbon monoxide, particulates, hydrocarbons, nitrogen oxides, photochemical oxidants, and lead) identified by the Clean Air Act as the most serious threat of all pollutants to human health and welfare.

**convergent evolution**   Species evolve from different origins but under similar environmental conditions to have similar traits.

**coral bleaching**   Whitening of corals when stressors, such as high temperatures, induce corals to expel their colorful single-celled protozoa, known as zooxanthellae, or when zooxanthellae die. Death of the coral reef may result.

**coral reefs**   Prominent oceanic features composed of hard, limy skeletons produced by coral animals; usually formed along edges of shallow, submerged ocean banks or along shelves in warm, shallow, tropical seas.

**core**   The dense, intensely hot mass of molten metal, mostly iron and nickel, thousands of kilometers in diameter at the earth's center.

**core habitat**   A habitat patch large enough and with ecological characteristics suitable to support a critical mass of the species that make up a particular community.

**Coriolis effect**   The tendency for air above the earth to appear to be deflected to the right (in the Northern Hemisphere) or the left (in the South) because of the earth's rotation.

**corridors**   Strips of natural habitat that connect two adjacent nature preserves to allow migration of organisms from one place to another.

**cost-benefit analysis (CBA)**   An evaluation of large-scale public projects by comparing the costs and benefits that accrue from them.

**cover crops**   Plants, such as rye, alfalfa, or clover, that can be planted immediately after harvest to hold and protect the soil.

**creative thinking**   Original, independent thinking that asks, "How might I approach this problem in new and inventive ways?"

**criminal law**   A body of court decisions based on federal and state statutes concerning wrongs against persons or society.

**criteria pollutants**   See *conventional pollutants*.

**critical factor**   The single environmental factor closest to a tolerance limit for a given species at a given time.

**critical thinking**   An ability to evaluate information and opinions in a systematic, purposeful, efficient manner.

**crude birth rate**   The number of births per thousand persons in a given year (using the midyear population).

**crude death rate** The number of deaths per thousand persons in a given year; also called crude mortality rate.

**crust** The cool, lightweight, outermost layer of the earth's surface that floats on the soft, pliable underlying layers; similar to the "skin" on a bowl of warm pudding.

**cultural eutrophication** An increase in biological productivity and ecosystem succession caused by human activities.

# D

**debt-for-nature swaps** Forgiveness of international debt in exchange for nature protection in developing countries.

**deciduous** Trees and shrubs that shed their leaves at the end of the growing season.

**decomposer** Fungus or bacterium that breaks complex organic material into smaller molecules.

**deductive reasoning** "Top down" reasoning in which we start with a general principle and derive a testable prediction about a specific case.

**deforestation** Removing trees from a forest.

**demographic transition** A pattern of falling death rates and birth rates in response to improved living conditions; typically leads to rapid then stabilizing population growth.

**demography** The statistical study of human populations relating to growth rate, age structure, geographic distribution, etc., and their effects on social, economic, and environmental conditions.

**density-dependent factors** Either internal or external factors that affect growth rates of a population depending on the density of the organisms in the population.

**dependency ratio** The number of nonworking members compared with working members for a given population.

**dependent variable** Also known as the response variable; is one affected by other variables.

**desalinization (or desalination)** Removal of salt from water by distillation, freezing, or ultrafiltration.

**desertification** Denuding and degrading a once fertile land, initiating a desert-producing cycle that feeds on itself and causes long-term changes in soil, climate, and biota of an area.

**deserts** Biomes characterized by low moisture levels and infrequent and unpredictable precipitation. Daily and seasonal temperatures fluctuate widely.

**detritivore** Organisms that consume organic litter, debris, and dung.

**dieback** A sudden population decline; also called a population crash.

**disability-adjusted life years (DALYs)** A health measure that assesses the total burden of disease by combining premature deaths and loss of a healthy life that result from illness or disability.

**discharge** The amount of water that passes a fixed point in a given amount of time; usually expressed as liters or cubic feet of water per second.

**discount rate** The amount we discount or reduce the value of a future payment. When you borrow money from the bank at 10 percent annual interest, you are in effect saying that having the money now is worth 10 percent more to you than having the same amount one year from now.

**disease** A deleterious change in the body's condition in response to destabilizing factors, such as nutrition, chemicals, or biological agents.

**dissolved oxygen (DO) content** Amount of oxygen dissolved in a given volume of water at a given temperature and atmospheric pressure; usually expressed in parts per million (ppm).

**disturbance** Any force that disrupts the established patterns and processes, such as species diversity and abundance, community structure, community properties, or species relationships.

**disturbance-adapted species** Species that depend on repeated disturbance for their survival and propagation.

**diversity** The number of species present in a community (species richness), as well as the relative abundance of each species.

**DNA** Deoxyribonucleic acid; the long, double-helix molecule in the nucleus of cells that contains the genetic code and directs the development and functioning of all cells.

**double-blind experiment** Neither the subject (participant) nor the experimenter knows which participants are receiving the experimental or the control treatments until after data have been gathered and analyzed.

**dust domes** High concentrations of dust and aerosols in the air over cities.

# E

**earthquakes** Sudden, violent movement of the earth's crust.

**ecological diseases** Sudden, wide-spread epidemics among livestock and wild species.

**ecological economics** Application of ecological insights to economic analysis; incorporating ecological principles and priorities into economic accounting systems.

**ecological footprint** An estimate of our individual and collective environmental impacts. It is usually calculated and expressed as the area of bioproductive land required to support a particular lifestyle.

**ecological niche** The functional role and position of a species in its ecosystem, including what resources it uses, how and when it uses the resources, and how it interacts with other species.

**ecological services** Processes or materials, such as clean water, energy, climate regulation, and nutrient cycling, provided by ecosystems.

**ecological succession** The process by which organisms gradually occupy a site, alter its ecological conditions, and are eventually replaced by other organisms.

**ecosystem** A specific biological community and its physical environment interacting in an exchange of matter and energy.

**ecosystem management** An integration of ecological, economic, and social goals in a unified systems approach to resource management.

**ecosystem restoration** To reinstate an entire community of organisms to as near its natural condition as possible.

**ecotones** Boundaries between two types of ecological communities.

**ecotourism** A combination of adventure travel, cultural exploration, and nature appreciation in wild settings.

**edge effects** A change in species composition, physical conditions, or other ecological factors at the boundary between two ecosystems.

**electron** A negatively charged subatomic particle that orbits around the nucleus of an atom.

**element** A substance that cannot be broken into simpler units by chemical means.

**El Niño** A climatic change marked by shifting of a large warm water pool from the western Pacific Ocean toward the east. Wind direction and precipitation patterns are changed over much of the Pacific and perhaps around the world.

**emergent disease** A new disease or one that has been absent for at least 20 years.

**emergent properties** Properties that make a system more than the sum of its parts.

**emigration** The movement of members from a population.

**emission standards** Regulations for restricting the amounts of air pollutants that can be released from specific point sources.

**endangered species** A species considered to be in imminent danger of extinction.

**endemic species** A species that is restricted to a single region, country, or other area.

**endocrine hormone disrupters** Chemicals that interfere with the function of endocrine hormones such as estrogen, testosterone, thyroxine, adrenaline, or cortisone.

**energy** The capacity to do work, such as moving matter over a distance.

**energy intensity** The amount of energy needed to provide the goods and services consumed in an economy.

**energy recovery** The incineration of solid waste to produce useful energy.

**entropy** A measure of disorder and usefulness of energy in a system.

**environment** The circumstances or conditions that surround an organism or a group of organisms as well as the complex of social or cultural conditions that affect an individual or a community.

**environmental health** The science of external factors that cause disease, including elements of the natural, social, cultural, and technological worlds in which we live.

**environmental impact statement (EIS)** An analysis of the effects of any major program or project planned by a federal agency; required by provisions in the National Environmental Policy Act of 1970.

**environmental law** Legal rules, decisions, and actions concerning environmental quality, natural resources, and ecological sustainability.

**environmental literacy** A basic understanding of ecological principles and the ways society affects, or responds to, environmental conditions.

**environmental policy** The official rules or regulations concerning the environment adopted, implemented, and enforced by some government agency.

**environmental science** The systematic, scientific study of our environment as well as our role in it.

**epigenetics** Effects (both positive and negative) expressed in future generations that are not caused by nuclear mutations and are not inherited by normal Mendelian genetics.

**epigenome** DNA and its associated proteins and other small molecules that regulate gene function in ways that can affect multiple generations.

**epiphyte** A plant that grows on a substrate other than the soil, such as the surface of another organism.

**estuaries** Bays or drowned valleys where a river empties into the sea.

**eutrophic** Rivers and lakes rich in organic material (*eu* = well; *trophic* = nourished).

**evolution** A theory that explains how random changes in genetic material and competition for scarce resources cause species to change gradually.

**evolutionary species concept** A definition of species that depends on evolutionary relationships.

**e-waste** Discarded electronic equipment, including TVs, cell phones, computers, etc.

**exotic organisms** Alien species introduced by human agency into biological communities where they would not naturally occur.

**exponential growth** Growth at a constant rate of increase per unit of time; can be expressed as a constant fraction or exponent. See also *geometric growth*.

**externalizing costs** Shifting expenses, monetary or otherwise, to someone other than the individuals or groups who use a resource.

**extinction** The irrevocable elimination of species; can be a normal process of the natural world as species outcompete or kill off others or as environmental conditions change.

# F

**family planning** Controlling reproduction; planning the timing of birth and having only as many babies as are wanted and can be supported.

**famines** Acute food shortages characterized by large-scale loss of life, social disruption, and economic chaos.

**fauna** All of the animals present in a given region.

**fecundity** The physical ability to reproduce.

**federal laws (statutes)** Laws passed by the federal legislature and signed by the chief executive.

**fens** Wetlands fed mainly by groundwater.

**feral** A domestic animal that has taken up a wild existence.

**fetal alcohol syndrome** A tragic set of permanent physical, mental, and behavioral birth defects that result when mothers drink alcohol during pregnancy.

**first law of thermodynamics** States that energy is conserved; that is, it is neither created nor destroyed under normal conditions.

**flood** An overflow of water onto land that normally is dry.

**floodplains** Low lands along riverbanks, lakes, and coastlines subjected to periodic inundation.

**food security** The ability of individuals to obtain sufficient food on a day-to-day basis.

**food web** A complex, interlocking series of individual food chains in an ecosystem.

**fossil fuels** Petroleum, natural gas, and coal created by geologic forces from organic wastes and dead bodies of formerly living biological organisms.

**fragmentation** Disruption of habitat into small, isolated fragments.

**fuel assembly** A bundle of hollow metal rods containing uranium oxide pellets; used to fuel a nuclear reactor.

**fuel cells** Mechanical devices that use hydrogen or hydrogen-containing fuel, such as methane, to produce an electric current. Fuel cells are clean, quiet, and highly efficient sources of electricity.

**fugitive emissions** Substances that enter the air without going through a smokestack, such as dust from soil erosion, strip mining, rock crushing, construction, and building demolition.

**fungi** Nonphotosynthetic, eukaryotic organisms with cell walls, filamentous bodies, and absorptive nutrition.

**fungicide** A chemical that kills fungi.

# G

**gap analysis** A biogeographical technique of mapping biological diversity and endemic species to find gaps between protected areas that leave endangered habitats vulnerable to disruption.

**gene** A unit of heredity; a segment of DNA nucleus of the cell that contains information for the synthesis of a specific protein, such as an enzyme.

**genetically modified organisms (GMOs)** Organisms created by combining natural or synthetic genes using the techniques of molecular biology.

**genetic engineering** Laboratory manipulation of genetic material using molecular biology.

**genuine progress index (GPI)** An alternative to GNP or GDP for economic accounting that measures real progress in quality of life and sustainability.

**geographic isolation** Geographical changes that isolate populations of a species and prevent reproduction or gene exchange for a long enough time so that genetic drift changes the populations into distinct species.

**geometric growth** Growth that follows a geometric pattern of increase, such as 2, 4, 8, 16, etc. See also *exponential growth*.

**geothermal energy** Energy drawn from the internal heat of the earth, either through geysers, fumaroles, hot springs, or other natural geothermal features or through deep wells that pump heated groundwater.

**GIS** Geographical information systems that use computers to combine and analyze geographical data.

**global environmentalism** The extension of modern environmental concerns to global issues.

**grasslands** Biomes dominated by grasses and associated herbaceous plants.

**Great Pacific Garbage Patch** A vast area of the Pacific Ocean containing plastic debris concentrated by global ocean circulation currents. One of several oceanic garbage gyres.

**greenhouse effect** Trapping of heat by the earth's atmosphere, which is transparent to incoming visible light waves but absorbs outgoing longwave infrared radiation.

**greenhouse gas** A gas that traps heat in the atmosphere.

**green pricing** Plans in which consumers can voluntarily pay premium prices for renewable energy.

**green revolution** Dramatically increased agricultural production brought about by "miracle" strains of grain; usually requires high inputs of water, plant nutrients, and pesticides.

**gross domestic product (GDP)** The total economic activity within national boundaries.

**gross national product (GNP)** The sum total of all goods and services produced in a national economy. Gross domestic product (GDP) is used to distinguish economic activity within a country from that of offshore corporations.

**gully erosion** Removal of layers of soil, creating channels or ravines too large to be removed by normal tillage operations.

# H

**habitat** The place or set of environmental conditions in which a particular organism lives.

**half-life** The time required for one-half of a sample to decay or change into some other form.

**hazardous waste** Any discarded material containing substances known to be toxic, mutagenic, carcinogenic, or teratogenic to humans or other life-forms; ignitable, corrosive, explosive, or highly reactive alone or with other materials.

**health** A state of physical and emotional well-being; the absence of disease or ailment.

**heap-leach extraction** A technique for separating gold from extremely low-grade ores. Crushed ore is piled in huge heaps and sprayed with a dilute alkaline-cyanide solution, which percolates through the pile to extract the gold.

**heat** Total kinetic energy of atoms or molecules in a substance not associated with the bulk motion of the substance.

**heat islands** Areas of higher temperatures around cities.

**herbicide** A chemical that kills plants.

**herbivores** Organisms that eat only plants.

**heterotroph** An organism that is incapable of synthesizing its own food and, therefore, must feed upon organic compounds produced by other organisms.

**high-level waste repository** A place where intensely radioactive wastes can be buried and remain unexposed to groundwater and earthquakes for tens of thousands of years.

**high-quality energy** Intense, concentrated, and high-temperature energy that is considered high-quality because of its usefulness in carrying out work.

**HIPPO** Habitat destruction, Invasive species, Pollution, Population (human), and Overharvesting, the leading causes of extinction.

**holistic science** The study of entire, integrated systems rather than isolated parts. Often takes a descriptive or an interpretive approach.

**homeostasis** A dynamic, steady state in a living system maintained through opposing, compensating adjustments.

**hormesis** Nonlinear effects of toxic materials.

**human development index (HDI)** A measure of quality of life using data for life expectancy, child survival, adult literacy, education, gender equity, access to clean water and sanitation, and income.

**hydrologic cycle** The natural process by which water is purified and made fresh through evaporation and precipitation. This cycle provides all the freshwater available for biological life.

**hypothesis** A conditional explanation that can be verified or falsified by observation or experimentation.

# I

**igneous rocks** Crystalline minerals solidified from molten magma from deep in the earth's interior; basalt, rhyolite, andesite, lava, and granite are examples.

**independent variable** One that does not respond to other variables in a particular test.

**indicators** Species that have very specific environmental requirements and tolerance levels that make them good indicators of pollution or other environmental conditions.

**indigenous people** Natives or original inhabitants of an area, those who have lived in a particular place for a very long time.

**inductive reasoning** "Bottom-up" reasoning in which we study specific examples and try to discover patterns and derive general explanations from collected observations.

**insecticide** A chemical that kills insects.

**insolation** Incoming solar radiation.

**integrated gasification combined cycle (IGCC)** A process in which a fuel (coal or biomass) is heated in the presence of high oxygen levels to produce a variety of gases, mostly hydrogen and carbon dioxide. Impurities, including $CO_2$, can easily be removed and the synthetic hydrogen gas, or syngas, is burned in a turbine to produce electricity. Superheated gas from the turbine is used to generate steam that produces more electricity, raising the efficiency of the system.

**integrated pest management (IPM)** An ecologically based pest-control strategy that relies on natural mortality factors, such as natural enemies, weather, cultural control methods, and carefully applied doses of pesticides.

**Intergovernmental Panel on Climate Change (IPCC)** A large group of scientists from many nations and a wide variety of fields assembled by the United Nations Environment Program and World Meteorological Organization to assess the current state of knowledge about climate change.

**internalizing costs** Planning so that those who reap the benefits of resource use also bear all the external costs.

**international treaties and conventions** Agreements between nations on important issues.

**interspecific competition** In a community, competition for resources between members of different species.

**intraspecific competition** In a community, competition for resources among members of the same species.

**invasive species** Organisms that thrive in new territory where they are free of predators, diseases, or resource limitations that may have controlled their population in their native habitat.

**ionosphere** The lower part of the thermosphere.

**ions** Electrically charged atoms that have gained or lost electrons.

**island biogeography** The study of rates of colonization and extinction of species on islands or other isolated areas based on size, shape, and distance from other inhabited regions.

**isotopes** Forms of a single element that differ in atomic mass due to a different number of neutrons in the nucleus.

# J

**J curve** A growth curve that depicts exponential growth; called a J curve because of its shape.

**joule** A unit of energy. One joule is the energy expended in 1 second by a current of 1 amp flowing through a resistance of 1 ohm.

# K

**K-selected species** Organisms whose population growth is regulated by internal (or intrinsic) as well as external factors. Large animals, such as whales and elephants, as well as top predators, generally fall in this category. They have relatively few offspring and often stabilize their population size near the carrying capacity of their environment.

**keystone species** A species whose impacts on its community or ecosystem are much larger and more influential than would be expected from mere abundance. This could be a top predator, a plant that shelters or feeds other organisms, or an organism that plays a critical ecological role.

**kinetic energy** Energy contained in moving objects, such as a rock rolling down a hill, the wind blowing through the trees, or water flowing over a dam.

**Kyoto Protocol** An international treaty adopted in Kyoto, Japan, in 1997, in which 160 nations agreed to roll back $CO_2$, methane, and nitrous oxide emissions to reduce the threat of global climate change.

# L

**landscape ecology** The study of the reciprocal effects of spatial pattern on ecological processes.

**landslides** Mass wasting or mass movement of rock or soil downhill. Often triggered by seismic events or heavy rainfall.

**La Niña** The opposite of El Niño.

**latent heat** Stored energy in a form that is not sensible (detectable by ordinary senses).

**LD50** A chemical dose lethal to 50 percent of a test population.

**life expectancy** The average age that a newborn infant can expect to attain in a particular time and place.

**limiting factors** Chemical or physical factors that limit the existence, growth, abundance, or distribution of an organism.

**limits to growth** A belief that the world has a fixed carrying capacity for humans.

**Living Machine** A wastewater treatment system composed of tanks or beds or constructed wetlands in which living organisms remove contaminants, nutrients, and pathogens from water.

**logarithmic scale** One that uses logarithms as units in a sequence that progresses by a factor of 10 in each step.

**logical thinking** A rational way of thought that asks, "How can orderly, deductive reasoning help me think clearly?"

**logistic growth** Growth rates regulated by internal and external factors that establish an equilibrium with environmental resources. See also *S curve*.

**LULUs** Locally Unwanted Land Uses, such as toxic waste dumps, incinerators, smelters, airports, freeways, and other sources of environmental, economic, or social degradation.

# M

**magma** Molten rock from deep in the earth's interior; called lava when it spews from volcanic vents.

**malnourishment** A nutritional imbalance caused by lack of specific dietary components or inability to absorb or utilize essential nutrients.

**Malthusian growth** A population explosion followed by a population crash; also called irruptive growth.

**Man and Biosphere (MAB) program** A design for nature preserves that divides protected areas into zones with different purposes. A highly protected core is surrounded by a buffer zone and peripheral regions in which multiple-use resource harvesting is permitted.

**mangrove forests** Diverse groups of salt-tolerant trees and other plants that grow in intertidal zones of tropical coastlines.

**manipulative experiment** Altering a particular factor for a test or experiment while holding all others (as much as possible) constant.

**mantle** A hot, pliable layer of rock that surrounds the earth's core and underlies the cool outer crust.

**marasmus** A widespread human protein deficiency disease caused by a diet low in calories and protein or imbalanced in essential amino acids.

**marginal costs** The cost to produce one additional unit of a good or service.

**marshes** Wetlands without trees; in North America, this type of land is characterized by cattails and rushes.

**mass burn** The incineration of unsorted solid waste.

**matter** Anything that takes up space and has mass.

**megacities** See *megalopolis*.

**megalopolis** Also known as a megacity or supercity; megalopolis indicates an urban area with more than 10 million inhabitants.

**mesosphere** The atmospheric layer above the stratosphere and below the thermosphere; the middle layer; temperatures are usually very low.

**metamorphic rocks** Igneous and sedimentary rocks modified by heat, pressure, and chemical reactions.

**methane hydrate** Small bubbles or individual molecules of methane (natural gas) trapped in a crystalline matrix of frozen water.

**microlending** Small loans made to poor people who otherwise don't have access to capital.

**midocean ridges** Mountain ranges on the ocean floor where magma wells up through cracks and creates new crust.

**Milankovitch cycles** Periodic variations in tilt, eccentricity, and wobble in the earth's orbit; Milutin Milankovitch suggested these are responsible for cyclic weather changes.

**millennium assessment** A set of ambitious environmental and human development goals established by the United Nations in 2000.

**mineral** A naturally occurring, inorganic, crystalline solid with definite chemical composition, a specific internal crystal structure, and characteristic physical properties.

**minimills** Mills that use scrap metal as their starting material.

**minimum viable population** The number of individuals needed for long-term survival of rare and endangered species.

**modern environmentalism** A fusion of conservation of natural resources and preservation of nature with concerns about pollution, environmental health, and social justice.

**molecules** Combinations of two or more atoms.

**monoculture forestry** Intensive planting of a single species; an efficient wood production approach, but one that encourages pests and disease infestations and conflicts with wildlife habitat or recreation uses.

**morbidity** Illness or disease.

**mortality** Death rate in a population, such as number of deaths per thousand people per year.

**Müllerian (or Muellerian) mimicry** Evolution of two species, both of which are unpalatable and have poisonous stingers or some other defense mechanism, to resemble each other.

**municipal solid waste**   The mixed refuse produced by households and businesses.

**mutagens**   Agents, such as chemicals or radiation, that damage or alter genetic material (DNA) in cells.

**mutation**   A change, either spontaneous or by external factors, in the genetic material of a cell; mutations in the gametes (sex cells) can be inherited by future generations of organisms.

**mutualism**   A symbiotic relationship between individuals of two different species in which both species benefit from the association.

# N

**National Environmental Policy Act (NEPA)**   The law that established the Council on Environmental Quality and that requires environmental impact statements for all federal projects with significant environmental impacts.

**natural experiment**   Observation of natural events to deduce causal relationships.

**natural increase**   Crude death rate subtracted from crude birth rate.

**natural resource economics**   Economics that takes natural resources into account as valuable assets.

**natural resources**   Goods and services supplied by the environment.

**natural selection**   The mechanism for evolutionary change in which environmental pressures cause certain genetic combinations in a population to become more abundant; genetic combinations best adapted for present environmental conditions tend to become predominant.

**negative feedbacks**   Factors that result from a process and, in turn, reduce that same process.

**neoclassical economics**   The branch of economics that attempts to apply the principles of modern science to economic analysis in a mathematically rigorous, noncontextual, abstract, predictive manner.

**net primary productivity**   The amount of biomass produced by photosynthesis and stored in a community after respiration, emigration, and other factors that reduce biomass.

**neurotoxins**   Toxic substances, such as lead or mercury, that specifically poison nerve cells.

**neutron**   A subatomic particle, found in the nucleus of the atom, that has no electromagnetic charge.

**new source review**   A permitting process required by 1977 amendments to the Clean Air Act, required when industries expand or modify facilities. The rule is contentious because vague language in the law allows industries to avoid oversight.

**NIMBY**   Not-In-My-Back-Yard: the position of those opposed to LULUs.

**nitrogen cycle**   The circulation and reutilization of nitrogen in both inorganic and organic phases.

**nitrogen-fixing bacteria**   Bacteria that convert nitrogen from the atmosphere or soil solution into ammonia that can then be converted to plant nutrients by nitrite- and nitrate-forming bacteria.

**nitrogen oxides**   Highly reactive gases formed when nitrogen in fuel or combustion air is heated to over 650°C (1,200°F) in the presence of oxygen or when bacteria in soil or water oxidize nitrogen-containing compounds.

**noncriteria pollutants**   See *unconventional pollutants*.

**nongovernmental organizations (NGOs)**   Pressure and research groups, advisory agencies, political parties, professional societies, and other groups concerned about environmental quality, resource use, and many other issues.

**nonpoint sources**   Scattered, diffuse sources of pollutants, such as runoff from farm fields, golf courses, and construction sites.

**nonrenewable resources**   Minerals, fossil fuels, and other materials present in essentially fixed amounts (within human time scales) in our environment.

**nuclear fission**   The radioactive decay process in which isotopes split apart to create two smaller atoms.

**nuclear fusion**   A process in which two smaller atomic nuclei fuse into one larger nucleus and release energy; the source of power in a hydrogen bomb.

**nucleic acids**   Large organic molecules made of nucleotides that function in the transmission of hereditary traits, in protein synthesis, and in control of cellular activities.

**nucleus**   The center of the atom; occupied by protons and neutrons. In cells, the organelle that contains the chromosomes (DNA).

# O

**obese**   Pathologically overweight, having a body mass greater than 30 kg/m², or roughly 30 pounds above normal for an average person.

**oil shales**   Fine-grained sedimentary rock rich in solid organic material called kerogen. When heated, the kerogen liquefies to produce a fluid petroleum fuel.

**old-growth forests**   Forests free from disturbance for long enough (generally 150 to 200 years) to have mature trees, physical conditions, species diversity, and other characteristics of equilibrium ecosystems.

**oligotrophic**   Condition of rivers and lakes that have clear water and low biological productivity (*oligo* = little; *trophic* = nourished); are usually clear, cold, infertile headwater lakes and streams.

**omnivores**   Organisms that eat both plants and animals.

**open access system**   A commonly held resource for which there are no management rules.

**open canopy**   A forest where tree crowns cover less than 20 percent of the ground; also called woodland.

**open system**   A system that exchanges energy and matter with its environment.

**organic compounds**   Complex molecules organized around skeletons of carbon atoms arranged in rings or chains; includes biomolecules, molecules synthesized by living organisms.

**organophosphates**   Organic molecules to which a phosphate group is attached. A group of highly toxic pesticides that are primarily neurotoxins.

**overgrazing**   Allowing domestic livestock to eat so much plant material that it degrades the biological community.

**overharvesting**   Harvesting so much of a resource that it threatens its existence.

**overnutrition**   Receiving too many calories.

**oxygen sag**   Oxygen decline downstream from a pollution source that introduces materials with high biological oxygen demands.

**ozone**   A highly reactive molecule containing three oxygen atoms; a dangerous pollutant in ambient air. In the stratosphere, however, ozone forms an ultraviolet absorbing shield that protects us from mutagenic radiation.

# P

**paradigms**   Overarching models of the world that shape our worldviews and guide our interpretation of how things are.

**parasite**   An organism that lives in or on another organism, deriving nourishment at the expense of its host, usually without killing it.

**parasitism**   A relationship in which one organism feeds on another without immediately killing it.

**particulate material**   Atmospheric aerosols, such as dust, ash, soot, lint, smoke, pollen, spores, algal cells, and other suspended materials; originally applied only to solid particles but now extended to droplets of liquid.

**passive solar absorption**   The use of natural materials or absorptive structures without moving parts to gather and hold heat; the simplest and oldest use of solar energy.

**pastoralists**   People who live by herding domestic animals.

**pathogens**   Organisms that produce disease in host organisms, disease being an alteration of one or more metabolic functions in response to the presence of the organisms.

**peat**   Deposits of moist, acidic, semidecayed organic matter.

**pelagic**   Zones in the vertical water column of a water body.

**permafrost**   A permanently frozen layer of soil that underlies the arctic tundra.

**permanent retrievable storage**   Placing waste storage containers in a secure location where they can be inspected periodically and retrieved, if necessary, for repacking or for transfer if a better means of disposal or reuse is developed.

**persistent organic pollutants (POPs)**   Chemical compounds that persist in the environment and retain biological activity for a long time.

**pest**   Any organism that reduces the availability, quality, or value of a useful resource.

**pesticide**   Any chemical that kills, controls, drives away, or modifies the behavior of a pest.

**pH**   A value that indicates the acidity or alkalinity of a solution on a scale of 0 to 14, based on the proportion of H⁺ ions present.

**phosphorus cycle**   The movement of phosphorus atoms from rocks through the biosphere and hydrosphere and back to rocks.

**photochemical oxidants**   Products of secondary atmospheric reactions. See also *smog*.

**photodegradable plastics**   Plastics that break down when exposed to sunlight or to a specific wavelength of light.

**photosynthesis**   The biochemical process by which green plants and some bacteria capture light energy and use it to produce chemical bonds. Carbon dioxide and water are consumed while oxygen and simple sugars are produced.

**photovoltaic cell**   An energy-conversion device that captures solar energy and directly converts it to electrical current.

**phylogenetic species concept**   A definition of species that depends on genetic similarities (or differences).

**phytoplankton**   Microscopic, free-floating, autotrophic organisms that function as producers in aquatic ecosystems.

**pioneer species**   In primary succession on a terrestrial site, the plants, lichens, and microbes that first colonize the site.

**plankton**   Primarily microscopic organisms that occupy the upper water layers in both freshwater and marine ecosystems.

**point sources** Specific locations of highly concentrated pollution discharge, such as factories, power plants, sewage treatment plants, underground coal mines, and oil wells.

**policy** A societal plan or statement of intentions intended to accomplish some social or economic goal.

**policy cycle** The process by which problems are identified and acted upon in the public arena.

**pollution** To make foul, unclean, dirty; any physical, chemical, or biological change that adversely affects the health, survival, or activities of living organisms or that alters the environment in undesirable ways.

**pollution charges** Fees assessed per unit of pollution based on the "polluter pays" principle.

**population** All members of a species that live in the same area at the same time.

**population crash** A sudden population decline caused by predation, waste accumulation, or resource depletion; also called a dieback.

**population explosion** Growth of a population at exponential rates to a size that exceeds environmental carrying capacity; usually followed by a population crash.

**population momentum** A potential for increased population growth as young members reach reproductive age.

**positive feedbacks** Factors that result from a process and, in turn, increase that same process.

**potential energy** Stored energy that is latent but available for use. A rock poised at the top of a hill or water stored behind a dam are examples of potential energy.

**power** The rate of energy delivery; measured in horsepower or watts.

**precautionary principle** The rule that we should leave a margin of safety for unexpected developments. This principle implies that we should strive to prevent harm to human health and the environment even if risks are not fully understood.

**predator** An organism that feeds directly on other organisms in order to survive; live-feeders, such as herbivores and carnivores.

**predator-mediated competition** A situation in which the effects of a predator dominate population dynamics.

**preservation** A philosophy that emphasizes the fundamental right of living organisms to exist and to pursue their own ends.

**primary pollutants** Chemicals released directly into the air in a harmful form.

**primary producers** Photosynthesizing organisms.

**primary productivity** Synthesis of organic materials (biomass) by green plants using the energy captured in photosynthesis.

**primary standards** Regulations of the 1970 Clean Air Act; intended to protect human health.

**primary succession** Ecological succession that begins in an area where no biotic community previously existed.

**primary treatment** A process that removes solids from sewage before it is discharged or treated further.

**principle of competitive exclusion** A result of natural selection whereby two similar species in a community occupy different ecological niches, thereby reducing competition for food.

**probability** The likelihood that a situation, a condition, or an event will occur.

**producer** An organism that synthesizes food molecules from inorganic compounds by using an external energy source; most producers are photosynthetic.

**productivity** The amount of biomass (biological material) produced in a given area during a given period of time.

**prokaryotic** Cells that do not have a membrane-bounded nucleus or membrane-bounded organelles.

**pronatalist pressures** Influences that encourage people to have children.

**prospective study** A study in which experimental and control groups are identified before exposure to some factor. The groups are then monitored and compared for a specific time after the exposure to determine any effects the factor may have.

**proteins** Chains of amino acids linked by peptide bonds.

**proton** A positively charged subatomic particle found in the nucleus of an atom.

# R

**r-selected species** Organisms whose population growth is regulated mainly by external factors. They tend to have rapid reproduction and high mortality of offspring. Given optimum environmental conditions, they can grow exponentially. Many "weedy" or pioneer species fit in this category.

**radioactive decay** A change in the nuclei of radioactive isotopes that spontaneously emit high-energy electromagnetic radiation and/or subatomic particles while gradually changing into another isotope or different element.

**random sample** A subset of a collection of items or observations chosen at random.

**rational choice** Public decision making based on reason, logic, and science-based management.

**recharge zones** Areas where water infiltrates into an aquifer.

**reclamation** Chemical, biological, or physical cleanup and reconstruction of severely contaminated or degraded sites to return them to something like their original topography and vegetation.

**recycling** Reprocessing of discarded materials into new, useful products; not the same as reuse of materials for their original purpose, but the terms are often used interchangeably.

**reduced tillage systems** Farming methods that preserve soil and save energy and water through reduced cultivation; includes minimum till, conserve-till, and no-till systems.

**reflective thinking** A thoughtful, contemplative analysis that asks, "What does this all mean?"

**reformer** A device that strips hydrogen from fuels such as natural gas, methanol, ammonia, gasoline, or vegetable oil so they can be used in a fuel cell.

**refuse-derived fuel** Processing of solid waste to remove metal, glass, and other unburnable materials; organic residue is shredded, formed into pellets, and dried to make fuel for power plants.

**regenerative farming** Farming techniques and land stewardship that restore the health and productivity of the soil by rotating crops, planting ground cover, protecting the surface with crop residue, and reducing synthetic chemical inputs and mechanical compaction.

**relative humidity** At any given temperature, a comparison of the actual water content of the air with the amount of water that could be held at saturation.

**remediation** Cleaning up chemical contaminants from a polluted area.

**renewable resources** Resources normally replaced or replenished by natural processes; resources not depleted by moderate use; examples include solar energy, biological resources such as forests and fisheries, biological organisms, and some biogeochemical cycles.

**renewable water supplies** Annual freshwater surface runoff plus annual infiltration into underground freshwater aquifers that are accessible for human use.

**replacement rate** The number of children per couple needed to maintain a stable population. Because of early deaths, infertility, and nonreproducing individuals, this is usually about 2.1 children per couple.

**replication** Repeating studies or tests.

**reproducibility** Making an observation or obtaining a particular result consistently.

**residence time** The length of time a component, such as an individual water molecule, spends in a particular compartment or location before it moves on through a particular process or cycle.

**resilience** The ability of a community or ecosystem to recover from disturbances.

**resource partitioning** In a biological community, various populations sharing environmental resources through specialization, thereby reducing direct competition. See also *ecological niche*.

**resources** In economic terms, anything with potential use in creating wealth or giving satisfaction.

**restoration ecology** Seeks to repair or reconstruct ecosystems damaged by human actions.

**retrospective study** A study that looks back in history at a group of people (or other organisms) who suffer from some condition to try to identify something in their past life that the whole group shares but that is not found in the histories of a control group as near as possible to those being studied but who do not suffer from the same condition.

**riders** Amendments attached to bills in conference committee, often completely unrelated to the bill to which they are added.

**rill erosion** The removing of thin layers of soil as little rivulets of running water gather and cut small channels in the soil.

**risk** The probability that something undesirable will happen as a consequence of exposure to a hazard.

**risk assessment** Evaluation of the short-term and long-term risks associated with a particular activity or hazard; usually compared with benefits in a cost-benefit analysis.

**rock** A solid, cohesive aggregate of one or more crystalline minerals.

**rock cycle** The process whereby rocks are broken down by chemical and physical forces; sediments are moved by wind, water, and gravity; sedimented and reformed into rock; and then crushed, folded, melted, and recrystallized into new forms.

**rotational grazing** Confining grazing animals in a small area for a short time to force them to eat weedy species as well as the more desirable grasses and forbes.

**runoff** The excess of precipitation over evaporation; the main source of surface water and, in broad terms, the water available for human use.

# S

**salinity** The amount of dissolved salts (especially sodium chloride) in a given volume of water.

**salinization** A process in which mineral salts accumulate in the soil, killing plants; occurs when soils in dry climates are irrigated profusely.

**salt marsh** A wetland with salt water and salt tolerant plants, usually coastal.

**saltwater intrusion** The movement of saltwater into freshwater aquifers in coastal areas where groundwater is withdrawn faster than it is replenished.

**sample** To analyze a small but representative portion of a population to estimate the characteristics of the entire class.

**sanitary landfills** Landfills in which garbage and municipal waste are buried every day under enough soil or fill to eliminate odors, vermin, and litter.

**savannas** An open prairie or grassland with scattered groves of trees.

**scavengers** In biology, organisms that consume carrion, or organisms not killed by the scavenger.

**science** The orderly pursuit of knowledge, relying on observations that test hypotheses in order to answer questions.

**scientific consensus** A general agreement among informed scholars.

**scientific method** A systematic, precise, objective study of a problem. Generally this requires observation, hypothesis development and testing, data gathering, and interpretation.

**scientific theory** An explanation or idea accepted by a substantial number of scientists.

**S curve** A curve that depicts logistic growth; called an S curve because of its shape.

**sea-grass beds** Large expanses of rooted, submerged, or emergent aquatic vegetation, such as eel grass or salt grass.

**secondary pollutants** Chemicals modified to a hazardous form after entering the air or that are formed by chemical reactions as components of the air mix and interact.

**secondary succession** Succession on a site where an existing community has been disrupted.

**secondary treatment** Bacterial decomposition of suspended particulates and dissolved organic compounds that remain after primary sewage treatment.

**second law of thermodynamics** States that, with each successive energy transfer or transformation in a system, less energy is available to do work.

**secure landfills** Solid waste disposal sites lined and capped with an impermeable barrier to prevent leakage or leaching.

**sedimentary rocks** Rocks composed of accumulated, compacted mineral fragments, such as sand or clay; examples include shale, sandstone, breccia, and conglomerates.

**sedimentation** The deposition of organic materials or minerals by chemical, physical, or biological processes.

**selection pressure** Limited resources or adverse environmental conditions that tend to favor certain adaptations in a population. Over many generations, this can lead to genetic change, or evolution.

**selective cutting** Harvesting only mature trees of certain species and size; usually more expensive than clear-cutting but less disruptive for wildlife and often better for forest regeneration.

**shade-grown coffee and cocoa** Plants grown under a canopy of taller trees, which provides habitat for birds and other wildlife.

**sheet erosion** Peeling off thin layers of soil from the land surface; accomplished primarily by wind and water.

**shelterwood harvesting** Mature trees are removed from the forest in a series of two or more cuts, leaving young trees and some mature trees as a seed source for future regeneration.

**sick building syndrome** A cluster of allergies and other illnesses caused by sensitivity to molds, synthetic chemicals, or other harmful compounds trapped in insufficiently ventilated buildings.

**sinkholes** A large surface crater caused by the collapse of an underground channel or cavern; often triggered by groundwater withdrawal.

**sludge** A semisolid mixture of organic and inorganic materials that settles out of wastewater at a sewage treatment plant.

**smart growth** The efficient use of land resources and existing urban infrastructure that encourages in-fill development, provides a variety of affordable housing and transportation choices, and seeks to maintain a unique sense of place by respecting local cultural and natural features.

**smart metering** A system of meters that give information about the source and price of electricity used by individual appliances and that can time usage to take advantage of the lowest cost power.

**smelting** Roasting ore to release metals from mineral compounds.

**smog** The combination of smoke and fog in the stagnant air of London; now often applied to photochemical pollution.

**social justice** Equitable access to resources and the benefits derived from them; a system that recognizes inalienable rights and adheres to what is fair, honest, and moral.

**soil creep** The slow, downhill movement of soil due to erosion.

**Southern Oscillation** The combination of El Niño and La Niña cycles.

**speciation** Evolution of new species.

**species** All the organisms genetically similar enough to breed and produce live, fertile offspring in nature.

**species diversity** The number and relative abundance of species present in a community.

**specific heat** The amount of heat energy needed to change the temperature of a body. Water has a specific heat of 1, which is higher than most substances.

**sprawl** Unlimited, unplanned growth of urban areas that consumes open space and wastes resources.

**stability** In ecological terms, a dynamic equilibrium among the physical and biological factors in an ecosystem or a community; relative homeostasis.

**state shift** An abrupt response to a disturbance that causes a persistent change in a system to a new set of conditions and relationships.

**statutory law** Rules passed by a state or national legislature.

**steady-state economy** Characterized by low birth and death rates, use of renewable energy sources, recycling of materials, and emphasis on durability, efficiency, and stability.

**stratosphere** The zone in the atmosphere extending from the tropopause to about 50 km (30 mi) above the earth's surface; temperatures are stable or rise slightly with altitude; has very little water vapor but is rich in ozone.

**stress** Physical, chemical, or emotional factors that place a strain on an animal. Plants also experience physiological stress under adverse environmental conditions.

**strip-cutting** Harvesting trees in strips narrow enough to minimize edge effects and to allow natural regeneration of the forest.

**strip-farming** Planting different kinds of crops in alternating strips along land contours; when one crop is harvested, the other crop remains to protect the soil and prevent water from running straight down a hill.

**strip-mining** Extracting shallow mineral deposits (especially coal) by scraping off surface layers with giant earth-moving equipment; creates a huge open pit; an alternative to underground or deep open-pit mines.

**Student Environment Action Coalition (SEAC)** A grassroots coalition of student and youth environmental groups, working together to protect our planet and our future.

**subduction (subducted)** Where the edge of one tectonic plate dives beneath the edge of another.

**subsidence** Settling of the ground surface caused by the collapse of porous formations that result from withdrawal of large amounts of groundwater, oil, or other underground materials.

**subsoil** A layer of soil beneath the topsoil that has lower organic content and higher concentrations of fine mineral particles; often contains soluble compounds and clay particles carried down by percolating water.

**sulfur cycle** The chemical and physical reactions by which sulfur moves into or out of storage and through the environment.

**sulfur dioxide** A colorless, corrosive gas directly damaging to both plants and animals.

**Superfund** A fund established by Congress to pay for containment, cleanup, or remediation of abandoned toxic waste sites. The fund is financed by fees paid by toxic waste generators and by cost recovery from cleanup projects.

**surface mining** Some minerals are also mined from surface pits. See also *strip-mining*.

**surface soil** The A horizon in a soil profile; the soil just below the litter layer.

**surface tension** The tendency for a surface of water molecules to hold together, producing a surface that resists breaking.

**sustainability** Ecological, social, and economic systems that can last over the long term.

**sustainable agriculture (regenerative farming)** Ecologically sound, economically viable, socially just agricultural system. Stewardship, soil conservation, and integrated pest management are essential for sustainability.

**sustainable development** A real increase in well-being and standard of life for the average person that can be maintained over the long term without degrading the environment or compromising the ability of future generations to meet their own needs.

**sustained yield** Utilization of a renewable resource at a rate that does not impair or damage its ability to be fully renewed on a long-term basis.

**swamps** Wetlands with trees, such as the extensive swamp forests of the southern United States.

**symbiosis** The intimate living together of members of two species; includes mutualism, commensalism, and, in some classifications, parasitism.

**sympatric speciation** A gradual change (generally through genetic drift) so that offspring are genetically distinct from their ancestors even though they live in the same place.

**synergism** When an injury caused by exposure to two environmental factors together is greater than the sum of exposure to each factor individually.

**synergistic effects** The combination of several processes or factors is greater than the sum of their individual effects.

**systems** Networks of interdependent components and processes.

# T

**taiga** The northernmost edge of the boreal forest, including species-poor woodland and peat deposits; intergrading with the arctic tundra.

**tailings** Mining waste left after mechanical or chemical separation of minerals from crushed ore.

**taking** The unconstitutional confiscation of private property.

**tar sands** Geologic deposits composed of sand and shale particles coated with bitumen, a viscous mixture of long-chain hydrocarbons.

**tectonic plates** Huge blocks of the earth's crust that slide around slowly, pulling apart to open new ocean basins or crashing ponderously into each other to create new, larger landmasses.

**telemetry** Locating or studying organisms at a distance using radio signals or other electronic media.

**temperate rainforest** The cool, dense, rainy forest of the northern Pacific coast; enshrouded in fog much of the time; dominated by large conifers.

**temperature** A measure of the speed of motion of a typical atom or molecule in a substance.

**temperature inversions** Atmospheric conditions in which a layer of warm air lies on top of cooler air and blocks normal convection currents. This can trap pollutants and degrade air quality.

**teratogens** Chemicals or other factors that specifically cause abnormalities during embryonic growth and development.

**terracing** Shaping the land to create level shelves of earth to hold water and soil; requires extensive hand labor or expensive machinery, but it enables farmers to farm very steep hillsides.

**tertiary treatment** The removal of inorganic minerals and plant nutrients after primary and secondary treatment of sewage.

**thermal pollution** Artificially raising or lowering of the temperature of a water body in a way that adversely affects the biota or water quality.

**thermocline** In water, a distinctive temperature transition zone that separates an upper layer that is mixed by the wind (the epilimnion) and a colder deep layer that is not mixed (the hypolimnion).

**thermodynamics** The branch of physics that deals with transfers and conversions of energy.

**thermohaline circulation** A large-scale oceanic circulation system in which warm water flows from equatorial zones to higher latitudes where it cools, evaporates, and becomes saltier and more dense, which causes it to sink and flow back toward the equator in deep ocean currents.

**threatened species** While still abundant in parts of its territorial range, this species has declined significantly in total numbers and may be on the verge of extinction in certain regions or localities.

**thresholds** Conditions where sudden change can occur in a system.

**throughput** The flow of energy and/or matter into and out of a system.

**tide pools** Small pools of water left behind by falling tides.

**tolerance limits** See *limiting factors*.

**total fertility rate** The number of children born to an average woman in a population during her entire reproductive life.

**total growth rate** The net rate of population growth resulting from births, deaths, immigration, and emigration.

**total maximum daily loads (TMDL)** The amount of particular pollutant that a water body can receive from both point and nonpoint sources and still meet water quality standards.

**Toxic Release Inventory** A program created by the Superfund Amendments and Reauthorization Act of 1984 that requires manufacturing facilities and waste handling and disposal sites to report annually on releases of more than 300 toxic materials. You can find out from the EPA whether any of these sites are in your neighborhood and what toxins they release.

**toxins** Poisonous chemicals that react with specific cellular components to kill cells or to alter growth or development in undesirable ways; often harmful, even in dilute concentrations.

**tradable permits** Pollution quotas or variances that can be bought or sold.

**"Tragedy of the Commons"** An inexorable process of degradation of communal resources due to selfish self-interest of "free riders" who use or destroy more than their fair share of common property. See *open access system*.

**transpiration** The evaporation of water from plant surfaces, especially through stomates.

**trophic level** Step in the movement of energy through an ecosystem; an organism's feeding status in an ecosystem.

**tropical rainforests** Forests near the equator in which rainfall is abundant—more than 200 cm (80 in.) per year—and temperatures are warm to hot year-round.

**tropical seasonal forests** Semi-evergreen or partly deciduous forests tending toward open woodlands and grassy savannas dotted with scattered, drought-resistant trees.

**tropopause** The boundary between the troposphere and the stratosphere.

**troposphere** The layer of air nearest to the earth's surface; both temperature and pressure usually decrease with increasing altitude.

**tsunami** Far-reaching waves caused by earthquakes or undersea landslides.

**tundra** Treeless arctic or alpine biome characterized by cold, dark winters; a short growing season; and potential for frost any month of the year; vegetation includes low-growing perennial plants, mosses, and lichens.

# U

**unconventional pollutants** Toxic or hazardous substances, such as asbestos, benzene, beryllium, mercury, polychlorinated biphenyls, and vinyl chloride, not listed in the original Clean Air Act because they were not released in large quantities; also called noncriteria pollutants.

**urban agglomerations** Urban areas where several cities or towns have coalesced.

**utilitarian conservation** The philosophy that resources should be used for the greatest good for the greatest number for the longest time.

# V

**vertical stratification** The vertical distribution of specific subcommunities within a community.

**vertical zonation** Vegetation zones determined by climate changes brought about by altitude changes.

**volatile organic compounds** Organic chemicals that evaporate readily and exist as gases in the air.

**volcanoes** Vents in the earth's surface through which molten lava (magma), gases, and ash escape to create mountains.

**vulnerable species** Naturally rare organisms or species whose numbers have been so reduced by human activities that they are susceptible to actions that could push them into threatened or endangered status.

# W

**warm front** A long, wedge-shaped boundary caused when a warmer advancing air mass slides over neighboring cooler air parcels.

**waste stream** The steady flow of varied wastes, from domestic garbage and yard wastes to industrial, commercial, and construction refuse.

**waterlogging** Water saturation of soil that fills all air spaces and causes plant roots to die from lack of oxygen; a result of overirrigation.

**water scarcity** Having less than 1,000 $m^3$ (264,000 gal) of clean fresh water available per person per year.

**watershed** The land surface and groundwater aquifers drained by a particular river system.

**water stress** Countries that consume more than 10 percent of renewable water supplies.

**water table** The top layer of the zone of saturation; undulates according to the surface topography and subsurface structure.

**watt** One joule per second.

**weather** The physical conditions of the atmosphere (moisture, temperature, pressure, and wind).

**weathering** Changes in rocks brought about by exposure to air, water, changing temperatures, and reactive chemical agents.

**wetlands** Ecosystems of several types in which rooted vegetation is surrounded by standing water during part of the year. See also *swamps, marshes, bogs, fens*.

**withdrawal** A description of the total amount of water taken from a lake, a river, or an aquifer.

**work** The application of force through a distance; requires energy input.

**world conservation strategy** A proposal for maintaining essential ecological processes, preserving genetic diversity, and ensuring that utilization of species and ecosystems is sustainable.

# Z

**zero population growth (ZPG)** A condition in which births and immigration in a population just balance deaths and emigration.

**zone of aeration** Upper soil layers that hold both air and water.

**zone of saturation** Lower soil layers where all spaces are filled with water.

# Photo Credits

## Design Elements

Title page: © Getty RF; Brief contents:
© StockTrek/Getty RF; A Closer Look icon:
© Corbis RF; Exploring Science icon: © PhotoDisc/
Getty RF; Active Learning icon: © MasterFile RF;
What Do You Think? Icon: © BananaStock/
Jupiter RF; What Can You Do? Icon, Appendices
opener, front/endmatter graphic: © Brand X
Pictures/PunchStock RF

## Chapter 1

Opener: © Author's Image/PunchStock RF; 1.1:
© Vol. DV13/Getty RF; 1.2: © Stocktrek/age
fotostock RF; 1.3: © Vol. 6/Corbis RF; 1.6a:
NOAA Geophysical Fluid Dynamics Laboratory;
1.6b: © Norbert Schiller/The Image Works; 1.6c:
© Getty RF; 1.7a: © Dimas Ardian/Getty; 1.7b:
© Christopher S. Collins, Pepperdine University;
1.7c & 1.8: © William P. Cunningham; 1.11:
© The McGraw-Hill Companies, Inc./Barry
Barker, photographer; 1.14: David L. Hansen,
University of Minnesota Agricultural Experiment
Station; 1.15: © Mary Ann Cunningham; 1.16:
© The McGraw-Hill Companies, Inc./John A.
Karachewski, photographer; 1.17: © Mary Ann
Cunningham; 1.18a: Courtesy of the Bancroft
Library at the University of California, Berkeley
#Muir, John-POR 65; 1.18b: Courtesy of Grey
Towers National Historic Landmark; 1.18c:
© Bettmann/Corbis; 1.18d: © AP/Wide World
Photos; 1.19: © Joe Klune/iStockphoto; CL 1.1:
© Digital Vision/PunchStock RF; CL 1.2:
© Cynthia Shaw; CL 1.3: © Dimas Ardian/Getty;
CL 1.4: © William P. Cunningham; CL 1.5:
© Getty RF; CL 1.6: Food and Agriculture Orga-
nization photo/R. Faidutti; CL 1.7: © Photodisc/
Getty RF; CL 1.8: © Designpics.com/PunchStock
RF; 1.20a: AP/Wide World Photos; 1.20b:
© Tom Turner/ The Brower Fund/Earth Island
Institute; 1.20c: Columbia University Archives;
Columbia University in the City of New York;
1.20d: © AP/Wide World Photos; 1.21:
© Dr. Parvinder Sethi

## Chapter 2

Opener: Courtesy of Rookery Bay National Estua-
rine Research Reserve; 2.4: Courtesy National Park
Service; p. 34: © G.I. Bernard/Animals Animals;
2.11: © William P. Cunningham; 2.12: NOAA;
p. 39 Fig. 2: The SeaWIFS Project, NASA/Goddard
Space Flight Center and ORBIMAGE; CL2.3:
© Creatas/PunchStock RF; 2.21: © Nigel Cattlin/
Visuals Unlimited

## Chapter 3

Opener: © Galen Rowell/Corbis; 3.1: Portrait of
Charles Darwin, 1840 by George Richmond (1809–
96). Down House, Downe, Kent, UK/Bridgeman
Art Library; 3.2: © Vol. 6/Corbis RF; 3.3:
© William P. Cunningham; 3.5: © visual safari/
Alamy RF; 3.6: © William P. Cunningham; CL
3.1a: © OS50/Getty RF; CL 3.1b: © Cynthia
Shaw; CL 3.1c: © David Shaw; CL 3.1d: © Tom
Cooper; CL 3.1e: © PhotoDisc/Getty RF; CL 3. 1f:
© Ingram Publishing/Alamy RF; CL 3.1g: © David
Shaw; CL 3.5: © Mary Ann Cunningham; CL 3.6:
© Alamy RF; CL 3.7: © Creatas/ PunchStock RF;
CL 3.8: © David Zurick; CL 3.10 © The McGraw-
Hill Companies, Inc./Jill Braaten, photographer;
3.10: © William P. Cunningham; 3.11: © Corbis
RF; 3.12: © D.P. Wilson/Photo Researchers; 3.13:
© Creatas/PunchStock RF; 3.14a, b: © Edward
Ross; 3.15: Courtesy Tom Finkle; 3.16a:
© William P. Cunningham; 3.16b: © PhotoDisc RF;
3.16c: © William P. Cunningham; 3.17: © Vol. 6
PhotoDisc/Getty RF; 3.22a: © Digital Vision/Getty
RF; 3.22b: © Stockbyte RF; 3.22c: © PhotoDisc
RF; 3.22d: © Corbis RF; 3.23a: © Corbis RF;
3.23b: © Eric and David Hosking/ Corbis; 3.23c:
© image100/PunchStock RF; 3.25: © Vol. 262/
Corbis RF; p. 71: Courtesy of David Tilman; 3.29
& 3:30: © William P. Cunningham

## Chapter 4

Opener: © Pierre Tremblay/Masterfile; 4.1: © AP/
Wide World Photos/Apichart Weerawong; 4.2:
© Vol. EP39/PhotoDisc/Getty RF; 4.4: © William
P. Cunningham; 4.5: © Frans Lemmens/Getty; CL
4.4: © Nigel Hicks/Alamy RF; CL 4.5: © Corbis
RF; CL 4.6: © Getty RF; CL 4.7: © Goodshoot/
Punchstock RF; CL 4.8: © Cynthia Shaw; CL
4.9: © William P. Cunningham; p. 86: © Alain Le
Garsmeur/Corbis; 4.11a: © William P. Cunningham;
4.11b: © Vol. 17/PhotoDisc/Getty RF

## Chapter 5

Opener: © Digital Vision RF; 5.2: © Mary Ann
Cunningham; 5.7: © Vol. 60/PhotoDisc/Getty
RF; 5.8: © Vol. 6/Corbis RF; 5.9: © William
P. Cunningham; 5.10: © Mary Ann Cunningham;
5.11: © William P. Cunningham; 5.12: © Vol. 90/
Corbis RF; 5.13: © William P. Cunningham; 5.14:
© Mary Ann Cunningham; 5.15: Courtesy of
SeaWIFS/NASA; 5.17: Courtesy NOAA; 5.18a:
© Vol. 89/PhotoDisc/Getty RF; 5.18b: © Mary Ann
Cunningham; 5.18c: © Andrew Martinez/Photo
Researchers; 5.18d: © Pat O' Hara/Corbis; 5.20a:

© Vol. 16/PhotoDisc RF; 5.20b: © William
P. Cunningham; 5.20c: © Mary Ann Cunningham;
5.21: © The McGraw-Hill Companies, Inc./Barry
Barker, photographer; CL 5.1: © Cynthia Shaw;
CL 5.5: © William P. Cunningham; CL 5.6: © IT
Stock/age fotostock RF; CL 5.7: © Cynthia Shaw;
p. 117: © L. David Mech; 5.26: © Mary Ann
Cunningham; 5.27: Courtesy U.S. Fish and Wildlife
Service, photographer Dave Menke; 5.28: Courtesy
USGS; 5.29: © Mary Ann Cunningham; 5.30:
© William P. Cunningham; 5.31: © Lynn
Funkhouser/Peter Arnold/Photolibrary; 5.32:
© 2009 J.T. Oris

## Chapter 6

Opener: © Ron Thiele; 6.3: © Digital Vision/
Getty RF; 6.5 & 6.6: © William P. Cunningham;
6.7a-c: Courtesy United Nations Environment
Programme; 6.8: © Digital Vision/PunchStock
RF; 6.9: © William P. Cunningham; 6.10: © Gary
Braasch/Stone/Getty; CL 6.1: © Digital Vision/
PunchStock RF; CL 6.2: NASA; CL 6.4:
© Comstock/Alamy RF; CL 6.5a: © Creatas/
Punchstock RF; CL 6.5b: © PhotoDisc/Getty RF;
CL 6.6: © Mary Ann Cunningham; CL 6.7: Data
from United Nations Food and Agriculture Orga-
nization, 2002; CL 6.8: © Amazon Conservation
Team; CL 6.9: © Amazon Conservation Team;
p. 138: Courtesy U.S. Fish & Wildlife Service/
J & K Hollingworth; 6.11: Courtesy of John
McColgan, Alaska Fires Service/Bureau of Land
Management; 6.12: © William P. Cunningham;
6.14: Courtesy of Tom Finkle; 6.15, 6.16 & 6.18:
© William P. Cunningham; 6.20: © National
Parks–Yellowstone–Wildlife Photo File, American
Heritage Center, University of Wyoming # 20475;
6.21: © William P. Cunningham; 6.22: © Digital
Vision/Getty RF; 6.23: © PictureQuest RF; 6.24:
© William P. Cunningham; 6.27: Courtesy of R.O.
Bierregaard

## Chapter 7

Opener: © John Maier/The New York Times/
Redux Pictures; 7.5: © Norbert Schiller/The Image
Works; 7.6a: © Scott Daniel Peterson; 7.6b:
© Lester Bergman/ Corbis; 7.10: © William
P. Cunningham; 7.12a: Photo by Jeff Vanuga, USDA
Natural Resources Conservation Service; 7.13:
© Novastock/PhotoEdit; 7.14: © FAO photo/
R. Faidutti; 7.15: © William P. Cunningham; 7.18:
Food and Agriculture Organization photo/R. Faidutti;
7.21a: Photo by Lynn Betts, courtesy of USDA
Natural Resources Conservation Service; 7.21b:
Photo by Jeff Vanuga, courtesy of USDA Natural

Resources Conservation Center; 7.21c & 7.22: © Corbis RF; 7.24: © Vol. 120/Corbis RF; CL 7.1 (background): National Agricultural Imagery Program, USDA; CL 7.5: © Golden Rice Humanitarian Board www.goldenrice.org; CL 7.6: © S. Meltzer/PhotoLink/Getty RF; CL 7.7: © Corbis RF; CL 7.8: © Corbis RF; 7.25: © William P. Cunningham; 7.27: © Michael Rosenfeld/Stone/ Getty; 7.29: Photo by Lynn Betts, courtesy of USDA Natural Resources Conservation Service; p. 176 & 7.30: © William P. Cunningham; 7.31: © 2008 Star Tribune/Minneapolis-St. Paul; 7.32 © William P. Cunningham

## Chapter 8

Opener: © The Carter Center/Emily Staub; 8.1: Courtesy of Donald R. Hopkins; 8.3: © William P. Cunningham; 8.4a: © Vol. 40/Corbis RF; 8.4b: © Image Source/Getty RF; 8.4c: Courtesy of Stanley Erlandsen, University of Minnesota; 8.7: © Getty RF; p. 199: © Dana Dolinoy, University of Michigan; 8.17: © The McGraw-Hill Companies, Inc./Sharon Farmer, photographer

## Chapter 9

Opener: NASA; 9.7: Courtesy Candace Kohl, University of California, San Diego; CL 9.1 (background): © T.O'Keefe/PhotoLink/Getty RF; CL 9.2: © Corbis RF; CL 9.3 & CL 9.4: © Brand X Pictures/PunchStock RF; CL 9.5: © Getty RF; CL 9.6: © Hisham F. Ibrahim/Getty RF; CL 9.7: © PhotoDisc/Getty RF; CL 9.8: © Corbis RF; CL 9.9: © G.K. & Vikki Hart/Getty RF; CL 9.10: © The McGraw Hill Companies, Inc./ Barry Barker, photographer; 9.15b: © Corbis RF; 9.15c (left & right): Photographer Lisa McKeon, courtesy of Glacier National Park Archives; 9.19: Courtesy of Dr. Delbert Swanson; 9.21: © China Tourism Press/Getty; 9.22: Image courtesy of Norman Kuring, SeaWIFS Project; 9.23: NASA; 9.25a, b & 9.27: © William P. Cunningham; 9.28: © John D. Cunningham/Visuals Unlimited; 9.30: © vario images GmbH & Co. KG/Alamy

## Chapter 10

Opener: © David McNew/Getty; 10.4: © William P. Cunningham; 10.9: Courtesy of National Renewable Energy Laboratory/NREL/PIX; 10.10: Courtesy of USDA, NRCS, photo by Lynn Betts; 10.11a-c: EROS Data Center, USGS; 10.11d Courtesy NASA's Earth Observatory; 10.13: © William P. Cunningham; 10.15: © Simon Fraser/ SPL/Photo Researchers; 10.17: © William P. Cunningham; 10.19: © Lawrence Lowry/Photo Researchers; 10.22 © William P. Cunningham; 10.23: © Les Stone/Sygma/Corbis; 10.25a: Courtesy of Joe Lucas/Marine Entanglement Research Program/National Marine Fisheries Service NOAA; 10.25b: Courtesy of NOAA and Georgia Department of Natural Resources; 10.26: © Steve Allen/Brand X Pictures RF; 10.28: © Cedar Grove Cheese Inc.; CL 10.1: © ThinkStock/Corbis RF; CL 10.2: © Brand X/Alamy RF; CL 10.4: © Peter Essick/Aurora/Getty; CL 10.6: Courtesy of National Renewable Energy Laboratory/NREL/PIX; CL 10.7 & CL 10.8: © William P. Cunningham; CL 10.9: © Mary Ann Cunningham

## Chapter 11

Opener: © Damon Winter/The New York Times/ Redux Pictures; 11.8: © Vol. 16/PhotoDisc/ Getty RF; 11.9: Courtesy of David McGeary; 11.11: © Bryan F. Peterson; 11.12: Courtesy Mike Williams, Ohio Department of Natural Resources Division of Mineral Resources Management; 11.13: © AP Photo/Bob Bird; 11.14: © Digital Vision/ PunchStock RF; 11.15 © Damon Winter/The New York Times/Redux Pictures; CL 11.1: © William P. Cunningham; CL 11.2: © Creatas/PunchStock RF; CL 11.3: © Mvemba Dizolele; CL 11.4: © Photo- Disc/ Getty RF; CL 11.5: © Vol 12/Corbis RF; CL 11.6: © William P. Cunningham; CL 11.7: © Vol. 160/Corbis RF; CL11.8: © Index Stock RF; 11.17: Courtesy of Chris G. Newhall/U.S. Geological Survey; 11.19: © David Greedy/Getty; 11.20: © Nick UT/AP/Wide World Photos; 11.21: U.S. Geological Survey

## Chapter 12

Opener: © Fotosearch/Photolibrary RF; 12.1: Courtesy Jean Ku/DOE/NREL; 12.7: © George Steinmetz/Corbis; 12.11: Courtesy U.S. Coast Guard; 12.13: © Regis Martin/The New York Times/Redux Pictures; 12.14: © Vol. 160/Corbis RF; 12.17: Courtesy Office of Civilian Radioactive Waste Management, Department of Energy; 12.20: National Renewable Energy Lab/NREL/ PIX; 12.21: © William P. Cunningham; 12.23: © University of Tennessee Institute of Agriculture; CL 12.1 (background): © Mary Ann Cunningham; CL 12.3: © The McGraw-Hill Companies, Inc./Doug Sherman, photographer; CL 12.4: U.S. Geological Survey; CL 12.6: © Vol. 17/Getty RF; 12.26: National Renewable Energy Lab; 12.28: © The McGraw-Hill Companies, Inc./ Doug Sherman, photographer; 12.29: © Digital Stock/Corbis RF; 12.31: National Renewable Energy Lab/NREL/PIX; 12.32: © Digital Stock/ Corbis RF; 12.33: © Ocean Power Delivery Ltd.; 12.36: Courtesy of Long Island Power Authority

## Chapter 13

Opener: © Ray Pfortmer/Peter Arnold/Photolibrary; 13.4: © William P. Cunningham; 13.5a: © Vol. 31/ Photodisc RF; 13.5b: Courtesy National Marine Sanctuary, photographer Claire Fackler; 13.6: © Doug Sherman/Geofile; 13.7a: Basel Action Network (www.ban.org); p. 326: © Barbara Gauntt; 13.9: © William P. Cunningham; 13.10: © Alamy RF; 13.13: © Vol. 42/Getty RF; 13.14: Courtesy of Urban Ore, Inc. Berkeley, CA; CL 13.1: © Punch-Stock RF; CL 13.4: © Creatas/PunchStock RF; CL 13.6: © Digital Vision RF; CL 13.8: © Vol. 67/ Corbis RF; CL 13.10 © Stockbyte/PunchStock RF; CL 13.13: © Alamy RF; 13.16: © PhotoDisc/Getty RF; 13.19: © Michael Greenlar/The Image Works; 13.21: Courtesy U.S. Department of Energy

## Chapter 14

Opener: © Martin Specht/The New York Times/ Redux Pictures; 14.2: © Corbis RF; 14.5: © William P. Cunningham; 14.6: © Louie Psihoyos/Science Faction; 14.7: © The McGraw-Hill Companies, Inc./ Barry Barker, photographer; 14.8: © 2003 Regents of the University of Minnesota. All rights reserved. Used with permission of the Design Center for American Urban Landscape; 14.9: © Vol. 62/ Corbis RF; 14.10 & 14.11: © William P. Cunningham; CL 14.0 (background): Library of Congress, Geography and Map Division; CL 14.1: © Mary Ann Cunningham; CL 14.2: © William P. Cunningham; CL 14.3a, b & CL 14.4: © Mary Ann Cunningham; CL 14.5: © William P. Cunningham; CL 14.6: © Mary Ann Cunningham; CL 14.7: © William P. Cunningham; CL 14.8: © Corbis RF; CL 14.9 & CL 14.10: © Mary Ann Cunningham; CL 14.11: © Getty RF; 14.12: © William P. Cunningham; 14.13: © Roofscapes, Inc. Used by permission; all rights reserved; 14.14: © William P. Cunningham; 14.18: © Vol. 6/Corbis RF; p. 360: © William P. Cunningham; 14.24: © Mark Luthringer

## Chapter 15

Opener: © Bettmann/Corbis; 15.1: © iStockphoto; 15.2: Courtesy of Tom Finkle; 15.5, 15.6 & 15.7: © Getty RF; CL 15.0 (background:) © William P. Cunningham; CL 15.1: © Jennifer Shelton; CL 15.2: © Brand X RF; CL 15.3 & CL 15.4: © Mary Ann Cunningham; CL 15.5: © Image Source RF; CL 15.6: © M. L. Heinselman; 15.8: © William P. Cunningham; 15.9: © Gary Fablano/ Pool/Corbis; 15.10: © William P. Cunningham; 15.12: © PunchStock RF; 15.13: Official White House Photo by Pete Souza; 15.14: © Corbis RF; 15.15: Courtesy of Dave Hansen, College of Agriculture Experiment Station, University of Minnesota; p. 380: © William P. Cunningham; 15.17: © Esther Henderson/Photo Researchers; 15.18: Courtesy of National Renewable Energy Laboratory/NREL/PIX; 15.19: © Doug Sherman/ Geofile; 15.20 & 15.21: © William P. Cunningham; 15.22: © Justin Guariglia/Corbis; 15.23: © Jerry Alexander/Getty Images.

## Illustrations

### Chapter 5

Figure 5.25 Reprinted with permission from J. Curtis in William L. Thomas (ed.), *Man's Role in Changing the Face of the Earth.* © 1956 by The University of Chicago Press. All rights reserved.

### Chapter 12

Figure 12.16 Courtesy of Northern States Power Company. Minneapolis, MN

### Chapter 14

Figure 14.20 Reprinted from Beyond the Limits, ©1992 by Meadows, Meadows, and Randers. With permission from Chelsea Green Publishing Co., White River Junction, Vermont.
Figure 14.21 Reprinted from Beyond the Limits, ©1992 by Meadows, Meadows, and Randers. With permission from Chelsea Green Publishing Co., White River Junction, Vermont.

### Chapter 15

Figure 15.9 Source: Comprehensive Everglades Restoration Plan.
Figure 15.16 ©1990 Bruce von Alten

# Index

International environmental organizations, 385–86
International Geophysical Year, 213
International Monetary Fund, 155
International Paper, 123, 124
International Rice Institute, 172
International Soil Reference and Information
    Centre, 141, 165
International trade, 359, 361
International treaties and conventions, 124–25,
    376–79
International Union for Conservation of Nature
    and Natural Resources, 123, 144, 148
Interplanting, 175
Interpretation, 13
Interspecific competition, 59
Intertidal zones, 53, 70, 106
Intraspecific competition, 57, 59
Inuit people, 230
Invasive species, 116, 118–19
Inversions, 231
Invertebrates, 110
Iodine deficiency, 158
Ionic bonds, 31
Ions, 30, 31
Iowa Revolving Loan Fund, 316
I=PAT formula, 80
Iran, family planning in, 90
Irrigation
    aquifer depletion for, 247
    importance to agriculture, 167, 245–46
    water-saving methods, 251
Island biogeography, 113, 116
Isolation, 55, 56
Isotopes, 30, 211
Ivory Coast, 324
Izaak Walton League, 384

# J

J curves, 63, 64
Jackson, Richard, 352
Jacobson, Mark, 316
Jakarta population density, 344
Janzen, Dan, 133–34
Japan
    life expectancy in, 85
    population trends, 81
    recycling in, 328
    reforestation in, 132
Jasper Ridge building, 383
Jet streams, 213
Jobs, environmental protection and, 363
Johnson, Hazel, 345
Jones, Van, 385
Joules, 34, 293
Judicial branch of government, 375–76
Junk science, 16

# K

K-selected species, 65–66, 354
Kelp forests, 63, 70
Kemp's Ridley sea turtles, 147
Kenya, 23
Kerala population control, 90–91

Kermode bears, 129
Kerry, John, 385
Keystone species, 62–63, 70, 123
Kinetic energy, 34
Kingdoms, 58
King's Canyon National Park, 19
Kingston Plains, 73
Kompogas, 320
Kropotkin, Peter, 340
Kruger National Park, 149
Kudzu vine, 118
Kuhn, Thomas, 14
Kuna Indians, 11
Kwashiorkor, 158
Kyoto Protocol, 223, 378

# L

La Niña, 212, 213
Laboratory animals, 196–97
Lake Erie, 258
Lake Mead, 239, 240, 247, 251
Lake Nasser, 314
Lake Powell, 240
Lakes
    ecosystems, 108–9
    eutrophication, 254
    as fresh water resources, 244
    invasive species, 116, 118
*Lancet*, 202
Land conflicts, 154
Land-use planning, 348–49, 352
Landes, Lynn, 319
Landfills, 319, 320, 323–24, 337–38
Landless Workers Movement, 154
Landowner opposition to ESA, 124, 125
*Landsat*, 39
Landscape ecology, 150–51
Landslides, 288
Languages, loss of, 10
Las Vegas, water conservation efforts, 250
Latent heat, 209, 212
Latin names, 58
Latitudes, biomes named for, 98–99
Lawns, 250
Laws and regulations
    clean air, 235–36, 374
    clean water, 257–59, 265, 374
    endangered species, 123, 124–25, 374
    environmental policy role, 368–71, 374–76
    hazardous waste, 334
Laws of thermodynamics, 34, 209
Lawsuits, 13
LD50 dose, 196
Lead
    as air pollutant, 228–29
    environmental persistence, 194
Lead poisoning, 120, 193, 228–29
Leafy spurge, 118
LED traffic signals, 303
Legislation. *See* Laws and regulations
Legislatures, 374–75
Legumes, 44
Leidy's comb jelly, 119
Leopold, Aldo, 19, 22
Less-developed countries. *See* Developing countries

Leukemias, 112, 200
Levees, 287
Liability for toxic waste, 334, 374
Liberian forest loss, 133
Liberty Link crops, 174
Lichens, 54, 61
Life
    biogeochemical cycles supporting, 40–41, 44–47
    earth's diversity, 3
    elemental properties, 29–33
    energy sources for, 35–37
    soil organisms, 163
Life cycle analysis of solid waste, 324
Life expectancy (human), 85–87, 182, 232
Life span, 85
Lifestyle, affluent, 8
Light-dependent reactions, 37
Light-independent reactions, 37
Lima, 344
Limestone, 31, 41, 275, 277
Limits to growth, 355–56
Line graphs, 24
Liquefied natural gas, 298–99
Literacy, environmental, 4, 380
Litter, recycling, 329
Littoral zones, 106, 109
Livestock production. *See also* Overgrazing
    antibiotic use in, 161, 162, 187
    land areas devoted to, 140
    resource requirements, 160–61
    sustainable practices, 177, 178
    water pollution from, 258–59
Living Machines for water treatment, 264
Living standards, energy use and, 293, 294
Lobbying influence, 384–85
Local chapters, 384
Locavores, 178
Lodgepole pine, 73, 74
Logarithmic scales, 365
Logging
    active resistance to, 129, 133–35, 138
    clear-cut practices, 73, 129, 135, 151
    Endangered Species Act resistance from, 124
    and fire management, 139
    as first step in deforestation, 134
    leaving preserves after, 151
    methods, 135
    of redwood forests, 104
    threat to Great Bear rainforest, 129
    on U.S. government-owned land, 135, 138–39
    varying biome responses to, 99, 101
Logical thinking, 17
Logistic population growth, 64–65
London Dumping Convention, 265
Long Island Power Authority, 316
Longhorn beetles, 61
Los Angeles temperature inversions, 231
Lotka-Volterra model, 64
Love Canal, 335
Lovins, Amory B., 302
Low-flush toilets, 250, 251
Low-income nations, 8–9
Low-input agriculture, 177
Low-level radioactive wastes, 301
Low-quality energy, 35
Low-risk problems, 201

# A Guide to Map Reading

## *Prepared by Peter Konovnitzine*

### Chaffey College

Maps can be compared to computers—they contain a lot of information that needs to be viewed, interpreted, and decoded. Every map should have several essential bits of information.

## The Parts of a Map

1. A **name** or **title** prevents confusion by clearly stating what it is you are looking at.

2. A **date** tells the map viewer how current the information is. Without a date on a map, you need to look for other clues, such as political boundaries and countries. For example, if a map shows a country called the Soviet Union, you know that the map was printed before 1991.

3. A **legend** or **key** box—usually placed at the bottom of a map—decodes all the colors and symbols used on the map. For example, most students who see the color green on a map associate it with vegetation, such as trees, grass, or forests. However, on most maps, the color green indicates low elevation. The color blue is almost always used to indicate water—oceans, seas, lakes, streams, or rivers. In addition, the legend box contains vital information useful in decoding other map markings.

4. **Direction** is usually indicated by placing a compass rosette on the map showing where the major cardinal points are: north, south, east, and west. However, today most cartographers (mapmakers) omit this symbol, assuming that the map viewer knows that the top of the map is north, the bottom is south, the left-hand side is west, and the right-hand side is east.

5. **Location** refers to the geographic grid that is usually overlaid on every map. The geographic grid is the "netting" that consists of latitude and longitude lines. Parallels of latitude lines run east to west across maps, while meridians of longitude lines go north to south. At the intersection points of these lines, you will find geographic coordinates. An example would be the geographic coordinates for the city of Los Angeles, California: 34 degrees north (of the equator) and 118 degrees west (of the prime meridian). This geographic coordinate is unique to Los Angeles. No other place on Earth has this geographic coordinate.

6. **Scale** helps in understanding the relationship between map distances and actual Earth distances. You will usually find scale in the legend or key box. There are three types of scales, and most maps made today have all three types:

   a. The linear or bar scale is a horizontal line drawn with markings placed at specific intervals indicating distances. The spacing between the markings indicates actual Earth distances. For example, if you take a ruler and measure the distance between two spacing ticks on the bar line, this distance will help you understand the actual distance between places on the Earth.

   b. Verbal scale is simply a sentence that states the relationship of distances on the map to actual distances on the Earth. For example, it may say: "One inch equals 100 miles." This means that 1 inch on the map would actually equal 100 miles on the Earth's surface.

   c. A representative fraction (RF) scale is the most useful, since it does not require prior knowledge of any particular distance measuring system. Let's say that you are not familiar with the metric system, and the map you are looking at has both the linear and verbal scales in metric notation. It may state "1 cm = 100 km." If you are not familiar with centimeters or kilometers, you will not be able to relate the scale used on the map to actual distances on the Earth's surface. The representative fraction scale has two advantages over the other two types of scale. First, it allows you to choose the distance measuring system that you are familiar with—either inches and miles or centimeters and kilometers (or any other system you want to use); and second, it always uses the same units both on the map and as it translates to actual Earth distances. For example, a common RF would be 1:62,500. To decode this, you would use one unit of your choosing—let's say inches—so that 1-inch on the map would be 62,500 inches on the Earth's surface. (By the way, this would come out to be about 1 inch to 1-mile.) Another way an RF is shown is as a fraction: 1/125,000. Notice again that the first number is always 1. This indicates that one unit on the map equals 125,000 identical units on the Earth's surface.

## Additional Map Information for Environmental Science Students

One of the key map features you can easily remember as you learn about environmental science is the relationship between major Earth grid lines and the Earth's vegetative regions. Here is a quick summary of this unique relationship. (Note: There are some minor exceptions.)

### Major Earth Grid Lines

| Name | Degree Value | Significance |
|---|---|---|
| Equator | 0 degrees | Earth's main **rainforest belt;** also starting point for parallels (lines of latitude) |
| Prime meridian (meridian of Greenwich) | 0 degrees | Starting point for meridians (lines of longitude) and Earth's **time zones** |
| Tropic of Cancer | 23.5 degrees N | Major **northern desert belt** (except southeast Asia) |
| Tropic of Capricorn | 23.5 degrees S | Major **southern desert belt** |
| Arctic Circle | 66.5 degrees N | **Tundra** usually found north of this grid line; **taiga** forest south of this grid line |
| Antarctic Circle | 66.5 degrees S | World's **storm belt** |

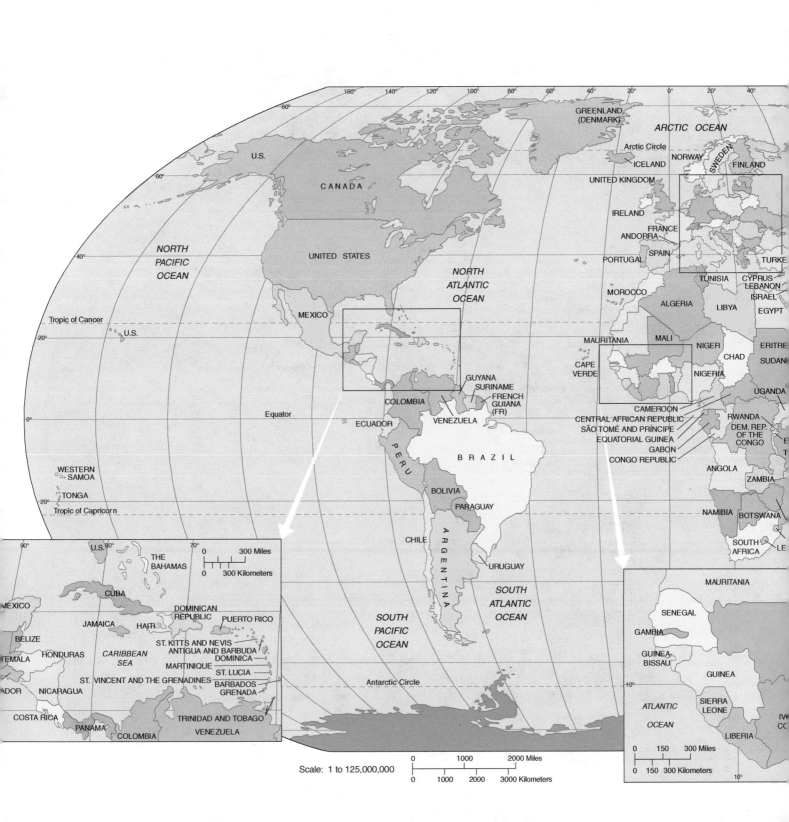

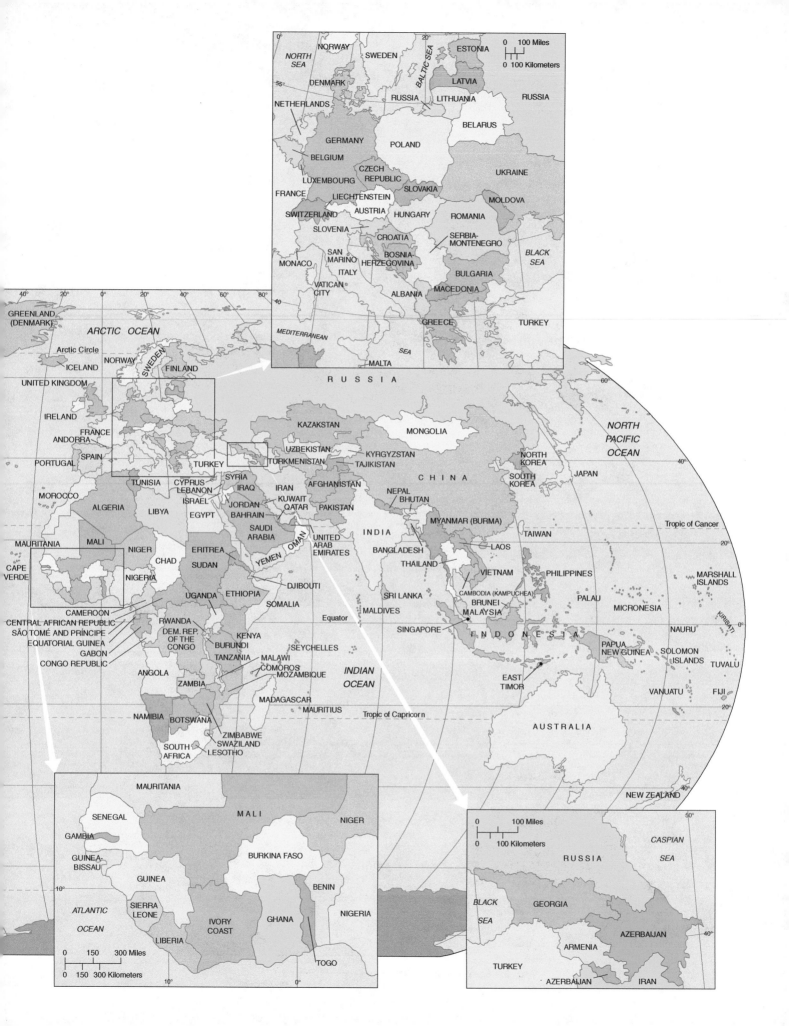

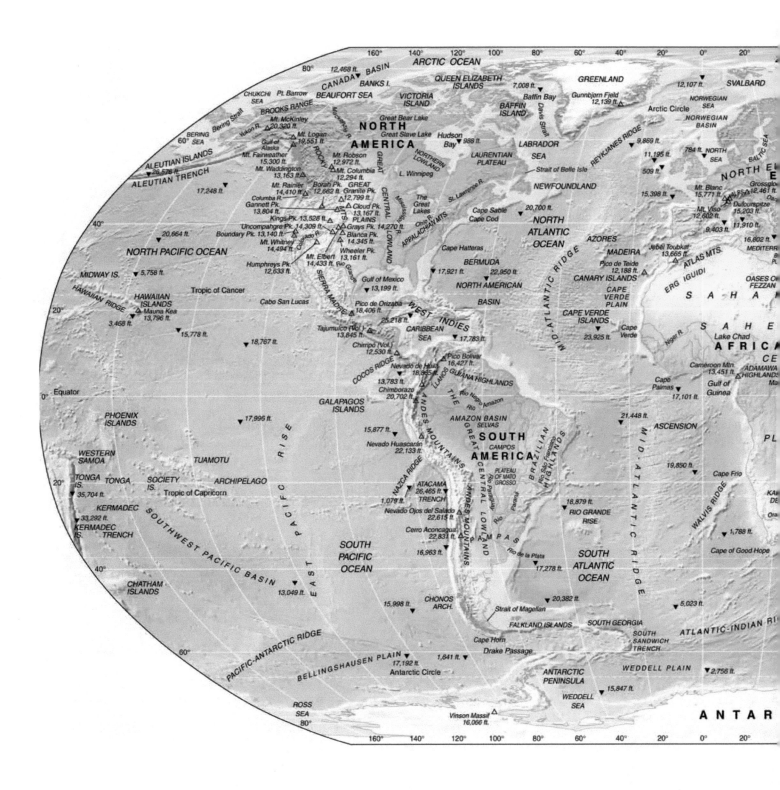

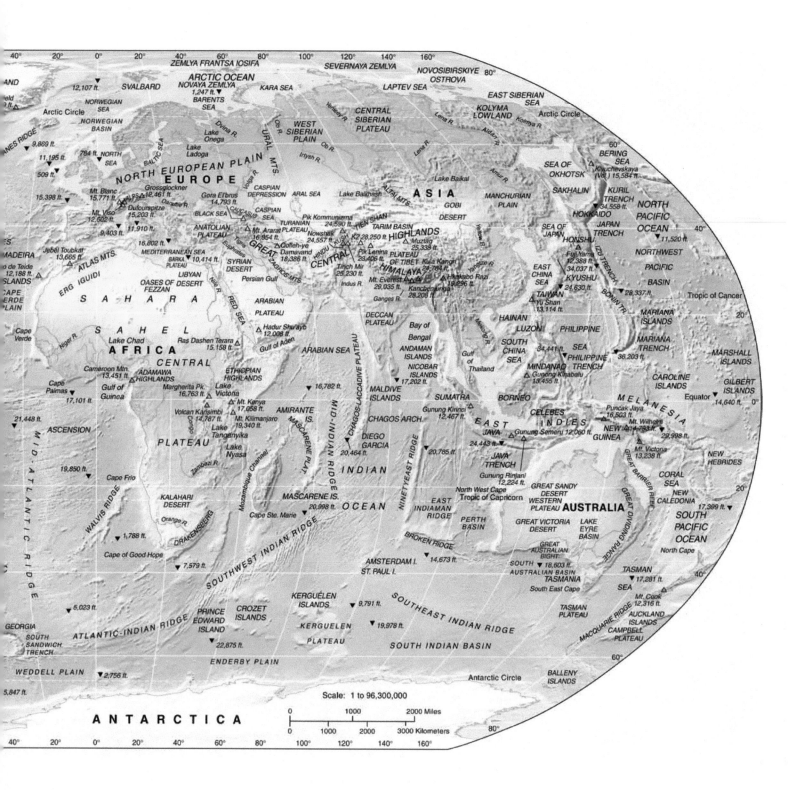

# Periodic Table of the Elements

**Key**

| |
|---|
| 1 |
| Hydrogen |
| **H** |
| 1.0079 |

Atomic number
Name
Symbol
Atomic weight

☐ Metals
☐ Metalloids
☐ Nonmetals
☐ Lanthanides
☐ Actinides

Period

| IA | IIA | IIIB | IVB | VB | VIB | VIIB | VIIIB | | | IB | IIB | IIIA | IVA | VA | VIA | VIIA | VIIIA |
|---|---|---|---|---|---|---|---|---|---|---|---|---|---|---|---|---|---|
| **1** Hydrogen **H** 1.0079 | | | | | | | | | | | | | | | | | **2** Helium **He** 4.0026 |
| **3** Lithium **Li** 6.941 | **4** Beryllium **Be** 9.0122 | | | | | | | | | | | **5** Boron **B** 10.811 | **6** Carbon **C** 12.0112 | **7** Nitrogen **N** 14.0067 | **8** Oxygen **O** 15.9994 | **9** Fluorine **F** 18.9984 | **10** Neon **Ne** 20.179 |
| **11** Sodium **Na** 22.989 | **12** Magnesium **Mg** 24.305 | | | | | | | | | | | **13** Aluminum **Al** 26.9815 | **14** Silicon **Si** 28.086 | **15** Phosphorus **P** 30.9738 | **16** Sulfur **S** 32.064 | **17** Chlorine **Cl** 35.453 | **18** Argon **Ar** 39.948 |
| **19** Potassium **K** 39.098 | **20** Calcium **Ca** 40.08 | **21** Scandium **Sc** 44.956 | **22** Titanium **Ti** 47.90 | **23** Vanadium **V** 50.942 | **24** Chromium **Cr** 51.996 | **25** Manganese **Mn** 54.938 | **26** Iron **Fe** 55.847 | **27** Cobalt **Co** 58.933 | **28** Nickel **Ni** 58.71 | **29** Copper **Cu** 63.546 | **30** Zinc **Zn** 65.38 | **31** Gallium **Ga** 69.723 | **32** Germanium **Ge** 72.59 | **33** Arsenic **As** 74.992 | **34** Selenium **Se** 78.96 | **35** Bromine **Br** 79.904 | **36** Krypton **Kr** 83.80 |
| **37** Rubidium **Rb** 85.468 | **38** Strontium **Sr** 87.62 | **39** Yttrium **Y** 88.905 | **40** Zirconium **Zr** 91.22 | **41** Niobium **Nb** 92.906 | **42** Molybdenum **Mo** 95.94 | **43** Technetium **Tc** (99) | **44** Ruthenium **Ru** 101.07 | **45** Rhodium **Rh** 102.905 | **46** Palladium **Pd** 106.4 | **47** Silver **Ag** 107.868 | **48** Cadmium **Cd** 112.40 | **49** Indium **In** 114.82 | **50** Tin **Sn** 118.69 | **51** Antimony **Sb** 121.75 | **52** Tellurium **Te** 127.60 | **53** Iodine **I** 126.904 | **54** Xenon **Xe** 131.30 |
| **55** Cesium **Cs** 132.905 | **56** Barium **Ba** 137.34 | *57 Lanthanum **La** 138.91 | **72** Hafnium **Hf** 178.49 | **73** Tantalum **Ta** 180.948 | **74** Tungsten **W** 183.85 | **75** Rhenium **Re** 186.2 | **76** Osmium **Os** 190.2 | **77** Iridium **Ir** 192.2 | **78** Platinum **Pt** 195.09 | **79** Gold **Au** 196.967 | **80** Mercury **Hg** 200.59 | **81** Thallium **Ti** 204.37 | **82** Lead **Pb** 207.19 | **83** Bismuth **Bi** 208.980 | **84** Polonium **Po** (209) | **85** Astatine **At** (210) | **86** Radon **Rn** (222) |
| **87** Francium **Fr** (223) | **88** Radium **Ra** (226) | **89** Actinium **Ac** (227) | **104** Rutherfordium **Rf** (261) | **105** Hahnium **Ha** (262) | **106** Seaborgium **Sg** (263) | **107** Neilsbohrium **Ns** (261) | **108** Hassium **Hs** (265) | **109** Meitnerium **Mt** (266) | | | | | | | | | |

| **58** Cerium **Ce** 140.12 | **59** Praseodymium **Pr** 140.907 | **60** Neodymium **Nd** 144.24 | **61** Promethium **Pm** 144.913 | **62** Samarium **Sm** 150.35 | **63** Europium **Eu** 151.96 | **64** Gadolinium **Gd** 157.25 | **65** Terbium **Tb** 158.925 | **66** Dysprosium **Dy** 162.50 | **67** Holmium **Ho** 164.930 | **68** Erbium **Er** 167.26 | **69** Thulium **Tm** 168.934 | **70** Ytterbium **Yb** 173.04 | **71** Lutetium **Lu** 174.97 |
|---|---|---|---|---|---|---|---|---|---|---|---|---|---|
| **90** Thorium **Th** 232.038 | **91** Protactinium **Pa** (231) | **92** Uranium **U** 238.03 | **93** Neptunium **Np** (237) | **94** Plutonium **Pu** 244.064 | **95** Americium **Am** (243) | **96** Curium **Cm** (247) | **97** Berkelium **Bk** (247) | **98** Californium **Cf** 242.058 | **99** Einsteinium **Es** (254) | **100** Fermium **Fm** 257.095 | **101** Mendelevium **Md** 258.10 | **102** Nobelium **No** 259.10 | **103** Lawrencium **Lr** 260.105 |

The periodic table arranges elements by atomic number (number of protons). The rows and columns are organized to show groups of similar chemical characteristics. For example, the rightmost column contains "noble" gases that do not react readily with other elements, and the next column to the left (F, Cl, Br, I, At) includes highly reactive elements known as halogens.